THE BIOLOGY OF
MARINE ANIMALS

THE BIOLOGY OF
MARINE ANIMALS

by

J. A. COLIN NICOL

Zoologist at the Plymouth Laboratory
of the Marine Biological Association

Second Edition

John Wiley & Sons, Inc.—New York
Interscience Publishers Division

Second Edition 1967
Reprinted 1969

Published in Great Britain by
Sir Isaac Pitman & Sons, Ltd., London

PRINTED AND BOUND IN ENGLAND

To the memory of my Father

PREFACE TO SECOND EDITION

IN THE preparation of this second edition I have incorporated the results of important advances made in the comparative physiology of marine animals during the past ten years. The text has been kept to the same length by removal of some antiquated material and by shortening elsewhere. Some errors, erroneous notions and time-honoured fallacies have been removed. To correct a misapprehension, I wish to point out that the references given in the first edition were not intended to be complete, but works were quoted that had useful bibliographies. A great spate of reviews and books in English is now upon us, and in the second edition reference is made to those works having exhaustive bibliographies. I thank friends and reviewers for criticisms of the first edition; some of these criticisms have been met in the revision.

1966   J. A. C. N.

PREFACE TO FIRST EDITION

EACH YEAR many young biologists make an excursion to the sea, not on idle pleasure bent but for the purpose of studying and investigating marine organisms. For some of these visitors it is perhaps their first actual experience of marine animals in their natural environment, and they will be captivated but bewildered by the multiplicity of life and by the diversity of biological adaptations which they will encounter. It is for these young men and women and for undergraduates specializing in marine zoology that this book has been written, but it is hoped that lecturers and investigators in other fields may find some diversion, if not actual instruction, in the following chapters.

This book is concerned with the comparative physiology of marine animals, and a knowledge of comparative morphology and general biology has been presumed on the part of the reader. There are limited excursions into allied fields of animal behaviour and ecology, when these can be related to the main theme. In the pages which follow I have tried to show some of the manifold ways in which marine animals, from all kinds of environments, have been able to maintain themselves in the face of hostile physical conditions and severe biotic competition. Whenever possible, at the risk of prolixity, I have cited specific examples in the belief that the functioning and adjustments of each animal deserve particular consideration, as revealing how it has managed to solve certain problems of existence.

Only animals belonging to the marine environment are considered.

Probably no apology is needed for this, since the ocean forms a remarkably stable and uniformly graded environment, with far less range of variation than that encountered on land or in fresh water. I have given some consideration to problems of littoral and estuarine ecology at the transition between sea, land and fresh water, and of animal associations, when these present features of particular interest to the marine zoologist. Of course, the great majority of examples are taken from littoral and inshore species, for these are the ones most readily available and therefore most thoroughly investigated.

This book has been in preparation for six years, and during that time many aspects have received extensive treatment elsewhere. Full bibliographies of earlier work in comparative physiology are now available and I have therefore confined myself principally to quoting works of the past two decades, including sources in which extensive reference lists may be found. Whenever possible I have attempted to use the presently accepted scientific name for each species mentioned, but there are undoubtedly many instances in which this goal has not been achieved. All measurements are given in the c.g.s. system.

During the preparation of this book I have received much assistance and advice from friends and colleagues. I am grateful to the following for reading certain chapters and for critical comments: the late Dr. W. R. G. Atkins, Professor C. M. Yonge, Dr. J. D. Robertson, Dr. D. Davenport, Dr. G. Y. Kennedy, Dr. H. W. Harvey, Mr. F. A. J. Armstrong, Dr. E. D. S. Corner and Dr. R. D. Keynes. Their criticisms and suggestions have done much to give the book any merit it deserves, but for the errors and egregious blunders which remain I reserve for myself full credit. Finally, I wish to acknowledge the great debt I owe to my wife for her encouragement and for assistance in preparing the text. She is also responsible for preparing many of the illustrations, which have been redrawn from the original sources.

J. A. C. N.

Plymouth, 1956

ACKNOWLEDGEMENTS

THE author wishes to thank the Editorial Boards and the Proprietors of the following scientific periodicals, and the authors concerned, for permission to reproduce the following figures:

Acta Physiologica Scandinavica, Fig. 3.13
Allgemeine Zoologie und Abstammungslehre, Figs. 8.4, 8.5
American Journal of Physiology, Fig. 9.21
Annales de l'Institut Océanographique, Figs. 14.11, 15.2, 15.4
Archiv für Anatomie und Physiologie, Fig. 3.14 (*a*)
Archiv für Protistenkunde, Fig. 9.1
Archives Néerlandaises de Physiologie de l'Homme et des Animaux, Fig. 4.23
Archives de Zoologie Expérimentale et Générale, Fig. 14.14 (*c*)
Archives des Sciences Physiologiques, Figs. 9.19, 9.20
Biological Bulletin, Figs. 3.15, 3.16, 3.19 (*b*), 4.17, 5.3, 6.8, 8.6, 8.9, 8.10, 8.17, 9.9 (*b*), 11.6 (*b*), 12.7
Biological Reviews of the Cambridge Philosophical Society, Figs. 2.8, 4.11, 5.11, 6.5, 8.13, 8.26 (*a*), 10.8, 10.9, 14.22, 14.23
British Museum Economic Series No. 10, Figs. 5.13, 15.15, 15.16
British Museum Guide to the Fish Gallery, Fig. 15.17
Bulletin No. 19 of the Cranbrook Institute of Science, Fig. 8.12
Bulletin of the U.S. Bureau of Fisheries, Figs. 6.4, 11.6 (*a*), 11.9
Bulletin of the U.S. Fisheries Commission, Fig. 15.3
Cold Spring Harbour Symposia on Quantitative Biology, Figs. 8.20 (*b*), 10.13
Commonwealth of Australia Council for Scientific and Industrial Research Bulletin 159, Fig. 15.18
Comptes Rendus des Travaux du Laboratoire Carlsberg, Fig. 4.8
Discovery Reports of the National Institute of Oceanography, Fig. 8.15
Ergebnisse der Biologie, Fig. 3.12
Experimental Cell Research, Fig. 9.7
Fauna e Flora del Golfo di Napoli, Fig. 14.14
The Feeding Mechanisms of a Deep-sea Fish Choliodus sloani, Fig. 5.28
Handbuch der vergleichenden Anatomie der Wirbeltiere, Figs. 8.1, 8.31
Harvey Lectures, Fig. 8.19
Hvalrådets Skrifter, No. 22, Fig. 4.15
Journal of Biological Chemistry, Figs. 6.7, 6.10
Journal of Comparative Neurology, Figs. 8.27, 10.17
Journal of Cellular and Comparative Physiology, Figs. 2.3, 3.14 (*b*), 3.18, 4.9, 4.25, 8.22, 9.15, 9.16, 10.6, 13.26
Journal of Experimental Biology, Figs. 2.4, 2.6, 2.8, 2.9, 2.10, 2.11, 2.12, 4.5, 4.10, 4.14, 4.19, 5.20, 6.1, 6.2, 6.11, 8.8, 8.17, 8.23, 9.4, 9.6, 9.10, 9.11, 9.12, 10.5, 10.10, 10.21, 10.22, 12.11
Journal of General Physiology, Figs. 8.17, 8.18, 8.25, 13.24
Journal of the Linnean Society of London, Fig. 5.10 (*b*)
Journal of Morphology, Figs. 5.9, 5.12 (*a*), 8.3, 12.6

Journal of Neurophysiology, Fig. 10.19
Journal of Physiology, Figs. 3.7, 8.30, 9.8, 9.14, 9.15, 10.3, 10.14 (*a*), 12.4
National Geographic Magazine, Fig. 13.18 (*b*)
Oceanic Birds of South America, Fig. 5.23
Pacific Science, Fig. 1.1
Le Parasitisme (Librairie de l'Université Lausanne), Fig. 14.12
Physiologia Comparata et Oecologia, Figs. 3.11, 9.13
Physiological Zoology, Figs. 3.21, 4.12, 4.13, 12.14
Proceedings of the Cambridge Philosophical Society: Biological Sciences, Fig. 6.5
Proceedings of the National Academy of Sciences, Fig. 12.13
Proceedings of the Royal Society: Series B, Figs. 4.21, 5.27, 8.11, 8.28, 8.33, 9.18, 10.2, 10.4, 10.8, 10.12, 10.16, 10.18, 10.25, 11.1, 11.3, 11.7 (*c*), 12.8, 15.1
Proceedings of the Royal Society of Edinburgh, Fig. 5.16
Proceedings of the Zoological Society of London, Figs. 4.1, 11.12, 14.3
Quarterly Journal of Microscopical Science, Figs. 3.17, 5.6, 5.7, 5.13 (*b*), 5.14, 5.19 (*b*), 7.1, 7.2, 8.2, 8.24, 9.3, 10.14 (*b*), 14.19, 14.21, 15.5
Rapports et Procès-Verbaux des Réunions: Conseil Permanent International pour l'Exploration de la Mer, Fig. 1.7
Schriften des Naturwissenshaftlichen Vereins für Schleswig-Holstein, Fig. 5.18
Scientific Reports of the Great Barrier Reef Expedition, 1928–29, Fig. 15.14
Transactions of the Illuminating Engineering Society, Fig. 1.8
Transactions of the Royal Society of Edinburgh, Figs. 5.5, 5.21, 6.6, 6.9, 15.12
Verhandlungen der deutschen zoologischen Gesellschaft, Figs. 5.25, 13.19, 13.20
Zeitschrift für vergleichende Physiologie, Figs. 3.2, 8.14, 12.1
Zeitschrift für Zellforschung, Fig. 10.20
Zoologia, Figs. 3.4, 3.5
Zoologica, Fig. 3.18 (*a*), (*c*), (*d*)
Zoologischer Anzeiger, Fig. 5.1

Acknowledgement is made also to the following publishers for permission to reproduce illustrations from their publications:

Cambridge University Press: Frontispiece from *Plant-animals: a Study in Symbiosis*, F. Keeble
Gustav Fischer Verlag: *Grundzüge einen Lehre vom Licht- und Farbensinn*, Frölich
Methuen and Co., Ltd.: Fig. 72 from *Adaptive Coloration in Animals*, H. B. Cott
Prentice Hall, Inc.: Fig. 20 from *The Oceans, their Physics, Chemistry, and General Biology*, H. U. Sverdrup *et al.*
Volharding: Figs. 20 and 21 from *Dissertation on the Utilization of Oxygen and Regulation of Breathing in Some Aquatic Animals*, L. van Dam

CONTENTS

CHAPTER 1

INTRODUCTORY

The sea, therefore, we may safely infer, has its offices and duties to perform; so, may we infer, have its currents, and so, too, its inhabitants; consequently, he who undertakes to study its phenomena must cease to regard it as a waste of waters. He must look upon it as a part of that exquisite machinery by which the harmonies of nature are preserved, and then he will begin to perceive the developments of order and the evidences of design; these make it a most beautiful and interesting subject for contemplation.

LIEUT. M. F. MAURY, 1883

THE REALM OF MARINE LIFE

THE oceans in their vast expanses cover seven-tenths of the earth's surface and in their deepest reaches extend downwards into the earth's crust to some 10,000 metres below sea level. The mean depth of the ocean has been estimated at about 4,000 metres, which is considerably greater than the mean height of land above sea level, namely some 850 metres. All this tremendous expanse and depth are inhabited by living things; animals have been secured from beneath the polar ice sheets, and from the ocean deeps more than 10 kilometres beneath the surface. These abyssal forms are normal inhabitants of that world and know no other, and similarly at intermediate depths there are other animals which tend to remain at definite levels.

The ocean is not evenly populated throughout its extent. The density and total volume of living organisms are greatest in coastal waters and at the surface, and decrease rapidly with depth in the waters of the open ocean. The food of all animals in the sea is ultimately derived from marine plants, phytoplankton and, to a small extent, seaweeds. Since the energy for their synthetic activities is provided by sunlight, plants can thrive only in shallow or surface waters within the range of adequate light penetration. In these regions the herbivores graze upon the plants, but at deeper levels, extending down to the deepest waters of the abyss, the animals are dependent upon the remains of dead or dying surface organisms which slowly shower upon them from above, and to some extent upon the spatial organization of food chains in vertical series.

VARIETY OF MARINE ANIMALS

Of the nineteen or so phyla recognized by zoologists all except one or two are found in the sea. Of these, five are exclusively and four are predominantly marine in habit, while many of the remaining phyla are well represented. The entirely marine phyla are the Brachiopoda, Chaetognatha,

1

Phoronidea, Pognophora and Echinodermata. Of the three most highly evolved groups of animals, the molluscs, arthropods and vertebrates, all have marine representatives. The cephalopods are without doubt the most highly developed of marine invertebrates, and approach the vertebrates in the complexity of their sensori-neural organization and behaviour. Arthropods reached their evolutionary peak in the insects, few of which have returned to the sea. But more remarkable, from the historical viewpoint, has been the repeated re-invasion of the seas by most of the major groups of vertebrates. So successful was this colonization that the teleosts were able to exploit all marine environments from the tidal zone to the ocean abyss, and occupy a dominant position in the oceanic fauna. The maritime birds and mammals, partly through their acquisition of homoiothermism, have been able to spread through the surface waters of all the oceans from arctic to antarctic ice, and in speed and agility they even outclass the fish and squid in their own element. On the invertebrate animals hitherto occupying the seas the effects of these evolutionary changes have been tremendous. From our point of view they enter into a consideration of the morphological and functional adaptations which have permitted the exploitation of a marine environment.

MARINE HABITATS

On the basis of their distribution and habits marine animals are generally classified as plankton, nekton and benthos. The first-named comprises all those small drifting organisms, both plants and animals, which have only feeble powers of locomotion and are carried helplessly at the mercy of currents and tides. Nekton refers to strong swimming animals, such as squid, fish and whales, whose movements are powerful enough to make them independent of water movements to a considerable degree. And thirdly, the benthos embraces all those bottom-living organisms which crawl over the substratum, burrow into it, or are sedentary in habit and remain fixed to one spot, for example, starfish, bivalves and sponges.

In addition to this classification of marine animals on the basis of habitat it is usual to recognize certain well-defined environments in the sea, each with special characteristics of its own. These are the littoral or inter-tidal region, the continental shelf and slope, the pelagic zone and the abyssal region. Subdivision of these various regions is often necessary for oceanographical and ecological purposes, and is briefly described in the following paragraphs. More extended treatment will be found in works on marine natural history and oceanography (11, 12, 27, 31, 32, 37). (References are given at the end of the chapter.)

The Inter-tidal Zone

At the junction between sea and land lies the shore or littoral zone, subject to tidal ebb and flow. This is the region bounded by extreme high- and low-water levels of spring tides. Its vertical range depends on the extent of the tides, and the area involved is also governed by the slope of the shore. Conditions of life in the littoral zone are quite dissimilar from those occurring elsewhere. When the tide is in the inhabitants are bathed by sea water, a relatively constant medium, but during tidal ebb they are periodically uncovered and exposed to the rigours of aerial climate. Quantitatively the fauna of the shore is very rich, but the vicissitudes of existence associated with this environment have led to a high degree of specialization. Consequently the population of the shore is peculiar in many respects and contains a high proportion of animals not found elsewhere. Because the littoral zone is more readily accessible to the zoologist than the waters offshore, and the animals living there can be observed directly, this region has received much attention.

In the tidal zone several environmental levels can be distinguished, determined by the degree of atmospheric exposure to which they are subjected. On the lower shore, lying below low-water neaps, there are long periods during neap tides when the shore is not exposed. Here live many sublittoral animals which can tolerate only limited exposure to the air. Other sublittoral animals invade the inter-tidal region during tidal flow only, or come inshore on occasion to spawn. Lying between the limits of low- and high-water neaps is a region which is covered twice daily by the sea, and which contains a rich fauna of typical inter-tidal species. Above high-water neaps there are long periods when the shore is exposed for days on end. The fauna of this region contains fewer species than lower levels, and many of these are restricted to higher regions of the shore. Consequently, zonation of animals is a conspicuous feature of the shore, and is illustrated in Fig. 1.1 depicting conditions on a rocky shore in New Zealand (30, 36, 43, 44).

The environmental variables which adult animals encounter in the inter-tidal zone, and which they endeavour to counter by morphological, physiological and behavioural means, are manifold and complex. No other region in the ocean presents such diversity of habitats and range of physical conditions as the inter-tidal zone. The variables with which we are concerned may be considered as follows.

Water Movements. In the littoral region water movements result from waves, swell and tidal action. In sheltered bays and estuaries such movements may be slight and gentle, but on rocky coast lines facing the open ocean the mechanical force of the waves is tremendous.

Animals living on wave-swept shores resist the destructive effects of wave action by suitable structural devices, and by modifications of form, or they actively seek shelter and cover. Acorn barnacles live cemented to rocks, chitons and limpets adhere firmly with their broad feet, and mussels attach themselves by strong byssus threads. Certain shore-fish, for example *Lepadogaster*, have their pelvic fins modified into strong suckers. Finally, the depressed or conical shape of littoral chitons and limpets offers minimal resistance to water movements.

Emersion. As the result of tidal movements animals on the shore are periodically exposed to air, either daily, or for longer intervals if they live

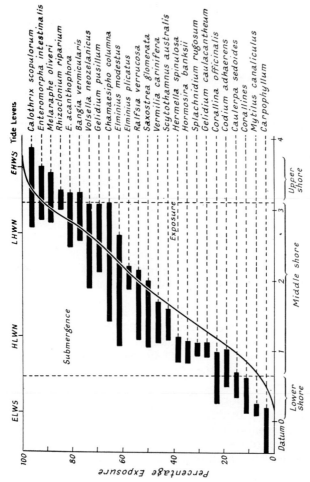

FIG. 1.1. ZONATION OF LITTORAL ANIMALS AND PLANTS ON A PROTECTED ROCKY
SHORE (NARROW NECK REEF) IN NEW ZEALAND

Tide levels shown on the left: EHWS, extreme high-water springs; LHWN, lowest
level of high-water neaps; HLWN, highest level of low-water neaps; ELWS, extreme
low-water springs. Organisms at top. Algae, *Calothrix, Enteromorpha, Rhizoclonium,
Bangia, Gelidium, Ralfsia, Scytothamnus, Hormosira, Splachnidium, Corallina, Codium,
Caulerpa, Carpophyllum.* Polychaetes, *Vermilia, Hermella.* Molluscs, *Melaraphe,
Volsella, Saxostrea, Mytilus.* Barnacles, *Chamaesipho, Elminius.* (After Dellow (16).)

above the level of high-water neaps (Fig. 1.1). Such animals may possess thick integuments which reduce the water lost through evaporation when the animal is in air (e.g. shore crabs) or hard shells which can be clamped firmly together during the period of exposure (e.g. shore barnacles and mussels). Still other forms obtain protection by burrowing into the substratum, creeping under rocks or into crevices, or among the fronds of shore-wrack, e.g. inter-tidal polychaetes and teleosts. The amount of exposure to the atmosphere which an animal can tolerate, and the pattern of its behaviour when the tide ebbs, are important factors governing its distribution on the shore.

Temperature. The inter-tidal zone experiences to a great degree the vicissitudes of terrestrial climate, and at low water animals are subject to the full range of aerial temperatures. Shore temperatures show great variation with latitude and season. On the shores of temperate regions ground temperatures may fall below 0°C in winter and reach 40°C in the heat of the summer sun, and higher temperatures will be encountered on tropical shores. Rock pools vary greatly in temperature, depending on their volume, on the air temperature and the length of time they are separated from the sea.

Littoral animals must of necessity be eurythermal in order to survive, and this is illustrated in investigations dealing with the heat tolerance of littoral gastropods. Broekhuysen (5) determined the lethal temperatures and the survival times at high temperatures for a series of shore gastropods at False Bay (South Africa), and he discovered that these factors were graded according to the zonal sequence of the species on the shore. Evans (19) has investigated the thermal death-points of littoral gastropods in Cardigan Bay. Mean lethal temperatures varied from 46·3°C for *Littorina neritoides* which lives above mean high-water neaps, to 36·2°C for *Gibbula cineraria* which occurs in damp shaded positions below mean low-water neaps. The highest temperatures recorded on the shore were 40·5°C for sun-baked rocks and 30°C in tidal pools. Both workers concluded that the degree of heat tolerance shown by these various snails is related to the temperature range which they encounter in nature, and the safety factor is sufficiently high so that they rarely, if ever, are exposed on the shore to temperatures that are lethal.

Active animals on the shore can escape the extremes of thermal fluctuations by seeking shelter; others, in the open and exposed to sunlight, may have body temperatures depressed by evaporation from their surfaces (17, 29). Also, there are some shore crabs which blanch when illuminated, and thereby reflect more of the incident light and heat. When these crabs are exposed on the shore this mechanism would tend to reduce the liability to heating in sunshine.

Salinity. Large variations in salinity occur in the inter-tidal region and in estuaries. During low tide the shore may be washed by rain water and those animals that are active and remain in the open may be surrounded by water which is almost fresh until the return of the sea. Freshwater seepage on the shore forms areas of reduced salinity, and these are favoured by certain species. Tidal pools are subject to considerable fluctuations in salinity, particularly those pools high on the shore which are cut off from the sea for some days during the period of neap tides. Wide environmental variations in salinity demand tolerance or functional methods of regulation against osmotic stress, and these will be considered in the next chapter.

In estuaries the salinity conditions are peculiar owing to the effects of tidal oscillations and river discharge, leading to variable admixture of

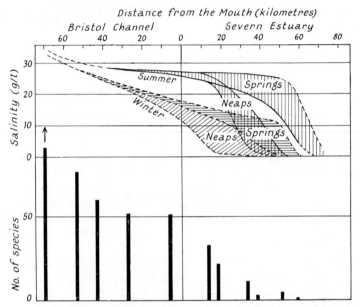

FIG. 1.2. SALINITY CHANGES IN AN ESTUARY (SEVERN), AND THE DECREASE IN THE NUMBER OF MARINE INTER-TIDAL ANIMALS AWAY FROM THE MOUTH

(*Above*) tidal and seasonal changes in salinity in the Bristol Channel and Severn Estuary (1940). (*Below*) number of species of marine inter-tidal animals recorded at various stations. (After Bassindale (4).)

fresh and salt waters. Only a restricted number of marine animals can exist under such conditions of reduced and variable salinity, and it is found that the number of marine species decreases as the estuary is ascended (Fig. 1.2). The distance which any given species can penetrate up the estuary depends on the lowest salinity it can tolerate for a given time. For fixed or sedentary animals such as molluscs, this is determined by the lowest salinity at springs during the season of maximal run-off. Active and migratory animals such as shrimps, however, are able to execute seasonal movements up and down the estuary, moving towards the mouth in winter and upstream during the spring and summer (4, 23, 29, 44).

The Sea Floor

Below low-tide mark the sea floor slopes gently at first across the continental shelf to the continental edge at about 200 metres. The gradient then increases and the floor falls off rapidly down to a depth of around 4,000 metres. This region of sharp descent is the continental slope below which the floor tends to level out again as the abyssal plain. The continental shelf has an average width of about 50 kilometres, but the actual extent varies widely in different parts of the world. In certain areas, such as the Grand Banks of Newfoundland and the North Sea, the shelf extends several hundred kilometres offshore, whereas off steep coasts, such as Spain and Chile, it is only a few kilometres wide. The abyssal plain is far from even, and presents great depressions and ridges; the greatest depressions, called deeps, extend down to 10,500 metres.

Pelagic Zone

The pelagic zone comprises the waters of the open ocean, and because of its volume, expanse and the density of its population, it forms the major oceanic environment which the biologist has to consider. It is sometimes divided into three horizontal regions on the basis of light penetration in the following manner.

1. An upper photosynthetic zone in which the light intensity is sufficient to provide plants with energy for growth. This will vary in depth according to the amount of light falling upon the water, and with the transparency of the water. In clear tropical oceanic waters the photosynthetic zone will extend down to some 100 metres, but will be less elsewhere. This region is often rich in plankton and herbivorous animals.

2. A twilight zone extending below the photosynthetic zone to the limit of light penetration.

3. An aphotic zone extending from the limit of light penetration to the sea bottom. This region is dark, without living plant life and is populated solely by carnivorous animals and detritus feeders.

Planktonic Organisms. The most important members of the phytoplankton, upon which all pelagic animals are ultimately dependent for food, are the diatoms, followed by dinoflagellates. These plants can flourish only in the photosynthetic layer and, correspondingly, zooplankton is densest near the surface and diminishes with depth. The character of the plankton also changes qualitatively as well as quantitatively in hauls from deeper waters, surface species giving way to mesopelagic and bathypelagic forms. The quantity of zooplankton in surface waters also shows great geographical variation, becoming more abundant over the continental shelf and in higher latitudes. In general there is a tendency for a few species of planktonic animals to predominate in catches made in far northern and southern waters, but these occur in immense numbers. In tropical waters, on the other hand, the population density is low but there is great diversity and richness of species.

In temperate and sub-polar waters there is a rich seasonal growth of nutritive phytoplankton which in turn regulates the abundance of planktonic animals. Around the British Isles the seasonal increase in plankton first becomes noticeable between February and March as a rapid blooming of the diatom pasturage. This is followed in April by the hatching of

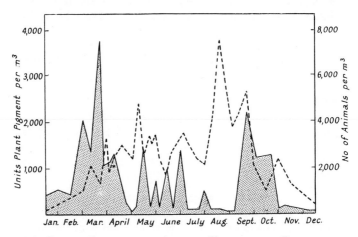

FIG. 1.3. GRAPHS SHOWING THE ANNUAL VARIATION OF PHYTOPLANKTON AND ZOOPLANKTON IN THE ENGLISH CHANNEL (1934)

Continuous line, phytoplankton; broken line, zooplankton. (From Harvey, Cooper, Lebour, and Russell (1935).)

vast hordes of planktonic animals which batten upon the phytoplankton. Owing to the depletion of nutrient salts and the grazing effect of planktonic animals, the plants decline in abundance. A second minor outburst of phytoplankton may follow in the autumn (Fig. 1.3). During the winter months the plankton content of the surface waters sinks to a low ebb. In arctic and antarctic waters there is only a single annual outburst of planktonic life, in the summer.

The permanent members of the zooplankton are animals such as foraminifers, copepods, euphausiids, siphonophores, ctenophores, salps, chaetognaths, pteropods and so on, which spend all their life adrift. These are the holopelagic forms. In coastal waters another element comes into prominence, namely the temporary plankton. This embraces the drifting larval stages of numerous littoral and benthic species such as polychaetes, decapod crustacea, echinoderms and molluscs. With these should be included young stages of fish and cephalopods. The temporary members of the plankton attain great abundance during the spring and summer, only to disappear after metamorphosing, settling on the bottom or perishing. In addition there are certain temporary planktonic forms which are characteristic of the open ocean, such as the Phyllosoma larva of the rock lobster *Scyllarus*, and the Leptocephalus larva of the eel.

CHEMICAL AND PHYSICAL PROPERTIES OF SEA WATER

Physical and chemical conditions in the oceans have been investigated actively since the voyage of the *Challenger* in 1872–6, and extensive data are at hand for forming an appreciation of sea water as an environmental medium for animal life. The environmental variables which are of immediate interest to the biologist are temperature, density, viscosity, pressure, light, salinity, suspended matter and dissolved gases. These are briefly reviewed in the following pages and are related, in so far as is practicable, to their biological effects.

Chemical Composition of Sea Water

Sea water contains a characteristic assemblage of dissolved solids and gases, and a variable amount of suspended inorganic and organic material. As first shown by Dittmar on the *Challenger* expedition samples, the main constituents of sea water, with minor exceptions, show remarkable uniformity throughout the oceans of the world. This fact is of fundamental

TABLE 1.1

AVERAGE COMPOSITION OF SEA WATER (CHLORINITY $19^0/_{00}$, SALINITY $34.325^0/_{00}$)

Ion	Composition % of sea salt	Concentration g/kg of sea water	Concentration mM/kg	Concentration g/l. at 20°C (S.G. 1·024)
Na^+	30·61	10·556	459·02	10·809
K^+	1·10	0·380	9·72	0·389
Mg^{++}	3·69	1·272	52·30	1·303
Ca^{++}	1·16	0·400	9·98	0·410
Sr^{++}	0·04	0·0085	0·15	0·013
H_3BO_3	0·07	0·026	0·42	0·027
Cl^-	55·04	18·980	535·30	19·435
$SO_4^=$	7·68	2·649	27·57	2·713
HCO_3^-*	0·41	0·140	2·29	0·143
Br^-	0·19	0·065	0·81	0·067
F^-	0·004	0·001	0·05	0·001

* Bicarbonate and carbonate will vary according to the pH of the sea water.

importance in oceanography and marine biology, since it ensures that the results of studies on the physical properties of sea water in any part of the world are of general and universal significance. Table 1.1 shows mean values for the principal dissolved substances in sea water of chlorinity $19‰$[1] (salinity $34.325‰$).

[1] See p. 10 for explanation of $^0/_{00}$.

Since the major constituents of sea water retain the same relative proportions wherever the sample is taken, it is possible, by determining the concentration of any one of them, to estimate the concentrations of the others. Because of this constant composition the relations between chlorinity, salinity, density and temperature are fixed, and interconversion of values is readily carried out. Finally, the biologist recognizes, in the constant ionic composition of sea water, a stable environmental factor of the utmost importance in the physiology of marine animals.

The constancy in composition of sea water is due to the system of oceanic circulation and to the continual mixing which occurs. This soon equalizes any local variations resulting from the discharge of rivers, the activity of living organisms, formation and melting of sea ice, the interaction of suspended material with dissolved substances and exchange with bottom deposits. There are, however, restricted areas, such as the Black and Baltic Seas and the mouths of large rivers, where dilution and peculiarities of circulation bring about changes in the relative concentrations of dissolved substances. In such regions modifications of the chlorinity ratios with respect to sodium, potassium, calcium and sulphate ions may be encountered.

Salinity. The salt concentration of sea water is known as salinity. Salinities are always expressed as grammes per kilogramme of sea water (parts per mille, ‰) and, in practice, are usually obtained by measuring the chlorinity, using argentometric titration. The reader will find a simplified procedure in Harvey (25). The relationship between the two quantities, salinity and chlorinity, is given by the expression

$$\text{Salinity (‰)} = 0.03 + 1.8050 \times \text{chlorinity (‰)}$$

For most biological purposes, the concentrations of substances in solution are usually expressed on a volume basis as percentages or grammes per litre. It is convenient, therefore, to have corresponding values for chlorine content, and this is available in the use of the term chlorosity, which is the equivalent of chlorinity expressed as grammes per litre at 20°C. The calculations involved are

$$\text{molarity of Cl in sample} = \frac{(\text{vol AgNO}_3)\,(\text{molarity AgNO}_3)}{\text{vol sample c.c.}}$$

$$\text{chlorosity} = 35.5\,(\text{molarity Cl})$$

$$\text{chlorinity} = \frac{\text{chlorosity}}{\text{density of sample at 20°C}}.$$

The chlorinity may be read from the graph shown in Fig. 1.4 relating it to chlorosity, or may be calculated with greater accuracy from the data given in Knudsen's hydrographical tables.

The salinity range in the open oceans is rather small, and usually lies between 33‰ and 37‰ in surface waters, with a mean of nearly 35‰. Marked deviations from these values are due to peculiar conditions. In regions where there is much dilution by heavy rainfall, discharge of rivers or melting ice the surface salinity may be much less, for example in semi-enclosed areas such as the Baltic Sea and Gulf of Bothnia, where surface salinities may fall to 5‰ or less. On the other hand, in partially isolated regions such as the Red Sea, where temperatures are high and evaporation excessive, salinities may exceed 41‰.

Certain general features of salinity distributions may be noted. Surface salinities, on the average, reach a maximum around latitudes 20°N. and 20°S. Salinities tend to be low in high latitudes due to low temperatures and little evaporation. The range is less for intermediate and deep waters

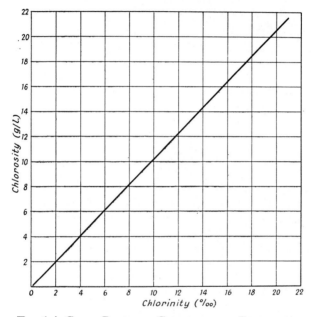

FIG. 1.4. CURVE RELATING CHLORINITY TO CHLOROSITY

than at the surface, which is more directly affected by evaporation and precipitation. Values for deep waters generally lie between 34·5‰ and 35‰; exceptions are the Red Sea and Mediterranean where deep waters of high salinity are found. Charts showing surface salinities and lines of isohalinity over the oceans of the world may be found in standard text-books of oceanography.

Minor Constituents. Besides the major constituents shown in Table 1.1, sea water contains small amounts of some forty other elements, apart from dissolved gases (22). The more important of these are silicon, phosphorus, nitrogen, iron, manganese, copper and vanadium. The concentrations are very low, 7 mg/kg or less (Table 1.2).

Some of these minor constituents, despite their low concentrations, are necessary for the continued existence of all organisms. Phosphates and

TABLE 1.2

A PARTIAL LIST OF THE MINOR ELEMENTS IN SEA WATER
(CHLORINITY $19^o/_{oo}$)

(From various sources)

Element	mg/kg
Boron	5·0
Silicon	0·01–7·0
Nitrogen (as NH_4, NO_3, NO_2)	0·001–0·7
Phosphorus	0·001–0·17
Iron	0·001–0·29
Manganese	0·001–0·01
Copper	0·01–0·024
Zinc	0·005–0·014
Molybdenum	0·0003–0·016
Vanadium	0·0002–0·007
Chromium	0·001–0·003
Cobalt	0·0001–0·0005

nitrogen-containing salts are essential nutrient substances for the growth of marine plants. An evaluation of this subject, which is outside the scope of the present work, is available elsewhere (21, 26). Phosphorus is an essential element in the composition of animals, and as inorganic and organic phosphates it occurs in the skeleton, body and cellular fluids. Iron, copper and vanadium are found in blood pigments, and iron is also an essential element in certain intracellular enzymes; silicon is utilized in the coverings and skeletons of diatoms, radiolarians, sponges, etc.

Organic Matter. Sea water contains a small quantity of dissolved and suspended organic matter, which is derived from the excreta of living organisms and from the decomposition of their tissues when dead. The amounts present are very small, and have been estimated at 1·2–2 mg of carbon per litre. There appears to be more organic matter in inshore than offshore waters, and some decrease during the winter months. A part of the organic matter in solution is utilized by bacteria, but it does not appear to contribute directly to the nourishment of marine animals (25, 37). On the other hand, the presence of minute quantities of organic substances in solution may well exert physiological effects out of all proportion to their concentration. It has been demonstrated that the development of certain echinoderm and polychaete larvae shows differing degrees of success in samples of sea water from different localities, owing to the presence of unknown factors. Studies of this kind may point the way towards determining the more elusive biological differences which exist between different waters (42).

Hydrogen Ion Concentration (pH). Sea water is normally alkaline in reaction and shows a range rarely exceeding pH 8·0 to pH 8·4 in surface waters, although values above and below these limits are sometimes met with under extraordinary conditions. Thus, in tidal pools, the pH sometimes rises to 9·6 owing to the activity of plants; and in isolated basins, where decomposition of organic matter is taking place and H_2S is given off, it may fall to 7·0. Sea water which is in equilibrium with the atmosphere has a hydrogen ion concentration of nearly pH 8·1, which can be taken as a normal value.

Sea water is alkaline as a consequence of excess of cations over anions derived from strong acids. The excess base is equivalent to ions of bicarbonate, carbonate and borate, and in consequence, sea water possesses limited buffering power. The removal or addition of 1·25 ml of CO_2 per litre will produce alterations in the hydrogen ion concentration of pH $\pm$ 0·1. The resistance of sea water to changes in hydrogen ion concentration is a factor of some importance to marine animals, many of which are very sensitive to changes in the pH of the medium.

Dissolved Gases. In sea water the dissolved gases which are of particular biological interest are oxygen and carbon dioxide. The partial pressures of these two gases in the atmosphere are 20·99 and 0·03 vols% (partial pressures of 159·52 and 0·23 mm Hg). The amount of gas present in aqueous solution is proportional to the partial pressure exerted by the gas. The solubilities of gases and therefore the amounts held in solution decrease with rise of temperature and increase of salinity. Solubility values are given in Table 1.3 for oxygen in sea water of different temperatures and salinities.

The dissolved oxygen content of ocean waters varies from 0–8·5 ml/l. It is greater in the surface layers, where free exchange with the atmosphere can take place, than in subsurface waters, which obtain their oxygen through mixing, wind action, etc. The oxygen content of sea water is significantly influenced by marine organisms. Both animals and plants consume oxygen, but the latter also release oxygen as the result of photosynthetic activity. Deeper water masses have derived their oxygen originally from the atmosphere prior to submergence, and this is depleted by the respiratory needs of animals and the oxidation of organic material. In the Atlantic Ocean, for example, maximal values of 8·2 ml O_2 per litre are found in surface layers; central water near the equator shows minimal values of 0·5 ml; and intermediate and deep waters have oxygen contents of 4·5–6 ml/l.

Although oxygen varies irregularly in distribution, the amounts present are usually adequate for the existence of animal life at all levels. Exceptions are certain enclosed seas, basins and fjords, in which there is deficient circulation, with the consequence that the bottom layers become stagnant and deficient in oxygen.

Carbon dioxide varies in concentration from 34–56 ml/l. in sea water, and is not a limiting factor in animal life. Part is dissolved as free CO_2 and as H_2CO_3, but most is present as carbonate and bicarbonate in

TABLE 1.3

Solubility of Oxygen in Sea Water (ml/l.)
(From Fox (20))

Salinity ⁰/₀₀ Chlorinity ⁰/₀₀	27·11 15	28·91 16	30·72 17	32·52 18	34·33 19	36·13 20
Temperature (°C)						
− 2	9·01	8·89	8·76	8·64	8·52	8·39
− 1	8·78	8·66	8·54	8·42	8·30	8·18
0	8·55	8·43	8·32	8·20	8·08	7·97
1	8·33	8·22	8·11	8·00	7·88	7·77
2	8·12	8·02	7·91	7·80	7·69	7·58
3	7·93	7·82	7·72	7·61	7·51	7·40
4	7·74	7·64	7·53	7·43	7·33	7·23
5	7·56	7·46	7·36	7·26	7·16	7·07
6	7·39	7·29	7·20	7·10	7·01	6·91
7	7·22	7·13	7·04	6·95	6·85	6·76
8	7·06	6·97	6·89	6·80	6·71	6·62
9	6·91	6·83	6·74	6·66	6·57	6·48
10	6·77	6·69	6·60	6·52	6·44	6·35
11	6·63	6·55	6·47	6·39	6·31	6·23
12	6·50	6·43	6·35	6·27	6·19	6·11
13	6·38	6·31	6·23	6·15	6·08	6·00
14	6·26	6·19	6·11	6·04	5·97	5·89
15	6·14	6·07	6·00	5·93	5·86	5·79
16	6·03	5·96	5·89	5·82	5·76	5·69
17	5·93	5·86	5·79	5·72	5·66	5·59
18	5·83	5·76	5·69	5·63	5·56	5·49
19	5·73	5·66	5·60	5·53	5·47	5·40
20	5·63	5·56	5·50	5·44	5·38	5·31
21	5·53	5·47	5·41	5·35	5·29	5·22
22	5·44	5·38	5·32	5·26	5·20	5·13
23	5·35	5·29	5·23	5·17	5·11	5·04
24	5·26	5·20	5·14	5·09	5·03	4·95
25	5·17	5·12	5·06	5·00	4·95	4·86

combination with the excess base, which allows sea water to hold larger amounts of CO_2 than distilled water at the same partial pressure.

Laboratory Sea Water

The sea water which is used in the aquaria of marine laboratories often differs substantially from natural sea water for various reasons. Different laboratories have their own methods of maintaining a sea-water circulation. The majority use sea water pumped from the sea and circulated in a closed system for variable periods. This, of course, is subject to evaporation and liable to concentration. Owing to the death and decomposition of animals, especially in warm weather, there may be an increase in the amount of organic matter in circulation. Oxygen levels in tanks may fall well below saturation, depending on total respiratory exchanges of aquarium animals. The hydrogen ion concentration tends to rise owing to the absence of plants, and some laboratories raise the pH by liming, or by the addition of sodium bicarbonate. In the Plymouth Laboratory, for example, water of salinity 38‰ and pH 7·9 had a calcium content of 0·62 g/l., compared with 0·39 g/l. in outside sea water. The experimental worker should take these factors into consideration when planning experiments which involve the use of aquarium water (1, 13, 41).

Physical Properties of Sea Water

These are outlined below under the headings of temperature, viscosity and density, light and pressure.

Temperature. The range of temperatures encountered in the sea is notably small when compared with conditions over the land surface. This is true whether diurnal variations, seasonal variations or changes with latitude are considered. The narrow temperature range of oceanic water results from the steady system of oceanic circulation and the high specific heat of water. The coldest waters are those of antarctic seas, where temperatures of $- 1·9°C$ are encountered at the edge of the ice pack. The warmest waters are found in partially enclosed areas north of the equator —the Red Sea, Gulf of Oman and the Persian Gulf—where temperatures of 35°C are attained, while the temperatures in small tropical lagoons and tidal pools may reach 40°C. In the open oceans, however, temperatures are much lower and rarely reach 30°C. The annual and latitudinal range of temperatures throughout all temperate and sub-tropical seas lies between 0 and 28°C, and at no place in the open ocean is the annual range of temperature more than 10°C.

These are surface temperatures, and it is found that with increasing depth not only does the temperature drop, but seasonal variations become negligible and disappear below depths of 200 metres. Thus in tropical waters, when the surface temperature is say, 25°C, the temperature at 200 metres is 20°C, at 1,200 metres is 5°C, below which the temperature continues to fall to minimal values of 1–2°C in abyssal regions (37).

Average surface temperatures for all the oceans range from about 27°C near the equator to $- 1°C$ in arctic and antarctic regions. In the northern hemisphere the mean surface temperature is about 3°C higher than in the southern, and there are also differences between the average temperatures of the several oceans.

It is apparent, therefore, that the oceans furnish a relatively stable thermal environment for the animals occurring therein. Some marine organisms are very sensitive to temperature changes, but the relative uniformity of water temperatures over vast areas minimizes the effects of this environmental variable. Temperature affects animals in several ways; extremes of temperature establish lethal parameters which can restrict the distribution of a species. By its effect on metabolism, temperature regulates spawning and affects development and growth. Because of the inverse relationship between viscosity and temperature, it also influences the rate of sinking of small planktonic organisms, as described in the next section.

Few animals have a universal distribution, a notable exception being the ctenophore *Beroë cucumis*. This species ranges from arctic to tropical regions, but there are probably physiological differences between animals from warm and cold waters, which are either due to acclimatization or have a genotypic basis. The widely distributed common solitary sea-squirt *Ciona intestinalis* has been shown to comprise several distinct physiological races which have different temperature optima for breeding.

In addition, some species, which are found at the surface in colder seas, extend across the equator, but in deeper and colder waters around 400 metres or more (18).

Temperature is a major environmental factor determining the range of a species, and many examples of this effect may be found among benthic as well as pelagic animals. The reef-building madreporarians are unable to tolerate temperatures below 20°C and are restricted to shallow inter-tropical waters between latitudes 25°N. and 25°S. The restrictive effect of temperature may be operative on somatic metabolism, or on reproductive activity. Thus the native British oyster *Ostrea edulis* breeds when the temperature rises above 15°C whereas the Portuguese oyster *Crassostrea angulata* requires a sea temperature of 20°C before it will commence spawning, and hence cannot reproduce itself in British waters where the temperature in inshore waters does not exceed 16°C.

The rate of metabolism is greatly increased in poikilothermic animals by rise of temperature. According to van't Hoff's rule the increase in metabolic rate for each 10°C rise in temperature (Q_{10}) is two- to threefold. External temperatures, therefore, will profoundly affect all the vital activities of the organism, development, growth, reproduction, digestion, etc. In species inhabiting temperate and boreal waters, vital activities occur at a lower level than in corresponding forms from tropical regions, and will be further depressed during the colder winter months of the year. Similar conditions may be expected in bathypelagic and bathybenthic animals (*vide* Chapter 4).

Viscosity and Density. The viscosity and density of sea water are proper-ties of great biological significance in relation to movement and suspension of marine organisms. The viscosity of sea water is slightly greater than that of fresh water, and increases gradually with rise in salinity, and to a much greater extent with fall in temperature. At a salinity of 35‰, for example, the increase of viscosity is almost twofold for a temperature drop from 25–0°C.

The viscosity of sea water is high compared with that of air, and offers much frictional resistance to the passage of bodies through it. Neverthe-less, some active nektonic animals are able to swim at surprisingly high speeds, e.g. whales, porpoises, penguins and scombrid fishes. We usually find that active swimmers are streamlined in some manner as an adapta-tion for securing higher locomotory efficiency. Streamlining is rather a loose term, but it refers usually to the possession of a smooth tapering shape with a minimal amount of projecting surface that could offer resistance to progression. Some animals with large rounded heads and tapering trunks are almost ideally streamlined, for example sperm whales. Besides laminar viscosity, which is concerned with the movement of thin uniform layers of fluid gliding smoothly over one another, progression nearly always involves some degree of eddy viscosity and turbulence as well. A streamlined form produces less turbulence and drag, and the animal accordingly encounters less resistance to its progress through the water.

The density of sea water is correlated with salinity and temperature. At atmospheric pressure and 0°C the specific gravity of sea water of salinity 35‰ is about 1·028. The specific gravity decreases with rise in temperature, and is increased slightly by high pressures (Fig. 1.5).

The cells and tissues of marine animals have nearly the same specific gravity as sea water, which accordingly forms a circumambient medium supporting their bodies. The density and viscosity of sea water are also important statically in the flotation of planktonic organisms. To maintain themselves in the surface waters, or at particular levels, the organisms concerned must either be no heavier than the water, if they are quiescent, or expend energy actively in order to counteract the pull of gravity and maintain their position.

Among animals that have an overall specific gravity less than or equal to sea water are siphonophores which have gas-filled floats (pneumatophores), such as the Portuguese man-o'-war *Physalia* and the by-the-wind sailor *Velella*. Those teleosts with swim-bladders are able to achieve the same result by controlling the volume of gases in the air-bladder, which acts as a buoyancy organ. The pelagic cephalopods *Nautilus* and *Spirula* have a chambered shell containing air, and the planktonic snail *Glaucus* is said to contain intestinal gases which fulfil a similar role.

Other adaptations serve to lower the specific gravity of marine organisms relative to sea water, and thus reduce the sinking factor. Pelagic animals frequently have the skeleton reduced compared with benthic forms, or have lost it altogether, e.g. the pelagic holothurian *Pelagothuria*, heteropods, pteropods, the pelagic lamellibranch *Planktomya*, pelagic crustaceans, cephalopods and fishes. A relative decrease in weight is also achieved by incorporating large amounts of water in the body tissues. This phenomenon is widespread in pelagic animals, many of which have soft transparent tissues of a jelly-like consistency (coelenterates, pelagic annelids, chaetognaths, pelagic cephalopods, salps and fish).

Light. Light is rapidly absorbed when passing through the surface waters of the sea and the intensity falls off with depth. Transmission of light through sea water is of great biological importance from several aspects. Since daylight provides the energy for photosynthetic activity it is one factor regulating the growth of plants, upon which animals ultimately depend for foodstuffs. The majority of animals are sensitive to light which acts as an environmental stimulus. Some of the more complex biological phenomena that are governed by changes in light intensity are phototactic responses, the diurnal migrations of planktonic animals, the incidence of reproductive activity, colour-responses and alterations in pigment-density. The absence of daylight in the deeper waters of the ocean has resulted in peculiar morphological and ethological specializations, and

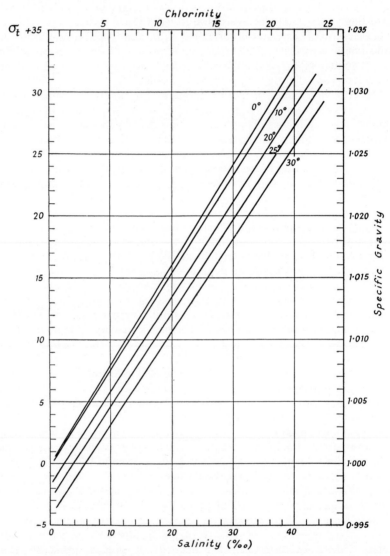

FIG. 1.5. GRAPHS SHOWING THE RELATIONSHIP BETWEEN THE SPECIFIC GRAVITY OF SEA WATER AT SELECTED TEMPERATURES, AND SALINITY AND CHLORINITY

many marine animals have developed luminescent organs for use at night or in the ocean depths.

When light passes through sea water it suffers diminution in intensity owing to the absorptive power of water and solutes and the scattering effects of water molecules and suspended particles. Pure water allows maximal penetration of radiant energy in the visible portion of the spectrum from 400 mμ to 580 mμ (violet to yellow), less of light waves from 580 mμ to 700 mμ (orange and red), while ultra-violet and infra-red are heavily absorbed. In oceanographical work the rate of decrease of light with depth is given by the extinction coefficient

$$\mu_v = 2\cdot30 \ (\log_{10} p_1 - \log_{10} p_2)/d$$

where p_1 and p_2 are the percentage illuminations at two points differing in depth by d metres. The extinction coefficient is a measure of the true absorption by sea water, absorption by coloured substances in solution if any, and scattering of light by suspended particles (34).

The amount of light which penetrates into the sea depends on several factors, namely surface intensity and the transparency of the water. There are obvious diurnal, seasonal and latitudinal changes in the intensity of incident light. A variable amount of the light that falls on the surface of the sea is reflected back, the amount being minimal when the sun is at the zenith. Oblique rays, on entering the water, must travel farther than vertical rays to reach the same depth, and are quickly absorbed before they penetrate far beneath the surface (37).

Studies in different regions have shown that the transmission of light in the sea varies widely with locality. Light penetration is maximal in the open ocean in the tropics, where turbidity and plankton density are low and the sun's rays at noon fall vertically on the surface, and is reduced at higher latitudes. In general, absorption is much greater in coastal than in oceanic waters because of the greater turbidity of the former (Fig. 1.6). Oceanic waters off the coast of Washington, for example, show minimal extinction coefficients twice that of pure water, and maximal values up to ten times as great. In coastal waters (Strait of Juan de Fuca), minimal and maximal values are sixteen times and thirty-four times as great as those for pure water.

Absorption changes across the visible spectrum according to the character of the water. In clear oceanic water, with a minimal content of suspended matter and organisms, penetration is greatest in the blue and least in the red region of the spectrum, whereas in coastal waters containing more suspended material, maximal penetration shifts to the green. This is due to the differential scattering effects of particulate matter on light of different wave-lengths, the blue end of the spectrum being affected most.

Utterback (38), who has investigated light penetration off the coast of Washington, found that clear oceanic water had maximal transparency at wave-length 480 mμ, at which 97·5% of the radiation penetrated 1 metre; and in coastal waters, maximal transparency occurred at 530 mμ, with

84·5% penetration. Similar results have been obtained elsewhere, and contrasting data for the Sargasso Sea and the English Channel are shown in Figs. 1.7 and 1.8. Very turbid coastal and estuarine waters show much lower values than these, and maximal penetration shifts towards the red end of the spectrum under such conditions (2, 3, 9, 14, 15).

Earlier estimates of illumination levels in deep waters have been superseded by photo-electric measurements, and data are now available showing how light intensities change during the day at various depths in the water column. Detectable light from the surface has been recorded down to 950 metres in the Caribbean (light intensities around $10^{-6}\ \mu W/cm^2$ receptor

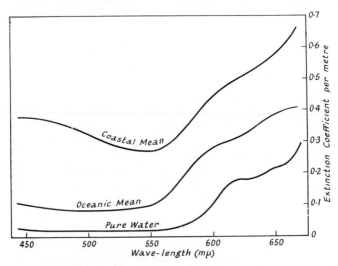

FIG. 1.6. SMOOTHED GRAPHS SHOWING THE EXTINCTION COEFFICENTS FOR LIGHT OF DIFFERENT WAVE-LENGTHS IN PURE WATER, AND IN DIFFERENT KINDS OF SEA WATER

(After Sverdrup, Johnson, and Fleming (37) from Utterback's data)

surface). At greater depths the light produced by animals becomes more pronounced and interferes with detection of attenuated surface light. At certain stations in the West Atlantic, background light remained constant or increased at depths greater than 300 metres, and individual flashes at 600 metres were as much as 1,000 times brighter than background illumination (9, 10, 28).

There is little information available for the photo-sensitivity of marine animals in weak illumination, but what there is suggests that some species possess a sensitivity at least equal to that of man, about $1 \times 10^{-8}\ \mu W/cm^2$ receptor surface, and special adaptations in deep-sea fishes may result in greater sensitivity (*see* Chapter 8).

Light and Pelagic Animals. Many plankton species in upper pelagic waters exhibit vertical migrations of great magnitude. These are responses

to changes in light intensity and are discussed in Chapter 8. Other phenomena of great interest concern differences in the pigmentation, eyes and
luminescent organs of pelagic animals from different depths. In the upper
waters many animals are transparent, or are tinted with blue. Below the
photosynthetic zone, where the light becomes weak, silvery fishes form a
conspicuous element of the fauna, and there is an increase in the number
of reddish or dark-coloured species. At greater depths, where daylight
fails, uniform dark colours, black, violet or red, prevail. Since the longer
wave-lengths of visible light are rapidly absorbed in the open sea, reddish-

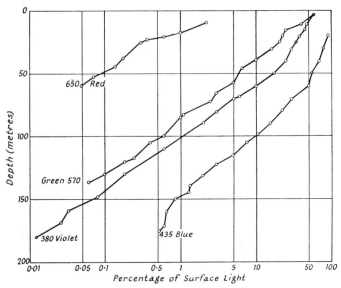

FIG. 1.7. PENETRATION OF DAYLIGHT INTO OCEANIC WATER (SARGASSO SEA)

The numbers on the graphs refer to the median of the spectral ranges which are as
follows: red, 600–700; blue, 346–526; violet, 310–450; green, 490–620 mμ. (From
Clarke and Backus (9).)

coloured crustaceans in the twilight zone will reflect little incident light
and in fact appear black at levels below about 25 metres.

The eyes also exhibit great transformations, and those of mesopelagic
animals are sometimes large and specialized in shape and structure.
Degeneration of eyes is uncommon among abyssal cephalopods and fish,
but in some genera—e.g. *Macrurus* (Teleostei)—the species occurring
below the level of light penetration tend to have smaller eyes than mesopelagic forms inhabiting the twilight zone. Certain bathypelagic species of
crustaceans, squid and fish, however, have completely degenerate eyes and
are blind. Some groups also show a correlation between the size of the
eyes and the presence or absence of photophores. There are luminescent
animals at all levels in the sea, but it is estimated that luminescence is most

common among crustaceans, cephalopods and fishes of the dimly lighted mesopelagic region. Complex photophores are characteristic of animals in this region, but many light-producing organisms are also found at greater depths, either in abyssal pelagic waters or on the bottom (31, 39, 40).

Pressure. Pressure alterations with depth form a major environmental variable in the bionomics of marine animals. Pressure increases by about

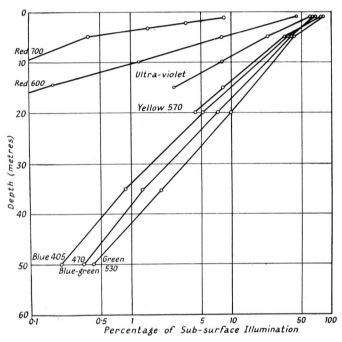

FIG. 1.8. PENETRATION OF DAYLIGHT INTO COASTAL WATER (ENGLISH CHANNEL)

The graphs refer to spectral ranges as follows: red 700+; red 600+; ultra-violet, 330–420; yellow, 550–80; blue, 330–480; blue-green, 455–80; green, 480–580 mμ. (After Atkins (2).)

1 atmosphere for each 10 metres increase in depth, and shows a range from zero at the surface to some 1,000 atmospheres in the ocean deeps.

Great pressures such as occur in the ocean depths are known to have profound effects on certain physiological and biochemical processes, but relatively little is known about how they influence marine animals. It has long been recognized that life exists in the abyssal regions, and the organisms occurring there are certainly physiologically adjusted to the great pressures which they encounter. Specimens have been obtained from the Philippine trench at over 10,400 metres, namely actinians, lamellibranchs, holothurians and echinoids, all of which were dead on reaching the surface (7).

The biological effects of pressure are certain to be complex. The volume of water changes only slightly under compression: this amounts to about 0·46% at 1,000 m, 3·30% at 8,000 m, and 5·01% at 10,000 m (0°C). At any given depth the pressures inside and outside the animal will be the same, and even if the animal changes its level, mechanical changes due to alterations in volume will be very small and will be equally distributed so long as air is absent. It is conjectural whether pressure limits the vertical range of motile species, since other factors may intervene before they exceed the pressure change which they can tolerate. Some species carry out vertical migrations of up to 400 metres (equivalent to 40 atmospheres), and can be designated eurybathic, or tolerant of pressure change. There are other benthic species which are known to have extraordinary vertical ranges, e.g. *Henricia sanguinolenta*, an asteroid, has been reported from inshore waters to depths of some 2,500 metres, equivalent to a pressure range of 0–250 atmospheres. Conditions in vertebrates are somewhat different, since many pelagic teleosts have an air-filled hydrostatic organ, and cetaceans dive with inflated lungs. Teleosts are often brought to the surface with inflated sounds as the result of the sudden pressure change, but this gives no indication of their powers of accommodation to pressure alterations which take place more gradually. The reader is referred to p. 399 for a discussion of the physiology of the teleostean air-bladder, and to p. 170 for a discussion of problems of respiration in cetaceans. Baro-sensitivity is discussed on p. 347.

The ability of marine organisms to survive great changes in pressure has been investigated experimentally to a limited extent. Particularly interesting data have been obtained for bacteria, which may be expected to throw some light on the effect of pressure changes on biochemical processes. Marine bacteria are abundant in nearly all bottom deposits, and Zobell (45) has obtained samples from the Philippine trench at depths exceeding 10,000 metres. When cultured, many of the bacteria from these abyssal depths survived at a temperature of 30°C and at atmospheric pressure. Significantly larger bacterial counts, however, were obtained in cultures incubated at 2·5°C and under pressures of 1,000 atmospheres, than at 30°C and at atmospheric pressure (46).

Some experiments have been carried out on the ability of marine animals to withstand great changes in pressure. Beebe attached a lobster (*Panulirus argus*?) to his bathysphere during one of his descents, and recorded that the animal survived a dive to 671 metres (pressure of about 67 atmospheres). The effect of hydrostatic pressures up to 1,000 atmospheres has been tested by Regnard (35) on a wide variety of organisms. Experiments of this sort have shown that it is always possible to kill shallow-water animals by exposure to a sufficiently high pressure, somewhere between 400 and 1,000 atmospheres. Molluscs (*Cardium*), annelids (*Nereis*), crustaceans (*Eupagurus*) and tunicates are inactivated by an exposure of one hour to 400–600 atmospheres. Some other forms are more resistant and survive an hour's exposure to 1,000 atmospheres, but considerable swelling takes place and normal activity returns only after some hours (8, 35).

Animals are usually dead when brought to the surface from great depths. In this process various factors besides pressure changes are also operative, such as mechanical disturbance and temperature alterations, and these may be lethal in themselves, quite apart from changes in pressure *per se*.

The effect of these pressure changes on the functioning of tissues is still imperfectly understood. It has been shown that the compressibility of muscle (rabbit) is approximately 88% of that of pure water, and at 500 atmospheres the volume of the muscle is decreased by almost 2%. Some interesting data are available about the physiological effect of pressure on various tissues and extracts, but all derived from shallow-water or terrestrial animals. Pressure inhibits gelation of protoplasm, solation results, and the cell loses its power of contraction. Disappearance of movement and contraction following rise of pressure has been observed in *Amoeba*, dividing egg cells (*Arbacia*) and chromatophores (*Fundulus*). Effective pressures for producing these effects lie between about 350–550 atmospheres. Pressure also reduces the beat of the embryonic fish heart (*Fundulus*), affects ciliary movement (*Mytilus*), abolishes muscle contraction (striated muscle, frog) and blocks nerve conduction (frog), the effective absolute pressures varying with the tissues under investigation (8, 33).

Moderate hydrostatic pressures (300–500 atmospheres) are known to affect many biochemical processes. On luminous bacteria the effect of pressure is to alter light intensity at temperatures departing from the optimum. When highly purified preparations of luciferin and luciferase (luminescent substrate and activating enzyme) are tested, it is found that pressure reversibly increases light intensity over a wide temperature range once the reaction is under way. Effects of this kind are explained on the grounds that some oxidative enzyme reactions proceed with a large volume increase, which is opposed by pressure and results in change of reaction rate and displacement of equilibrium. Each reaction displays its own peculiarities and must be interpreted separately. For example, the positive pressure effect shown by the luminescent reaction of ostracod extracts is due to a shift in equilibrium of a non-luminous oxidation of substrate, which proceeds with volume increase and is opposed by pressure. As a result, the concentration of luciferin substrate available for the luminescent oxidation reaction is increased (6, 24).

It is generally believed that the most significant effect of pressure on biological systems lies in the volume changes which it brings about. At high pressures protein molecules are compressed, denatured and altered in structure and chemical activity. In the ocean depths two factors, low temperatures and high pressures, both of which affect the rate of biological processes, are acting concomitantly, and the animals of the abyss must be genotypically modified to withstand the conditions obtaining there.

REFERENCES

1. ATKINS, W. R. G., "Note on the condition of the water in a marine aquarium," *J. Mar. Biol. Ass. U.K.*, **17**, 479 (1931).
2. ATKINS, W. R. G., "Daylight and its penetration into the sea," *Trans. Illum. Engng. Soc.*, **10** (7), 12 pp. (1945).
3. ATKINS, W. R. G. and POOLE, H. H., "The photo-electric measurement of the penetration of light of various wave-lengths into the sea and the physiological bearing of the results," *Phil. Trans. Roy. Soc. B.*, **222**, 129 (1933).
4. BASSINDALE, R., "Studies on the biology of the Bristol Channel. XI," *J. Ecol.*, **31**, 1 (1943).
5. BROEKHUYSEN, G. J., "A preliminary investigation of the importance of desiccation, temperature and salinity as factors controlling the vertical distribution of certain intertidal marine gastropods in False Bay, South Africa," *Trans. Roy. Soc. S. Afr.*, **28**, 255 (1941).
6. BRONK, J. R., HARVEY, E. N. and JOHNSON, F. H., "The effects of hydrostatic pressure on luminescent extracts of the ostracod crustacean, *Cypridina*," *J. Cell. Comp. Physiol.*, **40**, 347 (1952).
7. BRUNN, A. F., "The Philippine trench and its bottom fauna," *Nature*, **168**, 692 (1951).
8. CATTELL, M., "The physiological effects of pressure," *Biol. Rev.*, **11**, 441 (1936).
9. CLARKE, G. L. and BACKUS, R. H., "Measurements of light penetration in relation to vertical migration and records of luminescence of deep-sea animals," *Deep-Sea Research*, **4**, 1 (1956).
10. CLARKE, G. L. and WERTHEIM, G. K., "Measurements of illumination at great depths and at night in the Atlantic Ocean by means of a new bathyphotometer," *Deep-Sea Research*, **3**, 189 (1956).
11. COKER, R. E., *This Great and Wide Sea* (Chapel Hill, Univ. N.C. Press, 1947).
12. COLMAN, J. S., *The Sea and its Mysteries* (London, Bell, 1950).
13. COOPER, L. H. N., "On the effect of long-continued additions of lime to aquarium sea water," *J. Mar. Biol. Ass. U.K.*, **18**, 201 (1932).
14. COOPER, L. H. N. and MILNE, A., "The ecology of the Tamar estuary. 2. Under-water illumination," *ibid.*, **22**, 509 (1938).
15. COOPER, L. H. N. and MILNE, A., "The ecology of the Tamar estuary. 5. Under-water illumination. Revision of data for red light," *ibid.*, **23**, 391 (1939).
16. DELLOW, V., "Inter-tidal ecology at Narrow Neck Reef, New Zealand. (Studies in inter-tidal zonation. 3)," *Pacif. Sci.*, **4**, 355 (1950).
17. EDNEY, E. B., "Body temperature of arthropods," *Nature*, **170**, 586 (1952).
18. EKMAN, S., *Zoogeography of the Sea* (London, Sidgwick and Jackson, 1953).
19. EVANS, R. G., "The lethal temperatures of some common British littoral molluscs," *J. Anim. Ecol.*, **17**, 165 (1948).
20. FOX, C. J. J., "On the coefficients of absorption of the atmospheric gases in distilled water and sea water. 1. Nitrogen and oxygen," *Publ. Circ. Cons. Explor. Mer.*, No. 41, 23 pp. (1907).

21. GOLDBERG, E. D., "The oceans as a chemical system," *The Sea, Ideas* and *Observations on Progress in the Study of the Seas*, (Hill, M. N., general editor), **2**, 3 (New York, London, Interscience, 1963).

22. GOLDSCHMIDT, V. M., *Geochemistry*, Muir, A.Ed. (Oxford, Clarendon Press, 1954).

23. GUNTER, G., "Seasonal population changes and distributions as related to salinity, of certain invertebrates of the Texas coast," *Publ. Inst. Mar. Sci. Univ. Tex.*, **1** (2), 7 (1950).

24. HARVEY, E. N., *Bioluminescence* (New York, Academic Press, 1952).

25. HARVEY, H. W., *Recent Advances in the Chemistry and Biology of Sea Water* (Cambridge Univ. Press, 1945).

26. HARVEY, H. W., *The Chemistry and Fertility of Sea Waters* (Cambridge Univ. Press, 1955).

27. HEDGPETH, J. W. (Ed.), *Treatise on Marine Ecology and Paleoecology*, **1**, Ecology (*Mem. Geol. Soc. Amer.*, **67**, 1957).

28. HILL, M. N. (Ed.), *The Sea*, I and II (New York and London, Interscience, 1962).

29. LEWIS, J. B., "Environmental and tissue temperatures of some tropical intertidal marine animals," *Biol. Bull.*, **124**, 275 (1963).

30. MACGINITIE, G. E. and MACGINITIE, N., *Natural History of Marine Animals* (London, McGraw-Hill, 1949).

31. MARSHALL, N. B., *Aspects of Deep Sea Biology* (London, Hutchinson, 1954).

32. MOORE, H. B., *Marine Ecology* (London, Chapman & Hall, 1958).

33. PEASE, D. C. and KITCHING, J. A., "The influence of hydrostatic pressure upon ciliary frequency," *J. Cell. Comp. Physiol.*, **14**, 135 (1939).

34. POOLE, H. H. and ATKINS, W. R. G., "The penetration into the sea of light of various wave-lengths as measured by emission or rectifier photo-electric cells," *Proc. Roy. Soc. B.*, **123**, 151 (1937).

35. REGNARD, P., *Recherches Expérimentales sur les Conditions Physiques de la Vie dans les Eaux* (Paris, Masson, 1891).

36. RICKETTS, E. F. and CALVIN, J., *Between Pacific Tides*, 3rd ed., revised by Hedgpeth, J. W. (California, Stanford Univ. Press, 1952).

37. SVERDRUP, H. U., JOHNSON, M. W. and FLEMING, R. H., *The Oceans, their Physics, Chemistry and General Biology* (New York, Prentice Hall, 1942).

38. UTTERBACK, C. L., "Spectral bands of submarine solar radiation in the North Pacific and adjacent inshore waters," *Rapp. Cons. Explor. Mer*, **101** (2), 4, 15 pp., 1936).

39. WELSH, J. H. and CHASE, F. A. JR., "Eyes of deep-sea crustaceans. 1. Acanthephyridae," *Biol. Bull.*, **72**, 57 (1937).

40. WELSH, J. H. and CHASE, F. A. JR., "Eyes of deep-sea crustaceans. 2. Sergestidae," ibid., **74**, 364 (1938).

41. WILSON, D. P., "The aquarium and sea-water circulation system at the Plymouth Laboratory," *J. Mar. Biol. Ass. U.K.*, **31**, 193 (1952).

42. WILSON, D. P. and ARMSTRONG, F. A. J., "Biological differences between sea waters: experiments in 1953," ibid., **33**, 347 (1954).

43. YONGE, C. M., *A Year on the Great Barrier Reef* (London, Putnam, 1930).

44. YONGE, C. M., *The Sea Shore* (London, Collins, 1949).

45. ZOBELL, C. E., "Bacterial life at the bottom of the Philippine trench," *Science*, **115**, 507 (1952).

46. ZOBELL, C. E. and JOHNSON, F. H., "The influence of hydrostatic pressure on the growth and viability of terrestrial and marine bacteria," *J. Bact.*, **57**, 179 (1949).

CHAPTER 2

WATER, SALTS AND MINERALS

The stability of the *milieu intérieur* is the primary condition for freedom
and independence of existence; the mechanism which allows of this is
that which insures in the *milieu intérieur* the maintenance of all the
conditions necessary to the life of the (tissue) elements.

CLAUDE BERNARD

THE total amount of water contained in the body varies greatly from
species to species, but for each kind of animal there is usually a characteristic value, or range of values for different functional states. The water
content is high in many transparent pelagic forms, amounting to about
96% in the common jellyfish *Aurelia aurita*. Generally the water content
of animals lies between 70 and 85% (Table 2.1). In any given animal
there are differences in the amounts of water contained in the various
tissues. Nevertheless, the osmotic concentrations throughout an organism
are approximately equal and animals with greatly different water contents
may have similar osmotic concentrations. This is explained by the fact
that only a proportion of the substances composing an organism are
osmotically active; bone, connective tissue and shell, for example, may
be considered as osmotically inert (16).

The osmotically active substances found in animals comprise, broadly,
electrolytes, organic non-electrolytes and colloids (proteins). Within the
organism the cells are in osmotic equilibrium with their surroundings—
blood, lymph and tissue fluids. The concentrations of individual ions
within the cells, however, are markedly different from the concentrations
existing in the circumambient tissue fluids, and the presence of selectively
permeable cellular membranes bars the passage of certain ions, or retains
diffusible organic molecules at relatively high levels.

OSMOTIC ADJUSTMENT AND REGULATION

In the normal environment characteristic of the species, animals tend to
maintain their water content at a constant level referable to some basic
relationship such as water/protein ratio. In the maintenance of a steady
and optimal water content, osmotic adjustments and regulations are
fundamentally concerned. Marine animals, vertebrates excepted, generally
are in osmotic equilibrium with their environment. This is true of most
members of predominantly marine groups (e.g. Scyphomedusae, Polychaeta, Mollusca, Crustacea, Echinodermata, Ascidiacea). Marine
animals have repeatedly invaded fresh waters and the land by various
routes, through estuaries, up the shore or across brackish reaches of

meadows and swamps, and many instances of such transitions may be found on the margins of the oceans at the present time. But the sea has also been reinvaded from estuaries and the land, as witness the existence of marine pulmonates, insects, birds and mammals. In these transitional reaches between different environments the osmotic conditions present special difficulties to organisms, and these have been solved in various ways.

On entering aqueous media of different salt concentration, or emerging into the atmosphere where there is risk of desiccation, organisms are subjected to osmotic stress. Under the former conditions some animals adjust themselves osmotically by passive alteration of the concentration of their body fluids towards that of the external medium, and are said to be poikilosmotic. Others possess powers of osmotic homoeostasis to greater or lesser degree, and are able to regulate the osmotic level of their internal fluids within certain limits independently of the environment, and these organisms are termed homoiosmotic. Other terms in common use are stenohaline referring to animals which can tolerate only limited changes in salinity, and euryhaline referring to animals which can stand wide fluctuations in salinity.

Physico-chemical Relations

In experiments dealing with osmoregulation the osmotic pressures of the body fluids are usually expressed as depressions of the freezing point, although chloride concentrations sometimes are given as a rough measure of osmotic pressure. The salt concentrations of sea water are expressed variously as salinities (‰), chlorinities (‰), grammes per litre, or as percentages (grammes per 100 c.c.). Sea water of chlorinity 19‰ (salinity 34·325‰) has a freezing-point depression of $-1·872°C$. This is equivalent osmotically to 0·56 molal NaCl (32·15 g/l). The depression of the freezing point of sea-water samples can be calculated from the chlorinity by means of the equation

$$\varDelta = -0·0966\ Cl - 0·0000052\ Cl^3$$

Values of $\varDelta$ for sea water of different salinities are plotted in Fig. 2.1, and the graphs in Fig. 1.5 show the variation in specific gravity of sea water at five selected temperatures as a function of salinity and chlorinity. Some workers, on occasion, have expressed salt concentrations in terms of osmotically equivalent solutions of NaCl. For the convenience of the reader concentrations of NaCl and sucrose are related to freezing-point depressions in the graphs of Fig. 2.2 (for further details *see* Appendix).

Osmotic Adjustment in Poikilosmotic Animals

Most marine invertebrates are isosmotic with their environment and some of the poikilosmotic forms can endure a certain amount of dilution of the medium and still function effectively. When the outer coating is permeable, water flows in or out of the animal according to the external

M.A.—2*

TABLE 2.1
Composition of Marine Animals
Percentage of Wet Weight

Animal	Water	Total organic matter	Protein	Fat	Carbo-hydrate	Total inorganic matter	Salt (a) Ash (b)	Source
Coelenterata								
Aequorea aequorea	96·45	0·85	—	—	—	—	2·70 (b)	9
Aurelia aurita	95·56–96	—	0·67	—	—	—	3·2 (a)	10, 11, 12
Anemonia sulcata	87·56	10·68	—	—	—	1·60	—	14
Turbellaria								
Thysanozoon brocchii	73·92	—	—	1·22[5]	—	—	3·21 (b)	13
Nemertinea								
Cerebratulus marginatus	77·56–81·17	—	13·98–14·56	1·33–2·19[5]	1·26–2·47[2]	—	2·35–3·36 (b)	13
Polychaeta								
Perinereis cultrifera	75·35	21·46	16·85	2·58[5]	—	—	3·19 (b)	13
Arenicola marina	78·6	7·91	—	0·54[5]	0·38[2]	—	13·49 (b)	13
Chaetopterus variopedatus	85·61	10·66	8·36	0·89[5]	—	—	3·73 (b)	13
Gastropoda								
Archidoris pseudoargus	82·4	—	5·1[4]	0·32[1]	0·23[2]	—	10·51[8]	16
Lamellibranchia								
Mytilus edulis (whole mussel)	43	—	4·8	0·7	1·53	—	1·0 (b)	1
M. edulis (edible portion)	83·8	—	9·94	1·64	1·74	—	1·95 (b)	1
Pecten gibbus (edible portion)	80·3	—	14·8[4]	0·1	3·4	—	1·4 (b)	1
Mya arenaria	49·9[6]	—	5·0[4]	0·6	1·1	—	1·5[8]	1
Venus mercenaria (whole animal)	28·0[7]	—	2·1[4]	0·1	1·4	—	0·9[8]	1
V. mercenaria (edible portion)	80·8	—	10·6[4]	1·1	5·2	—	2·3[8]	1
Ostrea virginica (edible portion)	86·0	—	6·2	1·2	3·7	—	2·0 (b)	1
Crustacea								
Calanus finmarchicus	80	—	11–14	2–9	—	—	0·7 (b)	6, 7

	Water		N × 6.25[4]	[1]	[2]/[3]		[b]	Source
Homarus americanus (whole animal)	67·33	21·01	10·32[4]	0·95[1]	0·16[2]	11·66	—	1
H. americanus (edible portion)	81·84	—	14·49[4]	1·84[1]	—	—	1·71 [b]	3
Callinectes sapidus (edible portion)	79·04	—	17·95[4]	0·39[1]	0·47[3]	—	2·15 [b]	1
Echinodermata								
Asterias forbesii	67	—	11·3[4]	1·8[1]	—	—	11·7 [b]	8
Selachii								
Squalus brevirostris	87·56	—	—	—	—	—	—	5
Dasyatis akajei	80·26	—	—	—	—	—	—	5
Teleostei								
Clupea harengus (edible portion)	60—76·8	—	18·33[4]	2·2–19·5[1]	—	—	1·66 [b]	2
Gadus callarias (edible portion)	81·35	—	18·44[4]	0·09	—	—	1·23 [b]	2
Melanogrammus aeglifinus (edible portion)	79·17–81·68	—	14·56–16·19[4]	0·09–0·15	—	—	1·01–1·11 [b]	2
Scomberomorus maculatus (edible portion)	64·3–66·99	—	19·31–19·56[4]	12·59–16·24	—	—	1·11–1·2 [b]	2
Pseudopleuronectes americanus (edible portion)	78·4–82·5	—	15·88–16·0[4]	0·2–0·37	—	—	1·17–1·34 [b]	2
Centropristis striatus (edible portion)	77·98–80·56	—	6·04–6·06[4]	1·6–1·61	—	—	1·09–1·23 [b]	2
Ophiodon elongatus (flesh)	79·2	—	18·1	0·7	—	—	1·2 [b]	4

Notes: (1) ether extract;. (2) glycogen; (3), difference; (4) total N × 6·25; (5) petrol-ether extract; (6, 7) refuse, shell, waste, etc., 6–41·9 %, 7–67·5 %; (8) mineral matter.
Sources: 1, Tressler and Lemon (148); 2, Clark and Almy (24); 3, Atwater (1); 4, White (152); 5, King-Li-Pin *et al.* (64); 6 Gunther (42); 7, Orr (102); 8, Hutchinson, *et al.* (52); 9, Hyman (53); 10, Lowndes (82) 11, Hyman (54); 12, Lowndes (83); 13, Brand (18); 14, Bottazz (16); 15, Lovern and Wood (80); 16, McCance and Masters (86).

salt concentration, osmotic equilibrium is attained by transfer of water, and swelling or shrinkage of the body ensues. Probably in all poikilosmotic species some diffusion of salts takes place in addition to water transfer; when salt transfer is rapid the internal body fluids soon approach the external medium in salt concentration, and there is little or no alteration in body volume.

Marine Protozoa are probably isotonic with sea water and the plasma membrane is permeable to water. The outer covering usually possesses

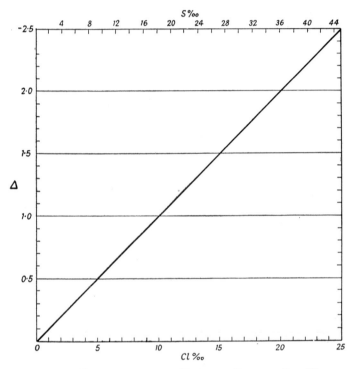

FIG. 2.1. DEPRESSION OF THE FREEZING POINT OF SEA WATER
AS A FUNCTION OF SALINITY AND CHLORINITY

little power of resisting hydrostatic pressure and even in skeletogenous forms (Radiolaria and Foraminifera) there are openings through which the protoplasm stands fully exposed to the external medium. Marine protozoans, as a rule, are slightly heavier than sea water. The flagellate *Noctiluca miliaris*, on the contrary, is demonstrably lighter: when taken from sea water with a specific gravity of 1·024 and tested in more dilute media, *Noctiluca* will just float in sea water of specific gravity 1·014. The animal appears to be in osmotic equilibrium with sea water. The cell sap of *Noctiluca* displays several peculiar chemical features (low SO_4^-, high

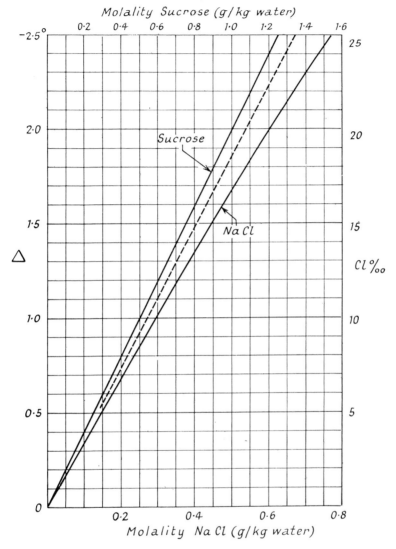

FIG. 2.2. CURVES FOR SOLUTIONS OF SUCROSE AND SODIUM CHLORIDE,
RELATING DEPRESSION OF FREEZING POINT TO CONCENTRATION

acidity, etc.), but it has not yet been possible to relate these to the flotation mechanism with any certainty (26).

Among Metazoa osmotic adjustment has been studied in several species with interesting results. Sipunculid worms such as *Golfingia* (= *Phascolosoma*), *Sipunculus* and *Dendrostoma* tolerate a certain degree of osmotic stress, adjusting to anisosmotic media. *Golfingia gouldii* survives exposure to sea-water concentrations of 55% and 160%, and *Dendrostoma* recovers after loss of 43% of body weight by desiccation. Superficially these animals behave like osmometers, and on transferring to dilute or concentrated

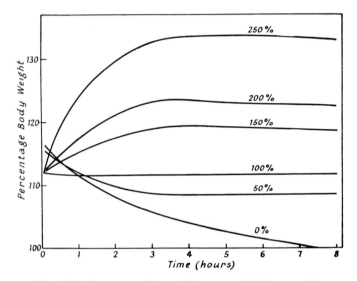

FIG. 2.3. CHANGES IN BODY WEIGHT OF *Golfingia gouldii*
WHEN INJECTED WITH DILUTE AND CONCENTRATED SEA WATER

Worms were injected at 0·2 hour with 12–17% body weight of sea water having the concentrations shown, after which they were immersed in normal sea water. Gradual decrease in weight about four hours after injecting concentrated sea water indicates salt loss. (From Adolph, 1936.)

sea water they swell or shrink rapidly, reaching equilibrium in a day or less. On returning the animals to normal sea water they tend to regain original volume. Again, on injecting sea water of different concentrations, animals subsequently alter in volume to a degree corresponding to the concentrations of the fluids injected, i.e. when injected with hypertonic solutions they swell and when injected with hypotonic solutions they shrink, owing to osmotic transfer of water (Fig. 2.3).

The integument of sipunculids (*Golfingia*, *Dendrostoma*) is semipermeable, permitting osmotic transfer of water in anisosmotic media. In consequence, the body fluids remain isosmotic with the external medium when the concentration of the latter is altered, i.e. osmotic adjustment takes place. Nevertheless, there is some regulation of volume. Specimens of *Dendrostoma* immersed in slightly dilute sea water (90%) swell, but after 24 hours they lose weight and return to normal (Fig. 2.4). Volume control is also shown in concentrated media (120% sea water). Critical studies reveal that the body wall of *Dendrostoma* is highly permeable to water, but only slightly permeable to salts; permeability to water and salts is greater inwards than outwards. Other loci, gut or nephridiopores, how-ever, are more permeable to salt. The increase in volume which occurs

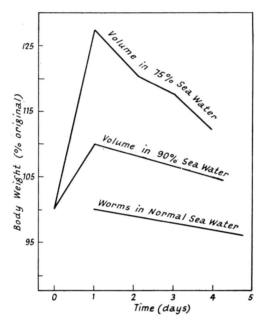

FIG. 2.4. VOLUME CONTROL EXHIBITED BY *Golfingia gouldii* IN
MODERATELY DILUTE SEA WATER (75% AND 90%)
Loss of weight of worms (controls) in normal sea water shown for comparison
Simplified from a diagram of Gross (40).)

when worms are placed in hypo-osmotic media is due to passive diffusion of water across the semipermeable body wall; subsequent volume regula-tion is achieved by loss of salt through nephridiopores and outward diffu-sion of water. In addition to these processes, there is some release of osmotically active particles into the blood from the body wall, tending to counterbalance the loss of salts to the exterior (40).

Other poikilosmotic marine invertebrates which take up water and swell in dilute sea water are *Nereis pelagica*, *Perinereis cultrifera*, *Arenicola marina* and *Sabella pavonina* (Polychaeta); *Mytilus edulis* and "*Doris*" (Mollusca); and *Caudina chilensis* (Holothuria) (Fig. 2.5). Some of these animals, e.g. *Caudina,* suffer salt loss which reduces the degree of swelling.

Experiments with the sea hare *Aplysia punctata* in dilute sea water show that these animals swell rapidly during the first two hours as water is absorbed, but the weight then falls off as salt is lost. On returning to normal sea water there is a further loss in weight since the external medium is now hyperosmotic to the animal (Fig. 2.5). A converse experiment in which *Aplysia* was placed in a solution containing part sea water and part sugar caused the animal to shrink, since the body wall is impermeable to sugar whereas salt diffuses out. Similarly, starfish and echinoids suffer

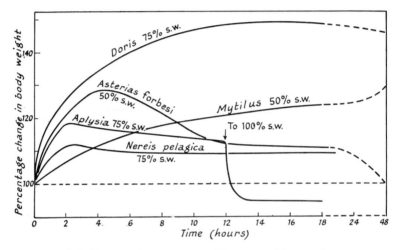

Fig. 2.5. Osmotic Adaptation in Different Marine Animals

Percentage change in body weight of animals placed in dilute sea water. (From Bethe, 1934, and Maloeuf, 1937.)

some weight increase in dilute media, but their hard skeletons restrict volume changes and considerable salt loss is believed to take place (77).

Some of these animals are partly estuarine in habit or occur in enclosed waters of reduced salinity. Thus *Arenicola marina* is found in nature in concentrations down to 23% sea water, and its tissues are capable of functioning in sea water diluted to that extent (Fig. 2.6). Some freezing-point values for this species in natural and experimental media are shown in Table 2.2 (cf. Fig. 2.7). Species such as *A. marina* which can tolerate considerable dilutions of their body fluids are able to live in brackish water of reduced salinities (8‰ and less), but they are unable to tolerate fresh water. To invade rivers and lakes, animals have needed some powers of osmoregulation, together with an integument which resists flooding by water and prevents salt loss.

During short periods some animals are able to fend off unfavourable

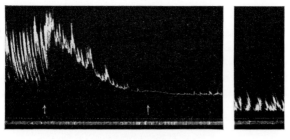

FIG. 2.6. ADAPTATION OF EXTROVERT OF *Arenicola marina* TO
DEPRESSION OF SALINITY

At beginning of experiment preparation was in normal sea water. First arrow indicates start of progressive dilution; second arrow, termination of dilution two hours later, when concentration had fallen to 28% sea water. Second record shows accommodation to diluted medium, at low amplitude, six hours later. Time scale in minutes. (From Wells and Ledingham (1940).)

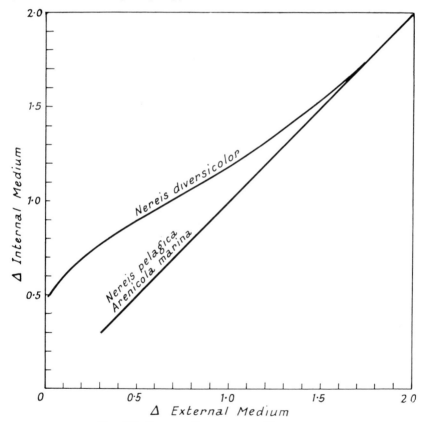

FIG. 2.7. OSMOTIC RELATIONS IN POLYCHAETES

The curves show variation in concentration of internal with external medium. *Nereis diversicolor* regulates at low concentrations; *N. pelagica* and *Arenicola marina* remain isosmotic with the environment. (Based on data of Schlieper's, 1929.)

conditions by shutting themselves off from the outside world, e.g. oysters, mussels and barnacles. In dilute media lamellibranchs such as *Mytilus* and *Scrobicularia* retract their siphons or close their shells, thus protecting the blood from extreme changes in concentration (35). The acorn barnacle *Balanus improvisus* is reported to be markedly euryhaline; specimens

TABLE 2.2

Arenicola marina

		Medium Δ	
		Internal	External
Heligoland	32°/$_{00}$	1·70	1·72
Kiel	14°/$_{00}$	0·76–0·77	0·75
Experimental 26 hours	5°/$_{00}$	0·28–0·30	0·29

of *B. balanoides* and *B. tintinnabulum* can survive for many days in fresh water, or the atmosphere, shutting their valves except for a minute breathing aperture (3). These, of course, are behavioural mechanisms for avoiding inclement conditions.

Littoral prosobranchs show well-marked zonation from permanently submerged to splash-levels and species exposed on the upper shore must be subject to considerable osmotic stress. The osmotic concentration of the blood of periwinkles (species of *Littorina*) follows that of sea water down to half dilution, but it is hyperosmotic in 50% sea water. Limpets (*Acmaea*) do not regulate; their extravisceral water (lying between tissues and shell), however, has limited capacity for osmotic buffering. In a South African investigation it was found that littoral snails could be arranged in a sequence according to tolerance of desiccation and changes of salinity, which sequence accorded with their vertical distribution and with gradation of like conditions in their environment (126, 146).

Among vertebrates hagfishes are poikilosmotic. The blood is slightly hyperosmotic to sea water, and in dilute or concentrated media (salinities, 25–40‰), the blood chloride follows that of the medium. The animals are very permeable to water: in dilute sea water they gain weight rapidly, and then slowly return to initial weight. Hagfishes are exclusively salt-water animals (87).

Osmoregulation

A number of mechanisms are available to euryhaline animals which attempt to keep their internal medium constant in the face of changing external salt concentrations, and these have been utilized in variable degree. Some animals show only very limited powers of osmotic regulation, and from this level there range all degrees of regulatory ability to that possessed by truly homoiosmotic species which are able to maintain their internal fluids fairly constant, irrespective of wide external fluctuations in salinity.

In waters of lowered salt concentration, such as estuaries, animals can passively oppose reduced salinities by means of membranes having reduced permeability to waters and salts. They can also react functionally by actively pumping out the water which tends to flow into the organism, and by absorbing salts from the surrounding medium so as to keep up the internal salt level in the face of various conditions tending to cause internal dilution. Waters of greatly raised salt content are not often encountered by marine animals and are most liable to be found in tidal pools high on the shore which are subject to evaporation during neap tides. Mechanisms utilized against high salinities involve membranes with lowered permeability to water and salts, active absorption of water against a salinity gradient, and secretion of excess salts. All processes involving active transfer of water and salts against osmotic gradients necessitate the expenditure of energy by the organism in the form of osmotic work, and theoretically, should be capable of detection in the form of a corresponding increased level of oxygen consumption.

PROTOZOA. Processes of osmoregulation among protozoans have been linked with activity of the contractile vacuole. This organ is especially characteristic of freshwater Protozoa, but it also occurs in many marine flagellates and ciliates and in freshwater sponges (Table 2.3). In its simplest

TABLE 2.3

SYSTEMATIC OCCURRENCE OF CONTRACTILE VACUOLES IN RELATION TO HABITAT

Class	Freshwater	Marine	Endoparasitic
Rhizopoda	Present	Absent from most	Absent
Mastigophora	Present	Present in many	Absent from nearly all
Ciliophora	Present	Present in most	Present in many
Sporozoa	—	—	Absent from all

form the contractile vacuole consists of a vesicle which contracts rhythmically and discharges its fluid contents through a temporary pore in the body surface. Vacuolar activity is less in marine than in freshwater forms, and there is general agreement that it operates in osmoregulation by pumping out water.

From collected data Kitching (65) has shown that the normal frequency of vacuolar contraction, expressed as vacuolar duration, varies from a few seconds to several minutes in freshwater Protozoa, but in marine Protozoa it is considerably longer (Table 2.4). When marine Protozoa possessing contractile vacuoles are placed in dilute sea water, vacuolar frequency and output increase (Fig. 2.8). It has also been observed that contractile vacuoles appear in certain marine protozoans normally lacking them, when they are kept in fresh water.

When marine peritrichs are subjected to dilute sea water below 75% vacuolar output is raised and body volume increases (Fig. 2.9). Cyanide (a respiratory inhibitor) interferes with this vacuolar activity so that

TABLE 2.4

VACUOLAR OUTPUT FOR SEVERAL FRESHWATER, ESTUARINE AND MARINE CILIATES
(selected data)

Species	Medium	Vacuolar duration	Rate of vacuolar output μ^3/sec
Vorticella convallaria	FW	11 sec	34·7
Rhabdostyla brevires	FW	20–100 sec	4·1–17·2
Zoothamnium sp.	FW	6–39 sec	7·8–17·9
Frontonia marina	SW 6·9⁰/₀₀	45–82 sec	330–560
Zoothamnium hiketes	SW 14·5⁰/₀₀	45–125 sec	2·5–4·6
Cothurnia curvula	SW ca 35⁰/₀₀	0·7–20 min	0·18–1·24
Vorticella marina	SW ca 35⁰/₀₀	13–32 min	1·1–3·4

individuals in diluted sea water continue to swell (Fig. 2.8). Removal of
the cyanide leads to recovery of vacuolar activity, and the vacuole pumps
at a faster rate than normal, with consequent decrease in body volume.

It appears, therefore, that contractile vacuoles are not indispensable to
marine Protozoa, since they are absent in most rhizopods and some

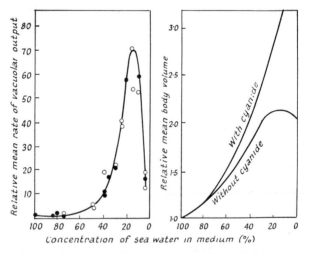

FIG. 2.8. OSMOREGULATION IN MARINE PERITRICHS

(*Left*) relation of rate of vacuolar output to concentration of sea water in *Zoothamnium
marinum* (solid circle) and *Cothurnia curvula* (open circle). (*Right*) relation of body
volume to concentration of the medium in the presence and absence of cyanide in
C. curvula. (From Kitching, 1936, 1938.)

ciliates, and they function at a much lower rate in marine peritrichs than
in comparable freshwater species. It may be that in marine forms they
serve to remove excess water taken in with the food and metabolic water,
and counteract the osmotic pressure of cellular colloids; the possibility of
ionic regulation by contractile vacuoles has also been raised. The rate of

vacuolar output in *Podophrya* (freshwater suctorian) increases tenfold during feeding. This increased vacuolar activity reduces hydration, resulting from ingestion of food, and reduces body volume (66, 68).

In dilute media, such as that encountered by estuarine ciliates, vacuolar output is increased. The cell membrane is considered to be semipermeable and to resist the passage of salts. Consequently, when the organism is in a hypotonic environment, water is drawn into the cell by osmosis and the increased activity of the contractile vacuole serves to bale out water as it pours into the cell. There are instances, however, of Protozoa lacking hard coverings and contractile vacuoles, which tolerate transfer to fresh water for some time, e.g. the marine variety of *Actinophrys sol* which has been acclimatized to fresh water (65, 67).

There are probably species differences in salt permeability and volume regulation among different protozoans. In marine ciliates studied by Kitching and others, swelling of the cytosome persists in dilute media, and

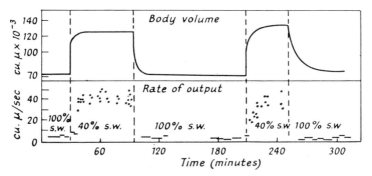

FIG. 2.9. EFFECT OF HYPOTONIC SEA WATER ON THE BODY VOLUME
AND VACUOLAR OUTPUT OF A MARINE PERITRICH, *Zoothamnium marinum*.
(From Kitching, 1934.)

vacuolar output remains at a high level. In the marine rhizopod *Amoeba mira* there is no contractile vacuole, but hyaline vacuoles appear during feeding, and the fluid in these vacuoles is eventually discharged. In dilute sea water the rate of elimination of fluid during feeding is inversely proportional to the osmotic concentration of the culture fluid. There is also an initial increase in cell volume, which gradually returns to normal. *Amoeba lacerta*, a freshwater species, possesses contractile vacuoles. Vacuolar output also varies inversely as the concentration of the medium. In concentrated media the *Amoeba* shrinks, then returns to normal size. These protozoans display volume regulation and seem to be permeable to salts: in anisosmotic media they soon approach the concentration of the external medium (49, 92).

METAZOA. Forms with limited powers of osmoregulation are described below.

Turbellaria. Many lower metazoans inhabiting brackish and fresh waters

obviously possess some osmoregulatory capacity. Among flatworms the
nephridial system of *Gyratrix hermaphroditus* has been implicated in
osmoregulation on morphological evidence. In freshwater varieties of
Gyratrix there is a well-developed protonephridial system, with flame cells,
ampullae and bladders. The nephridial system is reduced in brackish-
water varieties, and absent as far as we can tell from salt-water forms. In
dilute sea water and fresh water the nephridial system appears to function
in a manner analogous to the contractile vacuoles of Protozoa, by rhythmically pumping water out of the organism (78).

In the triclad *Procerodes* (= *Gunda*) *ulvae*, the role of the nephridial
system is doubtful. This species lives in estuarine reaches of small streams
where salinity conditions fluctuate from salt to fresh water according to
the state of the tide. When placed in dilute sea water *Procerodes* undergoes swelling but equilibrium is soon reached with some subsequent

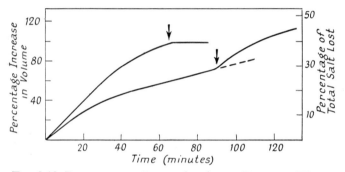

FIG. 2.10. BEHAVIOUR OF *Procerodes ulvae* IN DISTILLED WATER

Upper curve shows increase in volume; lower curve, loss of salts. Arrows indicate
dissolution of ectoderm. (Somewhat diagrammatic. Smoothed curves based on a figure
of Pantin's (105).)

decrease in weight. During this process there is loss of salt to the external
medium. In distilled water or in certain stream waters the animals die and
disintegrate, and it has been demonstrated that this is due to absence of
calcium in the external medium (Fig. 2.10). In nature *Procerodes* has been
found in streams with minimal calcium levels of 0·5 mg/l., where they are
exposed to fresh water for as long as 5 days during neap tides (105).

Much of the water that is taken up osmotically by *Procerodes*, when in
dilute sea water, passes through the parenchyma to the endoderm where it
is stored in large vesicles. Contrary to expectation, these vacuoles do not
discharge into the gut. In dilute sea water oxygen consumption is increased
once the worms have attained a steady state, and swelling proceeds beyond
normal when the animals are subjected to oxygen lack, or are poisoned
with cyanide (105).

Procerodes is probably isosmotic with sea water, and in dilute media the
tissues at first become flooded with water. Calcium is believed to act by

lowering the permeability of the body wall to water and salts, thereby
reducing the inflow until regulatory mechanisms become effective, while
excess water is stored in endodermal vesicles. In summary, active osmoregulatory processes in *Procerodes* appear to involve: the secretion of
water, by nephridia or through the body wall, against an osmotic gradient;
maintenance of depressed ectodermal permeability; retention of water in
endodermal vesicles having a low salt content.

Polychaeta. As indicated above, the sublittoral nereid worms *Nereis
pelagica* and *Perinereis cultrifera* adjust to low salt concentrations by
dilution of the body fluids and succumb when the external medium falls
much below 8‰. *N. diversicolor*, on the other hand, possesses limited
powers of osmoregulation and is able to tolerate brackish waters with
salinities as low as 0·5‰. The internal fluids of the latter species are
isosmotic with normal sea water, but in dilute media they maintain some
degree of hypertonicity (Fig. 2.7).

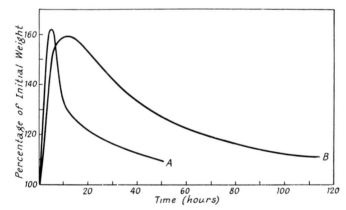

FIG. 2.11. REGULATION OF VOLUME IN *Nereis diversicolor* WHEN
TRANSFERRED FROM NORMAL TO DILUTE (20%) SEA WATER
A, Roscoff worms; *B*, Bangor worms. (From Ellis, 1937.)

In hypotonic media, water absorption and salt loss both take place
(Figs. 2.11 and 2.12). On transferring *N. diversicolor* from full strength to
20% sea water, the initial increase in weight is followed by a slow decline,
and on returning the animals to normal sea water they suffer a further loss
in weight. This is due to a reduction of internal salt concentration which
now leaves the animal hypotonic to its normal environment. Direct
measurements of ionic influx into the worm have been made with the aid
of ^{24}Na and ^{36}Cl. In normal sea water the uptake of sodium by *Nereis
diversicolor* is about 260 μg/g/hour wet weight. At high dilutions (9‰) permeability to water is reduced, and there is active uptake of NaCl against
the concentration gradient. Worms which have been exposed to dilute

media and then returned to normal sea water show increased uptake of sodium, which compensates for the loss of salt at lower salinities.

Calcium is also necessary for osmotic regulation, and in a dilute medium lacking this ion the animal remains swollen. The maintenance of hypertonicity in waters of lowered salt concentration must involve the expenditure of energy. In *N. diversicolor* and in *Neanthes virens*, another euryhaline species, oxygen consumption goes up in dilute sea water, and cyanide prevents the operation of regulatory processes with the consequence that the weight curve continues to rise (5, 29, 36, 56, 135, 136, 147).

Nereis diversicolor thus adjusts itself to a large extent when subjected to a hypotonic environment: first, by absorbing water and swelling;

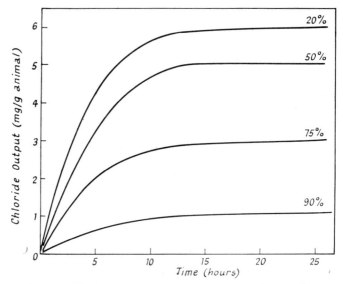

FIG. 2.12. OSMOTIC ADJUSTMENT IN *Nereis diversicolor*

Salt loss accompanying water intake in dilute sea water (concentrations shown against each curve). (From Ellis, 1937.)

second, by regulating its volume through salt loss. Calcium aids in diminishing the permeability of the integument to water but the ability of the animal to keep its internal fluids hypertonic to the environment shows that active regulatory processes come into operation. These involve the active uptake of ions (Na⁺ and Cl⁻) against a concentration gradient and possibly the secretion of water. It is interesting, in this regard, that the nephridial canal of *N. diversicolor* is longer and more convoluted than that of *P. cultrifera*, suggesting nephridial participation in osmoregulation.

Isolated tissues of *N. diversicolor* continue to function in low dilutions, and display spontaneous activity in 5–10% sea water. In *P. cultrifera*, on the other hand, the lower limits of salinity that will still permit muscular activity lie between 20–25% sea water.

Differences have been noted in the osmoregulatory performances of separate populations of one species, and between different estuarine species. *Nereis diversicolor* at Roscoff completes weight-regulation in 20% sea water in half the time taken by worms at Bangor and Plymouth (Fig. 2.11). *N. succinea* exhibits a higher rate of salt loss than do *N. diversicolor* and *N. limnicola*; the rates change in conformity with the degree of lowering of salinity tolerated by these species in their natural habitats, *N. succinea* inhabiting less brackish waters than the others (137).

Molluscs. Freshwater molluscs have well-developed osmoregulatory powers, and this rather suggests that brackish-water forms may be able to regulate their internal media. The bivalve *Mercenaria mercenaria* shows some hypertonicity in dilute sea water (blood 374 mM Cl, in sea water 319 mM Cl) (50). *Hydrobia* and *Potamopyrgus* are brackish water prosobranchs and the latter has invaded fresh water in recent historic times. *Hydrobia* remains slightly hyperosmotic in dilutions of sea water down to one-half, and *Potamopyrgus* in all dilutions down to fresh water. The osmotic balance is maintained, in part, by excretion of a urine hypo-osmotic to blood (146).

Osmoregulatory Powers in Crustacea. The majority of Crustacea are wholly marine, but various groups have representatives which have penetrated into brackish or even fresh waters, or have invaded the land and become terrestrial. As a class the Crustacea are characterized by a hard exoskeleton which may be strengthened by lime deposits. Among other functions the exoskeleton reduces permeability.

The strictly oceanic Crustacea found in the lower littoral zone or in sublittoral habitats are stenohaline and have body fluids isosmotic with sea water, e.g. *Maia, Portunus* and others. The blood concentrations of these animals follow closely that of sea water over the range Δ 2·5 to 1·5 or somewhat lower (Fig. 2.13). The spider crab *Maia* is unable to survive for more than a few hours in sea water diluted below one-fifth. In 80% sea water it quickly swells, but in less than a day its weight returns to normal as salts and water are lost, and its body fluids regain osmotic equilibrium with the environmental medium (Fig. 2.14).

A slight tendency to maintain the blood hypertonic to the external medium at concentrations below Δ 1·5 is shown by the edible crab *Cancer pagurus*. *Cancer* swells to a smaller extent in dilute media than *Maia*, its rate of swelling is less and volume regulation is also slower (Fig. 2.14). *Cancer* is less permeable to water and salts than *Maia*, and manifests a slight amount of osmoregulatory ability in hypotonic media.

By the use of iodide, which can be detected easily, estimations have been obtained of the permeability of the integument of various stenohaline and euryhaline crabs. In solutions containing this ion it has been found that the stenohaline brachyurans *Hyas araneus* and *Portunus depurator* are much more permeable than the relatively euryhaline *Cancer pagurus*

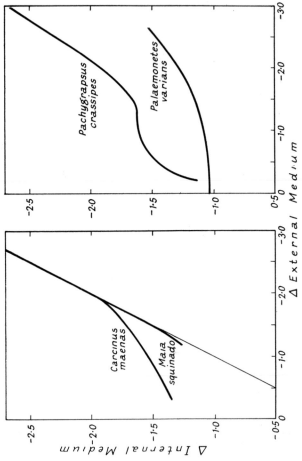

Fig. 2.13. Osmotic Relations of Representative Decapod Crustaceans

Variation of osmotic pressure of haemolymph with alterations in concentration of the external medium. (Data from Duval, 1925; Schlieper, 1929; Jones, 1941; Panikkar, 1941.)

and *Carcinus maenas*. Penetration takes place mostly through the gills but also proceeds at a slow rate through other external surfaces.

The common shore crab *Carcinus maenas* shows well-developed powers of osmoregulation in hypo-osmotic media and can survive dilutions down to Δ 0·6. In normal sea water the blood is isosmotic with the external medium, but in increasing dilutions it develops hypertonicity until at an external concentration of Δ 0·6 the internal concentration is maintained at twice that value; lower external concentrations are lethal (Fig. 2.13).

Carcinus shows little swelling in dilute sea water when compared with other brachyurans previously considered (Fig. 2.14). Permeability to water and salts is relatively low in *Carcinus*, but nevertheless some transfer still occurs across the gills in hypo-osmotic media, water being absorbed and salts lost. The water continually flowing in is eliminated by the kidneys, which produce a greater volume of urine under these conditions (cf. Fig. 7.3, p. 299).

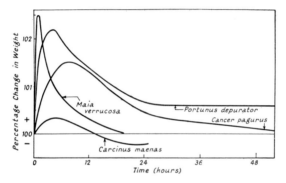

FIG. 2.14. CHANGES IN WEIGHT OF BRACHYURAN CRABS
WHEN TRANSFERRED TO DILUTE SEA WATER

Time, in hours, after placing in experimental medium. *Cancer pagurus* and *Portunus depurator* in 67% sea water (from Hukuda, 1932). *Maia verrucosa* and *Carcinus maenas* in 80% sea water (from Schwabe, 1933.)

In all concentrations of the external medium the urine of marine crustaceans tends to be isosmotic with the blood with some variation in either direction. In dilute sea water salt is lost in the urine and to a lesser extent across the body wall by diffusion, and the hyperosmotic level of the blood is maintained by active uptake of salt across the gill membranes, which offsets the loss of salt by the routes just mentioned. The kidney plays no part in salt conservation. Active uptake of salt by the gills is a process involving the expenditure of metabolic energy (117).

Many decapods are able to regulate the concentration of their blood in hyperosmotic as well as hypo-osmotic media, and some prawns and grapsoid crabs are actually hypo-osmotic to normal sea water under natural conditions (Fig. 2.13). The Australian rock crab *Leptograpsus variegatus*, which lives on the shore, displays definite hypotonicity to normal sea water (blood Δ 1·97, in sea water Δ 2·14) and similar conditions are found in *Heloecius cordiformis*, a crab inhabiting mangrove swamps where it is uncovered at low tide. The American shore crabs *Uca crenulata* and *Pachygrapsus crassipes* have blood concentration curves that reveal a high degree of osmotic regulation, the blood becoming hypotonic when the external medium exceeds 31·2‰, and remaining hypertonic when the external medium falls below this value. A hypo-osmotic condition is maintained either by secretion of salt across the gills or by active uptake of water (111, 117).

Some of these animals are normal inhabitants of brackish and estuarine waters where their osmoregulatory ability is of adaptive value. Blue crabs (*Callinectes sapidus*) from different environments show osmotic acclimation: those from low salinities (Cl about 6‰) survive in extreme dilution (Cl < 2·5‰) longer than crabs from high salinities (Cl about 25‰). Other examples of hyperosmotic regulating decapods are brackish-water crabs such as *Sesarma erythrodactyla*, and certain penaeid and palaemonid prawns such as *Metapenaeus monoceros* and *Palaemon serratus*. Some prawns even penetrate into fresh water, but the female returns to salt water to breed.

The final stage in euryhalinity, the penetration of fresh water, is dependent on the ability of the animal to regulate its blood concentration in highly dilute media, below 8‰. The blood of many euryhaline species becomes swamped at these low concentrations but in the Chinese crab *Eriocheir sinensis* the blood is maintained at a steady level under such conditions. This crab is an Asiatic species which was first noticed in Europe in 1912, and has since extended its range widely. Individuals grow to maturity in fresh water, but return to the sea to breed. The factors permitting *Eriocheir* to live in fresh water are low permeability to water and salts, and the ability of the gill membranes to absorb salt against an osmotic gradient (77, 111, 117).

During the moulting process of crabs there is a striking increase in size and weight which is correlated with osmotic changes in the blood. Prior to the moult water is lost, the osmotic pressure of the blood rises and the animal shrinks within its shell. Shortly after moulting sea water is absorbed osmotically and the osmotic pressure falls. In *Carcinus maenas*, an animal weighing about 50 g absorbs about 35 g during the moult. As a result the animal increases considerably in size and fills out its new exoskeleton (77).

In the inter-tidal zone crabs occurring at higher levels may be exposed to the atmosphere for several hours during tidal ebb and remain active. *Carcinus maenas* has been shown experimentally to live up to 8 days in air, during which time its blood concentration increased from about 610 mM to 815 mM. In an investigation of the effect of air exposure on a series of shore crabs (*Hemigrapsus, Pachygrapsus, Uca*) during ebb tide it has been found that the osmotic pressure of the blood increases, on the average,

Δ 0·18 during this period. A semi-terrestrial crab *Ocypode albicans*, which dwells near high-tide level, displays well-marked osmoregulatory capacity in air and in anisosmotic solutions. *Ocypode* is normally hypo-osmotic and possesses a blood-chloride level of 378 mM when the external chloride is 480 mM. Internal chloride levels are maintained constant for 24 hours in air, or in solutions ranging from 120–600 mM.

In warmer regions of the world some crabs (anomurans and brachyurans) have taken to a terrestrial existence, although they must return to the sea for reproduction. These animals are protected to a considerable degree against water loss by their relatively impermeable exoskeleton. Littoral and terrestrial crabs show much variation in their ability to withstand desiccation on exposure to air, but there is some tendency for crabs occurring near or above high-tide mark to survive longer in the atmosphere than more aquatic species. The terrestrial hermit crab *Coenobita diogenes* and the land crab *Gecarcinus lateralis* live in air for 4 days or more whereas the oceanic crabs *Portunus sulcatus* and *P. spinimanus* die in an hour. Some determinations of blood concentrations of littoral and terrestrial decapods made in Florida by Pearse appear in Table 2.5.

TABLE 2.5

BLOOD CONCENTRATIONS OF DECAPOD CRUSTACEANS FROM DIFFERENT HABITATS

Species	Δ Blood (mean)	Habits
Brachyura		
1. *Gecarcinus lateralis*	− 1·65	Terrestrial: in burrows
2. *Cardisoma guanhumi*	1·66	Terrestrial: in burrows
3. *Ocypode albicans*	1·70	Burrows near sea
4. *Grapsus grapsus*	1·92	Wave-swept rocky shore
5. *Mithrax verrucosus*	2·07	Coral reefs near low-tide mark
Anomura		
6. *Coenobita clypeatus*	2·09	Land hermit crab
7. *Petrochirus bahamensis*	2·09	Low-tide mark to sublittoral zone
Reptantia		
8. *Panulirus argus*	2·20	Shallow water: sublittoral
Sea water 36·05°/₀₀	2·04	

The majority of terrestrial and semi-terrestial crabs are hypo-osmotic to sea water, and are able to regulate in dilute and concentrated media. Hyperosmotic regulation in these terrestrial crabs is an expression of their ability to conserve water and discharge salts, both processes of adaptive value in dry environments. When desiccated, *Pachygrapsus* is able to take up water against a salinity gradient. The coco-nut crab *Birgus latro* shows specific behavioural adaptations for life on land: it can drink water from small puddles, moisten its respiratory membranes with external water, and control the concentration of its blood by selecting water of the appropriate salinity to drink (41, 108).

The shore isopod *Ligia oceanica* is also osmoregulatory to a notable degree. The blood of this animal shows a value of Δ 2·15 in normal sea water. The blood concentration is held fairly steady when the sea water is varied in concentration from 100–50%. Outside this range the blood concentration rises or falls, but osmoregulation still holds the blood hypo- or hyperosmotic to the external medium, when this deviates from accustomed values (106).

Amphipods are very common inhabitants of brackish and estuarine water. Various species of gammarids show well-marked temperature and salinity preferenda (Fig. 2.15). The typically marine species such as *Marinogammarus marinus* and *Gammarus locusta* can withstand sea water diluted down to 25%, under which conditions they maintain the blood markedly hyperosmotic. The brackish-water species *G. duebeni* shows a wide tolerance of concentrations from full strength to 2% sea water, and

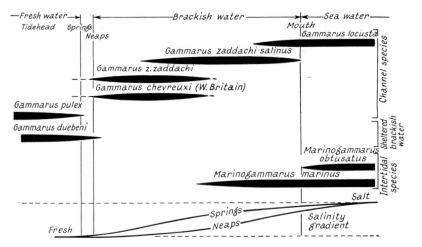

FIG. 2.15. DIAGRAM REPRESENTING THE RELATIVE DISTRIBUTIONS OF SOME
RELATED GAMMARIDS IN ESTUARINE AND CONTIGUOUS REGIONS OF RIVERS
(Suggested by a figure of Bassindale's, 1942)

keeps its blood hyperosmotic to the external medium when the concentration of the latter drops. In *G. pulex* the blood concentration is relatively low but is maintained above that of the external medium. The nephridium is larger and more complicated in *G. pulex* (fresh water) than in *G. locusta* (marine) and this suggests a functional role in salt resorption in the freshwater species (6, 140).

VERTEBRATES. All the major groups of vertebrates above the myxinoids have sea-water and freshwater representatives, and all of these exhibit osmotic and ionic regulation of body fluids. The concentration of inorganic ions in the body fluids is maintained at levels much below that of sea water (some two-fifths). On a functional basis two groups are distinguishable: (1) animals which are hypo-osmotic to sea water; (2) animals which are isosmotic or slightly hyperosmotic. Some lampreys are anadromous in habit, ascending rivers from salt water to spawn. In the sea they are markedly hypo-osmotic (blood of *Petromyzon marinus* from the Mediterranean, Δ 0·586°C) and regulate like teleosts, swallowing sea water and eliminating excess NaCl extrarenally (97). In fresh water, lampreys regulate by mechanisms similar to those of teleosts (*see* later section). Fresh-run lampreys (*Lampretra fiuviatilis*) can maintain their plasma chloride constant only in media more dilute than half sea water. Presumably, some change takes place in their capacity to osmoregulate during up-stream migration (95, 96, 115, 154).

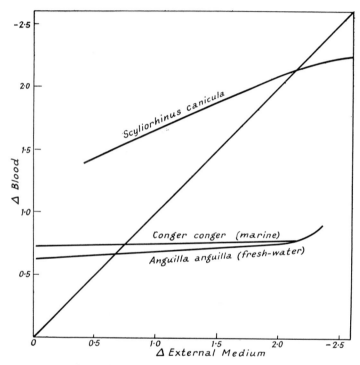

FIG. 2.16. VARIATION IN BLOOD CONCENTRATION OF THREE FISHES
IN WATERS OF DIFFERENT CONCENTRATIONS

A marine elasmobranch (dogfish), marine teleost (conger eel) and euryhaline teleost (freshwater eel). (Data from Duval, 1925.)

Gnathostomes are homoiosmotic to a considerable degree and their osmoregulatory mechanisms have been investigated extensively (Fig. 2.16). The blood of marine elasmobranchs is nearly isosmotic with sea water and has a higher osmotic pressure than that of marine teleosts (Table 2.6). The salt concentration of the blood is somewhat higher in elasmobranchs (about 240 mM Cl) than in teleosts (about 180 mM Cl). The greater osmotic pressure of elasmobranch blood is mainly due to its high urea content,

TABLE 2.6

Osmotic Concentrations of the Blood of some Marine Fish

	$\varDelta$ Blood	$\varDelta$ External medium
Elasmobranchs		
Mustelus mustelus	− 2·36	− 2·29
Squalus acanthias	1·62	1·33
Scyliorhinus canicula	2·22	2·15
Carcharias taurus	2·03	1·83
Raja laevis	1·93	1·86
Torpedo marmorata	2·20	2·15
Holocephali		
Callorhynchus milii	1·76	1·50–1·85
Chimaera monstrosa	1·99	SW
Teleosts		
Conger conger	0·77	2·14
Arna gigas	1·03	2·29
Charax puntazzo	1·04	2·29
Pleuronectes platessa	0·79–0·90	1·90
Anguilla anguilla	0·63	1·90
Gadus callarias	0·72	1·67
Cyclopterus lumpus	0·66	1·89
Lophius piscatorius	0·63	1·92
Mola mola	0·80	2·15
Scorpaena scrofa	0·71	2·15

(Various sources)

reaching 1·5% (250 mM) and responsible for about a third of the total osmotic pressure (133).

Urea is retained by elasmobranchs as a useful metabolite, much of the urea in the glomerular filtrate being absorbed in the kidney tubules. Moreover, the oral membrane, gills and integument are relatively impermeable

TABLE 2.7

Urea and Chloride Content of the Blood of some Cartilaginous Fishes

Species	Fluid	Chloride mM/l	Urea mM/l
Squalus acanthias	Blood plasma	234	248
Mustelus canis	Blood plasma	230–7	165–86
Carcharias taurus	Blood plasma	228–41	165–80
Raja laevis	Blood plasma	230–73	200–335
R. erinacea	Blood plasma	230–85	254–384
Ca lorhynchus milii	Blood	228	400–76
Chimaera monstrosa	Serum	394–96	244–87

to urea, which is thereby conserved. As the result of the osmotic gradient maintained by this high urea content water tends to flow into the blood from the surrounding medium. The water content of the tissues is maintained at a steady level by the excretion of a hypotonic urine at a relatively constant rate. Some data for urea levels in elasmobranchs are given in Table 2.7. There is some extrarenal excretion of urea and of salts (Na⁺,

K^+ and Cl^-) as in teleosts. The urea is diffused throughout the body, and appears to be osmotically and functionally neutral, as far as the tissues are concerned. In addition to this substance the blood contains relatively large amounts of trimethylamine oxide, in concentrations of 0·5–0·9% (66–120 mM) (Table 7.3). Like urea, it is resorbed in the kidney tubules and conserved by the fish, and is responsible for some 6–12% of the osmotic pressure of the blood (43, 60, 61, 132).

A few elasmobranchs have reinvaded estuaries and fresh waters from the sea. These animals have retained the same urea mechanisms as salt-water species, but the urea, and to a lesser extent the chloride, content of the blood are diminished. Threatened hydration of the tissues is to that extent reduced and the water balance is conserved by the production of a very dilute urine.

The chimaeroids also contain large quantities of urea, and have an osmoregulatory system similar to that of selachians (30, 133).

Teleosts. Unlike the great majority of marine animals the blood of marine teleosts is hypo-osmotic to sea water and the animals are confronted with the functional problem of avoiding osmotic dehydration in an aqueous medium. Blood osmotic pressures in these animals generally lie between $\varDelta$ 0·7 and $\varDelta$ 1·0, well below that of the external medium (Figs. 2.16 and 2.17). Marine fish drink large quantities of sea water; water

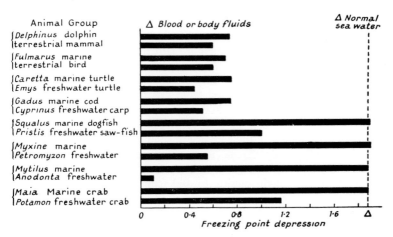

FIG. 2.17. HISTOGRAMS ILLUSTRATING OSMOTIC PRESSURES OF BLOOD AND BODY FLUIDS OF REPRESENTATIVE MARINE AND FRESHWATER ANIMALS FROM DIFFERENT GROUPS

together with sodium, potassium and chloride ions is absorbed through the gut wall, while most of the ionic magnesium and sulphate is rejected (*Anguilla, Myoxocephalus, Lophius*). Water conservation is aided by the production of only small quantities of urine, which is always isotonic or slightly hypotonic to the blood and low in ionic sodium, potassium and chloride. The constant salt uptake, which is a consequence of these processes, is compensated by the secretion of salts across the gills (15, 132).

In estuarine and freshwater environments the salt content of the blood is lowered, but the blood is still strongly hyperosmotic to fresh water (Δ 0·45–Δ 0·60, see Table 2·6). Water is absorbed by endosmosis through the exposed gill and oral membranes, but the rest of the body is relatively impermeable because of the covering of scales and mucus. Fish living in brackish or fresh water drink little water, and they get rid of the excess quantities absorbed by excreting copious amounts of a hypotonic urine. There is some loss of salts in the urine and in the faeces; the loss is partially made up in the food. In addition, as shown by Krogh, the gills of several species of freshwater fish are able to absorb chloride actively against a concentration gradient (*Salmo, Gasterosteus*, etc.).

It is therefore concluded that the ability of teleost fishes to regulate the osmotic concentration of their blood and thereby maintain a steady water content is due to two complementary mechanisms. In a hyperosmotic environment, sea water is absorbed through the alimentary canal and the excess salt is eliminated through the gills, while the kidneys produce minimal quantities of urine. In hypo-osmotic media, however, the gills resist the penetration of water, which is eliminated through the kidneys, and the necessary salts are obtained partly in the food but to a large extent in many species by absorption through mucous membranes in the buccal and branchial regions (77, 132).

The cells responsible for salt transfer have been identified as columnar acidophilic elements located in the gill filaments and elsewhere in the oral and pharyngeal region (*Conger, Fundulus, Pleuronectes*, etc.). In the euryhaline species *Fundulus heteroclitus*, cytological changes appear in these cells when the fish are transferred from salt to fresh water, and fresh to salt, and it is probable that salt transfer—absorption and excretion—is performed by the same cell under altered conditions (22, 25).

Teleosts vary greatly in their ability to tolerate salinity fluctuations, and the majority of strictly marine and freshwater species are stenohaline. Tolerance of osmotic changes is important in estuarine teleosts and in euryhaline species which migrate to and from the sea for spawning purposes. Examples are estuarine flounder *Platichthys flesus*; anadromous salmon; catadromous eels. The eel (*Anguilla anguilla*) tolerates an abrupt change from fresh to salt water, and after an initial loss in weight due to exosmosis, it re-establishes equilibrium in about 48 hours. Adjustment of the killifish *Fundulus heteroclitus* to both fresh and sea water has been investigated from several aspects. On transferring to fresh water from salt there is a temporary increase in weight, which returns to normal after 18 hours, and a loss of chloride amounting to 60% in 4 days. Adaptation to fresh water is complete after 24 hours. When returned to sea water they regain their normal chloride content and density within 6 hours. The presence of calcium in fresh water reduces chloride loss and water uptake under experimental conditions and is probably a factor influencing the distribution of euryhaline species, and permitting the colonization of fresh waters by marine species (13, 14, 45).

In the littoral zone some species must be able to resist desiccation when the tide is out. For example, the mud skipper *Periophthalmus* hops about actively on the mud in the heat of the sun during tidal ebb. Waters where the salinity rises above 35‰ present an analogous problem in the added strain imposed in resisting dehydration. In the Bitter Lakes and Lake Timsah of the Suez Canal Zone, salinities up to 53‰ have been reported. Normal inhabitants of these waters are sole *Solea solea* and grey mullet *Mugil cephalus*. In the desert brine pools bordering the Bitter Lakes a cyprinodont *Aphanius dispar* and a gastropod *Pirenella conica* live in waters where the salt concentration reaches 140π (about 6M NaCl). Osmotic stresses of this magnitude are most unusual (33).

Amphibia. The crab-eating frog *Rana cancrivora* and a few toads tolerate sea water but otherwise Amphibia are decidedly not marine creatures. The crab-eating frog inhabits mangrove areas and when adapted to sea water its blood is slightly hyperosmotic to the medium; it is most interesting that this is achieved by retaining urea in a manner similar to elasmobranchs. The salt concentration in the plasma of frogs in sea water is about twice that of frogs in fresh water; urea accounts for almost half the osmotic concentration (350 mM/l. in sea water 29‰). The formation of urine is drastically reduced when the frog is in sea water, and urea is conserved. The eggs of these frogs are enclosed in capsules impermeable to sea water (124).

REPTILES, BIRDS AND MAMMALS. The higher vertebrates which have re-invaded the sea have to some extent been functionally pre-adapted for a maritime life since their terrestrial ancestors have had to solve the problem of water conservation. Marine reptiles, birds and mammals are all provided with an impermeable integument which prevents the passage of water and salts. Since these animals are predominantly air-breathers, the respiratory surfaces are shielded from sea water.

Reptiles and Birds. Inshore species of birds such as gulls, cormorants and steamer ducks may periodically resort to fresh water, but many pelagic species (petrels, albatrosses, penguins) never taste fresh water throughout their lives. Maritime birds drink salt water and also derive water from their food and metabolic processes. A considerable amount of water is lost by evaporation from the lungs and air sacs. The chief marine reptiles are turtles (Sphargidae and Cheloniidae), Galápagos marine lizard (*Amblyrhynchus*), estuarine and salt water crocodiles (*Crocodylus*), and sea snakes (Hydrophiidae). Some of these animals, on occasion, have access to fresh water, but others, such as the leathery turtle *Dermochelys coriacea* and the pelagic sea snake *Pelamis platurus*, are wholly marine (122). The Galápagos lizard is littoral and eats seaweed.

In reptiles and birds the terminal portion of the cloaca serves to recover water from the faeces and kidney excreta. The main end-product of nitrogen metabolism (in birds and many reptiles) is uric acid, which possesses low solubility and is excreted in a nearly solid state. This is not the case in aquatic turtles, however, which excrete mainly urea and ammonia. The urine of reptiles is no more concentrated than the body fluids, and that of birds is only concentrated twofold. The osmotic concentration of the blood of marine turtles is somewhat higher than that of freshwater forms (*Caretta*, marine, Δ 0·76; *Emys*, fresh water, Δ 0·44), and that of the fulmar seems to be slightly elevated (Fig. 2.17). The more concentrated blood of marine species, by lowering the osmotic gradient, reduces the amount of osmotic work that must be performed in salt secretion (63, 99, 109, 132, 143).

Osmotic regulation in marine reptiles and birds is achieved largely through the activity of salt-excreting glands in the head. In marine reptiles they are located in the orbit, and it is by this route that excess sodium and potassium, taken in with the food, are eliminated. The concentrations of sodium and potassium in the urine of the green turtle are 12 and 8 m-equiv/l. respectively, less than in the blood; in the secretion of the salt-gland they are 685 and 21 m-equiv/l., respectively (48).

In marine birds a large salt gland lying in the nasal cavity is capable of excreting a very concentrated solution of sodium chloride (*c.* 800 mN). The gland, sometimes quiescent, becomes active when the bird ingests salt and becomes subject to osmotic stress. The efficiency of the gland can be illustrated by the behaviour of a gull which, when fed sea water equivalent to one-tenth of its body-weight, eliminated the salt load in 3 hours. The salt-gland is capable of the high rate of excretion of 30 c.c./kg body weight/h (124).

A peculiarity of petrels and their allies is the presence of a greatly enlarged proventriculus, responsible for secreting large amounts of lipoids. It appears that the secretion of stomach oil is confined to the breeding season and that it is used in feeding the young. Adult fulmars also show a preference for fatty foods. A highly adaptive lipoid metabolism is characteristic of animals which are exposed to water shortage. The metabolic oxidation of fats yields far more water than other foodstuffs, and probably is an important factor in maintenance of water balance among pelagic birds (93).

Mammals. Osmotic relations in marine mammals are similar to those in pelagic birds. The osmotic pressure of the blood is slightly higher than that of terrestrial species, but still well below sea water (Fig. 2.17), and active processes of osmoregulation are necessary to maintain the salt and water balance of the animal. Water is obtained largely from the food. Both birds and mammals that feed upon marine vertebrates obtain a food of relatively low salt content (about 1 % NaCl), not markedly different from the concentration of their own body fluids (fish-eating birds, seals, killer whales). Those species that feed upon marine invertebrates (some birds, crab-eating seals, walruses, whalebone whales) are in a rather different category since the salt concentration of their prey is practically equivalent to sea water, and the margin of water left for their functional needs is reduced.

Water is lost by evaporation at the respiratory surfaces, in the faeces and in the urine, but loss through the latter two routes is reduced by resorption in the rectum and production of a hypertonic urine. A further loss of water occurs during lactation and the production of a concentrated milk (rich in fat), in whales and seals, is related to the necessity for water economy (28, 77, 94, 130).

In the mammalian kidney the urine is concentrated by resorption of water in a special segment of the distal convoluted tubule. Measurements of osmotic pressures and chloride concentrations in the urine of marine animals show values of Δ 0·73–4·50 and 10–413 mM Cl for seals and Δ 1·83–3·41 and 75–820 mM Cl for whales. The majority of values lie within the range encountered in terrestrial species. In the harbour seal *Phoca vitulina* it has been found that the rate of urine formation is low between meals but increases markedly after a meal of fish. Loss of water in the urine is thus curtailed between meals, and the kidneys are enabled to function more effectively after feeding when additional water is available for renal excretion. Marine mammals drink little sea water: seals are able to swallow their prey while submerged without taking in salt water, and whalebone whales use their huge fleshy tongues to press out the water from the crustaceans trapped in the baleen plates. It appears, then, that marine mammals keep down their salt content by avoiding the ingestion of salt water, by excreting minimal amounts of water and by the production of a hypertonic urine (46, 55, 79, 134).

The data derived from seals which have been fed upon fish (herring) indicate that there is sufficient water available from this source to provide for the normal physiological requirements of the animal. Marine mammals which feed largely or exclusively upon invertebrates are subject to an additional osmotic strain. The salt content of the urine is generally less than 32 g/l., and accurate experiments on the dolphin *Tursiops truncatus* have shown that individuals of this species fail to regain their original state in 9 hours after administering 2 l. of 0·5 M NaCl. It is uncertain how the water requirements of marine mammals which feed largely upon invertebrates are met. Water absorption against an osmotic gradient or extrarenal salt secretion are possibilities. The fat content of the food of these animals (copepods, herring, etc.) is high (Table 2.1), and could provide a rich source of metabolic water. Fasting humpback whales draw upon their great stores of fat, and excrete a very concentrated urine (Δ 2·79). Osmotic regulation may be achieved by catabolism of fat, providing metabolic water, ingestion of sea water and the elimination of excess salt by the production of a highly hypertonic urine (9, 31, 32, 77).

All the vertebrates above the myxinoids have body fluids whose content of inorganic salts is only about half that of sea water, and it is now apparent that they have all developed salt pumps for bailing out surplus salt which tends to push inwards from the surrounding sea water. It is curious that so many different organs have assumed this function: rectal gland of selachians, gills of teleosts, the skin of frogs, orbital and nasal salt glands

TABLE 2.8

Concentrations of Ions in Tissues of Some Marine Organisms in Comparison with Body Fluids and Sea Water

Concentrations in mM per kg (a), mM per l. (b), or mM per kg H_2O (c)

Organism	Tissue or fluid	Na^+	K^+	Ca^{++}	Mg^{++}	Cl^-	$SO_4^=$	Source
Plants								
Valonia macrophysa	Cell sap (b)	90	500	1·7	trace?	597	trace?	1, 14
Halicystis	Cell sap (b)	557	6·4	8	16·7	603	trace	1, 14
Animals								
Golfingia sp.	Muscle (a)	122	106	4·25	—	91	—	2
	Body fluid (a)	378	38	10·5	—	430	—	2
Pecten maximus	Muscle (a)	48·7	112·3	2·7	3·3	53·6	—	6
	Blood (a)	475·8	13·1	13·47	43·17	541·5	29·35	6
Aplysia punctata	Muscle (a)	326·6	47·83	16·72	95·4	377·9	—	6
	Blood (a)	491·4	9·7	13·35	48·93	541·5	29·35	6
Loligo pealii	Muscle (a)	53·6	113·7	—	—	71	—	3
	Axoplasm (a)	—	310	—	—	130	—	4
L. forbesi	Blood (a)	429·7	21·1	11·6	53·04	535·3	7·70	5
Sepia officinalis	Axoplasm (a)	46	323	—	—	72	—	12
	Vitreous humour (a)	533	13·5	13·1	5·4	575	3·1	13
	Aqueous humour (a)	561	16·3	14·2	7·0	665	6·4	13
	Plasma (a)	465	21·9	11·6	57·7	591	6·3	13
Eledone cirrhosa	Muscle (a)	80·9	101	3·7	12·7	93	—	6
	Blood (a)	425·7	12·2	11·6	57·2	480	43·1	6
Carcinus maenas	Muscle (c)	54	120	6·9	17·9	54	—	15
	Blood (b)	468	12·1	17·5	23·6	524	—	15
Paracentrotus lividus	Eggs (c)	52	210	4	11	80	6	7
Caudina chilensis	Muscle (a)	191	138·5	88·7	39·2	122	65·3	8
	Blood cells (b)	202	176	6·9	14·5	126	131·5	9
	Plasma (b)	460	11·8	10·8	50·5	523	28·8	9
Clupea harengus	Eggs† (a)	35·7	45·7	2·4	6·4	83·0	—	11
Sea water: chlorinity 19‰ (a)		459	9·7	10·0	52·3	535·3	27·5	10

† Fresh ova. Presumably stripped from fish.

Sources: 1, Osterhout (103); 2, Steinbach (141); 3, Manery (89); 4, Bear and Schmitt (7); 5, Robertson (113); 6, Hayes and Pelluet (44); 7, Rothschild and Barnes (120); 8, Koizumi (73); 9, Koizumi (72); 10, Sverdrup, Johnson and Fleming (142); 11, Macallum (85); 12, Keynes and Lewis (62); 13, Robertson (114); 14, Höber (1945); 15, Shaw (129).

of reptiles and birds, kidney of mammals. Also the salt-excretory function of some, perhaps all of these organs, is regulated by adreno-cortical steroid hormones of the adrenal cortex (or its interrenal equivalent) (58).

OSMOTIC RELATIONS AMONG PARASITES. Parasitic animals are sometimes subjected to peculiar osmotic conditions as the result of their parasitic mode of life. These arise in relation to the external medium of the host (ectoparasites and free-living stages), the internal medium of the host (endoparasites) and the use of the host's fluids as a source of food (blood-sucking ectoparasites). Osmotic relations have been investigated in only a few species and information is limited, but from what is known of their life-histories parasites may be expected to display peculiar conditions of adaptation and regulation in relation to their biotic environments.

Highly specialized parasites, which have external phases and utilize a succession of hosts, may be exposed to widely different salt concentrations at different stages of their life-history. Examples are marine trematodes passing from marine invertebrates to vertebrate hosts. These soft-bodied animals appear to be poikilosmotic and osmolabile. Some marine cercariae will withstand sea water diluted to 50–25%. At least one species, *Spelotrema*, is restricted in distribution by salinities below 17‰ (8).

Cestodes from fish appear to be isotonic or slightly hypotonic to the hosts' fluids. Plerocercoid larvae of *Schistocephalus* from *Gasterosteus* are poikilosmotic, and shrink or swell when the external medium is made more concentrated or dilute (above or below 0·75% NaCl). Another cestode, *Bothriocephalus*, from the spiral valve of *Scyliorhinus*, is slightly hypotonic to the surrounding intestinal fluid ($\varDelta$ 2 against $\varDelta$ 2·08–2·65). This is an interesting problem since a large part of the osmotic pressure of selachian body (and intestinal) fluids is due to urea (p. 51). Evidence exists that intestinal nematodes possess some powers of osmotic and ionic regulation (47, 139).

Some parasites have become adapted to host animals which migrate into estuaries, fresh water or even upon land. Species of fish-lice *Argulus* infect both fresh- and salt-water fishes and will tolerate immediate transfer from one medium to the other. Some bopyrid and rhizocephalan parasites accompany their crustacean hosts into brackish or fresh water. In contrast are caligid copepods which are parasitic upon sea-run trout and salmon: these parasites are stenohaline, and are killed when the host returns to fresh water (2, 153).

Ectoparasites, which infect terrestrial crabs, face a somewhat different problem, namely threatened desiccation. An example is *Cancricola*, a harpacticid copepod found on the gills of littoral and land crabs. These parasites feed on blood and mucus, and benefit from the fact that the host must keep its gill surfaces moist.

External parasites which feed on the blood of marine vertebrates take in a fluid of much lower osmotic pressure than the surrounding medium, and tend to become flooded until the surplus water is eliminated. A peculiar degree of osmolability is displayed by the parasitic copepod *Lernaeocera branchialis* from the cod. *Lernaeocera* is normally isotonic with sea water but becomes hypotonic when living upon a fish and feeding upon the latter's blood (104).

MINERAL SALTS AND IONIC REGULATION

Osmotic relations are a function of the total concentrations of solutes in the media. Although osmotic pressures of external and internal media are usually equal in marine invertebrates, the concentrations of individual ions are frequently dissimilar. In this regard it is necessary to distinguish between intracellular and extracellular fluids. All cells appear to differ in inorganic composition from the surrounding media, whether tissue fluids or sea water (Table 2.8). The cell sap of the large unicellular alga *Valonia* differs greatly in ionic composition from surrounding sea water. Eggs of the sea urchin *Paracentrotus* show high levels of potassium and relatively low concentrations of sodium, chloride and sulphate ions. Muscles generally contain large amounts of potassium and low levels of sodium and chloride ions. Calcium and magnesium ions are present in greater (*Aplysia*) or lesser amounts (*Pecten*) than in sea water. Blood corpuscles of *Caudina* concentrate ionic potassium and sulphate, but reduce sodium, magnesium and chloride. Axoplasm contains particularly large amounts of potassium and low levels of sodium and chloride ions, in conjunction with special excitability characteristics of nerve fibres (Chapter 10). Cells both within the body and freely exposed to sea water can regulate individual ions at concentration-levels differing from sea water or tissue fluids. There is a general tendency for cells to concentrate K^+ and, to a lesser extent Ca^{++}, and to reduce Na^+ and Cl^-. Muscle fibres of *Carcinus* regulate Na^+ and K^+, Na^+ being secreted, and K^+ retained by the fibre. Much variation exists in the way in which Ca^{++}, Mg^{++} and $SO_4^=$ are treated (129).

In lower forms the intracellular osmotic concentration is largely due to inorganic electrolytes, but in certain higher marine invertebrates a tendency exists for a large proportion of these ions to be replaced, particularly in muscle cells, by organic substances. Considerable quantities of amino-acids occur in molluscan and crustacean muscle, where they are believed to be important in regulation of intracellular osmotic pressure (23, 34).

Ionic Concentrations in Body Fluids

Turning now to internal fluids (plasma, haemolymph, coelomic fluid) we find certain disparities in the ionic concentrations of different species. Nevertheless the ionic compositions of body fluids throughout the animal kingdom possess a general pattern of resemblance which is too great to have originated fortuitously. In lower animals the tissue fluids closely resemble sea water (coelenterates, polychaetes). Higher forms tend to accumulate K^+ relative to Na^+, and to reduce levels of Mg^{++} and $SO_4^=$. This trend is most pronounced in decapod crustaceans and vertebrates. Concentrations of ions in body fluids of representative species are shown in Table 2.9. Absolute values depend to some extent on the concentration

TABLE 2.9

Concentrations of Ions in Body Fluids of Marine Animals

(in mM per l. or mM per kg water†)

Animal	Fluid	Na$^+$	K$^+$	Ca^{++}	Mg^{++}	Cl$^-$	SO$_4^=$	Ext. Cl$^-$	Source
Coelenterata									
Aurelia aurita†	Tissue fluid	454·4	10·5	9·73	50·8	554·2	15·18	536	1
Aequorea coerulescens†	Tissue fluid	456	24·3	9·9	50·5	548	23·6	519	2
Cyanea capillata†	Tissue fluid	442	16·2	9·9	50	556	11·2	519	2
Polychaeta									
Aphrodit e aculeata	Coelomic fluid	467·3	12·59	10·24	52·93	549·9	28·2	548	1
Arenicola marina	Coelomic fluid	470·6	10·31	10·22	53·73	546·7	26·04	548	1
Amphitrite johnstoni	Blood	405·9	13·02	9·54	54·9	477	30·8	483	3
Glycera dibranchiata	Coelomic fluid	—	9·61	10·0	61·34	483	27·5	483	3
Sipunculoidea									
Golfingia sp.	Coelomic fluid	387·1	38·9	10·7	—	440·3	—	522	4
Echiuroidea									
Echiurus echiurus	Coelomic fluid	440·16	12·62	9·17	42·48	480	30·72	483	3
Crustacea									
Ligia oceanica	Blood	586	14	36·2	21	596	4·5	581	17
Palaemon serratus	Blood	394	7·7	12·6	12·6	430	2·6	581	19
Homarus americanus	Serum	465·13	8·56	10·66	4·73	498	5·0	525	3
Palinurus vulgaris†	Plasma	544·42	10·33	13·45	16·61	556·7	21·30	560	1
Nephrops norvegicus†	Plasma	517·5	7·57	13·85	8·88	518·9	18·53	530	1
Cancer borealis	Serum	459·84	10·2	11·5	21·89	479	18·78	492	3
Carcinus maenas†	Blood	514·84	11·94	12·9	18·91	541·22	15·93	542	5
Lithodes maia†	Plasma	476·6	12·48	12·35	52·18	536·7	25.7	530	1
Xiphosura									
Limulus polyphemus	Serum	386·4	12·76	9·01	40·9	468·4	14·79	—	7
Mollusca									
Mytilus edulis†	Blood	501·8	12·7	12·6	55·8	586·1	30·7	592·2	18
Mercenaria mercenaria	Blood	308·9	6·82	11·3	29·1	374	18·1	319	3
Pecten maximus	Blood	487·3	13·47	13·8	44·2	554·5	30·1	568	11
Aplysia punctata	Blood	587	11·6	13·87	51·8	645·9	—	—	13
Archidoris pseudoargus	Blood	517·5	15·0	12·6	56·7	528·8	—	525	13
Sepia officinalis†	Blood	465	21·9	11·6	57·7	591	6·3	575	14
Loligo forbesi†	Blood	419	20·6	11·3	51·6	522	7·3	506	14
Eledone cirrhosa†	Blood	438	13·0	11·0	54·6	513	20·7	510	14
Echinodermata									
Asterias vulgaris	Coelomic fluid	460·1	8·82	8·89	30·7	505	25·4	492	3
Marthasterias glacialis†	Perivisceral fluid	459·6	10·87	10·18	51·15	540·9	27·59	537	1
Echinus esculentus†	Perivisceral fluid	444·4	9·58	9·97	50·29	524·29	27·07	525	6
Strongylocentrotus drobachiensis	Coelomic fluid	461·0	9·59	8·82	31·0	510	25·3	483	3
Lytechinus variegatus	Perivisceral fluid	546	14·68	13·92	35·36	485	17·99	510	12
Cucumaria frondosa	Coelomic fluid	419·8	9·69	9·35	49·67	487	29·8	483	3
Tunicata									
Ascidia nigra	Blood	403·2	17·6	10·35	38·5	—	—	527·6	12
Phallusia mammillata†	Blood	467·3	9·98	9·54	52·93	567·5	14·83	548	15
Vertebrata									
Myxine glutinosa	Serum	401·9	9·09	5·29	22·48	448	6·03	483	3
Myxine glutinosa†	Serum	558	9·6	12·5	38·8	576	13·3	592	15
Squalus acanthias	Serum	257·3	7·01	4·01	6·0	276·93	—	—	7
Mustelus canis	Plasma	270	5·6	5·8	3·0	230	1·79	—	8
Raja laevis	Plasma	255	5·2	3·8	3·5	235	0·5	—	8
R. erinacea	Plasma	254	8	6	2·5	255	—	—	20
Muraena helena	Plasma	211·8	1·95	7·73	4·85	188·4	11·35	659	15
Gadus callarias	Serum	180·9	10·1(¹)	4·67	2·42	175·5	—	—	7
Syngnathus acus	Blood	206·8	16·5	3·50	9·68	190·7	—	—	9
Lophius piscatorius	Blood	242·1	6·60	2·61	4·56	182·2	—	—	9
Lophius piscatorius	Plasma	180	5·1	11	10	172	—	—	16
Sea water, chlorinity 19⁰/₀₀, density at 20°C 1·0243		470·15	9·96	10·24	53·57	548·30	28·24	—	10

(1) Haemolysis of erythrocytes may have raised level of K$^+$.

Sources: 1, Robertson (113); 2, Koizumi and Hosoi (74); 3, Cole (including earlier analyses) (1940); 4, Steinbach (141); 5, Webb (1940); 6, Robertson (112); 7, Macallum (85); 8, Smith (125); 9, Edwards and Condorelli (1928); 10, Sverdrup, Johnson and Fleming (142); 11, Hayes and Pelluet (44); 12, Valente and Bruno (149); 13, Bethe and Berger (11); 14, Robertson (114); 15, Robertson (115); 16, Brull and Nizet (19); 17, Parry (106); 18, Potts (110); 19, Parry (1954); 20, Hartman, et al. (43).

and ionic composition of the external medium. The relative ionic composition of the body fluids of a series of marine invertebrates and fishes is presented in Table 2.10 on a chloride basis of 100. This ion is in equilibrium with sea water in most animals, and forms a suitable basis for comparison. Of twenty invertebrates examined by Robertson (113), all had chloride values within 4% of sea water, and most within 1%. In marine fishes, which regulate osmotically and keep their blood concentrations below 200 mM, the internal chloride level is directly determined by the homoiosmotic powers of the species.

Physiological Media

Suitable physiological media for marine animals are described in the appendix (p. 668). Some of these are based on analyses of body fluids, others have been determined empirically.

TABLE 2.10

RELATIVE IONIC COMPOSITION OF BODY FLUIDS

Group Animal	Na^+	K^+	Ca^{++}	Mg^{++}	Cl^-	$SO_4^=$
Sea water	55·5	2·01	2·12	6·69	100	14·0
Coelenterata						
Aurelia aurita	53	2·05	1·96	6·3	100	6·3
Polychaeta						
Arenicola marina	56	2·09	2·12	6·7	100	12·9
Aphrodite aculeata	55	2·52	2·12	6·6	100	13·9
Sipunculoidea						
Golfingia vulgaris	58	2·24	2·25	4·7	100	12·9
Mollusca						
Pecten maximus	55	2·61	2·18	6·5	100	13·5
Mya arenaria	56	2·15	2·26	6·6	100	14·1
Ensis ensis	55	3·14	2·30	6·6	100	12·2
Pleurobranchus membranaceus	56	2·36	2·38	6·7	100	14·3
Neptunea antiqua	55	2·30	2·25	6·8	100	13·1
Buccinum undatum	54	2·88	2·31	7·0	100	12·6
Eledone cirrhosa	54	3·07	2·46	7·0	100	10·5
Sepia officinalis	51	4·10	2·22	6·7	100	2·9
Loligo forbesi	52	4·35	2·44	6·8	100	3·9
Crustacea						
Squilla mantis	64	2·69	2·59	2·2	100	11·2
Homarus vulgaris	62	1·75	3·20	1·0	100	4·4
Nephrops norvegicus	65	1·61	3·02	1·2	100	9·7
Palinurus vulgaris	63	2·05	2·73	2·0	100	10·4
Carcinus maenas	62	2·43	2·69	2·4	100	8·0
Cancer pagurus	64	2·44	3·00	3·2	100	13·8
Lithodes maia	58	2·56	2·60	6·7	100	13·0
Echinodermata						
Marthasterias glacialis	55	2·22	2·13	6·5	100	13·8
Echinus esculentus	55	2·09	2·15	6·6	100	14·0
Holothuria tubulosa	56	2·06	2·15	6·9	100	13·9
Tunicata						
Phallusia mammillata	53·3	1·95	1·91	6·38	100	7·1
Salpa maxima	54·4	2·22	1·99	6·20	100	8·8
Vertebrata						
Myxine glutinosa	62·9	1·84	1·23	2·31	100	3·1
Lampetra fluviatilis	80·9	3·69	2·32	1·51	100	7·7
Mustelus canis	76	2·68	2·79	0·82	100	2·11
Raja laevis	70	2·44	1·82	0·29	100	0·46
Gadus callarias	67	6·35*	2·62	0·95	100	—
Lophius piscatorius	86	4·0	1·62	1·72	100	—
Muraena helena	72·9	1·14	2·32	0·88	100	8·2

* Haemolysis of erythrocytes probably responsible for release of intracellular K^+.
(Data from J. D. Robertson and earlier sources)

Hydrogen Ion Concentration. Sea water is alkaline, about pH 8·1. The body fluids of marine animals are generally more acid than sea water, usually above neutrality, but slightly below in some species. Some values for several species are shown in Table 2.11. A small variation in hydrogen ion concentration is tolerated by tissues or organs. The lobster heart, which has a pH optimum of 7·4, continues to beat normally over the range pH 7·0–8·0, but values beyond these limits affect tonus, amplitude and frequency. Cardiac and smooth muscles of other animals show similar sensitivity. Herring eggs develop normally in sea water ranging from pH 6·7–8·7, but development is retarded in sea water with lower pH values (59).

Ionic Regulation

The ionic differences which exist between body fluids and the surrounding sea water could result from passive physical agencies or depend upon

TABLE 2.11

HYDROGEN ION CONCENTRATIONS (pH) OF BODY FLUIDS

Animal	Fluid	pH
Polychaeta		
Arenicola marina	Coelomic fluid	7·2–7·3
Amphitrite johnstoni	Coelomic fluid	6·80
Glycera dibranchiata	Coelomic fluid	7·40
Echiuroidea		
Echiurus echiurus	Coelomic fluid	7·60
Sipunculoidea		
Sipunculus nudus	Body fluid	7·25–7·79
Mollusca		
Strombus gigas	Blood	7·5
Aplysia fasciata	Blood	7·23–7·46
Mercenaria mercenaria	Mantle fluid	7·90
Crassostrea angulata	Blood	7·2
Sepia officinalis	Blood	7·24–7·90
Octopus vulgaris	Blood	7·8
Crustacea		
Homarus americanus	Serum	7·55–7·61
Palinurus vulgaris	Blood	7·7
Cancer borealis	Serum	7·81
Carcinus maenas	Blood	7·53 ± 0·37
Callinectes hastatus	Serum	7·24–7·49
Xiphosura		
Limulus polyphemus	Serum	6·98–7·47
Echinodermata		
Cucumaria frondosa	Coelomic fluid	7·3–7·8
Asterias vulgaris	Coelomic fluid	7·2–7·54
Solaster endica	Coelomic fluid	6·90
Strongylocentrotus drobachiensis	Coelomic fluid	7·20–7·84
Lytechinus variegatus	Coelomic fluid	7·7–7·8
Echinarachnius parma	Coelomic fluid	6·90
Tunicata		
Salpa maxima	Blood	7·5
Chelyosoma siboja	Pericardial fluid	7·2
Ciona intestinalis	Blood	6·47–6·56
Vertebrata		
Myxine glutinosa	Serum	7·63
Scyliorhinus stellaris	Blood	7·32
Torpedo ocellata	Blood	7·64
Conger conger	Blood	7·67
Scomber scombrus	Oxygenated blood at 2·17 mm CO_2	7·94
Prionotus carolinus	Oxygenated blood at 1·21 mm CO_2	7·79
Opsanus tau	Oxygenated blood at 1·37 mm CO_2	7·64

(Various sources)

TABLE 2.12

Composition of Body Fluids before and after Dialysis against Sea Water

Animal	Fluid	mg per g water						mg/ml	
		Na$^+$	K$^+$[1]	Ca^{++}	Mg^{++}	Cl$^-$	SO$_4$$^=$	Protein	Water
Aurelia aurita	Mesogleal exudate before dialysis	10·45	0·411	0·390	1·235	19·65	1·458	0·4	981
	after dialysis	10·59	0·380	0·408	1·270	19·00	2·642	0·4	981
Marthasterias glacialis	Perivisceral fluid before dialysis	10·57	0·425	0·408	1·244	19·18	2·650	0·6	983
	after dialysis	10·51	0·379	0·407	1·273	19·05	2·650	0·6	982
Echinus esculentus	Perivisceral fluid before dialysis	10·22	0·375	0·399	1·223	18·59	2·601	0·3[1]	985·4
	after dialysis	10·19	0·369	0·395	1·220	18·68	2·582	—	985·9
Homarus vulgaris	Plasma before dialysis	11·71	0·550	0·587	0·173	18·26	0·763	22·6[1]	971
	after dialysis	10·59	0·382	0·460	1·305	18·35	2·625	22·6[1]	969·3
Nephrops norvegicus	Plasma before dialysis	11·90	0·296	0·555	0·216	18·40	1·780	33	961
	after dialysis	10·54	0·384	0·448	1·297	18·59	2·572	33	961
Cancer pagurus	Plasma before dialysis	11·55	0·468	0·552	0·658	18·08	2·306	34·9[1]	963
	after dialysis	10·70	0·396	0·464	1·289	18·55	2·637	34·5[1]	961·2
Lithodes maia	Plasma before dialysis	10·96	0·488	0·495	1·269	19·03	2·470	38	954
	after dialysis	10·56	0·382	0·440	1·311	18·48	2·563	38	954
Normal sea water		10·45	0·380	0·400	1·264	18·89	2·646	—	986·1

[1] mg/g water

(Data from J. D. Robertson)

active regulation by the animals' tissues. The body fluids of more primitive groups, namely coelenterates, polychaetes and echinoderms, usually contain very little protein, but in more active crustaceans and cephalopods blood protein attains high levels, up to 100 g/l. in *Loligo* and *Eledone* (*see* Tables 2.12 and 2.13). The presence of protein affects ionic diffusion and concentrations in several ways. Proteins form undissociated complexes with calcium and retain calcium at high levels. Other cations may be bound by negatively charged protein molecules which are prevented from diffusing across bounding membranes because of their large size. According to the Donnan equilibrium, the product of diffusible cations and anions inside must equal the product of diffusible cations and anions outside, e.g. $Na_i \times Cl_i = Na_o \times Cl_o$. Since some of the cation is held by protein the actual situation is—

inside $\quad \dfrac{Na_iCl_i}{Na_iPr} \quad \Big\| \quad$ outside Na_oCl_o

therefore, $Na_i > Na_o$, and $Cl_i < Cl_o$.

For the Donnan equilibrium to be operating under these circumstances without endosmosis implies impermeability to certain ions, or an internal hydrostatic pressure equal to or greater than the colloidal osmotic pressure.

The magnitude of the ionic differences resulting from the undiffusibility of proteins and protein/calcium complexes across gills and other bounding membranes can be estimated by dialysing the body fluids against sea water and comparing the analyses of undialysed and dialysed samples. Data obtained by Robertson and Webb for a series of marine animals are shown in the accompanying tables (2.12 and 2.13). These investigations show that the ionic differences between body fluids and sea water become greatly reduced following dialysis, and reveal the small part played by protein-binding in determining the concentration levels of ions in blood and other internal media. Most of the disparity between internal and external media is due to controlled regulation of ionic levels by the animal. The extent to which different animals regulate separate ions can be appreciated from an examination of Table 2.10 (relative ionic composition of body fluids).

The ability to regulate ionically is a universal characteristic of marine animals, differing only in magnitude in various groups. In more primitive groups, embracing coelenterates, echinoderms, polychaetes, lamellibranchs, gastropods and ascidians, regulation is slight. There is some regulation of potassium and, to a lesser extent, of calcium ions; ionic sulphate is reduced slightly, except in *Aurelia* and *Phallusia*, where it is halved. Sodium, magnesium and chloride ions are in equilibrium with sea water. In contrast to these forms, the two active invertebrate groups, cephalopods and decapod crustaceans, show well-marked regulation of all ions in the haemolymph. Cephalopod bloods show a range (expressed as percentage of concentration in dialysed plasma): Na^+, 93–8; K^+, 152–219; Ca^{++}, 91–107; Mg^{++}, 98–103; Cl^-, 101–5; $SO_4^=$, 22–81. Potassium is held at

TABLE 2.13

Composition of Body Fluids as Percentages of Dialysis Values

Animal	Concentrations as percentages of dialysis values						mg/ml	
	Na^+	K^+	Ca^{++}	Mg^{++}	Cl^-	$SO_4^=$	Protein	Water
Echinus esculentus	100	102	101	100	100	101	—	—
Homarus vulgaris	110	85	131	14	101	32	29	964
Nephrops norvegicus	113	77	124	17	99	69	33	961
Eupagurus bernhardus	105	130	137	49	96	135	69	926
Cancer pagurus	109	115	118	44	98	99	37	961
Carcinus maenas	110	118	108	34	104	61	55	936
Lithodes maia	104	128	113	97	103	96	38	954
Pecten maximus	99·7	129·9	102·5	97·3	100·0	96·5	2·6	983
Mya arenaria	100·8	106·7	106·6	99·0	99·9	101·0	1·3	982
Ensis ensis	98·7	155·2	107·6	98·7	99·2	86·5	4·4	981
Neptunea antiqua	100·6	113·9	101·7	101·1	100·9	97·8	24·1	968
Buccinum undatum	97·3	141·9	104·3	102·8	99·6	90·0	25·3	966
Loligo forbesi	95·2	219·4	101·6	101·7	103·5	29·3	149·7	866
Sepia officinalis	92·5	205·2	90·5	98·1	105·1	22·1	109	892
	97·6	175·4	94·3	—	101·0	80·7	67·6	925
Eledone cirrhosa	97·4	152·1	107·1	102·7	101·7	77·2	105·0	896

(Data from Robertson)

high levels, magnesium is accumulated slightly and sulphate is greatly reduced. The range in decapod crustaceans is: Na^+, 94–113; K^+, 77–156; Ca^{++}, 84–137; Mg^{++}, 14–99; Cl^-, 87–104; $SO_4^=$, 32–135. Potassium is usually accumulated (anomurans and brachyurans) and calcium is maintained at higher levels than sea water in most species examined. The most striking feature is the great reduction in magnesium, ranging from equilibrium with sea water in *Maia* and *Lithodes*, to 14% of sea-water values in *Homarus*. Sulphate is likewise reduced. A peculiarity of decapod blood is seen in the accumulation of sodium, in correlation with a reduction of magnesium. Hermit crabs (*Eupagurus*) are unusual among decapods in accumulating sulphate, and in correlation with this fact have reduced levels of chloride to preserve the balance of anions. The isopod *Ligia oceanica* likewise shows well-marked ionic regulation (Table 2.9). Sodium, potassium, calcium and chloride are all more concentrated than in sea water, whereas magnesium and sulphate are much reduced.

Data relating to ionic regulation in lower vertebrates are presented in Table 2.10. Hagfishes are slightly hyperosmotic to sea water; the osmotically active constituents of the plasma are mostly inorganic ions. Potassium and divalent ions are reduced in the plasma relative to sea water. There is no regulation of sodium and chloride. The osmotic deficit between the plasma and tissues is made up largely of organic acids and trimethylamine oxide (98). Salt levels of lampreys and all higher forms are only about one-half sea-water values (280 mM in selachians and 200 mM or less in teleosts). Sodium, and often potassium, are accumulated in the plasma relative to chloride; magnesium is greatly reduced relative to chloride in correlation with the increase of sodium and sulphate is held at very low levels. Ionic regulation is more highly developed in vertebrates than in the most advanced invertebrate phyla (115).

Mechanisms of Ionic Regulation. There are two aspects of ionic regulation which have excited much interest, namely the historical basis for the ionic similarity of body fluids, and the mechanisms by which particular concentrations are maintained. The similarities in ionic composition of the body fluids of animals are more striking than the differences. Thus, all fluids show relatively high levels of Na^+ and Cl^-, and low levels of K^+, Mg^{++} and $SO_4^=$. Moreover, the relative concentrations are roughly of the same order as those found in sea water. This general similarity between body fluids and sea water has been regarded as a relic of the probable marine origin of animals. Macallum (85) has pointed out that the fluids of primitive marine animals closely resemble oceanic water in ionic properties. The blood of higher forms, particularly vertebrates, differs somewhat from sea water in the relative proportions of various ions. Macallum advanced the hypothesis that the chemical composition of the ancient seas differed profoundly from that of the oceans today. Marine animals were considered to have been originally in ionic equilibrium with sea water. As the oceans changed in composition, the fluids of more primitive animals altered correspondingly, whilst higher animals, which developed closed circulatory systems, tended to retain throughout their subsequent evolution the ionic composition possessed by sea water at the time their circulatory systems were closed off. The peculiar ionic conditions in the plasma of vertebrates were thus related to the composition of sea water at the time these animals first appeared in the ancient seas.

This interesting hypothesis has served to underline the essential similarity of body fluids and has directed attention to their probable origin. Evidence relating to the chemical composition of the oceans in past ages indicates that they have remained relatively stable throughout most of geological time, and any variations which have occurred have been within rather narrow limits. The problem no longer bears the original stamp that was impressed upon it, since the evidence just reviewed shows that all marine animals can regulate the chemical composition of their cellular and body fluids. Ionic regulation is an evolutionary acquisition and its mode of expression has been modified with time (85, 121).

Differences in ionic mobilities may be involved to some extent in establishing and maintaining ionic levels in animals, but the primary factors operative must be ascribed to active processes of absorption and excretion of particular ions. These processes result in the creation of ionic steady states, in conjunction with, or independent of, the maintenance of osmotic equilibrium.

Phyletic Review of Primitive Groups largely in Equilibrium with Sea Water

We have noted that ionic regulation is slight in inactive members of more primitive groups. The ionic composition of the mesogloea in *Aurelia* differs slightly from that of sea water, and is controlled by the bounding ectodermal and endodermal epithelia. Sulphate is actively eliminated together with associated cations. Active absorption of potassium appears to take place. The chloride increment is apparently a passive consequence of the reduction of sulphate, and thus acts to counterbalance the cations (74, 113).

One consequence of the reduction of sulphate is that the body fluid of jellyfish has a lower specific gravity than sea water since the protein content of the body is low (*vide* Table 2.1); the replacement of some 40% of that amount of sulphate occurring in sea water by chloride renders the animal neutrally buoyant (*vide* Table 9.4). The low densities, relative to sea water, of other gelatinous planktonic animals, such as ctenophores, etc., are due to alterations in the ionic concentrations of the body fluids, especially reduction of sulphate (Fig. 9.21) (27).

Peculiar conditions relating to floating devices have been noted in siphonophores. In various genera, e.g. *Agalma* and *Diphyes*, there are special bracts (hydrophyllia) or bells (nectocalyces) which are lighter than sea water. Suggested mechanisms to achieve this condition are hypotonicity (reduced internal salt concentration) or accumulation of substances with lower specific gravity than NaCl (77).

Various hydroids and anemones which inhabit brackish water appear to possess low salt concentrations, and to be in osmotic equilibrium with their environment. Internal concentrations of certain ions also follow closely those of the external medium. Sea anemones have calcium concentrations nearly equivalent to sea water. When placed in dilute sea water, animals absorb water and lose calcium; in sea water plus isotonic $CaCl_2$, calcium is absorbed. The body wall of anemones shows two-way permeability to water and calcium, but exchange of the latter is rather slow.

The concentrations of ions in coelomic fluids of echinoderms are very similar to those in sea water. Potassium appears to be regulated in all species, and magnesium in some instances. The quantities of protein are very small, less than 1 mg/g of water, too low to affect ionic concentrations. Concentrations of potassium in the water-vascular system are much higher than in the perivisceral fluid (*Marthasterias, Echinus*). Suggested mechanisms are, active absorption of potassium via the gills or outward diffusion of potassium through the same structures, thus maintaining a concentration gradient of potassium across the vascular system and coelom to the exterior (11, 113, 114).

The holothurian *Caudina chilensis* resembles coelenterates in the facility with which ions and water are exchanged with the environment. Swelling and shrinking take place in hypotonic and hypertonic media. When animals are placed in artificial sea water in which the concentrations of individual ions have been altered, the body fluids alter in conformity with the environment and reach equilibrium within 5 days. Relative rates for ionic movement across the body wall are $K^+ > Na^+ > Ca^{++} > Mg^{++}$, and $Cl^- > SO_4^= $ (70, 71).

The coelomic fluids of polychaetes, sipunculoids and echiuroids likewise contain very little protein, below 1 mg/ml of water (*Aphrodite, Arenicola* and *Golfingia*). There is slight regulation of ions: potassium is accumulated in most species, and sulphate is reduced in *Arenicola* and some others. The mechanism of ionic regulation in these animals is unknown. Selective absorption of ions by the body wall, and secretion of a urine low in potassium and rich in sulphate may be involved. It has been suggested that nephridia may be concerned in ionic regulation in these forms. *Arenicola marina* adjusts in dilute sea water and soon reaches osmotic equilibrium. Potassium and calcium are increased relative to the medium, sulphate reduced, while other ions attain equilibrium with the diluted medium (Table 2.14). Heightened values of potassium and calcium may be due to accentuated ionic regulation in dilute media, or to differences in diffusion rates. An analogous situation is presented by *Golfingia* muscle immersed in solutions of artificial sea water in which potassium or calcium is altered. Intracellular potassium is kept at a higher level, and calcium is held below that of the external medium over wide ranges of concentrations (141).

Decapod Crustacea. Marine decapod crustaceans generally possess high levels of sodium, potassium and calcium ions, and reduced levels of magnesium and sulphate ions. Lobsters are peculiar in having low potassium values. Protein occurs in high concentrations, up to 8% of the plasma, and forms indiffusible complexes with calcium. Ionic regulation involves: active absorption by the gills of sodium, potassium, calcium and chloride against a concentration gradient; inward diffusion of magnesium

TABLE 2.14

Ionic Regulation of Coelomic Fluid by *Arenicola marina* in Full Strength and Diluted Sea Water (75–50%)

Medium	Concentrations of coelomic fluids as percentages of sea-water values						mg/ml	
	Na$^+$	K$^+$	Ca^{++}	Mg^{++}	Cl$^-$	SO$_4^=$	Protein	Water
In normal sea water	100·1	103·5	99·8	100·3	99·7	92·2	0·2	983
In diluted sea water (15–23 hours)	100	118	113	100	100	90	—	—

(From Robertson (113))

and sulphate along the concentration gradient; differential excretion by the antennary glands, tending to lower blood magnesium and sulphate, and conserve sodium and potassium. The gills and integument of the lobster are relatively impermeable to magnesium and sulphate ions, which enter largely through the gut.

Permeability to ions has been measured in various ways. When *Carcinus* is placed in dilute sea water, changes take place in the relative proportions of ions in the blood. Sodium and chloride decrease more than potassium and calcium, and blood protein rises. Percentages of sodium, potassium, calcium and chloride increase relative to the medium, while magnesium and sulphate decrease (Table 2.15). The greater divergency between ionic

TABLE 2.15

Composition of the Haemolymph of *Carcinus maenas* in Normal and Dilute (67%) Sea Water

Medium	Percentages of concentration in external medium					
	Na$^+$	K$^+$	Ca^{++}	Mg^{++}	Cl$^-$	SO$_4^=$
In normal sea water	110·9	120·9	126·72	35·4	99·79	57·1
In dilute sea water	134·5	142·7	133·6	31·3	125·2	46·4

(From Webb (1940))

ratios of the blood and external medium which results is due to increased salt absorption and excretion. The overall effect is a reduction of osmotic gradient, largely owing to an absolute decrease of sodium and chloride and increased ionic regulation. Permeability has also been tested by altering the concentration of ions individually in the medium. When animals are placed in artificial sea water with one ion altered, there are corresponding

TABLE 2.16

EXCRETION IN MARINE ANIMALS

Ratios of concentrations of ions in urine to those in plasma

Animal	Na^+	K^+	Ca^{++}	Mg^{++}	Cl^-	$SO_1^=$	Source
Crustacea							
Palaemon serratus	0·82	0·86	0·95	6·70	1·06	3·80	8
Nephrops norvegicus	0·98	0·83	0·81	1·30	1·01	1·06	1
Homarus vulgaris	0·99	0·91	0·64	1·80	1·01	1·59	1
Palinurus vulgaris	0·98	0·65	0·86	1·37	1·01	0·98	1
Carcinus maenas	0·95	0·78	0·94	3·90	0·98	2·24	2
Cancer pagurus	0·97	0·80	0·89	1·25	0·96	1·33	3
Maia squinado	—	0·83	1·33	1·44	0·98	1·47	4
Eriocheir sinensis (sea water)	—	1·15	0·93	2·17	1·14	—	5
Cephalopoda							
Sepia officinalis	0·79	0·50	0·70	0·68	1·00	2·15	7
Eledone cirrhosa	1·02	0·90	0·87	0·89	0·97	1·36	1
Vertebrata							
Muraena helena	0·58	0·12*	3·60	26·2*	—	—	6
Syngnathus acus	0·38	0·25	1·85	10·75	1·01	—	6
Lophius piscatorius	0·34	0·39	5·74	16·15	0·69	—	6

* Ratio based on a figure for whole blood.

Sources: 1, Robertson (113); 2, Webb (1940); 3, Robertson (112); 4, Bialaszewicz (12); 5, Scholles (125); 6, Edwards and Condorelli (1928); 7, Robertson (114); 8, Parry (1954).

changes in the concentration of that ion in the blood. For example, *Carcinus* in calcium-free sea water suffers a reduction of internal calcium to one-fifth in 8 days.

The gills are far more permeable than the general integument. Those of *Carcinus* actively absorb sodium, potassium, chloride and probably calcium against a concentration gradient. The gills of *Eriocheir* take up the same ions from very dilute media. Measurements on isolated gills of *Eriocheir* show that NaCl is absorbed at a rate of 2·5 mg/g tissue/hour.

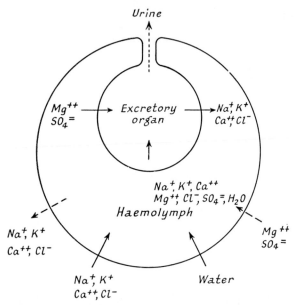

FIG. 2.18. DIAGRAM ILLUSTRATING THE SALT AND WATER EXCHANGE OF *Carcinus*

Broken arrows represent movement of solutes and water brought about by diffusion and ultrafiltration; continuous lines, movements (absorption and secretion) occasioned by active regulation on the part of the animal. (After Webb (1940).)

Absorption of NaCl is halted by cholinesterase inhibitors, and it is likely that cholinesterase is involved in the mechanism of ion-transport. The accompanying diagram (Fig. 2.18) illustrates salt and water exchange in *Carcinus*.

Examination of crustacean urine reveals differential excretion. Sodium, potassium and calcium are conserved, while magnesium and sulphate are eliminated (Table 2.16). Together, the patterns of absorption and excretion broadly account for the levels of individual ions in the haemolymph (20, 69, 77, 111, 116, 117).

Mollusca. In lamellibranchs and gastropods potassium and calcium are regulated, and in cephalopods regulation extends to all ions. Plasma protein is very high in certain prosobranchs and in cephalopods, largely owing to the occurrence of haemocyanin (Table 2.13). Mechanisms of ionic regulation in marine forms are imperfectly understood. Examination of fluid from the renal sac of cephalopods shows that resorption of potassium, calcium and magnesium ions, and secretion of sulphate ion take place in the formation of urine (Table 2.16). As a result, levels of the former ions are raised, and levels of the latter lowered in the blood. The low level of sodium in the renal fluid of *Sepia*, compared with plasma, is ionically balanced by secretion of ammonia (146 m-equiv./kg water). As far as absorption from the medium is concerned, it would appear that potassium, magnesium, etc., are taken up against a concentration gradient, while sodium and sulphate enter along a diffusion gradient. Gills and general integument are probably involved. The body wall of *Aplysia* (tectibranch) is freely permeable to the ions of sea water (110, 113, 114).

Tunicates. The body fluids of tunicates are in osmotic equilibrium with sea water and ionic regulation is feebly developed (Table 2.10). All ions except sodium are kept at different values from those of sea water: potassium is significantly raised in *Salpa*, and the divalent ions—calcium, magnesium and sulphate—are reduced in both Thaliacea and Ascidacea. The pattern of ionic regulation is not dissimilar from that of *Aurelia* (cf. Table 2.10). Excretory tubules being absent in tunicates, the whole burden of ionic regulation is borne by the external surfaces (114).

Fishes. Myxinoids, entirely marine, have fluids slightly hyperosmotic to sea water. There is no regulatory mechanism for sodium and chloride, but potassium and divalent ions—calcium, magnesium and sulphate—are secreted into the urine (98).

Marine elasmobranchs tend to be almost isosmotic with sea water owing to high internal concentrations of urea. From the fluids taken into the alimentary canal, magnesium and sulphate ions are absorbed to only a slight extent, compared with potassium, calcium and chloride ions. Excess magnesium, sulphate and chloride are excreted by the kidney (the latter at 320 mM/l. in the spur dog). The rectal gland is capable of secreting NaCl at twice the plasma concentration and supplements the kidney when necessary by pumping out excess influxing or dietary NaCl (21). Blood protein levels are rather high in elasmobranchs and teleosts (1–8%), and the proteins interact with inorganic ions.

Secretory organs on the genito-urinary tract of rays produce a concentrated alkaline fluid of pH > 9. These so-called alkaline glands seem to function as anion pumps, secreting hydroxyl and carbonate ions against a concentration gradient, as well as $Cl-$ and $SO_4=$. Their function, perhaps, is to neutralize the acidity of the urine and protect the sperm (90).

The mechanism of ionic regulation is somewhat similar in marine teleosts except that the blood is hypo-osmotic. Monovalent ions, sodium, potassium and chloride, are absorbed from the sea water which is drunk, while calcium and especially magnesium and sulphate are concentrated in the intestinal fluid. Excess magnesium and sulphate are excreted in the urine, while sodium, potassium and chloride are excreted extrarenally via the gills (Table 2.16). Branchial excretion of chloride has been measured by Keys in the heart-gill preparation of the eel *Anguilla* (77).

MINOR ELEMENTS IN TISSUES AND SKELETONS

In addition to the principal elements which we have just reviewed, we find various minor elements in many species. These show a random distribution, and their functional significance is not always known. We exclude here the common constituents of the three main groups of organic compounds—carbohydrates, fats and proteins.

Apart from chlorine, the three halogens, bromine, iodine and fluorine, are sometimes present in small amounts. Iodine is a normal constituent of thyroxine in vertebrates, and in *Amphioxus* it is localized in the endostyle and in mucous secretions of that gland. Further evidence is thus provided of the homology of the protochordate endostyle and the vertebrate thyroid gland. Both iodine and bromine occur in gorgonians and sponges, in haloaromatic amino-acids which are normal constituents of skeletal scleroprotein. Iodine is accumulated to some extent by lamellibranchs and other marine animals. Organic secretions of many species besides corals show high levels of iodine, possibly in combination with organic substances, namely tubes of *Diopatra*, *Chaetopterus*, *Bispira* (polychaetes), byssus of *Mytilus*, test of *Pyura* (tunicate), etc. Fluorine occurs in traces in the shells of some lamellibranchs, in remarkably large quantities in mantle and other tissues of the nudibranch *Archidoris* (2% of cations), and in the body wall of the brittle star *Ophiocomina* (3b, 17, 39, 51, 81, 118, 119, 144, 145, 150).

Some of the heavy metals are accumulated in appreciable amounts by various marine invertebrates. Certain metals, particularly iron, are essential elements in the prosthetic groups of many enzymes. Iron is found in cytochrome, a widely distributed intracellular haemochromogen, and in certain respiratory pigments (haemoglobin, chlorocruorin, haemerythrin, *see* Chapter 4). The radular teeth of chitons (Chitonidae) and limpets (Patellidae) contain large amounts of iron as Fe_2O_3 (54% of ash in *Patella vulgata*). The iron content of sea water is low (0·002–0·02 mg/kg), and *Patella* relies mainly on algal food for supplies of iron. The iron content of certain gastropods, *Lineus* (nemertine) and *Nephthys* (polychaete) is high (57).

Copper is probably universally distributed among animals. It occurs in the respiratory pigment of crustaceans, xiphosurans and molluscs (haemocyanin, Chapter 4), and in some respiratory enzymes. Marine invertebrates lacking haemocyanin generally have copper concentrations of 0·2–8 mg% dry weight, but oysters show unusually large concentrations of copper, up to 300 mg%. Manganese is another element which appears to be a normal constituent of all animals, and occurs in traces. Amounts in *Pecten* and *Ostrea* vary from 1–18 mg% dry weight. Gills and ripe ovaries contain the largest amounts and there is an increase of manganese during the reproductive period (37, 91).

Certain other trace elements have an interesting biological distribution. Vanadium is accumulated by some ascidians, *Stichopus mobii* (holothurian) and *Pleurobranchus* (nudibranch). In ascidians, at least, the vanadium is organically bound and is concentrated in blood corpuscles (Chapter 4). Other trace elements reported for various marine animals are aluminium, zinc, nickel, cobalt and titanium. Minor elements may be taken up directly from solution. However, certain ions are adsorbed by hydrated oxides of iron and manganese, and if the latter are collected by filter-feeders the adsorbed elements become available to the animals (10, 38, 75).

Calcium is extensively utilized in skeletons of animals, and in calcareous tubes. Because of their importance these structures are described in more detail in a separate chapter (15). We note here the occurrence of $CaCO_3$ in coral skeletons and molluscan shells, and of $CaCO_3$ and $Ca_3(PO_4)_2$ in the exoskeleton of decapod crustaceans. Magnesium is an important constituent of the skeleton of certain animals—Foraminifera, Alcyonaria, Echinodermata and Crustacea. Magnesium concentrations in some gastropods are very high ($1\cdot58\%$ wet weight in *Archidoris*). Strontium occurs in the skeleton of some radiolarians (Acantharia). Silicon is important in the skeleton of diatoms, most radiolarians and siliceous sponges. The radular teeth of limpets (*Patella*) contain much silica (33% of ash), as well as iron (57, 150).

EGGS, EMBRYOS AND LARVAE

Eggs of marine invertebrates are usually in osmotic equilibrium with the surrounding sea water, but differ considerably from the latter in ionic composition (Table 2.8). Echinoderm eggs have been extensively studied, and over a limited range of dilutions they behave in conformity with the gas laws. The plasma membrane is largely impermeable to salts and the egg behaves like an osmometer when placed in dilute sea water. Deviations from expected values for volume changes are explained as due to the presence of osmotically inactive materials. The osmotically inactive fraction amounts to $7\cdot3\%$ in unfertilized eggs of *Arbacia*, and increases to $27\cdot4\%$ after fertilization.

Cyclical changes take place in the egg prior to and subsequent to fertilization, one of which is permeability to water. Sensitivity to dilute sea water and rate of swelling in hypotonic media increase greatly after fertilization. The permeability of the egg membrane (*Arbacia*, *Paracentrotus*) alters greatly at this time: potassium, calcium and magnesium ions are released shortly after fertilization and are subsequently resorbed (101, 127).

A proportion of the total osmotic pressure of eggs is due to organic molecules, particularly in higher forms. Relative amounts of organic constituents are low in echinoderm eggs, whereas in eggs of *Maia*, *Sepia* and *Torpedo* they are responsible for one-quarter to one-half of the total osmotic concentration. Among mineral constituents potassium is high, as in many cells, sodium occurs in relatively low concentrations, calcium and magnesium are present in colloidal combinations and chloride is mostly dissociated, the relative amounts varying in different species. To maintain these ionic differences from the environmental medium requires a highly impermeable barrier about the egg. In reality, the egg is selectively permeable, and possesses the power of secreting and absorbing particular ions according to metabolic requirements. During the course of development salt is absorbed, and the ash content and density steadily increase (84, 100).

Ionic regulation in developmental stages of marine animals has been reviewed by Krogh (77), and Needham (100) has collated much relevant information. An interesting study of an estuarine polychaete *Marphysa gravelyi* reveals that the demersal eggs of this species are protected by a jelly coat. Eggs denuded of jelly swell or shrink in anisotonic media, and disintegrate in sea water of salinity less than 14‰, whereas eggs protected

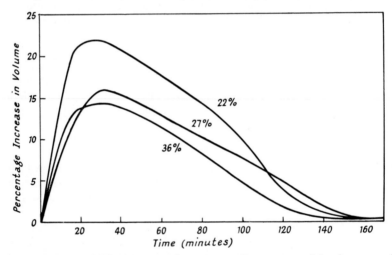

FIG. 2.19. VOLUME REGULATION IN LARVAE OF A POLYCHAETE, *Marphysa gravelyi*
Smoothed curves showing percentage increases of volume in waters of lowered salinity (After Krishnamoorthi (76).)

by jelly will develop even in distilled water. Larvae show volume regulation in hypotonic sea water (down to 22‰) presumably due to salt loss (Fig. 2.19). Sex cells and larvae of the California mussel *Mytilus californianus* are susceptible to dilutions below 29·6‰, and survival declines below this concentration. This species is characteristic of coasts with high salinity, and the narrow salinity tolerance of the larvae is one factor restricting its distribution (76).

The salinity tolerances of the eggs and larvae of two populations of *Nereis diversicolor* have been found to differ—*viz.* at Kristineberg and in the Gulf of Finland. The optimal salinity is higher and the lower and upper limits of tolerance are set higher at Kristineberg. Correlated with these differences is the generally lower salinity obtaining in the Gulf of Finland. Colonization towards fresh water is limited by the lowest tolerance of the developing eggs (at a salinity of 6‰). A closely related species, *N. limnicola* —occurring in fresh water at San Francisco—is viviparous. Its larvae, developing within the coelomic cavity of the parent, are protected against fresh water (138).

There is space to examine only certain aspects of water and salt relations in fish eggs and larvae. Oviparous selachians produce what Needham has termed a cleidoic type of egg which is independent of the medium for its supply of water and salts. The egg membrane is largely impermeable to urea, and the accumulation of this substance as the result of protein metabolism gives rise to final concentrations approaching those of the adult.

The eggs of marine teleosts are at first permeable to water and salts, but during the course of development osmoregulatory ability develops and the chloride content of the embryo is reduced. In contrast, eggs of the euryhaline killifish *Fundulus heteroclitus* are nearly impermeable to water and salt, and display ionic and osmotic regulation from earliest stages. The genital products, eggs and sperm, are initially in osmotic equilibrium with the parents' fluids. Plaice eggs (*Pleuronectes platessa*), which are hypotonic to sea water when laid (eggs Δ 0·70, sea water Δ 1·91), will develop in 20% sea water, and herring eggs (*Clupea pallasii* and *C. harengus*) will survive a wide range of salinities (from 5–37‰). Eggs of *Fundulus* (euryhaline) will develop and hatch in distilled water. Spermatozoa of the goby *Gillichthys mirabilis* (euryhaline) are active over the range Δ 0·33–3·82, and sperm of the flounder *Limanda schrenki* show similar tolerance (88, 100, 151, 155).

REFERENCES

1. ATWATER, W. O., "The chemical composition and nutritive values of food-fishes and aquatic invertebrates," Commissioner's Rept. 1888, U.S. Fish. Comm., p. 679 (1892).
2. BAER, J. G., *Ecology of Animal Parasites* (Urbana, Univ. Illinois Press, 1952).
3. BARNES, H. and BARNES, M., "Resistance to desiccation in intertidal barnacles," *Science*, **126**, 358 (1957).
4. BARRINGTON, E. J. W., "The localization of organically bound iodine in the endostyle of *Amphioxus*," *J. Mar. Biol. Ass. U.K.* **37**, 117 (1958).
5. BEADLE, L. C., "Adaptation to changes of salinity in the polychaetes," *J. Exp. Biol.*, **14**, 56 (1937).
6. BEADLE, L. C. and CRAGG, J. B., "Studies on adaptation to salinity in *Gammarus* spp.," *J. Exp. Biol.*, **17**, 153 (1940).
7. BEAR, R. S. and SCHMITT, F. O., "Electrolytes in the axoplasm of the giant nerve fibers of the squid," *J. Cell. Comp. Physiol.*, **14**, 205 (1939).
8. BELAYEW, G. M. and SELIKMAN, E. A., "Infection of some invertebrates of the White Sea by trematodes depending on their osmoregulatory capacity," *Rep. Acad. Sci. U.S.S.R.*, **71**, 813 (1950).
9. BENTLEY, P. J., "Composition of the urine of the fasting humpback whale (*Megaptera nodosa*)," *Comp. Biochem. Physiol.*, **10**, 257 (1963).
10. BERTRAND, D., "The biogeochemistry of vanadium," *Bull. Amer. Mus. Nat. Hist.*, **94**, 405 (1950).

11. BETHE, A. and BERGER, E., "Variationen im Mineralbestand verschiedener Blutarten," *Pflüg. Arch. ges. Physiol.*, **227**, 571 (1931).
12. BIALASZEWICZ, K., "Sur la régulation de la composition minéral de l'hémolymphe chez le Crabe," *Arch. Int. Physiol.*, **35**, 98 (1932).
13. BLACK, V. S., "Changes in density, weight, etc., in *Fundulus heteroclitus*, in fresh water and sea water," *Biol. Bull.*, **95**, 83 (1948).
14. BLACK, V. S., "Changes in body chloride, density and water content of salmon fry when transferred from fresh to sea water," *J. Fish. Res. Bd Can.*, **8**, 164 (1951).
15. BLACK, V. S., "Osmotic regulations in teleost fishes," *Publ. Ont. Fish. Res. Lab.*, No. 71, p. 53, (1951).
16. BOTTAZZI, F., "Das Cytoplasma und die Körpersäfte," *Handb. vergl. Physiol.*, **1** (1 Hälfte), 1 (1925).
17. BOWEN, V. T. and SUTTON, D., "Comparative studies of mineral constituents of marine sponges," *J. Mar. Res.*, **10**, 153 (1951).
18. BRAND, T. F. VON, "Stoffbestand und Ernährung einiger Polychäten und anderer mariner Würmer," *Z. vergl. Physiol.*, **5**, 643 (1927).
19. BRULL, L. and NIZET, E., "Blood and urine constituents of *Lophius piscatorius*," *J. Mar. Biol. Ass. U.K.*, **32**, 321 (1953).
20. BURGER, J. W., "The general form of excretion in the lobster, *Homarus*," *Biol. Bull.*, **113**, 207 (1957).
21. BURGER, J. W., "Further studies on the function of the rectal gland in the spiny dogfish," *Physiol. Zool.*, **35**, 205 (1962).
22. BURNS, J., and COPELAND, D. E., "Chloride excretion in the head region of *Fundulus heteroclitus*," *Biol. Bull.*, **99**, 381 (1950).
23. CAMIEN, M. N., SARLET, H., DUCHÂTEAU, G. and FLORKIN, M., "Non-protein amino acids in muscle and blood of marine and freshwater Crustacea," *J. Biol. Chem.*, **193**, 881 (1951).
24. CLARK, E. D. and ALMY, L. H., "A chemical study of food fishes," *J. Biol. Chem.*, **33**, 483 (1918).
25. COPELAND, D. E., "Adaptive behavior of the chloride cell in the gill of *Fundulus heteroclitus*," *J. Morph.*, **87**, 369 (1950).
26. DAVIS, C. C., "Concerning the flotation mechanism of *Noctiluca*," *Ecology*, **34**, 189 (1953).
27. DENTON, E. J., "Buoyancy mechanisms of sea creatures," *Endeavour*, **85**, 3 (1963).
28. EICHELBERGER, L., FETCHER, E. S. JR., GEILING, E. M. K. and VOS, B. J. JR., "The composition of dolphin milk," *J. Biol. Chem.*, **134**, 171 (1940).
29. ELLIS, W. G., "Comparative measurements of water and electrolyte exchange in a stenohaline and in a euryhaline polychaete," *J. Exp. Biol.*, **16**, 483 (1939).
30. FÄNGE, R. and FUGELLI, K., "Osmoregulation in chimaeroid fishes," *Nature*, **196**, 689 (1962).
31. FETCHER, E. S. JR., "The water balance in marine mammals," *Quart. Rev. Biol.*, **14**, 451 (1939).
32. FETCHER, E. S. JR. and FETCHER, G. W., "Experiments on the osmotic regulation of dolphins," *J. Cell. Comp. Physiol.*, **19**, 123 (1942).
33. FOX, H. M., "Zoological results of the Cambridge Expedition to the Suez Canal, 1924. 1. General Part," *Trans. Zool. Soc. Lond.*, **22**, 1 (1929).
34. FRASER, D., KERMACK, W. O., LEES, H. and WOOD, J. D., "Non-protein nitrogen fractions of the flesh of lobsters and crabs," *Biochem. J.*, **51**, 32 (1952).

35. FREEMAN, R. F. H. and RIGLER, F. H., "The responses of *Scrobicularia* to osmotic pressure changes," *J. Mar. Biol. Ass. U.K.*, **36**, 553 (1957).
36. FRETTER, V., "Uptake of radioactive sodium (^{24}Na) by *Nereis diversicolor* and *Perinereis cultrifera*," *J. Mar. Biol. Ass. U.K.*, **34**, 151 (1955).
37. GALTSOFF, P. S., "Accumulation of manganese and the sexual cycle in *Ostrea virginica*," *Physiol. Zool.*, **15**, 210 (1942).
38. GOLDBERG, E. D., "Chemical scavengers of the sea," *J. Geol.*, **62**, 249 (1954).
39. GORBMAN, A., LISSITZKY, S., MICHEL, R. and ROCHE, J., "Thyroidal metabolism of iodine in the shark," *Endocrinology*, **51**, 311 (1952).
40. GROSS, W. J., "Osmotic responses in the sipunculid *Dendrostomum zostericolum*," *J. Exp. Biol.*, **31**, 402 (1954).
41. GROSS, W. J., "Aspects of osmotic regulation in crabs showing terrestrial habit," *Amer. Nat.*, **89**, 205 (1955).
42. GUNTHER, E. R., "Observations on the fatty constituents of marine plankton," *J. Exp. Biol.*, **11**, 173 (1934).
43. HARTMAN, F. A., LEWIS, L. A., BROWNELL, K. A., SHELDEN, F. F. and WALTHER, R. F., "Some blood constituents of the normal skate," *Physiol. Zool.*, **14**, 477 (1941).
44. HAYES, F. R. and PELLUET, D., "The inorganic constitution of molluscan blood and muscle," *J. Mar. Biol. Ass. U.K.*, **26**, 580 (1947).
45. HEUTS, M. J., "On the mechanism and the nature of adaptive evolution," *La Ricerca Scientifica*, **19** (Suppl.), 35 (1949).
46. HIATT, E. P. and HIATT, R. B., "The effect of food on the glomerular filtration rate and renal blood flow in the harbor seal," *J. Cell. Comp. Physiol.*, **19**, 221 (1942).
47. HOBSON, A. D., STEPHENSON, W. and EDEN, A., "Studies on the physiology of *Ascaris lumbricoides*," *J. Exp. Biol.*, **29**, 22 (1952).
48. HOLMES, W. N. and McBEAN, R. L., "Some aspects of electrolytic excretion in the green turtle, *Chelonia mydas*," *J. Exp. Biol.*, **41**, 81 (1964).
49. HOPKINS, D. L., "The contractile vacuole and the adjustment to changing concentration in freshwater *Amoebae*," *Biol. Bull.*, **90**, 158 (1946).
50. HOPKINS, H. S., "Metabolic reactions of clams' tissues to change in salinity," *Physiol. Zool.*, **22**, 295 (1949).
51. HOSOI, K., "Contribution to the biochemistry of the coral. 4. Iodine in the polyp of *Fungia*," *Stud. Palao Trop. Biol. Sta.*, **2**, 49 (1940).
52. HUTCHINSON, G. E., SETLOW, J. K. and BROOKS, J. L. "Biochemical observations on *Asterias forbesi*," *Bull. Bingham Oceanogr. Coll.*, **9**, Art. 3 (1946).
53. HYMAN, L. H., "Observations and experiments on the physiology of medusae," *Biol. Bull.*, **79**, 282 (1940).
54. HYMAN, L. H., "Water content of medusae," *Nature*, **151**, 140 (1943).
55. IRVING, L., FISHER, K. C. and McINTOSH, F. C., "The water balance of a marine mammal, the seal," *J. Cell. Comp. Physiol.*, **6**, 387 (1935).
56. JØRGENSON, C. B. and DALES, R. P., "The regulation of volume and osmotic regulation in some nereid polychaetes," *Physiol. Comp. Oecol.*, **4**, 357 (1957).
57. JONES, E. I., McCANCE, R. A. and SHACKLETON, L. R. B., "The role of iron and silica in the structure of the radular teeth of certain marine molluscs," *J. Exp. Biol.*, **12**, 59 (1935).
58. JONES, I. C. and PHILLIPS, J. G., "Adrenocorticosteroids in fish," *Symp. Zool. Soc. Lond.*, No. 1, 17 (1960).

59. KELLEY, A. M., "Effect of abnormal CO_2 tension on development of herring eggs," *J. Fish. Res. Bd Can.*, **6**, 435 (1946).
60. KEMPTON, R. T., "Studies on the elasmobranch kidney," *J. Morph.*, **73**, 247 (1943).
61. KEMPTON, R. T., "Studies on the elasmobranch kidney. 2. Resorption of urea by the smooth dogfish, *Mustelus canis*," *Biol. Bull.*, **104**, 45 (1953).
62. KEYNES, R. D. and LEWIS, P. R., "The sodium and potassium content of cephalopod nerve fibres," *J. Physiol.*, **114**, 151 (1951).
63. KHALIL, F., "Excretion in reptiles," *J. Biol. Chem.*, **171**, 611 (1947).
64. KING-LI-PIN, HSUNG-MAO-CHEN and LIN-YU-SU, "Contribution to the study of the specific gravity, water content and volume of brain of salt-water fishes," *Contr. Inst. Physiol. Acad. Peiping*, **3**, 141 (1936).
65. KITCHING, J. A., "Contractile vacuoles," *Biol. Rev.*, **13**, 403 (1938).
66. KITCHING, J. A., "The physiology of contractile vacuoles. 4. A note on the sources of water evacuated, and on the function of contractile vacuoles in marine Protozoa," *J. Exp. Biol.*, **16**, 34 (1939).
67. KITCHING, J. A., "Contractile vacuoles," *Symp. Soc. Exp. Biol.*, **6**, 145 (1952).
68. KITCHING, J. A., "The physiology of contractile vacuoles. 8. The water relations of the suctorian *Podophrya* during feeding," *J. Exp. Biol.*, **29**, 363 (1952).
69. KOCH, H. J., "Cholinesterase and active transport of sodium chloride through the isolated gills of the crab *Eriocheir sinensis*," in *Recent Developments in Cell Physiology*, Ed. Kitching, J. A. (London, Butterworths, 1954).
70. KOIZUMI, T., "Studies on *Caudina chilensis*. 2. On the velocity of permeation of Cl′ and $SO_4″$," *Sci. Rept. Tôhoku Imp. Univ.*, Ser. 4, **10**, 33 (1935).
71. KOIZUMI, T., "Studies on *Caudina chilensis*. 3. On the velocity of permeation of K′, Na′, Ca″ and Mg″," ibid., Ser. 4, **10**, 269 (1935).
72. KOIZUMI, T., "Studies on *Caudina chilensis*. 4. On the inorganic composition of the corpuscles of the body fluid," ibid., Ser. 4, **10**, 277 (1935).
73. KOIZUMI, T., "Studies on *Caudina chilensis*. 5. On the inorganic composition of the longitudinal muscles," ibid., Ser. 4, **10**, 281 (1935).
74. KOIZUMI, T. and HOSOI, K., "On the inorganic composition of the medusae," ibid., Ser. 4, **10**, 709 (1936).
75. KORRINGA, P., "Recent advances in oyster biology," *Quart. Rev. Biol.*, **27**, 266 (1952).
76. KRISHNAMOORTHI, B., "Studies on the osmotic properties of the eggs and larvae of a brackish-water polychaete, *Marphysa gravelyi*," *Proc. Indian Acad. Sci. B.*, **34**, 199 (1951).
77. KROGH, A., *Osmotic Regulation in Aquatic Animals* (Cambridge Univ. Press, 1939).
78. KROMHOUT, G. A., "A comparison of the protonephridia of fresh-water, brackish-water and marine specimens of *Gyratrix hermaphroditus*," *J. Morph.*, **72**, 167 (1943).
79. LADD, M., RAISZ, L. G., CROWDER, C. H. JR. and PAGE, L. B., "Filtration rate and water diuresis in the seal," *J. Cell. Comp. Physiol.*, **38**, 157 (1951).
80. LOVERN, J. A. and WOOD, H., "Variations in the chemical composition of herring," *J. Mar. Biol. Ass. U.K.*, **22**, 281 (1937).
81. LOW, E. M., "Halogenated amino-acids of the bath sponge," *J. Mar. Res.*, **10**, 239 (1951).
82. LOWNDES, A. G., "Percentage of water in jelly-fish," *Nature*, **150**, 234 (1942).
83. LOWNDES, A. G., "Water content of medusae," ibid., **151**, 226 (1943).

84. LOWNDES, A. G., "Densities of the embryonic stages of sea-urchins," ibid., **154**, 55 (1944).
85. MACALLUM, A. B., "The paleochemistry of the body fluids and tissues," *Physiol. Rev.*, **6**, 316 (1926).
86. McCANCE, R. A. and MASTERS, M., "The chemical composition and the acid—base balance of *Archidoris britannica*," *J. Mar. Biol. Ass. U.K.*, **22**, 273 (1937)
87. McFARLAND, W. N. and MUNZ, F. W., "Regulation of body weight and serum composition by hagfish in various media," *Comp. Biochem. Physiol.*, **14**, 383 (1965).
88. McMYNN, R. G. and HOAR, W. S., "Effects of salinity on the development of the Pacific herring," *Canad. J. Zool.*, **31**, 417 (1953).
89. MANERY, J. F., "Electrolytes in squid blood and muscle," *J. Cell. Comp. Physiol.*, **14**, 365 (1939).
90. MAREN, T. H., RAWLS, J. A., BURGER, J. W. and MYERS, A. C., "The alkaline gland of the skate," *Comp. Biochem. Physiol.*, **10**, 1 (1963).
91. MARSTON, H. R., "Cobalt, copper and molybdenum in the nutrition of animals and plants," *Physiol. Rev.*, **32**, 66 (1952).
92. MAST, S. O. and HOPKINS, D. L., "Regulation of the water content of *Amoeba mira* and adaptation to changes in the osmotic concentration of the surrounding medium," *J. Cell. Comp. Physiol.*, **17**, 31 (1941).
93. MATTHEWS, L. H., "The origin of stomach oil in the petrels," *Ibis*, **91**, 373 (1949).
94. MEARA, M. L., "The component acids of the milk fat of a grey Atlantic seal," *Biochem. J.*, **51**, 190 (1952).
95. MORRIS, R., "The osmoregulatory ability of the lampern (*Lampetra fluviatilis*) in sea water during the course of its spawning migration," *J. Exp. Biol.*, **33**, 235 (1956).
96. MORRIS, R., "Some aspects of the structure and cytology of the gills of *Lampetra fluviatilis*," *Quart. J. Micr. Sci.*, **98**, 473 (1957).
97. MORRIS, R., "General problems of osmoregulation with special reference to cyclostomes," *Symp. Zool. Soc. Lond.*, No. 1, 1 (1960).
98. MORRIS, R., "Studies on salt and water balance in *Myxine glutinosa*," *J. Exp. Biol.*, **42**, 359 (1965).
99. MOYLE, V., "Nitrogenous excretion in chelonian reptiles," *Biochem. J.*, **44**, 581 (1949).
100. NEEDHAM, J., *Chemical Embryology*, 3 vols. (Cambridge Univ. Press, 1931).
101. ODDO, A. M. and ESPOSITO, M., "Changes in the potassium content of sea urchin eggs on fertilization," *J. Gen. Physiol.*, **34**, 285 (1951).
102. ORR, A. P., "On the biology of *Calanus finmarchicus*. 4. Seasonal changes in the weight and chemical composition in Loch Fyne," *J. Mar. Biol. Ass. U.K.*, **19**, 613 (1934).
103. OSTERHOUT, W. J. V., "Physiological studies of single plant cells," *Biol. Rev.*, **6**, 368 (1931).
104. PANIKKAR, N. K. and SPROSTON, N. G., "Osmotic relations of some metazoan parasites," *Parasitology*, **33**, 214 (1941).
105. PANTIN, C. F. A., "The adaptation of *Gunda ulvae* to salinity. 3. The electrolyte exchange," *J. Exp. Biol.*, **8**, 82 (1931).
106. PARRY, G., "Osmotic and ionic regulation in the isopod crustacean *Ligia oceanica*," ibid., **30**, 567 (1953).
107. PARRY, G., "Urine production by the antennal glands of *Palaemonetes varians*," ibid., **32**, 408 (1955).

108. PEARSE, A. S., *The Emigrations of Animals from the Sea* (Dryden, N.Y., Sherwood Press, 1950).
109. PORTIER, P., *Physiologie des animaux marins* (Paris, Flammarion, 1938).
110. POTTS, W. T. W., "The inorganic composition of the blood of *Mytilus edulis* and *Anodonta cygnea*," *J. Exp. Biol.*, **31**, 376 (1954).
111. POTTS, W. T. W. and PARRY, G., *Osmotic and Ionic Regulation in Animals* (Oxford, London, Pergamon Press, 1964).
112. ROBERTSON, J. D., "The inorganic composition of the body fluids of three marine invertebrates," *J. Exp. Biol.*, **16**, 387 (1939).
113. ROBERTSON, J. D., "Ionic regulation in some marine invertebrates," ibid., **26**, 182 (1949).
114. ROBERTSON, J. D., "Further studies on ionic regulation in marine invertebrates," ibid., **30**, 277 (1953).
115. ROBERTSON, J. D., "The chemical composition of the blood of some aquatic chordates, including members of the Tunicata, Cyclostomata and Osteichthyes," ibid., **31**, 424 (1954).
116. ROBERTSON, J. D., "Osmotic and ionic regulation in aquatic invertebrates," in *Recent Advances in Invertebrate Physiology* (Univ. Oregon Publ., 1957).
117. ROBERTSON, J. D., "Osmotic and ionic regulation," *The Physiology of Crustacea*, Waterman, T. H., (Ed.), Vol. 1, p. 317 (New York and London, Academic Press, 1960).
118. ROCHE, J., MICHEL, R. and YAGI, Y., "Sur la présence de monobromotyrosine dans les gorgonines," *C.R. Acad. Sci., Paris*, **232**, 570 (1951).
119. ROCHE, J. and YAGI, Y., "Sur la présence de la monoiodotyrosine dans la spongine," *C. R. Soc. Biol., Paris*, **146**, 288 (1952).
120. ROTHSCHILD, LORD and BARNES, H., "The inorganic constituents of the sea-urchin egg," *J. Exp. Biol.*, **30**, 534 (1953).
121. RUBEY, W. W., "Geologic history of sea water," *Bull. Geol. Soc. Amer.*, **62**, 1111 (1951).
122. SCHMIDT, K. P., "Annotated bibliographies of marine ecological relations of living amphibians and reptiles," *Mar. Life*, **1** (9), 43 and 47 (1951).
123. SCHMIDT-NIELSEN, K. and FÄNGE, R., "Salt glands in marine reptiles," *Nature*, **182**, 783 (1958).
124. SCHMIDT-NIELSEN, K., "Osmotic regulation in higher vertebrates," *Harvey Lect.*, **58**, 52 (1963).
125. SCHOLLES, W., "Über die Mineralregulation wasserlebender Evertebraten," *Z. vergl. Physiol.*, **19**, 522 (1933).
126. SEGAL, E. and DEHNEL, P. A., "Osmotic behaviour in an intertidal limpet," *Biol. Bull.*, **122**, 417 (1962).
127. SHAPIRO, H., "The change in osmotically inactive fraction produced by cell activation," *J. Gen. Physiol.*, **32**, 43 (1948).
128. SHAW, J., "Ionic regulation in the muscle fibres of *Carcinus maenas*. 1. The electrolyte composition of single fibres," *J. Exp. Biol.*, **32**, 383 (1955).
129. SHAW, J., "Ionic regulation in the muscle fibres of *Carcinus maenas*. 2. The effect of reduced blood concentration," ibid., **32**, 664 (1955).
130. SIVERTSEN, E., "On the biology of the harp seal," *Hvalråd. Skr.*, No. 26, 166 pp. (1941).
131. SMITH, H. W., "The composition of the body fluids of elasmobranchs," *J. Biol. Chem.*, **81**, 407 (1929).

132. SMITH, H. W., "Water regulation and its evolution in the fishes," *Quart. Rev. Biol.*, **7**, 1 (1932).
133. SMITH, H. W., "The retention and physiological role of urea in the Elasmobranchii," *Biol. Rev.*, **11**, 49 (1936).
134. SMITH, H. W., "The composition of urine in the seal," *J. Cell. Comp. Physiol.*, **7**, 465 (1936).
135. SMITH, R. I., "On the distribution of *Nereis diversicolor* in relation to salinity in the vicinity of Tvärminne, Finland, and the Isefjord, Denmark," *Biol. Bull.*, **108**, 326 (1955).
136. SMITH, R. I., "The ecology of the Tamar estuary. 7. Observations on the interstitial salinity of intertidal muds in the estuarine habitat of *Nereis diversicolor*," *J. Mar. Biol. Ass. U.K.*, **35**, 81 (1956).
137. SMITH, R. I., "A comparison of salt loss rate in three species of brackish-water nereid polychaetes," *Biol. Bull.*, **125**, 332 (1963).
138. SMITH, R. I., "On the early development of *Nereis diversicolor* in different salinities," *J. Morph.*, **114**, 437 (1964).
139. SMYTH, J. D., "Studies in tapeworm physiology. 1. The cultivation of *Schistocephalus solidus in vitro*," *J. Exp. Biol.*, **23**, 47 (1946).
140. SPOONER, G. M., "The distribution of *Gammarus* species in estuaries. Part 1," *J. Mar. Biol. Ass. U.K.*, **27**, 1 (1947).
141. STEINBACH, H. B., "The distribution of electrolytes in *Phascolosoma* muscle," *Biol. Bull.*, **78**, 444 (1940).
142. SVERDRUP, H. U., JOHNSON, M. W. and FLEMING, R. H., *The Oceans: their Physics, Chemistry, and General Biology* (New York, Prentice-Hall, 1942).
143. TANAKA, H., "Chemical studies on the urine of *Chelonia japonica*," *J. Biochem, Tokyo*, **36**, 313 (1944).
144. TEH PING LIN and GOLDBERG, E. D., "Accumulation of radio-iodine in the thyroid gland of elasmobranchs," *Endocrinology*, **48**, 485 (1951).
145. THOMAS, I. M., "The accumulation of radioactive iodine by *Amphioxus*," *J. Mar. Biol. Ass. U K.*, **35**, 203 (1956).
146. TODD, M. E., "Osmotic balance in *Hydrobia* and *Potamopyrgus*," *J. Exp. Biol.*, **41**, 665 (1964).
147. TOPPING, F. L. and FULLER, J. L., "The accommodation of some marine invertebrates to reduced osmotic pressures," *Biol. Bull.*, **82**, 372 (1942).
148. TRESSLER, D. K. and LEMON, J. McW., *Marine Products of Commerce* (New York, Reinhold Publ. Corp., 1957).
149. VALENTE, D. and BRUNO, A., "Conteúdo mineral do sangue de Invertebrados marinhos," *Zoologia, S. Paulo*, No. 16, p. 303 (1951).
150. VINOGRADOV, A. P., "The elementary chemical composition of marine organisms," Mem. 2, Sears Foundation Mar. Res. (1953).
151. WEISEL, G. F. JR., "Relation of salinity to the activity of the spermatozoa of *Gillichthys*, a marine teleost," *Physiol. Zool.*, **21**, 40 (1948).
152. WHITE, F. D., "The nutritive value of marine products. 10. Proximate analysis of ling cod," *J. Biol. Bd Can.*, **2**, 461 (1936).
153. WHITE, H. C., "Life history of *Lepeophtheirus salmonis*," ibid., **6**, 24 (1942).
154. WIKGREN, B., "Osmotic regulation in some aquatic animals with special reference to the influence of temperature," *Acta Zool. Fenn.*, **71**, 102 pp. (1953).
155. YAMAMOTO, K., "Studies on the fertilization of the egg of the flounder," *J. Fac. Sci. Hokkaido Univ. (Zool.)*, Ser. 6, **10**, 253 (1951).

CHAPTER 3

BODY FLUIDS AND CIRCULATION

> But the circulation which I discovered teaches clearly that there is a
> necessary outward and backward flow of the blood, and this at different
> times and places, and through other and yet other channels and pas-
> sages; that this flow is determined also, and for the sake of a certain
> end, and is accomplished in virtue of parts contrived for the purpose
> with consummate forecast and most admirable art.
> WILLIAM HARVEY: Letter to P. M. Slegel, 1651

GENERAL FUNCTIONS OF BODY FLUIDS

IN the preceding chapter the composition of body fluids has been described,
and it has been shown that many animals are capable of maintaining an
internal medium of composition different from the environment. In primitive animals the dissolved constituents of the body fluids consist predominantly of mineral substances, but in higher forms the blood and body
fluids are found to contain large amounts of organic substances, sometimes
in colloidal form, including respiratory pigments (Tables 2.12, 2.13,
4.9, 4.10).

The Protozoa are of such small size that functional exchange of material
between the protoplasm and environment is carried out efficiently by
diffusion across the plasma membrane. The simplest metazoans—sponges
and coelenterates—lack body cavities, and the spaces between the tissue
layers are filled with a solid gelatinous matrix. Internal and external membranes are exposed to sea water and even when the jelly layer becomes very
thick, as in the mesogloea of large pelagic medusae, it is noteworthy that
the cellular content is very sparse. Moreover, metabolic activity of these
lowly animals proceeds at a low rate, which can be satisfied by processes
of diffusion.

In higher groups tissue and body fluids of various kinds are invariably
present. These fluids are concerned with transporting oxygen, foodstuffs,
metabolic wastes, hormones, phagocytes, erythrocytes and other haemal
cells. In soft-bodied invertebrates the body fluids are also concerned with
maintenance of body turgor. Diffusion is such a slow process that in all
but the smallest animals some mechanism must exist for circulating body
fluids so that exchanges of substances may be facilitated. We shall now
consider the various kinds of body fluids, and the circulatory systems which
control their movements. Owing to the great diversity existing in the
organization of body spaces and circulatory systems in different animals,
any classification must be arbitrary and repetitive, but the following will
indicate the various categories which can be recognized.

CLASSIFICATION OF BODY FLUIDS

The External Milieu. This is utilized in some groups of marine animals as a fluid medium subserving transport. Sponges are literally a network of channels through which sea water is propelled by the unco-ordinated activity of numerous flagella. The sea water carries oxygen and food to the organism and waste products away. The hydraulics of this system are described in Chapter 5 dealing with feeding and nutrition. In coelenterates the gastrovascular cavity or coelenteron, with its ramifying passages, is filled with sea water which forms an internal vehicle for transporting dissolved substances and foodstuffs to various parts of the body. In *Cyanea*, for example, currents pass peripherally along the roof and return along the floor of the gastrovascular channels (62). The water vascular system in many echinoderms communicates with the exterior at the madreporite, and acts as a hydraulic mechanism. In the cavities and channels of these various animals the fluids are moved to and fro by ciliary activity or muscular contractions.

Tissue Fluids. These are important in all triploblastic animals as the intimate *milieu* bathing the cells of the body and filling the spaces between organs. It is through this medium that the cells receive or unload gaseous, mineral and organic substances, and it is *vis-à-vis* the interstitial fluids that ionic and other exchanges occur which are essential to the functioning of nervous and contractile tissues (122). In simple metazoans, such as platyhelminths which lack a body cavity, the fluids are confined to interstitial spaces. The tissue spaces of those animals with open circulatory systems, such as bivalve molluscs, are continuous with the haemocoele and contain haemolymph. But in various higher forms with closed circulatory systems, especially the vertebrates, a distinct interstitial fluid permeates the intercellular matrix, and communicates with the blood stream by diffusion through the walls of the finest blood vessels, and by the lymphatic circulation.

There are few estimates of the volume of intercellular fluid in lower animals. On the basis of thiocyanate determinations (injection of a known amount of thiocyanate and subsequent estimation of its concentration in body fluids), the total extracellular space in mammals is found to lie around 20–30% of body weight. About one-third of this volume is occupied by blood; the remainder is lymph and interstitial fluids. In the mussel *Mytilus edulis*, intercellular fluid or haemolymph is estimated to be about 12%; the extracellular space in crabs *Carcinus* and *Eriocheir* forms 33–37% of body volume. Haemolymph volume in these animals is equivalent to total extracellular space in vertebrates. In cephalopods, which also possess a closed vascular system, total extracellular fluid as measured by sucrose injection amounts to about 33% (81, 112).

In the open circulatory system of the mussel, the haemolymph follows alterations of the external medium fairly closely. *Mytilus californianus* maintains a constant ratio of about 1·6–1·0 between Cl⁻ concentrations of external medium and intercellular fluid over a restricted environmental range (Cl⁻ concentrations of 0·9–2·8 %). Within these limits, Cl⁻ exchange occurs only between haemolymph and external medium. Beyond this range, however, Cl⁻ exchange takes place between the cellular contents and the haemolymph, and the cells are unable to maintain a steady internal concentration in the face of marked changes in external chlorinity. Where a well-developed closed circulatory system is present, as in vertebrates, the tissue fluids form a reservoir of water and salts which can be called upon to buffer alterations in the composition of circulating fluids (39, 81).

Fluids in Primary Body Cavities. Many invertebrates retain the primary body cavity or blastocoele in the adult as spaces of various extent filled with intercellular fluid. In the preceding section reference has been made to the relationship between interstitial and circulatory fluids, and we have noted that in various primitive groups all the body fluids of the organism can be regarded as a continuous medium occupying primary body spaces, sinuses and intercellular meshes. In platyhelminths the parenchyma contains large intercellular spaces filled with tissue fluid. In nemertines the diffuse body cavity is reduced to a system of one or more definite vascular channels. Longitudinal vessels are connected together by contractile transverse vessels and these, aided by body movements, circulate the contained fluids. This is the beginning of a true circulatory system concerned, among other things, with transport of oxygen to more deeply lying tissues (25).

In those animals with open circulatory systems (Mollusca, Crustacea, Xiphosura) the primitive body cavity is retained in large haemocoelic spaces through which the blood or haemolymph slowly passes on its way back from the tissues to the heart.

Coelomic Fluids. Extensive coelomic spaces filled with fluid are found in polychaetes, sipunculoids, echiuroids, ectoproct polyzoans, phoronids, chaetognaths and echinoderms. In leeches the coelomic spaces are extensively invaded by mesenchymatous tissue and are reduced to a system of longitudinal channels. In molluscs the coelomic spaces are restricted to small cavities in the kidneys, gonads and pericardium. A similar condition obtains in crustaceans. Coelomic cavities are, of course, well developed in the lower chordates, and coelomic fluid occurs in the spaces between the body wall and the internal organs.

Blood in Closed Vascular Systems. Closed vascular systems are found in the following marine groups: nemertines, polychaetes, leeches, sipunculoids, phoronids, cephalopods, holothurians and chordates. Usually such systems contain a relatively small volume of blood which is pumped continuously around the organism. The hearts or other devices which provide the motive force for propelling the body fluids display great variation in structure and efficiency, and some are subject to various degrees of nervous control.

Lymphatic systems resembling those occurring in vertebrates are not encountered among invertebrates. Gnathobdellid leeches, however, are peculiar in having blood vessels communicating with coelomic sinuses and with intracellular capillaries of botryoidal tissue in a manner analogous with the lymphatic vessels of vertebrates.

In the following pages attention will be restricted to fluid systems of marine invertebrates and the lower chordates.

VOLUME OF CIRCULATING FLUIDS

In higher animals with closed circulatory systems the blood forms only a small and relatively fixed fraction of the body weight or volume. Some selected values for blood volumes of various animals are given in Table 3.1 (125). These have been obtained by several methods. One consists in determining the haemoglobin content of a sample of blood, and then bleeding the animal and washing out the vessels to obtain the total haemoglobin in the body; with these data the blood volume is computed. Others involve addition of a known quantity of some substance which remains confined to the blood stream, and determining the degree of dilution which takes place after it becomes uniformly distributed in the circulation. For this purpose dyes are usually employed (Evans' blue, vital red). Total extracellular fluid has been estimated by using substances such as thiocyanate and sucrose, which are not taken up by tissue cells.

Mean values for total extracellular fluid (sucrose spaces) in fishes are: lamprey, 23·9 %; chondrichthians, 21·2 %; marine teleosts, 15·4 % (125). Blood volumes in fishes are 8·5 % in the lamprey, 6·6 % in chondrichthians, and 2·9 % in marine teleosts. Cyclostomes, which have larger blood volumes per unit body weight than other vertebrates, have a peculiar circulatory feature, viz. extensive sinuses or lacunae in the venous system; these lacunae pose some interesting problems (67). Among lower vertebrates there is a tendency towards reduction of blood volume from more primitive cyclostomes to more complex bony fishes. These values contrast with the generally larger blood volumes found in invertebrates with open circulatory systems (17–37 % in crustaceans; 40–60 % in molluscs other than cephalopods). Utilization of a small volume of circulatory fluid is more efficient than a large one, when it is pumped around the body faster and made use of more often. In these terms the blood circulation of a fish is more efficient than that of the crab (open system). But the haemolymph of the latter is really equivalent to blood plus interstitial fluids of animals with closed circulatory systems, and a comparison on a basis of this kind is difficult. The values for *Arenicola* (minimal estimates) show that large blood volumes are not confined to animals with open circulatory systems. In addition to volumetric considerations, overall efficiency will also depend on hydrodynamic factors, especially the configuration of the peripheral bed and the mechanics of the pumping system. The amount of coelomic fluid in some of the soft-bodied lower invertebrates appears to be very high. Thus, in echiuroids and priapuloids it forms 30–50% of body weight or volume (9, 15, 20, 32, 37, 52, 77, 81, 85, 86, 87, 94, 109).

TABLE 3.1—Blood Volumes of Lower Animals

Animal	Blood volume ml/100 g body weight (or other)	Method
Teleostei		
Tautoga onitis	1·5†	Bleeding and Hb estimation
Sebastodes sp.	2·8†	Vital red
Ophiodon elongatus	3·1	Evans' blue
	1·6–4†	ditto
	1·9†	Vital red
Cottidae, sp.	2·7	ditto
	1·9–2·7†	ditto
Solea solea	1·76, 2·35†	Bleeding and estimation of erythrocyte volume
Belone belone	4·08, 4·44	ditto
♀ less roe	4·80, 5·91	ditto
Selachii		
Squalus acanthias	3·71†	Bleeding and Hb estimation
	6·66†–0·26	Evans' blue
S. acanthias male	5·2	Vital red
	3·9–5·9†	ditto
S. acanthias female	4·4	Vital red
	3·9–5·1†	ditto
	1·7–17·9†	Evans' blue
female with young (embryos small)	11·2	Vital red
	4·5–5·5†	ditto
(embryos large)	10·7–13†	ditto
	4·7†	Vital red and Evans' blue
Raja rhina	5·3	Evans' blue
	1·5–2†	Vital red
	3·6–7†	Evans' blue
R. binoculata	4·4	ditto
	2·2–7·3†	ditto
	0·8–2·7†	Vital red
R. binoculata and *R. erinacea*	4·3–4·5	Bleeding and Hb estimation
R. clavata	2·18–2·49†	Bleeding and estimation of erythrocyte volume
Chimaeroidea		
Hydrolagus colliei	6·7†	Vital red
	1·9, 3·3†	Evans' blue
Cyclostomata		
Petromyzon marinus	5	Evans' blue
Crustacea		
Carcinus maenas	37	Thiocyanate
Eriocheir sinensis	33	Thiocyanate
Homarus americanus	16·6	Evans' blue
Mollusca		
Cryptochiton stelleri	43·8	Inulin
Mytilus californianus	50·8	Inulin
Bullia digitalis	63–66	Amaranth
Aplysia californianus	51	Inulin
Octopus hongkongensis	5·8	Evans' blue
Echiuroidea		
Urechis caupo	37–38†	Bleeding
Priapuloidea		
Priapulus caudatus ⎫ *Halicryptus spinulosus* ⎭	30–50*	Bleeding
Polychaeta		
Arenicola marina	13–44	Bleeding and Hb estimation
	31–50	ditto

† blood per 100 g body weight.   * Volume per cent.
(Various sources.)

BLOOD VESSELS
In those animals with open circulatory systems the blood or haemolymph comes into direct contact with the tissue cells. When a closed vascular system is present the blood constituents must diffuse across the walls of sinuses, small capillaries, etc., to reach the tissue fluids and cells. In the tissues the blood unloads gases, nutrients, etc., and picks up metabolites originating in the tissue cells. The composition of the blood is restored by exchanges which take place in the circulatory bed of skin, gills, excretory organs, etc.

In vertebrates the walls of the larger vessels are composed of layers of muscular and connective tissue (elastic and collagen fibres), with an internal lining of endothelium. Changes in diameter of these vessels serve to accommodate alterations in blood volume, either locally or widespread, and changes in vascular tonus participate in regulation of blood pressure. The capillary wall is a semipermeable membrane, freely permeable to water, salts and small organic molecules. Temporary gaps between the endothelial cells allow the escape of colloidal particles (protein, particulate matter) and occasional blood cells. The residual osmotic pressure, exerted by plasma protein, counterbalances in large part capillary hydrostatic pressure. Colloidal osmotic pressures in the plasma of marine teleosts lie between 4–28 cm H_2O. Values are much lower in elasmobranchs, ranging from 17–46 mm H_2O (72, 127). Pressure-drop along the capillary results in some degree of circulation in the tissue spaces, fluid escaping from the arterioles and capillaries proximally returning again at the venous end.

Among invertebrates muscular blood vessels occur in many groups, but little is known of the role they play in regulation of circulatory conditions. The histology of vessels has been most intensively investigated in the Annelida. Generally these consist of endothelial, skeletal and peritoneal layers. The endothelium is discontinuous and is made up of flat branched cells. The skeletal coat consists of collagenous material. Muscle fibres are frequently present in the external peritoneal layer (28, 54, 55).

In holothurians the larger haemal vessels (intestinal vessels) have relatively thick walls composed of internal endothelium, loose connective tissue and muscle, and an external peritoneum. Vessels of the rete mirabile consist of two epithelial layers; capillaries and lacunae contain only a single layer of endothelium. Nemertines, the most primitive animals to possess a closed vascular system, have two kinds of vessels. The larger contractile vessels are provided with a wall of four layers, namely lining endothelium (flat or bulging cells), gelatinous connective tissue, circular and longitudinal muscles, and an outer non-nucleated covering. Smaller non-contractile vessels lack the muscle layer and consist of inner and outer epithelia, with intervening membrane (25, 63, 108).

Among other invertebrates with closed circulatory systems the cephalopods are worthy of special attention. There is a rich peripheral capillary network; arteries and veins are provided with striped muscle, which is hypertrophied in arterial and branchial hearts (119).

The vascular systems of lower chordates and invertebrates invite further investigations from many aspects. For each of the major groups in which the systems are closed it is desirable to obtain a sound histological picture of the structure of the vascular walls, and to relate this to permeability, inherent contractility, maintenance of tonus and nervous regulation. Partition of fluids and alterations of volume with changing functional states are obvious physiological variables. In the case of open systems there is much to be learnt about volume changes in different sinuses, participation in hydraulic mechanisms and pressure changes under different functional conditions. In all cases these factors have to be related to the output of the heart and the contribution of contractile vessels as main or subsidiary pumping agencies.

Pressure in Circulatory Systems

Blood is propelled through vascular channels by the pumping action of special hearts and contractile vessels, aided in many animals by somatic movements. The pressure head which is built up by the pumping system is gradually dissipated in the vascular channels through frictional losses. The level of blood pressure is determined by the volume of circulating fluid, the force exerted by the heart or other contractile structure and by the peripheral resistance.

Closed Circulatory Systems

Fishes. Haemodynamics and regulation of blood pressure in fishes have received increasing attention; some selected values for blood pressures in arterial vessels of fishes are given in Table 3.2 (57).

In fishes the blood which leaves the heart passes through the branchial vessels before reaching the dorsal aorta. Interposition of the branchial capillaries produces a pressure drop before the blood actually reaches the systemic circulation, and pressure continues to drop in peripheral vessels. Pressures are lower and circulation more sluggish in fishes than in homoeotherms of comparable size. Clark observes that the heart ratio (heart weight over body weight) of a fish is much lower than that of mammals. Since the oxygen requirements of fish are only a fraction of those of warm-blooded animals, a much smaller circulatory volume per minute is adequate for fish metabolism.

Cardiac activity in fish, as in other vertebrates, is subject to regulatory mechanisms bringing about changes in blood pressure. With increase of heart rate there is a rise of blood pressure and a decline of pulse pressure, as the arteries become increasingly distended. The circulation rate depends on the volume output of the heart per beat (stroke volume), and the frequency of heart beat, and as the latter increases there is an increase in the velocity of blood flow. Measurements made on the eel (*Anguilla anguilla*) show that the blood leaving the heart takes from 12 to 60 sec to reach the various posterior veins.

TABLE 3.2

BLOOD PRESSURES OF FISH

Species	Vessel	Blood pressure mm Hg
Myxine glutinosa	Dorsal aorta	3–8
	mean	5
	Pulse pressure	2
Scyliorhinus canicula	Ventral aorta	29·4–36·8
		36·8/33·1
	Branchial arteries	48/38·5
		45/38
	Skin artery	7–10
	Intestinal artery	8·1–8·9
Squalus acanthias	Ventral aorta	28·2/14·9
	Dorsal aorta	11–28
		mean 15·4
S. acanthias	Ventral aorta	39/28
	Dorsal aorta	30/23
Carcharias taurus	Ventral aorta	22–39
		mean 32
	Dorsal aorta	13–30
		mean 23·3
Raja "punctata"	Ventral aorta	16·1/7·4
	Intestinal artery	5·1
R. ocellata	Ventral aorta	16·9/12·5
		17·7/15·5
Torpedo torpedo	Ventral aorta	16·1/7·4
	Intestinal artery	5·1
Anguilla anguilla	Ventral aorta	30–40
		mean 35·5
	Pneumogastric artery	10–22
		mean 16
	Branchial arteries	65–70
Oncorhynchus tschawytscha	Ventral aorta	45–120
		mean 74·6
	Dorsal aorta	44–58
		mean 53·3
Dorosoma cepedianum	Bulbus arteriosus	47·7/38·2
Lophius piscatorius	Ventral aorta	36·8

Certain reflexes, initiated peripherally, affect cardiac activity and blood pressure. If respiratory flow over the gills of a shark or skate is stopped, cardiac inhibition ensues and blood pressure falls; mechanical handling and a variety of other external stimuli produce the same effect. Electrical stimulation of the central ends of cut vagus, hypobranchial and lateral line nerves results in respiratory and cardiac inhibition. When branchial arteries are perfused, raising the arterial pressure evokes sensory discharge in the branchial nerves (glossopharyngeal, vagus), and a similar rhythmic sensory discharge takes place in the normal animal at each heart beat when pressure in the branchial arteries rises. Raising the pressure in the first pair of afferent branchial arteries also produces cardio-inhibition. It seems likely that there is a normal branchial depressor reflex in fish: this reflex is stimulated by presso-receptors in the afferent branchial arteries, and produces cardio-inhibition and fall of blood pressure. Its function appears to be protection of the delicate branchial capillaries lying near the heart (93).

Afferent visceral impulses from many regions are fed into autonomic medullary centres, from which efferent impulses proceed peripherally in autonomic pathways. Efferent cardioregulatory routes available are

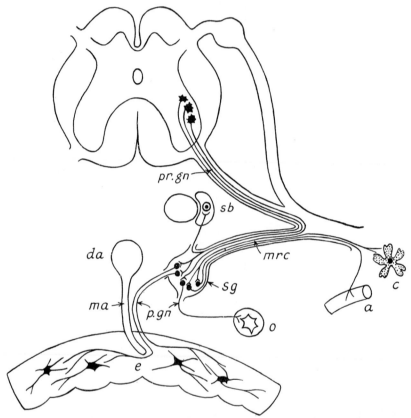

FIG. 3.1. DIAGRAM OF SYMPATHETIC PATHWAYS IN A TELEOST FISH

a, artery; *c*, chromatophore; *ma*, mesenteric artery; *mrc*, mixed ramus communicans; *pr.gn*, pre-ganglionic neurone; *o*, oviduct; *sg*, sympathetic ganglion; *sb*, suprarenal body; *da*, dorsal aorta; *e*, gut; *pgn*, post-ganglionic neurone.

cardiac branches of the vagus (inhibitory fibres) and pre-ganglionic sympathetic fibres to the suprarenal organs. There is no sympathetic supply to the heart in fish. Vagus activity stops the heart and results in fall of blood pressure. Experimentally, adrenaline and noradrenaline usually produce acceleration of the heart and increased strength of beat, as well as causing prolonged rise of blood pressure. It is possible that adrenaline and noradrenaline, secreted by chromaffine tissue of the suprarenal bodies, have pressor effects in the normal animal.

Efferent pathways to blood vessels in fish require further study. Peripheral somatic vessels in the trunk of elasmobranchs are innervated by sympathetic fibres only; visceral (gut) vessels are within sympathetic and parasympathetic fields: branchial and cephalic vessels receive parasympathetic fibres. The following pharmacological observations are pertinent to the morphological pattern. Injection of acetylcholine, although causing cardiac inhibition, raises blood pressure owing to a vasoconstrictor action on peripheral arteries. Adrenaline dilates branchial and constricts systemic vessels, resulting in overall rise of blood pressure (*Raja*). This suggests that sympathetic control of somatic vessels is mediated by adrenergic fibres; parasympathetic fibres to the branchial vessels may be cholinergic.

In teleosts the autonomic supply of heart and vessels is more complex: noteworthy features are a demonstrated sympathetic innervation of branchial and cephalic vessels, and sympathetic plexuses on splanchnic vessels (Fig. 3.1). Vagus activity causes inhibition of the heart. Stimulation of sympathetic trunks in the eel (*Anguilla*) causes vaso-constriction of peripheral vessels. Adrenaline has a vaso-dilator effect on branchial vessels and a constrictor effect on systemic vessels as in selachians (7, 20, 53, 65, 69, 70, 96, 97).

Invertebrates. In cephalopods, which have closed circulatory systems, blood pressures are high, greater than those of many cold-blooded vertebrates. In *Octopus* pressures in the cephalic artery range from 48–60 mm Hg, and in one large animal reached 88 mm Hg. Differences between systolic and diastolic pressures usually lie around 10 mm Hg, but may attain 25 mm. In the gill veins blood pressures fall to 5·4–6·1 mm Hg; pulse pressure here is small, around 0·8 mm Hg. Cephalopods are the largest and most active of invertebrates, with correspondingly high metabolic levels (119).

In contrast, pressures in the vessels of sluggish polychaetes are very low. In *Neanthes* pressure in the dorsal artery is 1·1–2·2 mm Hg when the animal is at rest, and increases to 17·6 mm Hg during activity.

Open Circulatory Systems

Animals with open circulations have low and highly variable blood pressures. In small crustaceans—e.g. some ostracods, copepods and cirripedes—a heart is often wanting and blood is circulated solely by movements of the body wall and alimentary canal. Increase in size and activity is attended by development of a heart pump, but even in large crustaceans the pressure head developed by the heart is low, and circulation of the blood owes much to movements of the appendages and the body wall. Recorded blood pressure in the sternal sinus of the shore crab *Carcinus maenas*, a relatively small but active animal, is 13 cm H_2O. In large specimens of *Maia*, a relatively sluggish crab, systolic pressure in the heart is 55 mm H_2O, and the difference between systolic and diastolic pressures is 8 mm H_2O. Pressure drop from the arteries to the thoracic sinus is about 25 mm H_2O (absolute pressures in the latter 24–34 mm H_2O). In the lobster (*Homarus*), a large active animal, the intraventricular blood pressure is 17·7–1·36 cm H_2O, and the aortic pressure immediately posterior to the ventricle is 17·7 cm during systole and 12 cm at diastole. Pressures in the haemocoele range from 27–82 mm H_2O; pericardial pressures are the lowest of the circulatory system, 0–16 mm H_2O. Vascular pressures vary with activity of the heart, with body tonus and body movements. In decapod crustaceans blood pressures in arteries and the haemocoele rise greatly during activity.

An open circulatory system is also characteristic of gastropods and lamellibranchs. Arterial pressures in freshwater mussels (*Anodonta*) are lower than in decapod crustaceans, about 35 mm H_2O at systole, falling to 10 mm H_2O during diastole. Muscular contraction, causing ejection of water from the exhalant siphon, doubles arterial pressure. Pressures in the haemocoele of the sea hare *Aplysia*, a gastropod, are much above those of *Anodonta*, and approximate those of decapod crustaceans. Pressures in the body cavity of a resting animal were 2·5–4 cm H_2O, and rose to 6 cm during activity.

The heart is a weak and rather inefficient pump in crustaceans and molluscs with open circulatory systems. Some of the work involved in moving the blood about the body is performed by the somatic musculature through changes in body tonus and activity; during periods of higher activity, when oxygen requirements are greater, blood pressure and circulatory movements are automatically increased (102, 119).

HYDROSTATIC PRESSURES IN BODY CAVITIES

Fluids in the body cavities of many soft-bodied animals, as we have already noted, have several functional roles including circulation of essential substances, removal of wastes, provision of a constant internal *milieu* and participation in hydraulic mechanisms essential for movement and locomotion.

In burrowing gastropods and lamellibranchs the foot is employed for locomotion and burrowing and the haemolymph supplies the necessary turgor for movements to be executed. When the foot is extended the pedal muscles relax and blood flows through the pedal artery into the foot. Retraction of the foot is brought about by contraction of the pedal muscles, and blood is shifted largely into spaces in the mantle. Burrowing movements are carried out with great rapidity by the razor-shell *Ensis*. In downward burrowing the foot is extended into the sand, blood flows into it and the tip swells out into a bulbous disc (Fig. 3.2). This acts as an anchor while the pedal muscles contract and draw the animal down. This is followed by return of the blood to the body, while the foot extends once more, repeating the manoeuvre. In upward progression the pedal muscles remain relaxed while the tip of the foot becomes distended with blood. With the tip anchored, blood is forced into the upper region of the foot, which elongates, thus pushing the animal upwards. The consecutive muscular contractions involved in burrowing can still take place in an exsanguinated animal, but in the absence of turgor these are weak and ineffective (40).

Bullia is a burrowing gastropod whose foot is capable of great expansion. Blood is shifted from the visceral into the pedal sinus, and the turgor of the foot is maintained by compression of the visceral sinus; at the same time the extravisceral spaces (between the shell and the tissues) fill with water (17).

Mechanisms used in siphonal extrusion vary in different species of lamellibranchs. The siphons of *Mya* are extended by water forced into their lumina from the mantle cavity. The mantle and siphonal cavities form a fluid-tight system, and force is applied by contractions of the adductor muscles. Elongation proceeds stepwise; water is taken into the system between successive elongations, so that the internal volume remains constant (Fig. 3.3). In *Scrobicularia*, in contrast, siphonal extension is effected by the intrinsic musculature of the siphonal walls acting on the blood within, the volume of which remains constant (24).

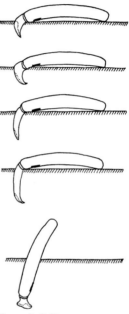

In tubular animals, such as annelids, echiuroids, sipunculoids, holothurians and enteropneusts, pressure of the body fluids is determined by tonus and contraction of the body wall. In these soft-bodied animals the body fluids constitute a hydrostatic skeleton against which the muscle systems can operate. In burrowing species, activity and burrowing movements are accompanied by increased turgor and elevation of fluid pressures in coelomic cavities. Muscle and fluid systems form a coordinated unit, proper changes in each of

FIG. 3.2 RAZOR-SHELL *Ensis*. SEQUENCE OF MOVEMENTS IN DOWNWARD BURROWING. (Redrawn from Fraenkel (40).)

which are necessary for locomotion and burrowing to be accomplished.

In the burrowing lugworm *Arenicola*, pressure in the coelomic cavity when the animal is at rest averages 13·6 cm H_2O; pressures in the anterior body cavity rise to 36 cm during muscular contraction, and to 27 cm during burrowing. Removal of a quarter of the coelomic fluid more than doubles burrowing time. Higher pressures are developed in the anterior branchial region than in posterior segments. This results from contraction of circular muscle in the posterior branchial region, driving fluid forwards in the anterior region, which is then sealed off by constriction of the body wall against the gut. In the ragworm *Neanthes* pressure of coelomic fluid rises from a resting value of 1–2 cm to 15 cm H_2O during activity; fluid pressures in *Glycera* are 0·5–2 cm. at rest, and 8 cm H_2O when the animal is active (23).

In sipunculoids high internal pressures are attained which provide body turgor essential for burrowing. In *Sipunculus nudus* and *Golfingia gouldii* fluid pressures increase from 2–3 cm H_2O in the relaxed condition to around 100 cm during maximal activity. When lying freely in the water and executing burrowing movements coelomic pressure in *Golfingia* rises to 25 cm and in *Sipunculus* to 40 cm H_2O. Pressures are higher during fast burrowing in sand, around 90 cm H_2O in *Sipunculus*. Burrowing is accomplished in these animals by protracting the proboscis and driving

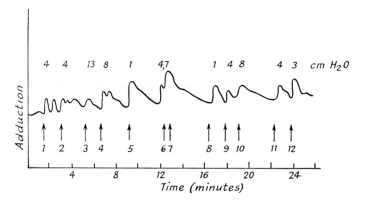

FIG. 3.3. HYDROSTATIC PRESSURE AND MOVEMENT IN *Mya arenaria*

Record showing movement of shell valves and simultaneous readings of internal hydrostatic pressure of mantle fluid. Movement upwards indicates adduction. Elongation of the siphons was noted at points 1–12. Each peak on the trace was accompanied by an elongation of the siphons until they reached a length of 40 cm. (Redrawn from Chapman and Newell (24).)

it into the sand, the loosened sand being carried backwards behind the animal. During burrowing activity there are regular rises and falls of pressure in the coelomic fluid, accompanied by eversion and retraction of the proboscis. Protrusion of the proboscis usually occurs during a rise of coelomic pressure; the proboscis can be withheld or retracted against high coelomic pressures by retractor muscles, however. When the body wall is perforated, fluid pressures can no longer be built up and eversion of the proboscis ceases (138.)

Hydraulic mechanisms are well developed in echinoderms, where they are involved in locomotory, feeding and burrowing activities. In these animals the coelom comprises (1) the perivisceral cavity, (2) a perihaemal system consisting of a perihaemal radial vessel in each radius, plus a ring vessel about the mouth, and (3) a water vascular system. The latter originates in an external opening, the madreporite, which is connected via an axial sinus and stone canal with a circumoral water vascular ring. The ring bears several Polian vesicles and from it a radial water vessel enters each radius and gives off lateral vessels to the tube feet. In crinoids and holothurians the madreporite opens into the perivisceral cavity. In addition there is a lacunar vascular system consisting of a ring of lacunar tissue around the mouth, from which a longitudinal strand penetrates into each radial perihaemal canal. In holothurians and echinoids dorsal and ventral vessels from the oral lacunar ring pass along the alimentary canal, on which they form plexuses. In some sea cucumbers the dorsal intestinal vessel gives rise to an intricate rete mirabile on the mesentery, and this rich network also becomes associated with the respiratory trees (27).

In those echinoderms in which the tube feet are used for walking, the radial water vessels bear contractile ampullae associated with the tube feet. These ampullae are able to drive water into the podia, causing the latter to protract (p. 426). A valve at the junction of the radial vessel and the lateral canal leading into each ampulla confines fluid to the ampulla-podial system during motor activity.

In holothurians the anterior podia are modified into tentacles, which are supplied by radial ducts of the ambulacral system. This originates in an oral ring which bears Polian vesicles, one or more sinuses leading into internal madreporites, and a set of five radial ducts. The latter connect with the tentacles and the tube feet, and the Polian vesicles form a reservoir of fluid for the entire podial system. The tentacular ducts leading off the radial vessels are guarded by valves, and usually possess tentacular ampullae which are employed in extruding the tentacles. Pressures vary independently in the Polian complex and tentacular ducts. In *Thyone* pressure is usually higher in the tentacular duct than in the Polian complex (10–25 cm as against 3–5·5 cm H_2O). In a relaxed animal pressure in the body cavity is low (0–2·5 cm H_2O), but rises during activity to 37 cm H_2O. Similar values are given for *Caudina*.

Thyone and *Caudina* are burrowing animals, and it is interesting to compare them with *Holothuria* which inhabits rock crevices. In *H. grisea* rhythmical cloacal contractions drive water into the cloaca and respiratory trees; after about ten contractions the cloaca opens and the accumulated water is driven out by contraction of the body wall. This expulsion generally results in a fall of about 5 mm in coelomic pressure (Fig. 3.4). Average coelomic pressure varies from 7 to 21 mm H_2O, and during normal body movements the coelomic pressure approaches 30 mm H_2O. Strong mechanical stimulation producing contraction of the body wall brings about a pressure rise of 4·5–16 cm H_2O (Fig. 3.5). A comparison of coelomic pressures of *Holothuria* with those recorded for *Thyone* and *Caudina* indicates that the stronger muscular contractions of these animals during the course of burrowing necessitate the development of much higher coelomic pressures.

In holothurians which possess Cuvierian organs, e.g. *Holothuria*, strong contractions of the body wall can lead to rupture of the cloaca and extrusion of the Cuvierian organs. This is usually attended by high coelomic

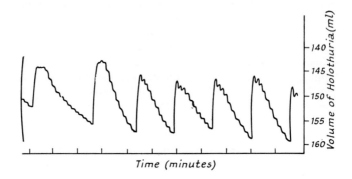

FIG. 3.4. PERIODIC CHANGES IN THE VOLUME OF AN INTACT *Holothuria grisea*

Time scale in minutes. Each cycle in the curve represents a series of about ten cloacal contractions, increasing the body volume by 10–15 ml, followed by a contraction of the body wall. Each contraction of the cloaca drives in about 1 ml; when the body wall contracts, all of the accumulated water is driven out and the volume falls. Read from right to left. (From Pantin and Sawaya (101).)

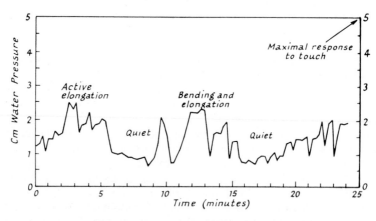

FIG. 3.5. GRAPH OF CHANGES IN COELOMIC PRESSURE OF *Holothuria grisea* (From Pantin and Sawaya (101).)

pressures (12–18 cm H$_2$O). But extrusion of the gut can sometimes occur at moderate pressures, and does not invariably involve high pressures. Consequently other factors besides development of high coelomic pressures must be involved (27, 35, 101).

PUMPING MECHANISMS

In order to utilize efficiently the fluids present in body cavities and vessels, some circulatory mechanism is necessary. Circulation of body fluids is accomplished in some animals of small size by the action of cilia, or by muscular movements of the body wall. When definite circulatory systems are present, either of the closed or open type, it is found that a rhythmically contractile pumping device is interpolated for keeping the fluid in constant motion.

Movement of body fluids is often aided greatly by general muscular activity. Peristaltic burrowing and other somatic movements assist in the circulation of coelomic and vascular fluids in polychaetes, sipunculoids and echinoderms. Ciliary tracts in the body cavities of these animals have a similar effect (89, 138).

Circulatory pumps can be classified as (a) contractile vessels, (b) tubular hearts, (c) chambered hearts, (d) ampullar accessory hearts. In some animals more than one kind of heart is present to suit particular circulatory needs. To direct the fluid in one direction while the heart is contracting, special mechanisms are necessary and these actually take two forms, mechanical and functional. When the heart is provided with valves at its exit and entrance these prevent retrograde flow of blood while the heart is filling or emptying (diastole and systole). In other hearts contraction takes the form of a progressive wave, driving the contained fluid forward. Frequently both mechanisms are employed.

Contractile Vessels

These are widely distributed among invertebrates, and are best known in annelids. In *Arenicola* blood is pumped forward in the dorsal vessel. The circulation follows the course: dorsal vessel → gastric plexus → lateral gastric vessel → lateral heart → ventral vessel → sub-intestinal and afferent vessels to body wall, nephridia and gills → intestinal plexus and vessels → gastric and dorsal vessels. Contractile vessels are the dorsal vessel, the lateral, oesophageal and some nephridial vessels. The two lateral hearts pump blood into the ventral vessel. Contraction begins in the auricle (a thin-walled expansion of the gastric vessel) and proceeds ventrally in the ventricle towards the ventral vessel. There is no relation between contractions of dorsal vessel and hearts, nor any correspondence in the beating of the two hearts. Usually the heart beats faster and more irregularly than the dorsal vessel; the auricular region sometimes contracts several times for each ventricular beat (110).

The blood vessels of many polychaetes contract rhythmically. The vascular system of *Nereis* contains a contractile dorsal and non-contractile ventral vessel, from each of which segmentally arranged branches extend to capillary plexuses in the body wall, gut and parapodia. Contraction in the dorsal vessel takes the form of a peristaltic wave which begins in the posterior region and travels anteriorly at about 7 mm/sec (17°C). Many of the smaller vessels also are contractile, including blindly ending capillaries serving internal organs. In sabellids nearly all vessels, including trunks and blind capillaries, are contractile; the latter fill up with successive lots of blood passing by in the trunk vessels. In these animals peristalsis in the main longitudinal vessels occasionally reverses direction, indicating absence of fixed functional polarization. The blood vessels of worms contract at rather slow frequencies, around 5–20 per min (Table 3.3) (28).

In *Amphioxus* the heart is a simple tube comparable to sinus venosus plus conus arteriosus, and many other vessels are also contractile. A peristaltic contractile wave begins in the hepatic vein and proceeds to sinus venosus (heart), endostyle artery (ventral aorta), bulbils and afferent branchial arteries. Velocity of propagation is slow, around 0·3 mm/sec. Contractile activity is rather irregular and after several heart beats there may be irregular pauses. In general, the glomus (a buccal plexus) and subintestinal vein beat with twice the frequency of the heart (Table 3.3). Antiperistaltic waves have also been observed (118, 134, 135).

The heart of brachiopods is a contractile muscular vessel lying above the gut. Rhythmically pulsatile vessels occur in the mantle of the oyster (*Ostrea*), where they drive blood into the circumpallial artery. Certain of the haemal (lacunar) vessels on the intestine of holothurians are spontaneously contractile. The beat is rather irregular and slow (2–10 per min) in different species (Table 3.3) (61, 108).

Chambered Hearts

Molluscs. These occur in vertebrates and molluscs. In the latter group they range in complexity from the rudimentary heart of scaphopods, connected by ostia with venous sinuses, to the highly developed organs of cephalopods. Typically the heart consists of two auricles (one in certain gastropods, four in tetrabranch cephalopods), opening into a ventricle. Auricles are receiving chambers with slight musculature; the ventricle is more muscular and strongly contractile. Cardiac muscles are sometimes striated (*Murex, Octopus*, etc.). Guarding the aperture between auricles and ventricles is an A.V. or semilunar valve. In lamellibranchs valves are also present at the origin of the aortae, and prevent blood from being driven backwards into the heart when the foot or siphons suddenly contract. Blood is carried away from the heart by anterior and posterior aortae, and is returned by veins, differently organized in the various groups.

In lamellibranchs and gastropods with open circulations the blood passes into lacunae and venous sinuses. The branchial circulation takes its origin largely from the renal sinus. Not all lamellibranchs have a complete branchial circulation; in *Mytilus*, for example, some of the venous blood returns to the heart without passing through the gills. In cephalopods the venous return from the peripheral capillary network involves vena cava, abdominal and pallial veins, which lead into a pair of branchial hearts. These are muscular dilatations serving to pump blood through the ctenidia, from which efferent vessels return blood to the auricles. Many of the veins are also contractile, showing peristaltic movements, and venous valves occur which regulate the direction of flow.

Rate of heart beat is generally slow in lamellibranchs and gastropods, around 10–20 beats per min, and higher in cephalopods, up to 80 beats per

TABLE 3.3

REPRESENTATIVE FIGURES FOR HEART FREQUENCIES

Animal	Vessel	Temperature (°C)	Frequency (beats per min)
Neanthes virens	Dorsal vessel	20	20
Perinereis cultrifera	Dorsal vessel	14·5	7–9
Arenicola marina	Lateral heart	—	13–22
Sabella pavonina	{ Branchial vessel	19	5·9
	Lateral vessels	19	7·1
	Ventral vessel	19	10·9
	Peri-intestinal sinus	19	24
Talorchestia longicornis	Heart	15	175–200
Homarus americanus	Heart	16–20	50–136 mode 100
Palaemon serratus	Heart	17	181
Spirontocaris securifrons	Heart	18	139–199
Cancer irroratus	Heart	16–20	150
Limulus polyphemus	Heart	—	12–28
Ostrea edulis	Heart	—	25–30
Pecten sp.	Heart	22	18–22
Mya arenaria	Heart	20	15
Cryptochiton sp.	Heart	—	5–7
Acmaea limatula	Heart	14	35–48
Phyllirrhoe sp.	Heart	20	46·5
Tiedemannia neapolitana	Heart	14–15	25
Pterotrachea coronata	Heart	14–15	50
Loligo vulgaris	Systemic heart	—	70–80
Octopus vulgaris	Systemic heart	—	33–40
Stichopus californicus	Intestinal vessel	18–22	4–5·5
Caudina chilensis	Intestinal vessel	—	1·2–2
Molgula manhattensis	Heart	—	43
Phallusia sp.	Heart	12	10
Salpa fusiformis	Heart	11	57–60
Amphioxus	{ Endostyle artery	20	0·88
	Glomus	20	1·70
	Vena sub-intestinalis	20	1·64
Scyliorhinus stellaris	Heart	16	44
Carcharias sp.	Heart	16	18, 30
Anguilla anguilla	Heart	13–16	46–68
Gadus callarias	Heart	16	26–40
Pleuronectes platessa	Heart	—	54–76
Dorosoma cepedianum	Heart	19	20–50

min (Table 3.3). Cephalopods are active animals with high respiratory rates, and have need of an efficient circulatory system. Blood pressures are high, due in part to rapid heart beat, and in part to the closed circulation and strength of the cardiac pump. Cardiac output of the octopus is 10 ml/kg/min, and blood volume is 5% (68). In consequence of these various factors the velocity of circulation is rapid and probably approaches that of bony fishes (68, 87).

Turning now to the properties of molluscan heart muscle, we find certain differences from vertebrate cardiac muscle. The molluscan heart is excitable at all stages of the cardiac cycle, but threshold is high during systole, and a strong stimulus is required to elicit a contraction. A condition approaching absolute refractoriness exists during early systole, after which excitability gradually returns (Fig. 3.6). It follows from these characteristics that the molluscan heart can be tetanized by repetitive stimulation.

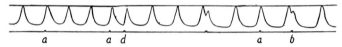

a   a d   a   b

FIG. 3.6. EFFECT OF ELECTRICAL STIMULI ON
VENTRICULAR CONTRACTION OF *Aplysia*

Stimulus ineffective during systole (*a*), but effective during diastole (*b*), and diastolic pause (*d*). (From Carlson, 1906.)

The frequency and force of contractions are dependent on the internal pressure (cf. Starling's law of the vertebrate heart), and some molluscan hearts fail to beat unless sufficiently distended. The heart of *Octopus* ceases to beat when the internal pressure falls below 2 cm H_2O, and the frequency increases with rise in pressure (80, 119).

Fishes. The fish heart is derived during ontogeny from a tubular structure and consists of three successive chambers, namely sinus venosus, auricle and ventricle. These are guarded by valves: S.V. (sinus venosus) valves where the ducts of Cuvier enter the sinus, S.A. (sino-auricular) valves between sinus and auricle, and A.V. (auriculo-ventricular) valves guarding the auriculo-ventricular junction. The ventricle leads into a muscular and contractile truncus arteriosus in elasmobranchs, and a fibrous bulbus arteriosus in teleosts. These latter structures are provided with semilunar valves. The heart discharges into a ventral aorta from which afferent branchial arteries carry the blood to the gills before it enters the systemic circulation.

The sequence of cardiac contraction is from sinus to ventricle. The sinus and auricle have thin muscular walls, especially the former, and are essentially receiving chambers; the ventricle has strong muscular walls and is the effective pump. The valves are arranged so as to prevent reflux of blood, and close when the pressure on the outgoing side exceeds that on the incoming side. Conditions affecting venous return in fishes are poorly understood; venous pressures measured near the heart lie around zero, and it is likely that swimming movements and contractions of the body wall are important in moving blood back to the heart. The sinus fills during diastole, and when contraction ensues the S.A. valves open and the auricle fills. As the auricle fills its pressure rises and during systole the S.A. valves close, the A.V. valves are forced open and blood fills the ventricle.

Systolic contraction of the ventricle in turn is accompanied by closure of the A.V. valves and discharge of blood into the ventral aorta, the semilunar valves in turn closing when the ventricle passes into diastole and intra-ventricular pressure falls below that in the ventral aorta.

Vertebrate heart muscle is striated, and it is divided into cellular units by intercalated discs, which are irregular cell boundaries or plasmademma membranes. When an electrical stimulus is applied to the intact heart, or to a piece of heart tissue, the excitatory wave which is evoked spreads throughout the tissue. The contraction of the vertebrate heart, either dur-ing rhythmic activity or following electrical stimulation, is all or nothing in character, i.e. it is maximal for the condition of the heart at that time and is not affected by stimulus-strength. When tested by electrical stimula-tion during various phases of a normal contractile cycle the heart proves to be inexcitable during most of systole (absolute refractory period), after

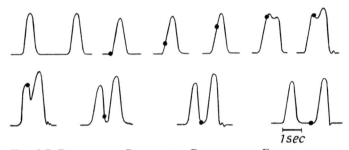

1 sec

FIG. 3.7. REFRACTORY PERIOD AND RECOVERY OF EXCITABILITY IN
THE HEART OF *Torpedo ocellata*

Effect of a strong induction shock on the ventricle at different intervals after the occurrence of an auricular contraction. Exact moment of stimulation is shown by the black spots on the tracings. (From Mines, 1913.)

which excitability gradually returns (Fig. 3.7). At the end of systole and throughout most of diastole an interpolated stimulus evokes a contraction of submaximal height (relative refractory period); recovery becomes com-plete by the end of diastole. Any extra contraction interposed between two normal contractions is followed by a compensatory pause longer than a normal diastolic pause. The long absolute and relative refractory periods preclude tetanization of heart muscle. When quiescent strips of vertebrate heart muscle are stimulated by repeated shocks at suitable intervals (longer than the refractory period), they respond by single contractions of increas-ing magnitude, an effect known as staircase.

According to Starling's law of the heart the strength of contraction is dependent on its degree of distension. This is an effect common to all muscle by which the force of contraction increases with stretching, up to some maximal value. By this means the heart adapts itself to a given load. The mechanics of cardiac output in several freshwater teleosts have been investigated by Hart (57). The blood pressure rises with increase in rate of heart beat up to frequencies of 45–50 beats per min, beyond which there would appear to be little opportunity for further increase of pressure. As the heart rate increases, pulse pressure declines, while systolic pressure rises.

The output per heart beat is known as the stroke volume and varies with the weight of the fish. The cardiac output (stroke volume) of the dogfish *Squalus acanthias* is 0·4–1·5 c.c. for a normal animal weighing 1,600 g, with a maximal value of 3 c.c. At a cardiac frequency of 36 per min this gives an average minute volume of about 20 c.c./kg fish. In a cod of 2·9 kg, the stroke volume is 0·9 c.c., the heart rate is 30/min, and the minute volume is 9·3 c.c./kg fish. Heart frequencies of some representative species of selachians and teleosts are given in Table 3.3. These show about the same range as in cephalopods, invertebrates of comparable size and blood pressures (20, 66, 117).

Tubular Hearts

Hearts of arthropods, when present, usually take the form of contractile tubes or are derived therefrom. In Crustacea the heart lies in a large pericardial sinus, with which it communicates by several ostia guarded by valves. Isopods and amphipods have long tubular hearts (Fig. 3.8). In decapods they are polygonal-shaped chambers, lying freely in the pericardium and suspended at several corners by strands (Fig. 3.17). Blood is discharged from the heart through several arteries (five in front and two behind in *Homarus*), which are also supplied with valves. The arteries carry blood to all parts of the body; after bathing the tissues the venous blood passes by a lacunar system into a large ventral sinus, whence it is carried by afferent branchial vessels to the gills. In the latter there is a complicated through circulation by which venous blood is brought close to the surface of the gill filaments in distinct afferent and efferent capillaries. From the gills the blood passes by efferent branchio-cardiac veins to the pericardium, and thence to the heart. The heart of *Limulus* is a long segmental tube perforated by eight pairs of ostia, which mark it off into eight segments (Fig. 3.9). In the anterior half are five pairs of arteries plus one anteromedian artery. A receiving chamber ("auricle") covers the posterior region of the heart. Arthropod heart muscle is cross striated, and consists of circularly or spirally arranged fibres. There is some doubt whether the heart muscle is truly syncytial.

Arthropod heart muscle resembles the molluscan heart in its contractile properties. There is a condition of reduced excitability early in systole, after which excitability gradually returns (Fig. 3.10). This condition is relative, however, and by increasing the strength of stimulus a contraction can be produced at any stage of the cardiac cycle. At slow frequencies of stimulation (1 per sec), staircase, or progressive increment of consecutive responses, can be demonstrated in crab heart (*Cancer*).

An investigation of haemodynamics in the lobster (*Homarus americanus*) shows that the cardiac stroke volume is about 0·1–0·3 c.c. An animal hav-

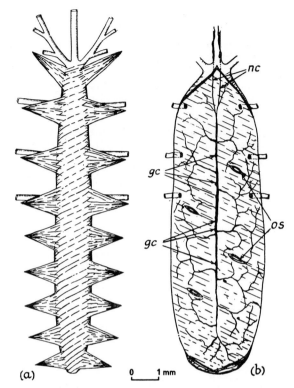

FIG. 3.8. HEART OF *Ligia oceanica*; (*a*) VIEW OF THE HEART FROM THE VENTRAL
SIDE, SHOWING ARTERIES AND ALARY MUSCLES; (*b*) INNER SURFACE OF THE
HEART, SHOWING NERVES AND GANGLIA

gc, nerve cells in nerve trunks; *nc*, nerves connecting local system with c.n.s.; *os*, ostia.
(From Alexandrowicz (1).)

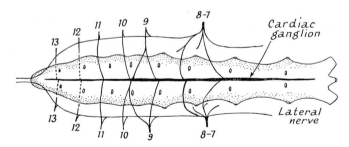

FIG. 3.9. HEART OF KING CRAB *Limulus*, SHOWING ARRANGEMENT OF NERVES

7–8, cardiac nerve from brain; 9–11, cardiac nerve from abdominal ganglia. (From
Carlson.)

ing a blood volume of 75 c.c. and a cardiac rate of 100 beats per min can turn over its entire blood volume in 3–8 min. The heart is the main pumping mechanism in decapod crustaceans, assisted by body movements which help in driving blood back to the heart. A structure called the blood pump is the main pumping organ in barnacles (Thoracica). This structure is a distended vessel which can be compressed by contiguous and extrinsic somatic muscles. In Malacostraca a blood pump (the *cor frontale*) on the anterior artery supplements the propulsive force of the heart (88).

In solitary ascidians such as *Ciona* the heart is a simple ∧-shaped tube. The walls are composed of curious muscle fibres, differentiated into an

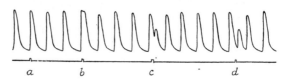

FIG. 3.10. MYOGRAM OF THE HEART OF *Palinurus*, STIMULATED WITH INDUCTION SHOCKS AT VARIOUS STAGES OF THE CARDIAC CYCLE

Stimulus ineffective at the beginning of systole (*a*), but effective during diastole (*b*, *c*, *d*). (From Carlson, 1906.)

inner striated, and an outer sarcoplasmic portion. There is no endothelium. Periodically, the heart reverses the direction of its beat, at the same time reversing the course of circulation about the body. Alternation of direction of heart beat is characteristic of all tunicates—salps, pyrosomae and ascidians. Blood pressure is very low, around 2 mm Hg in *Ascidia* (34, 91).

Ampullar Hearts

Accessory devices for propelling blood through peripheral channels sometimes take the form of contractile ampullae. In cephalopods the branchial hearts are booster devices which drive systemic venous blood through the gills towards the systemic heart. The walls consist of spongy tissue lined with faintly striated endothelial cells; exit and entrance are guarded by sets of valves. The two branchial hearts contract simultaneously and rhythmically (119, 126).

In lancelets there are small contractile bulbils at the bases of the gill bars. Propulsion of blood through the vessels and lacunar spaces (or blood sinuses) of hagfishes is aided by contractile activity of gill vessels and accessory hearts—portal, cardinal and caudal—on the venous return (67). Lymph vessels of fishes sometimes bear contractile lymph hearts which drive lymph into the veins. In the tail of *Anguilla*, for example, there is a lymph heart which opens into the caudal vein. Lymph hearts are composed of striped anastomosing muscle fibres, and are provided with valves to prevent reflux of blood or lymph. Evidence exists that activity of the lymph heart is controlled by the c.n.s. (central nervous system): it stops beating when the spinal cord is destroyed, and its frequency is altered by stimulation of the cord.

HEART RATES. Some representative data on heart rates of different animals are presented in Table 3.3. In general the frequencies of contractile vessels in such animals as polychaetes and holothurians are rather low, often less than 10 per min. The hearts of sluggish animals beat at slower rates than those of more active forms (e.g. lamellibranchs versus cephalopods). Heart rates are related to general metabolism and are an important factor, varying in significance in different groups, in maintaining an efficient circulation suited to the animal's requirements. Both cardiac rate and amplitude are usually subject to regulatory mechanisms, described in more detail in sections to follow.

Heart rates vary with temperature and Q_{10} values range between 2–3 in many species. Like certain other activities, there is evidence that heart rates tend to show temperature adaptation (acclimatization) in various species. This is established for the limpet *Acmaea limatula*, and is implicit in the adaptation of rate function to latitude shown by many forms. For example, the rate of pulsation of the dorsal blood vessel of *Perinereis cultrifera* has been compared in specimens at Plymouth (England) and Tamaris (Mediterranean). The rate in northern specimens was the same at 14°C as in Mediterranean specimens at 20°C (respective summer environmental temperatures). In a similar manner Crustacea from northern latitudes show faster heart rates than more southern forms, when comparison is made with the same or closely allied species at a given intermediate temperature. Differences in rate processes obtain even in a single locality. Thus, limpets (*Acmaea limatula*) from the low intertidal region have faster heart rates than high littoral animals at a given temperature of measurement. Adaptation of rate processes is one aspect of compensation for variable environmental temperature (19, 50, 111, 114, 135).

INITIATION AND REGULATION OF CARDIAC ACTIVITY. Hearts are characterized by rhythmic and continuous contractility, the initiation and maintenance of which are primary intrinsic functions. The classical object of cardiac research is the vertebrate heart, in which the beat is demonstrably muscular in origin (myogenic). There are certain invertebrate groups in which cardiac contractions are dependent on the nervous system (neurogenic hearts). Myogenic and neurogenic hearts are distinguished on several grounds. Myogenic hearts are usually inhibited by acetylcholine in low concentrations ($< 10^{-8}$), while neurogenic hearts are usually accelerated. Search should reveal ganglion cells in the latter type of heart, or in the immediate vicinity. The electrocardiogram of the myogenic heart consists of regular slow potentials, while that of the neurogenic heart shows fast oscillations. Other suggestive features are ease of tetanization, simultaneity or sequence of contraction throughout the organ, and degree of autonomous activity versus central nervous control. A differential effect of ether on the activity of the two types of hearts is explained by the greater sensitivity which the c.n.s. shows to this anaesthetic compared with heart muscle (95).

Myogenic Hearts

The hearts of vertebrates and molluscs are myogenic, and the beat originates in the cardiac musculature. Ontogenetically, contractions appear in the vertebrate heart before it is innervated, and automatic contractions sometimes continue in fragments of adult heart tissue which lack ganglion cells (6).

Fish Heart. In the fish heart contractions are initiated in the sinus venosus and spread to other chambers through the myocardium. Other regions capable of producing automatic rhythmic contractions under experimental conditions are: the veins of Cuvier, the auricle, the auriculo-ventricular canal and the ventricle. Local warming or cooling of the pace-makers alters cardiac rate and provides a means of delimiting their boundaries and observing their influence on other regions. Local warming of the sinus region, for example, increases cardiac rate. When a Stannius

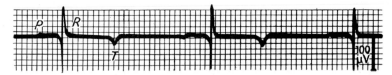

FIG. 3.11. ELECTROCARDIOGRAM OF THE HEART OF *Platichthys flesus*
PRT waves shown. Calibration, 100 μV. (From Oets (98).)

ligature, blocking conduction from sinus to ventricle, is applied to the heart of selachians and eels, the anterior chambers beat at a slower rate than the sinus. This effect is not always apparent in the teleost heart. A wave of excitation can proceed in either direction through the myocardium. The unidirectional course of excitation, from sinus to auricle to ventricle, results from differences in the rhythmicity of the several regions, the sinus showing a more rapid recovery of excitability and thus acting as pacemaker for the whole heart (117).

The electrocardiogram (ECG) from the fish heart resembles that of other vertebrates, and gives information about the spread of excitation and contractions of the several chambers. Typically there are a series of slow waves consisting of upward inflexions (negative *P*, *R* waves) and downward deflexions (positive *Q* and *S* waves) (Fig. 3.11). The electrocardiogram represents a wave front of excitation (depolarization) spreading over the heart. The *P* wave corresponds to conduction in the auricle, the *PQ* interval is delay at the auriculo-ventricular junction and the *QRS* complex represents conduction in the ventricle. A terminal *T* wave, which may appear negative or positive, follows after an interval and is linked with repolarization of the ventricular surface. Contraction of the S.V. is correlated with a small negative *V* wave, immediately preceding the *P* wave.

This appears as a simple diphasic wave in the isolated sinus, and stands revealed after extirpation of the ventricle. In selachians a *B* wave, representing activity of the truncus, is sometimes registered (73, 74, 98).

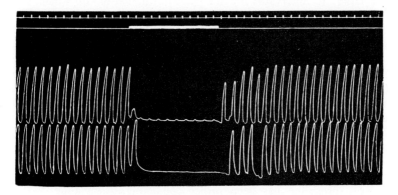

FIG. 3.12. EFFECT OF STIMULATION OF THE VAGUS NERVE
ON THE HEART OF *Scyliorhinus canicula*

Time scale, above, 1/sec; stimulation shown on second line from top. Lower two curves, heart contractions; auricle above, ventricle below. Some sinus activity is manifest during vagus-arrest of the auricle. (From von Skramlik (119).)

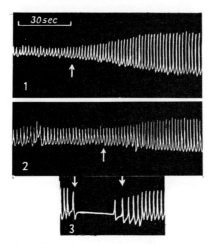

FIG. 3.13. EFFECT OF DRUGS ON THE FISH HEART (*Squalus acanthias*)

1: adrenaline (1×10^{-8}); 2: noradrenaline (5×10^{-7}); 3: acetylcholine (5×10^{-7}) (heart sensitized with physostigmine 4×10^{-5}). (From Östlund (97).)

The heart of the hagfish is not innervated. An increased venous return, stretching the ventricle, causes the heart to accelerate. This is a local effect, acting either directly on the myogenic pacemaker or indirectly on some intrinsic regulatory tissue in the wall of the heart (13, 67). The heart of the hagfish contains chromaffin cells; it is insensitive to acetylcholine, but responds to the catecholamines adrenaline and noradrenaline after pretreatment with dihydroergotamine. The heart of the lamprey, on the other hand, is innervated by the vagus, stimulation of which causes cardio-acceleration (13, 67).

In gnathostome fishes the heart receives inhibitory fibres in cardiac branches of the vagus nerve, and these terminate around the sino-auricular opening on post-ganglionic neurones which influence the pacemaker. Stimulation of the vagus slows the heart or brings it to a standstill (Fig. 3.12). The vagus is believed to exert its effect on the cardiac musculature, especially the pacemaker of the sinus, by release of a chemical transmitter, acetylcholine. Acetylcholine and pilocarpine have a vagomimetic action (Fig. 3.13) and are blocked by atropine (p. 438). It has been observed that the inhibitory potentialities of these drugs are not realized in fish embryos (*Fundulus*) until the heart is innervated. There is no sympathetic acceleratory supply, either in selachians or teleosts. Evidence dealing with the effect of adrenaline has been rather conflicting. Adrenaline and noradrenaline usually accelerate the elasmobranch heart and increase the force of beat (*Squalus*, *Raja*) (Fig. 3.13). There is occasionally an initial inhibitory effect, which is blocked by atropine. The effect of these amines on the teleost heart is slight (6, 20, 60, 97). There is a tendency for heart beat and breathing to be synchronized in resting teleosts, and the heart beat decreases when breathing ceases or deoxygenated water reaches the gills; these effects on the heart seem to be reflex expressions (115).

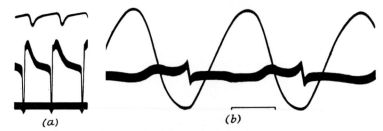

(a)   *(b)*

FIG. 3.14. ELECTROCARDIOGRAMS OF MOLLUSCAN HEARTS

(*a*). *Aplysia*. From above downwards, myogram, electrocardiogram, time in seconds (from Hoffmann, 1911.)

(*b*). *Crassostrea virginica*. Electrical record, small waves; mechanical tracing, large waves. Upward deflexion of myogram indicates contraction. Time scale below, 1 sec. Temp. 22°C (from Taylor and Walzl (124).)

Molluscan hearts are myogenic, and all regions can show autonomous contractions. During contraction there is a well-marked A–V interval, amounting to about 0·5 sec. Electrocardiograms have been recorded from several mulluscan hearts, and show the slow waves characteristic of myogenic types. In *Octopus* there is an initial fast deflexion succeeded by a prolonged wave of negativity, and the same sort of pattern is shown by the gill heart of *Loligo*. The electrocardiogram of *Aplysia* consists of slow waves with superimposed irregular deflexions; those of bivalves (*Ostrea*, *Anodonta*) normally display a diphasic component near the beginning of contraction and one or several slow waves associated with contraction (Fig. 3.14). Apparently the fast component in the ECG represents the spread of excitation; and the slow waves, potential changes taking place during contraction.

Although showing automaticity, the hearts of molluscs are subject to nervous regulation. Cardiac nerves arise from the visceral ganglion in lamellibranchs; the presence of nerve cells in the heart is disputed. In gastropods cardiac nerves arise from the visceral or accessory visceral

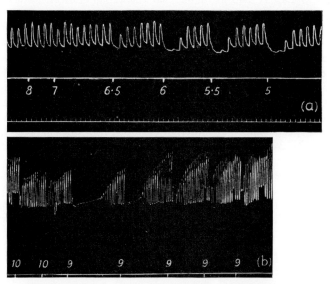

FIG. 3.15. INHIBITION OF THE HEART OF *Mercenaria mercenaria* BY
STIMULATION OF THE VISCERAL GANGLION

(*a*). Brief bursts of shocks; figures indicate position of secondary of induction coil (in centimetres). (*b*). Effect of repeated bursts of shocks. Time scale in (*a*) 3 sec. (From Prosser (104).)

ganglion, and terminate in auricle and ventricle. The existence of nerve cells is in doubt; if present they probably represent secondary regulatory neurones. The nervous supply of the cephalopod heart has been traced in detail. In these animals the cardiac branches arise from the visceral nerves and proceed to the heart via ganglia. From the latter, branches pass to auricles, ventricle and branchial hearts.

Inhibitory and acceleratory cardiac fibres have been identified in certain molluscs. Inhibitory nerves are particularly in evidence among lamellibranchs but are also recorded for certain gastropods (nudibranchs and pulmonates). Stimulation of the visceral nerves and ganglia causes well-marked inhibition of the lamellibranch heart (Fig. 3.15). Acceleratory nerves have also been demonstrated in various amphineurans, gastropods and lamellibranchs: these arise from the pleuro-visceral cords in chitons, and the visceral ganglia of prosobranchs and tectibranchs. Stimulation of these nerves causes acceleration of the heart, or initiates contractions in a quiescent organ.

In cephalopods both branchial and systemic hearts receive inhibitory fibres. Stimulation of the visceral nerves causes slowing or inhibition of the heart. The distribution of the two visceral nerves is such that each nerve causes inhibition of ventricle and ipsilateral auricle. Reflex afferent pathways linking the two auricles are believed to traverse the visceral nerves. Evidence is also available that the cephalopod heart is provided with acceleratory fibres. In some preparations stimulation of the visceral nerves produces acceleration of rhythm in the systemic and branchial hearts, and augmentation of beat in the systemic ventricle (*Eledone*, *Octopus*). Under repetitive stimulation the amplitude of beat rises with increase in number of stimuli, the augmentation amounting to 40–300% with thirty stimuli (*Octopus*). It is believed that both inhibitory and acceleratory fibres coexist in the cardiac nerves, the latter showing higher threshold to electrical stimulation, and that these two categories of fibres exert their specific effects by different chemical transmitters (41, 42, 43, 44, 80, 105, 119, 124).

Much recent work is concerned with the participation of chemical mediators in the neural regulation of cardiac activity. Acetylcholine inhibits the hearts of certain gastropods, lamellibranchs and cephalopods, sometimes in very low concentration (10^{-12} in *Mercenaria* (= *Venus*) (Fig. 3.16)). Among lamellibranchs, acetylcholine usually depresses at low con-

FIG. 3.16. EFFECT OF ACETYLCHOLINE ON THE HEART OF *Mercenaria mercenaria*
Concentrations: 1: 2×10^{-12}; 2: 2×10^{-11}; 3: 2×10^{-10}. (From Wait (1943).)

centrations, and excites at high concentrations (48). Within the body acetylcholine is quickly hydrolysed and rendered ineffective by acetylcholine esterase, the activity of which is blocked by certain tertiary ammonium compounds, e.g. eserine (physostigmine) and prostigmine. Eserine sensitizes the heart of *Mercenaria* to acetylcholine, resulting in enhanced inhibition when the latter drug is applied. This effect, however, is not apparent in the cephalopod heart.

If we accept the hypothesis that acetylcholine may be a normal chemical transmitter produced by inhibitory fibres in the molluscan heart, other direct evidence should be forthcoming. Acetylcholine, by assay, has been demonstrated in hearts of gastropods, lamellibranchs and cephalopods, and acetylcholine esterase in the first two groups. Acetylcholine content of the myocardium is rather low among lamellibranchs and opisthobranch gastropods, but higher among prosobranchs. Cholinesterase activity is proportional to acetylcholine levels.

Eserine prolongs cardiac inhibition produced by stimulation of the visceral ganglion in *Mercenaria*, and the perfusate from an animal subjected to stimulation of the visceral ganglion causes inhibition of a second, test heart. There is no comparable evidence for acetylcholine participation in cardio-regulation of cephalopods. In these animals eserine fails to potentiate nervous inhibition caused by stimulation of the visceral ganglion, and tests for acetylcholine in the perfusate are negative.

Adrenaline and noradrenaline have an acceleratory effect on various molluscan hearts (*Aplysia, Ostrea, Loligo*). Ergotamine excites the hearts of *Mercenaria* and *Loligo*, and abolishes or reduces the stimulatory effect of adrenaline. Tyramine resembles adrenaline in causing acceleration of the cephalopod heart, but only in high concentrations. Recent studies show that some molluscan hearts are excited by serotonin (5-hydroxytryptamine), e.g. *Mercenaria, Aplysia, Octopus*. Tyramine, noradrenaline, serotonin occur in appreciable quantities in the posterior salivary glands of some octopods, and serotonin has been found in ganglia of *Mercenaria* and *Busycon* and in the hypobranchial gland of *Murex*. It is believed that serotonin is the normal mediator of the cardiac excitatory nerves of *Mercenaria*. Cephalopods contain much amine oxidase, an enzyme capable of oxidizing serotonin, tyramine and related compounds (8, 11, 12, 36, 42, 44, 82, 97, 100, 103, 104, 105, 132, 133).

Holothuria. The intestinal vessels of holothurians are weakly contractile, and show localized peristaltic waves. By analogy with the pharmacology of other hearts, contractions of the intestinal vessel of *Stichopus* appear to be myogenic. It beats spontaneously, and is inhibited by acetylcholine in rather low concentrations (threshold 10^{-14}). Eserine potentiates the response to acetylcholine, and nicotine inhibits vascular contractility. The action potential of the intestinal vessel appears to be a simple wave of negativity (108).

Neurogenic Hearts

Arthropods. Neurogenic hearts are best exemplified by arthropods. In this type the rhythm of the heart beat is controlled by the nervous system. Among some of the lower Crustacea (Cladocera) the heart appears to be myogenic, whereas neurogenic hearts are characteristic of higher forms. During development the larval heart shows myogenic automaticity, pulsating rhythmically before the advent of the nervous system (lobster, king crab). Later, the nervous system predominates in control of movement, although it is reported that even the deganglionated heart of adult *Limulus* displays myogenic automatism, but the rhythm is slower and the beat is peristaltic in character (78).

In the hearts of Malacostraca and Xiphosura (*Limulus*) there are nerve cells in which the excitatory process originates. These intrinsic cardiac neurones are termed the local cardiac system by Alexandrowicz. They consist of a small and fixed number of nerve cells situated along the course

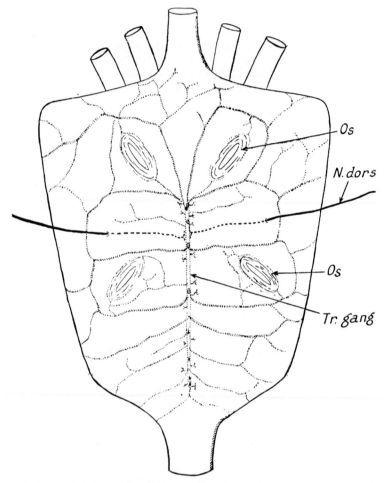

FIG. 3.17. NERVOUS SYSTEM IN THE DORSAL WALL OF THE HEART OF
Palinurus vulgaris

N. dors, dorsal cardiac nerve piercing the heart wall; *Os*, ostium; *Tr. gang*, ganglionic trunk with its nerve cells (from Alexandrowicz, 1932.)

of a ganglionic trunk in the dorsal wall of the heart (Malacostraca) (Fig. 3.17). Small and large neurones are distinguished in most groups: there are six neurones in isopods (*Ligia*); sixteen in stomatopods; nine in decapods; five or six in the cardiac trunk of amphipods and mysids. The axonal processes of these cells proceed to the heart muscles. This local system is connected to the central nervous system by extrinsic cardiac nerves. In addition, the arterial valves and alary muscles receive a separate innervation of their own from the c.n.s.

Various experimental methods have been utilized in studying the activity of the intrinsic nervous system. In *Ligia* the activity of the heart is ruled by the dorsal ganglionic trunk, and by severing this trunk different pulsatory rhythms are produced in various parts of the heart. Such experiments indicate that nervous continuity is necessary for co-ordination of heart-beat. Removed from the heart, the cardiac ganglion of decapods remains active; isolated portions of the heart normally contract spontaneously only when some ganglion cells are present. The electrical discharge of the ganglion precedes by a brief interval (10–14 msec) both the electrical and mechanical activities of the myocardium. From this kind of evidence it is concluded that the hearts of higher crustacea are neurogenic, and that the cardiac ganglion is the pacemaker (88).

In the heart of *Limulus* there are lateral nervous trunks linked by thin connectives to a median ganglionic trunk (Fig. 3.9). The latter contains scattered small multipolar neurones and large unipolar neurones. Excitation originates in the large ganglion cells of the middle cardiac segments and is relayed via the smaller neurones to the heart muscle. When the median nerve cord is progressively removed the amplitude of contractions diminishes, and when the longitudinal nerves are cut through, the beating of anterior and posterior regions of the heart becomes asynchronous. Local warming and excitation are most effective in altering heart rate when applied to the central segments of the ganglion. It is of interest that a deganglionated heart, which has ceased beating, may be stimulated into activity by tension or application of NaCl, but the resulting contractions are slow, local or peristaltic, of quite a different kind from the neurogenic heart beat (1, 3, 4, 78).

Electrocardiograms of the neurogenic hearts of arthropods show fast and slow components like those of myogenic hearts, but in addition a complex oscillatory pattern is present (*Astacus, Libinia, Limulus*) (Fig. 3.18). The larger slow waves in the arthropod ECG correspond to processes of muscular contraction and repolarization, while the fast oscillations represent nervous discharge. Electrical recording from the isolated pacemaker ganglion of *Limulus* shows bursts of impulses corresponding to each heart beat. Each neurone discharges several times during a burst lasting about 0·5 sec (range, 2–15 discharges per heart beat). The rate of discharge of each neurone is initially high and gradually falls off. Records secured from the middle segments where the large unipolar neurones are located reveal slow waves lasting more than 0·1 sec, with superimposed axon spikes. The excitatory wave originates in these large unipolar cells, the pacemakers, and their slow potentials electrically synchronize the discharge of the smaller multipolar neurones. In fatigue, or after treatment with abnormal concentrations of K^+ and Ca^{++}, the individual ganglion cells begin to discharge at random and asynchrony appears (106, 107).

The normal heart beat in higher crustaceans likewise originates in a burst of nervous activity in the cardiac ganglion. The ganglionic cells fire off a series of impulses at regular intervals: the frequency of bursts determines the frequency of heart beats, and the number of motor impulses in

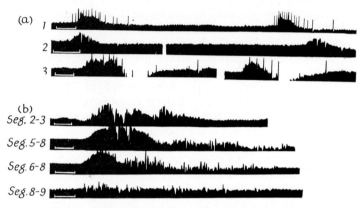

FIG. 3.18. RECORDS OF SLOW POTENTIALS FROM THE
CARDIAC GANGLION OF *Limulus*

(*a*). Records from three preparations showing axon spikes of single units superimposed on slow spikes. 1: Spikes from two units; 2: One unit discharging twice during each slow wave; 3: Spikes of one large unit. (*b*). Records from different segments of one ganglion. Position of leads on segments noted. Time signal, 0·1 sec. (From Prosser (106).)

each burst determines the amplitude of contraction. Of the various kinds of neurones in the cardiac ganglion, the small cells behave as pacemakers controlling the larger cells; the latter are motoneurones and cause rapid contraction of the heart muscle. With intracellular recording it has been found that the large motor neurones produce slow generator potentials which are succeeded by propagated spike potentials. Arriving at the myocardium the nerve impulses produce local depolarization of muscle cells; from these points an electrotonus spreads through the muscle network and passively depolarizes the rest of the muscle membrane (18, 51, 64, 88).

There is suggestive evidence for local reflex pathways in the arthropod heart. In the heart of *Limulus* the frequency and amplitude of beat are influenced by the condition of the heart muscle, but this effect depends on the presence of the cardiac ganglion. In the cardiac ganglia of crustacea it has been observed that the pacemaker and motor neurones bear dendritic processes, which make contact with the cardiac muscle fibres: these processes, it has been suggested, are afferent in function (78).

The intrinsic cardiac ganglia of crustaceans and *Limulus* receive regulatory nerves from the c.n.s. Both inhibitory and acceleratory fibres have been distinguished. In Crustacea the extrinsic cardiac nerves originate from suboesophageal and thoracic ganglia. In *Limulus* there are inhibitory fibres which arise from the brain, and acceleratory fibres which are believed to originate in abdominal ganglia. Stimulation of the cerebral ganglia inhibits the heart of *Limulus*, and stimulation of the inhibitory fibres reduces the output of impulses from the cardiac ganglion.

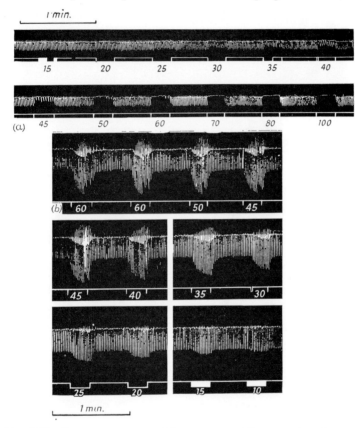

FIG. 3.19. CARDIO-REGULATIVE NERVES OF THE HEART OF *Panulirus argus*

(*a*). Effect of stimulation of cardio-inhibitor fibres on heart beat. Frequency of stimulation varied (pulses per sec). (*b*). Effect of stimulation of cardio-accelerator fibres on heart beat. Frequency varied (pulses per sec). (From Maynard (1953).)

In decapod crustacea, acceleratory and inhibitory fibres have been distinguished by the effects of transection and electrical stimulation (Fig. 3.19). The extrinsic cardiac nerves of the spiny lobster *Panulirus* consist of two pairs of cardio-accelerators and one pair of cardio-inhibitors. Stimulation of the cardio-inhibitory nerves causes a reduction in amplitude and frequency of heart beat. Effective limits of stimulation lie between 15 and

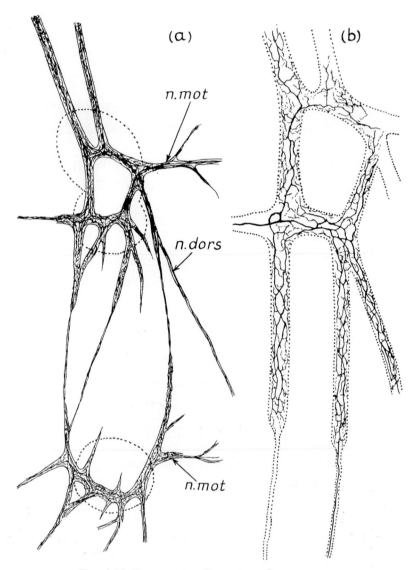

FIG. 3.20. PERICARDIAL ORGANS OF *Cancer pagurus*

(*a*). Organ of right side; vein-openings are indicated by dotted lines. *n. mot*, motor nerves; *n. dors*, dorsal nerve of the heart; (*b*), ramifications of a nerve fibre to form a neuropile in the pericardial wall (from Alexandrowicz (2).)

90 shocks per sec, and between these limits the rate and amplitude of beat can be graded by varying the frequency of stimuli. Conversely, stimulation of the cardio-accelerators increases the frequency and amplitude of heart beat (effective stimulation frequencies lie between 5 and 60 shocks per sec). The extrinsic cardiac nerves appear to achieve their effects by depressing or enhancing excitabilities of ganglionic pacemaker cells (78, 88, 120).

In the pericardial cavity of Malacostraca (decapods, stomatopods, isopods) there are peculiar ramifying networks of nerve fibres forming a neuropile termed the pericardial organs (Fig. 3.20). It has been suggested that these have a neurosecretory function. Extracts of the pericardial organs produce marked changes in heart action: their effect is usually excitatory and resembles that produced by adrenaline and noradrenaline (2, 5, 76).

The hearts of higher crustaceans (amphipods, isopods, decapods) and Limulus are accelerated by acetylcholine, and the excitatory action of acetylcholine is enhanced by eserine. Pilocarpine and eserine resemble acetylcholine in accelerating the heart. Nicotine initially accelerates, followed by a paralysing effect. Adrenaline and serotonin have an acceleratory effect on the hearts of crustaceans and Limulus. These pharmacological observations are of interest for the light they may shed on processes of cardiac regulation. The excitatory effect of acetylcholine resembles that produced by stimulation of cardio-acceleratory fibres. The blocking and paralysing effects reported for atropine and nicotine appear to take place in the pacemaker ganglion. A schema has been suggested ascribing cholinergic activity to extrinsic acceleratory nerves and pacemaker (large intrinsic) neurones, and adrenergic activity to the intrinsic (small) motor cells (29, 30, 56, 78, 105, 113, 120, 131).

Polychaetes. The contractile vessels of two polychaetes have been investigated, namely *Nereis* and *Arenicola*. Nerve cells have been found in the lateral hearts of *Arenicola*, but not in the contractile dorsal vessel of *Nereis* (*Neanthes*). There appear to be avenues for extrinsic nervous control, since stimulation of the ventral cord inhibits the lateral hearts of *Arenicola*, and increases the rate and amplitude of contractions of the dorsal vessel in *Nereis*. It appears from the electrocardiogram that the heart beat of *Arenicola* is neurogenic in origin. The electrical response shows an initial rapid negative wave, followed by a positive deflexion, often with several superimposed oscillations. The oscillations and the fast spike would appear to represent the summated discharge of ganglionic pacemakers in a neurogenic heart. Acetylcholine has an acceleratory and augmentor action on the heart of *Arenicola*, and the effects are increased by eserine (107).

Tunicates. The nature of the pacemaker mechanism in the heart of tunicates has not been resolved. Nerve cells appear to be absent, although some uncertainty exists about this point since the hearts are rather refractory to methylene-blue staining methods. The heart-beat normally originates at one or other end of the heart, which are pacemaker regions, but even isolated middle pieces of the heart of *Molgula* will continue to beat for some time. The heart regularly reverses the direction of beat, pacemaker centres at each end of the heart taking control alternately. To explain this regular reversal of control it has been argued that a back pressure is gradually built up in the circulatory system, compelling the heart to stop, and allowing the opposite centre to take over. Against this it is pointed out that completely isolated hearts show periodic reversal in the absence of back pressure: a controlling mechanism for reversal inherent in the pacemaker is thus implied. Krijgsman suggests that reversal is due to periodic fatigue (adaptation) followed by recovery, alternately, in the pacemakers (34, 58, 79, 90).

IONIC EFFECTS AND BALANCED SALT SOLUTIONS

Like all excitable tissues the heart is dependent on a proper ionic balance in the fluids surrounding it for optimal activity. Hearts will continue to beat for many hours outside the body when suspended in properly balanced salt solutions, especially when an energy source (glucose) is added. Some of the perfusion fluids described in the appendix have been devised for hearts and tested on them. For many marine invertebrates, in which the salt composition of the blood closely approximates sea water, the latter provides a satisfactory medium for sustained cardiac activity. Where a high degree of ionic regulation takes place, e.g. in decapod crustacea, the perfusion fluid must closely resemble the blood in salt composition and alkalinity for optimal heart activity. The heart of *Maia*, for example, will beat in sea water, but the amplitude is much stronger in a perfusate resembling normal plasma in heightened levels of potassium and calcium, and reduced magnesium. Only in a few invertebrates, e.g. in certain brachyurans, is the osmotic pressure different from that of the external medium. Fish regulate ionically and osmotically.

The ionic composition of invertebrate heart tissue is not known, but it probably resembles that of somatic muscles, which are high in K^+, and low in Na^+, Ca^{++} and Mg^{++}, compared with blood and sea water. These ionic differences are maintained by a polarized bounding membrane. Any radical changes in concentrations and ratios of cations in the surrounding medium bring about depolarization and deterioration of conduction and contractility in the myocardium. In addition, when control is neurogenic, altered ionic conditions affect the neural pacemakers. It is apparently only cations which influence cardiac activity to any perceptible degree. The nature of the anion (save that it be non-toxic) is of small significance, and chlorides are usually employed in artificial media. Sodium is the predominant cation; small and definite amounts of potassium and calcium must also be present for normal functioning; magnesium is also necessary for some, but not all, invertebrate hearts. Rather than list the manifold effects of altered ionic ratios on the many invertebrate hearts which have been tested, some representative examples have been selected from the major phyla.

Mollusca. Excess sodium has a stimulatory effect on the oyster heart (*Ostrea*), arresting it in systole. Potassium in excess increases rate and tonus, and at a concentration six times normal arrests the heart in systole. The effects of these cations are offset by calcium, high levels of which slow the heart and stop it in diastole. In the absence of calcium the cardiac rate increases (pacemaker-stimulation), but the heart comes to rest in diastole, owing to interference with contractility. Magnesium is essential for normal cardiac functioning in *Ostrea*: absence of magnesium results in cardiac acceleration and arrest in systole; high magnesium inhibits the pacemaker and arrests the heart in diastole (100, 128).

Ionic effects on the cephalopod heart (*Loligo*, *Octopus*) are probably somewhat similar. Raised potassium accelerates the heart and increases the force of the beat. High calcium stops the heart in diastole; low calcium increases rate and arrests in systole. The heart will beat in the absence of magnesium, but addition of magnesium increases the amplitude of the beat.

Crustacea and Xiphosura. Excess sodium generally has a stimulatory effect on the crustacean heart, increasing rate and amplitude. In a solution of NaCl alone, the heart ceases beating in systole. Low sodium depresses cardiac function and the heart stops in diastole. In the presence of excess potassium, the beat of the lobster heart becomes irregular, and amplitude and tonus increase. In a solution containing only KCl the heart stops in systole; in low potassium the heart continues beating normally or stops in diastole. These effects are ascribed to stimulation of the cardiac pacemaker. Calcium also acts on the pacemaker of the lobster heart, high calcium depressing the heart and stopping it in diastole, low calcium causing acceleration and reducing amplitude. Magnesium is not essential for continued beating, but high magnesium inhibits and arrests in diastole (26).

Comparable effects have been observed in *Limulus* where high concentrations of ionic sodium and potassium excite the heart and arrest it in systole. The heart beat becomes fast and weak in excess KCl. High potassium increases the frequency of neuronal discharge in the cardiac ganglia; low potassium decreases the number of impulses, and in absence of potassium ganglionic discharge gradually ceases. With high calcium, cardiac frequency decreases and the heart becomes arrested in diastole. Decreased calcium is accompanied by an increase in ganglionic discharge frequency and in the number of active ganglionic units, effects which cause acceleration of the heart (22, 106).

Selachii. The vertebrate heart is accelerated by excess sodium, with tendency to arrest in systole, whereas high potassium at first stimulates, and then arrests in diastole. The predominant effect of Ca^{++} is enhanced cardiac contraction, resulting in systolic arrest, while in the absence of Ca^{++} the heart relaxes and stops in diastole. As far as known the fish heart, exemplified by *Scyliorhinus* and *Raja*, reacts in a similar manner. Magnesium levels are low in vertebrate blood, and heightened magnesium sepresses the heart and brings about diastolic arrest. A peculiarity of delachian blood is the existence of high levels of urea (p. 51). This substance appears to be osmotically neutral so far as internal tissues are concerned, since it freely penetrates blood cells and heart muscle. Removal of urea arrests the heart of *Raja*; substitution of urea by sucrose is ineffective. It thus appears that urea has become necessary to the functional activity of elasmobranch heart muscle (47, 116).

Conclusions. Since the heart depends upon a balanced medium for functional integrity, it is difficult to judge an ion in isolation. The effects of any one ion vary with the levels of others and demand a consideration of ionic ratios. Calcium antagonizes the stimulatory effect of sodium and potassium on the pacemaker of hearts, and a proper balance of (Na^+ + K^+)/Ca^{++} is essential for optimal functioning. A proper total osmotic concentration is also essential, but within certain limits an increase in one ion is counterbalanced by proportional increases of the others. Since Na^+ already occurs in high concentrations it is difficult to raise the concentration of this ion without increasing the osmotic effect; reduction of Na^+ or of other ions can be osmotically balanced by addition of some neutral substance such as sucrose. Replacement of all Na^+ by sucrose usually results in reduction of heart rate, and in these circumstances there is probably some loss of electrolytes from the cells. Na^+ generally has a stimulative action on pacemakers and contractility. In both molluscs and arthropods K^+ appears to stimulate the pacemakers (myal and neural, respectively). Ca^{++} ion may affect the contractile process as well as the pacemaker, the exact effect differing in various groups. Mg^{++} appears to be essential for rhythmic beating in only certain groups, especially gastropods and lamellibranchs. In these animals alterations of Ca^{++} and Mg^{++} may have analogous effects, but the ions are not interchangeable. In general, it appears that the nervous pacemaker of the arthropod heart is more sensitive to changes in the K^+/Ca^{++} ratio than the myogenic molluscan heart. Changes from normal in the hydrogen ion concentration of the bathing fluid are also deleterious to continued functioning, and perfusates are usually buffered to normal pH to secure optimal activity.

BLOODS CELLS

The blood, haemolymph and coelomic fluids of animals usually contain formed elements of various kinds. These are chromocytes and leucocytes, the latter including amoebocytes, lymphocytes, phagocytes, thrombocytes, thigmocytes, motile cells etc. In the accompanying table (3.4) are given some figures for cell counts of certain animals, and data for erythrocytes are summarized in Table 4.9. Probably the most striking feature of these figures is the variation, amounting in some species to 50 % or more (16, 99).

There is no doubt that corpuscular numbers fluctuate greatly under various conditions: during growth, seasonally, in response to stress, disease, infection and with short- and long-term cycles of organic activity. The figures for *Limulus*, young and adult, are illustrative of ontogenetic changes. Maluf (84) relates the large variation in corpuscular numbers in crustaceans to fluctuations in blood volume, which is known to alter during the moult cycle (p. 48). Seasonal changes in erythrocyte numbers do take place in certain teleosts (71).

Chromocytes are coloured blood cells often containing respiratory blood pigments. Erythrocytes containing haemoglobin are found in vascular and coelomic fluids of many animals (Table 4.8). Certain cells in the coelomic fluid of echinoids (elaeocytes) contain naphthoquinone pigments. The blood of pycnogonids (*Anoplodactylus*) contains numerous nucleated corpuscles, pink to purple in colour, of unknown function. Vanadium chromogens are enclosed in blood corpuscles (vanadocytes) in certain ascidians. The role of respiratory pigments in oxygen transport is described in the following chapter (p. 171) (45, 82, 130).

Phagocytic amoebocytes are of common occurrence in blood and coelomic fluids of animals. Ever since Metchnikoff discovered phagocytes in the body fluids of starfish these cells have been recognized as playing an important role in the phagocytic ingestion and elimination of foreign particles, including bacteria. In the perivisceral fluids of echinoderms (urchins, cucumbers) there are amoeboid and flagellated phagocytes which take up particulate matter. Three categories of leucocytes are described in the haemolymph of crustacea. These are explosive corpuscles forming 40–50 % of the total; thigmocytes forming 20–30 %; and amoebocytes forming the remainder. The thigmocytes, which produce fine processes in shed blood, are mainly responsible for phagocytosis, and ingest particulate matter such as India ink; the amoebocytes are less phagocytic. In lamellibranchs amoebocytes are abundant and are distributed throughout the body, being especially common about the gut. These cells readily take up indigestible particulate matter, such as India ink, carmine granules, etc., injected into the blood stream. Eventually the particle-laden amoebocytes migrate through epithelial layers of the alimentary tract, mantle, pericardium and elsewhere, where they are voided together with their enclosed material. An equally important role of amoebocytes in lamellibranchs is digestion, since these animals do not produce an extracellular protease or lipase. Amoebocytes in the gut take up particulate food material, which is broken down by intracellular enzymes (amylases, proteases and lipases), and made available to the organism in assimilable form (14, 46, 59, 121, 123, 137).

Peculiar corpuscular elements occur in the body fluids of certain groups. The body fluids of brachiopods and phoronids contain large anucleate bodies termed spindle cells. These are thought to be metamorphosed derivatives of blood corpuscles. Perhaps the most peculiar blood inclusions are small ciliated urns found in the coelomic fluid of sipunculoid worms. Their function is unknown.

Blood Coagulation and Haemostasis

Among animals with circulatory systems, defence mechanisms exist for minimizing loss of blood when a blood vessel or sinus is perforated. In more primitive phyla the ionic composition of the blood is not greatly

TABLE 3.4

CELL COUNTS IN BODY FLUIDS

Animal	Fluid	Corpuscle	Mean cell count per mm^3
Annelids			
Nereis (Neanthes) virens	Body fluids	Leucocytes	29,600
Amphitrite ornata	ditto	ditto	47,400 ± 20,100 (SD)
Sipunculoid			
Golfingia gouldii	Coelomic fluids	Total cells (leucocytes and erythrocytes)	78,900 ± 31,900 (SD)
Priapulids			
Priapulus caudatus	ditto	Erythrocytes	45,000–160,000
		Amoebocytes	9,000–30,000
Halicryptus spinulosus	ditto	Erythrocytes	40,000
Crustacea			
Talorchestia longicornis	Haemolymph	Leucocytes	5,100 ± 2,600 (SD)
Hippa talpoida	ditto	ditto	10,600 ± 4,100 (SD)
Crangon vulgaris	ditto	ditto	8,300 ± 2,700 (SD)
Palaemonetes vulgaris	ditto	ditto	2,700 ± 800 (SD)
Homarus americanus	ditto	ditto	18,700 ± 6,500 (SD)
Pagurus pollicaris	ditto	ditto	26,000 ± 11,500 (SD)
Cancer borealis	ditto	ditto	14,200 ± 7,200 (SD)
Uca minax	ditto	ditto	12,400 ± 4,400 (SD)
Xiphosura			
Limulus polyphemus			
young	ditto	ditto	14,600 ± 5,000 (SD)
adult	ditto	ditto	30,000 ± 11,400 (SD)
Mollusca			
Mya arenaria	ditto	ditto	20,200 ± 7,700 (SD)
Mercenaria mercenaria	ditto	ditto	9,000 ± 5,900 (SD)
Ostrea virginica	ditto	ditto	22,400 ± 6,800 (SD)
Loligo pealei	Blood	ditto	7,000 ± 3,600 (SD)
Echinoderms			
Asterias forbesii	Coelomic fluid	ditto	6,300 ± 2,400 (SD)
Arbacia punctulata	ditto	ditto	11,300 ± 5,600 (SD)
Fish			
Scomber scombrus	Blood	ditto	25,000, 32,000
Anguilla bostoniensis	ditto	ditto	97,000, 165,000
Mustelus canis	ditto	ditto	60,000–81,000
Raja laevis	ditto	ditto	25,000
Dasyatis centroura	ditto	ditto	75,000

(Data from Yeager and Tauber (137); Maluf (84); Kisch (75); Fänge and Åkesson (37).)

dissimilar from sea water and the content of organic matter is small. In such animals the loss of relatively large volumes of body fluids is probably not serious metabolically, although there will be interference with the efficiency of hydraulic mechanisms. In higher forms, however, in which the blood constitutes a specialized fluid markedly dissimilar from sea water, the maintenance of a stable internal medium is essential for the continued functioning of the tissues of the body. In these animals continued haemorrhage is disastrous, because of the slump of blood pressure and interference with the metabolic exchanges taking place between the tissue cells and body fluids.

Methods of defence against haemorrhage come under the heading of haemostasis, and show a progressive evolution in the animal kingdom. The most primitive mechanism, found in all animals, consists of a constriction of the body wall or of the injured blood vessel, whereby the flow of blood is reduced or stopped. Soft-bodied animals, such as polychaetes and holothurians, constrict the body wall and contain their body fluids until such time as the ruptured surface can regenerate. Animals with rigid coverings, e.g. arthropods, must have recourse to other means. It is noteworthy that even when a limb is autotomized in crustacea, very little blood is lost. In decapods practising autotomy a diaphragm extends across the breaking plane and a valve, closed by blood pressure from within, shuts off the blood sinus when the limb is lost (136).

Vertebrates. In vertebrates, and in several invertebrate phyla, it is found that shed blood coagulates and seals the wound. Constriction of the ruptured vessel aids the process of coagulation, since the flow of blood is reduced and the blood cells have an opportunity to gather and clump together. The simplest type of coagulation is due to an aggregation and clumping together of blood leucocytes in the wound. This in turn may be followed by the formation of a true (fibrin) clot derived from circulating plasma proteins. When both mechanisms are operating, the clot or thrombus is made up partly of formed (cellular) elements and partly of fibrin-clot. Before examining haemostasis in invertebrates it will be useful to review briefly the situation in vertebrates, about which more is known.

When blood vessels of a vertebrate are injured, the walls constrict and platelets gather at the wound, contributing to the thrombus. At the same time the platelets disintegrate and release a thromboplastic factor, which participates in the chemical changes culminating in coagulation of the blood plasma. Coagulation is essentially a conversion of a circulating protein, fibrinogen, dissolved in the plasma, into an insoluble form, fibrin, which forms a gel and so closes the wound. The clotting process takes place in two stages. The first phase consists of the formation of a catalyst, thrombin, from a precursor, prothrombin, occurring in the blood plasma. This takes place under the influence of Ca^{++} ions and a thromboplastic factor, found in blood platelets, muscle and other tissues. In the second phase fibrinogen is converted into insoluble fibrin through the action of thrombin. For this phase the presence of Ca^{++} is unnecessary.

The same processes are involved in blood clotting in all vertebrates. Prothrombin and thrombin are protein substances; the latter is classified with proteolytic enzymes, and related to trypsin. The thromboplastic factor (thromboplastin) is a phospholipoid (e.g. cephalin) or a conjugated lipo-protein. Fibrinogen is a globulin; fibrin is a crystalline protein having the form of needle-like micellae. The course of clotting is summarized as follows —

$$\left.\begin{array}{l} \text{platelets} \xrightarrow{\text{dissolution}} \\[1em] \text{plasma} \xrightarrow{\text{activation}} \end{array}\right\} \text{thromboplastin (cephalin-protein)}$$

$$\text{prothrombin} + Ca^{++} + \text{thromboplastin} \longrightarrow \text{thrombin}$$

$$\text{fibrinogen} \xrightarrow{\text{catalysis by thrombin}} \text{fibrin}$$

These substances are found throughout the vertebrates, but thrombin and fibrinogen appear to show some specificity. Levels of prothrombin in fishes are around 2–7 mg%; average values of blood fibrinogen are 0·11% in *Scyliorhinus*, and 0·26–0·36% in teleosts (129, 139).

Blood platelets are replaced in lower vertebrates by nucleated spindle cells (thrombocytes). Plasma concentrations are about 2,000 thrombocytes/mm³ of blood (trout). Thrombocytes also show a tendency to agglutinate and disintegrate in shed blood, and probably release a thromboplastic factor concerned in the formation of thrombin (21).

Coagulation can be retarded or prevented in shed vertebrate blood by the use of waxed collecting vessels which retard agglutination and disintegration of formed elements, and by the addition of Na citrate or K oxalate, which reduce the Ca^{++} ion content of the blood. The erythrocytes of fish blood are comparatively fragile, and are progressively haemolysed by K oxalate; 5% haemolysis occurs in teleost blood with 0·1% K oxalate and complete haemolysis with 0·3%. Clotting is also inhibited by heparin, a naturally occurring polysaccharide (mucoitin-polysulphate-ester) in vertebrates and by hirudin, an anti-coagulant from the leech (10, 140, 141).

Invertebrates. In the majority of invertebrates with definite circulatory systems blood coagulation is effected solely by the formation of a cellular thrombus, and it is only in arthropods (certain crustaceans and insects) that a fibrin-clot is formed. Earlier work dealing with haemostasis in different invertebrates is reviewed in Winterstein's *Handbuch der vergleichenden Physiologie* (1925, Bd 1).

In polychaetes, echinoderms and molluscs coagulation is a cellular process resulting from aggregation of amoebocytes at the wound. In extravasated perivisceral fluid of sea urchins and other echinoderms, the amoebocytes tend to collect and send out long processes which contract and form fibres. Apparently a protein material is liberated from the white cells and this, in association with material from the plasma, quickly forms a retractile clot. Free calcium and some factor released from injured tissues are necessary for clotting, which can be prevented by addition of citrate and oxalate. In molluscs a similar situation is found. Blood corpuscles of *Cardium*, for example, adhere to foreign surfaces and to one another when blood is collected, and a structureless plasmodium of agglutinated cells is formed, which closely resembles a fibrin-clot. The cellular agglutinations of gastropods possess little haemostatic value. The haemolymph of *Limulus* lacks fibrinogen, and clotting is initiated by cellular aggregation. This is followed by the formation of a gelatinous mass or pseudo-clot. Aggregation times are 6–20 sec, and gelation times (first appearance of a gel) are 24–55 sec. Clot retraction (syneresis) subsequently occurs. Gelation is ascribed to the liberation of cell-fibrin (31, 49).

In crustaceans the situation is more complex. Coagulation in many species is due largely or solely to aggregation of blood cells, and there is no subsequent gelation of the plasma, e.g. *Cancer pagurus, Maia squinado,* etc. A true fibrin-clot, however, is formed by many species. This is rather weak in *Carcinus maenas* and *Palaemon serratus.* Firm fibrin-clots are formed by lobster blood (Palinura, Astacura), isopods (*Ligia*) and by *Gammarus locusta.* Gelation of the plasma is said to take place in two stages in the shed blood of *Homarus* and *Ligia.* In the first stage blood cells known as explosive corpuscles stick to foreign surfaces and quickly disintegrate, giving rise to localized clots; in the second, related to disintegration of blood thigmocytes, gelation spreads to involve the whole plasma. The two stages are fundamentally similar.

Mean coagulum weights for decapods range from 3·6 g/l. plasma in *Gecarcinus* to 16·6 g/l. in *Panulirus.* The coagulum includes cellular elements which are responsible for around a third to a fifth of the total. Much individual variation is encountered in fibrinogen levels of various species, and there is some evidence that fibrinogen concentration is minimal at time of moult (*Carcinus, Callinectes*). Coagulation in shed blood usually takes place within a minute, although many minutes often elapse before flow is stopped at a wound. The heaviest fibrin-clots are formed by macrurans (lobsters, crayfish). These are nearly equalled by the coagulum of *Dardannus* (anomuran). Values for brachyurans are about a quarter of those for *Panulirus.* Attempts have been made to correlate clotting ability with other defensive properties, and in general it appears that blood clotting is best developed in species lacking very hard external coverings and showing low incidence of autotomy (92).

Clotting in the blood of the lobster *Homarus vulgaris* and allied forms is essentially different from the process in vertebrates. The haemolymph contains a dissolved fibrinogen, which is converted into fibrin in shed blood through the action of a thrombin-like catalyst termed coagulin. The latter occurs in blood leucocytes (explosive cells, thigmocytes), in muscle and other tissues. Coagulation begins with the disintegration of blood leucocytes, which release coagulin. In the presence of Ca^{++} ions this factor accelerates the conversion of fibrinogen to fibrin, which forms a homogeneous clot (38, 84).

Some properties of lobster fibrinogen (*Homarus*) are as follows. The concentration in the haemolymph is around 0·4%, but decreases greatly in animals kept in captivity, apparently as the result of inanition. Clotting is ineffective at concentrations below 0·15%. Fibrinogen can be salted out of blood by the addition of half-saturated ammonium sulphate or sodium chloride. Its isoelectric point lies at pH 4·1, and it shows optimal activity (as measured by clotting time) at pH 7·2. Fibrin clotting is prevented by the addition of citrate or oxalate, but not by hirudin or heparin except in high concentrations.

Various methods have been described for the separation of lobster fibrinogen, including electrophoresis. The following are procedures which have been used for obtaining noncoagulated crustacean (lobster) plasma. Collect blood in a paraffin tube containing 1 ml of 0·2 M Na citrate per 10 c.c. of blood or 1 mg K oxalate per ml of blood. Centrifuge the fluid to remove the cell coagulum. Clotting is produced in this citrated or oxalated plasma by the addition of $CaCl_2$ and muscle extract. The coagulation factor is not specific among crustaceans, and is not interchangeable with vertebrate thromboplastic factor and thrombin (33, 38).

REFERENCES

1. ALEXANDROWICZ, J. S., "Innervation of the heart of *Ligia oceanica*," *J. Mar. Biol. Ass. U.K.*, **31**, 85 (1952).
2. ALEXANDROWICZ, J. S., "Nervous organs in the pericardial cavity of the decapod Crustacea," ibid., **31**, 563 (1953).
3. ALEXANDROWICZ, J. S., "Innervation of an amphipod heart," ibid., **33**, 709 (1954).
4. ALEXANDROWICZ, J. S., "Innervation of the heart of *Praunus flexuosus* (Mysidacea)," ibid., **34**, 47 (1955).
5. ALEXANDROWICZ, J. S. and CARLISLE, D. B., "Some experiments on the function of the pericardial organs in Crustacea," ibid., **32**, 175 (1953).
6. ARMSTRONG, P. B., "The role of the nerves in the action of acetylcholine on the embryonic heart," *J. Physiol.*, **84**, 20 (1935).
7. BABKIN, B. P., BOWIE, D. J. and NICHOLLS, J. V. V., "Structure and reactions to stimuli of arteries (and conus) in the elasmobranch genus *Raja*," *Contr. Canad. Biol. Fish.*, **8**, 207 (1933).
8. BACQ, Z. M., "L'acétylcholine et l'adrénaline chez les Invertébrés," *Biol. Rev.*, **22**, 73 (1947).
9. BARCROFT, J. and BARCROFT, H., "The blood pigment of *Arenicola*," *Proc. Roy. Soc. B*, **96**, 28 (1924).
10. BLACK, E. C. and IRVING, L., "The effect of hemolysis upon the affinity of fish blood for oxygen," *J. Cell. Comp. Physiol.*, **12**, 255 (1938).
11. BLASCHKO, H. and HAWKINS, J., "Observations on amine oxidase in cephalopods," *J. Physiol.*, **118**, 88 (1952).
12. BLASCHKO, H. and HIMMS, J. M., "Enzymic oxidation of amines in decapods," *J. Exp. Biol.*, **31**, 1 (1954).
13. BLOOM, G., ÖSTLUND, E. and FÄNGE, R., "Functional aspects of cyclostome hearts," in *The Biology of Myxine*, Eds. Brodal, A. and Fänge, R, p. 317 (Oslo, Universitetsforlaget, 1963).
14. BOOLOOTIAN, R. A., "The perivisceral elements of echinoderm body fluids," *Amer. Zool.*, **2**, 275 (1962).
15. BORDEN, M. A., "A study of the respiration and of the function of haemoglobin in *Planorbis corneus* and *Arenicola marina*," *J. Mar. Biol. Ass. U.K.*, **17**, 709 (1931).
16. BOTTAZZI, F. et al., "Das Cytoplasma und die Körpersäfte," *Handb. vergl. Physiol.*, **1**, Pt. 1 (1925).
17. BROWN, A. C., "Blood volumes, blood distribution and sea-water spaces in relation to expansion and retraction of the foot in *Bullia*," *J. Exp. Biol.*, **41**, 837 (1964).
18. BROWN, H. F., "Electrophysiological investigations of the heart of *Squilla*," *J. Exp. Biol.*, **41**, 701, 723 (1963).

19. BULLOCK, T. H., "Compensation for temperature in the metabolism and activity of poikilotherms," *Biol. Rev.*, **30**, 311 (1955).

20. BURGER, J. W. and BRADLEY, S. E., "The general form of circulation in the dogfish, *Squalus acanthias*," *J. Cell. Comp. Physiol.*, **37**, 389 (1951).

21. CATTON, W. T., "Blood cell formation in certain teleost fishes," *Blood*, **6**, 39 (1951).

22. CHAO, I., "Action of electrolytes on the dorsal median nerve cord of the *Limulus* heart," *Biol. Bull.*, **64**, 358 (1933).

23. CHAPMAN, G. and NEWELL, G. E., "The rôle of the body fluid in relation to movement in soft-bodied invertebrates. 1. The burrowing of *Arenicola*," *Proc. Roy. Soc. B.*, **134**, 431 (1947).

24. CHAPMAN, G. and NEWELL, G. E., "The rôle of the body fluid in the movement of soft-bodied invertebrates. 2. The extension of the siphons of *Mya arenaria* and *Scrobicularia plana*," *ibid.*, **145**, 564 (1956).

25. COE, W. R., "Biology of the nemerteans of the Atlantic coast of North America," *Trans. Conn. Acad. Arts Sci.*, **35**, 129 (1943).

26. COLE, W. H. and KAZALSKI, L. A., "A perfusing solution for the lobster heart and the effects of its constituent ions on the heart," *Bull. Mt. Desert I. Biol. Lab.*, p. 40 (1939).

27. CUÉNOT, L., "Échinodermes," in *Traité de Zoologie*, Ed. Grassé, P. P., Tome XI (Paris, Masson, 1948).

28. DALES, R. P., *Annelids* (London, Hutchinson Univ. Library, 1963).

29. DAVENPORT, D., "The effects of acetylcholine, atropine, and nicotine on the isolated heart of the commercial crab, *Cancer magister*," *Physiol. Zool.*, **14**, 178 (1941).

30. DAVENPORT, D., "Further studies in the pharmacology of the heart of *Cancer magister*," *Biol. Bull.*, **82**, 255 (1942).

31. DAVIDSON, E., "Clotting of the perivisceral fluid of the sand dollar, *Echinarachnius parma*," *Biol. Bull.*, **105**, 372 (Abstr.) (1953).

32. DERRICKSON, M. B. and AMBERSON, W. R., "Determination of blood volume in the lower vertebrates by the direct method," *Biol. Bull.*, **67**, 329 (1934).

33. DUCHÂTEAU, G. and FLORKIN, L., "La coagulation du sang des Arthropodes. 4. Sur le fibrinogène et sur la 'coaguline' musculaire du Homard," *Bull. Soc. Chim. Biol., Paris*, **36**, 295 (1954).

34. EBARA, A., "The periodic reversal of the heart-beat in *Salpa fusiformis*," *Sci. Rep. Tokyo Univ. Lit. Sci.*, **7**, 199 (1954).

35. ENDEAN, R., "The Cuvierian tubules of *Holothuria leucospilota*," *Quart. J. Micr. Sci.*, **98**, 455 (1957).

36. ERSPAMER, V., and GHIRETTI, F., "The action of enteramine on the heart of molluscs," *J. Physiol.*, **115**, 470 (1951).

37. FÄNGE, R. and ÅKESSON, B., "The cells of the coelomic fluid of Priapulides and their content of haemerythrin," *Ark. Zool.*, **3**, 25 (1952).

38. FLORKIN, M., "Blood chemistry," in *The Physiology of Crustacea*, Vol. 1, p. 141 (New York, London, Academic Press, 1960).

39. FOX, D. L., "Changes in the tissue chloride of the California mussel in response to heterosmotic environments," *Biol. Bull.*, **80**, 111 (1941).

40. FRAENKEL, G., "Die Grabbewegung der Soleniden," *Z. vergl. Physiol.*, **6**, 167 (1927).

41. FREDERICQ, H., "Action des nerfs du coeur d'*Aplysia limacina*: analyse au moyen de la caféine," *Arch. Int. Physiol.*, **49**, 299 (1939).

42. Fredericq, H., "Les nerfs cardio-régulateurs des Invertébrés et la théorie des médiateurs chimiques," *Biol. Rev.*, **22**, 297 (1947).

43. Fredericq, H. and Bacq, Z. M., "Analyse quantitative des effets cardiaques de la stimulation du nerf viscéral des Céphalopodes," *Arch. Int. Physiol.*, **49**, 490 (1939).

44. Fredericq, H. and Bacq, Z. M., "Sur la possibilité d'une médiation chimique dans l'action des nerfs cardiaques chez les Céphalopodes; influence de la caféine," ibid., **50**, 169 (1940).

45. George, W. C., "A comparative study of the blood of the tunicates," *Quart. J. Micr. Sci.*, **81**, 391 (1939).

46. George, W. C. and Ferguson, J. H., "The blood of gastropod molluscs," *J. Morph.*, **86**, 315 (1950).

47. Green, J. W. and Hoffman, J. F., "Erythrocyte volume and urea in elasmobranchs," *J. Cell. Comp. Physiol.*, **37**, 506 (1951).

48. Greenberg, M. J., "A compendium of responses of bivalve hearts to acetylcholine," *Comp. Biochem. Physiol.*, **14**, 513 (1965).

49. Gregoire, C. and Tagnon, H. J., "Blood coagulation," *Comparative Biochemistry*, Ed. Florkin, M. and Mason, H. S., Vol. IV, p. 435 (New York and London, Academic Press, 1962).

50. Grodziński, Z., "The influence of temperature upon the rate of the heart in the embryos of teleost fishes," *Bull. Acad. Polonaise Sci. Lettres, Cl. Sci. Math. Nat.*, Ser. B. II, **1948**, p. 255 (1949).

51. Hagiwara, S. and Bullock, T. H., "Intracellular potentials in pacemaker and integrative neurons of the lobster cardiac ganglion," *J. Cell. Comp. Physiol.* **50**, 25 (1957).

52. Hall, V. E., "The muscular activity and oxygen consumption of *Urechis caupo*," *Biol. Bull.*, **61**, 400 (1931).

53. Halsey, J. T. and Minnich, B., "A study of the action of certain drugs on the vessels of the dogfish," *Bull. Mt. Desert I. Biol. Lab.*, p. 16 (1938).

54. Hanson, J., "The histology of the blood system in Oligochaeta and Polychaeta," *Biol. Rev.*, **24**, 127 (1949).

55. Hanson, J., "The blood-system in the Serpulimorpha. 3. Histology," *Quart. J. Micr. Sci.*, **92**, 255 (1951).

56. Hara, J., "On the hormones regulating the frequency of the heart beat in the shrimp, *Paratya compressa*," *Annot. Zool. Jap.*, **25**, 162 (1952).

57. Hart, J. S., "The circulation and respiratory tolerance of some Florida freshwater fishes," *Proc. Fla Acad. Sci.*, **7**, 221 (1945).

58. Haywood, C. A. and Moon, H. P., "The mechanics of the blood vascular system of *Ascidiella aspersa*," *J. Exp. Biol.*, **27**, 14 (1950).

59. Hetzel, H. R., "Studies on holothurian coelomocytes. II," *Biol. Bull.*, **128**, 102 (1965).

60. Hiatt, E. P., "The action of adrenaline, acetylcholine and potassium in relation to the innervation of the isolated auricle of the spiny dogfish (*Squalus acanthias*)," *Amer. J. Physiol.*, **139**, 45 (1943).

61. Hopkins, A. E., "Pulsation of blood vessels in oysters," *Biol. Bull.*, **70**, 413 (1936).

62. Hyman, L. H., *The Invertebrates: Protozoa through Ctenophora*, Vol. I (London, McGraw-Hill, 1940).

63. Hyman, L. H., *The Invertebrates: Platyhelminthes and Rhynchocoela*, Vol. II (London, McGraw-Hill, 1951).

64. IRISAWA, H. and IRISAWA, A. F., "The electrocardiogram of a stomatopod," *Biol. Bull.*, **112**, 358 (1957).
65. IRVING, L., SOLANDT, D. Y. and SOLANDT, O. M., "Nerve impulses from branchial pressure receptors in the dogfish," *J. Physiol.*, **84**, 187 (1935).
66. JOHANSEN, K., "Cardiac output and pulsatile aortic flow in the cod," *Comp. Biochem. Physiol.*, **7**, 169 (1962).
67. JOHANSEN, K., "The cardiovascular system of *Myxine*," *The Biology of Myxine*, Eds. Brodal, A. and Fänge, R., p. 289 (Oslo, Universitetsforlaget, 1963).
68. JOHANSEN, K., "Cardiac output in the large cephalopod *Octopus dofleini*," *J. Exp. Biol.*, **42**, 475 (1965).
69. JULLIEN, A. and RIPPLINGER, J., "Le rameau cardiaque du pneumogastrique des poissons est formé d'au moins deux nerfs: un nerf chronotrope, cholinergique, et un nerf tonotrope, non cholinergique," *C.R. Acad. Sci., Paris*, **230**, 867 (1950).
70. JULLIEN, A. and RIPPLINGER, J., "De l'action des nerfs inhibiteurs sur le coeur entier et les segments cardiaques d'un poisson marin, la Rascasse," *C.R. Soc. Biol., Paris*, **145**, 401 (1951).
71. KAWAMOTO, N., "Physiological studies on the eel. 1. The seasonal variation of the blood constituents," *Sci. Rept. Tohôku Imp. Univ.*, Ser. 4, **4**, 635 (1929).
72. KEYS, A. and HILL, R. M., "The osmotic pressure of the colloids in fish sera," *J. Exp. Biol.*, **11**, 28 (1934).
73. KISCH, B., "Electrographic investigations of the heart of fish," *Exp. Med. Surg.*, **6**, 31 (1948).
74. KISCH, B., "The electrical topography of the surface of the univentricular heart," ibid., **7**, 55 (1949).
75. KISCH, B., "Observations on the haematology of fishes and birds," ibid., **7**, 318 (1949).
76. KNOWLES, Sir FRANCIS G. W., Bt. and CARLISLE, D. B., "Endocrine control in the Crustacea," *Biol. Rev.*, **31**, 396 (1956).
77. KORJUIEV, P. A. and NIKOLSKAYA, I. S., "The blood-volume of some marine and fresh water fishes," *C.R. Acad. Sci. U.R.S.S.*, **80**, 989 (1951).
78. KRIJGSMAN, B. J., "Contractile and pacemaker mechanisms of the heart of arthropods," *Biol. Rev.*, **27**, 320 (1952).
79. KRIJGSMAN, B. J., "Contractile and pacemaker mechanisms of the heart of tunicates," ibid., **31**, 288 (1956).
80. KRIJGSMAN, B. J. and DIVARIS, G. A., "Contractile and pacemaker mechanisms of the heart of molluscs," ibid., **30**, 1 (1955).
81. KROGH, A., *Osmotic Regulation in Aquatic Animals* (Cambridge Univ. Press, 1939).
82. LOEB, L., "Amoeboid movement and agglutination in amoebocytes of Limulus and the relation of these processes to tissue formation and thrombosis," *Protoplasma*, **2**, 512 (1927).
83. LOVELAND, R. E., "5-hydroxytryptamine, the probable mediator of excitation in the heart of *Mercenaria* (*Venus*) *mercenaria*," *Comp. Biochem. Physiol.*, **9**, 95 (1963).
84. MALUF, N.S.R., "The blood of arthropods," *Quart. Rev. Biol.*, **14**, 149 (1939).
85. MARTIN, A. W., "The blood volume of some elasmobranchs," *Fed. Proc. Amer. Soc. Exp. Biol.*, **6**, 164 (Abstr.) (1947).

86. MARTIN, A. W., "Some remarks on the blood volume of fish," in *Studies honoring Trevor Kincaid*, Ed. Hatch, M. H., p. 125 (Seattle, Univ. Wash. Press, 1950).

87. MARTIN, A. W., HARRISON, F. M., HUSTON, M. J. and STEWART, D. M., "The blood volumes of some representative molluscs," *J. Exp. Biol.*, **35**, 260 (1958).

88. MAYNARD, D. M., "Circulation and heart function," *The Physiology of Crustacea*, Vol. 1, p. 161 (New York, London, Academic Press, 1960).

89. MEYER, A., "On the coelomic cilia and circulation of the body-fluid in *Tomopteris helgolandica*," *J. Mar. Biol. Ass. U.K.*, **16**, 271 (1929).

90. MILLAR, R. H., "Reversal of the heart-beat in Tunicates," *Nature*, **170**, 851 (1952).

91. MILLAR, R. H., *Ciona*, L.M.B.C. Mem. 35 (Liverpool Univ. Press, 1953).

92. MORRISON, P. R. and MORRISON, K. C., "Bleeding and coagulation in some Bermudan Crustacea," *Biol. Bull.*, **103**, 395 (1952).

93. MOTT, J. C., "Some factors affecting the blood circulation in the common eel (*Anguilla anguilla*)," *J. Physiol.*, **114**, 387 (1951).

94. NAGEL, H., "Die Aufgaben der Exkretionsorgane und der Kiemen bei der Osmoregulation von *Carcinus maenas*," *Z. vergl. Physiol.*, **21**, 468 (1934).

95. NEEDHAM, A. E., "The neurogenic heart and ether anaesthesia," *Nature*, **166**, 8 (1950).

96. NICOL, J. A. C., "Autonomic nervous systems in lower chordates," *Biol. Rev.*, **27**, 1 (1952).

97. ÖSTLUND, E., "The distribution of catechol amines in lower animals and their effect on the heart," *Acta Physiol. scand.*, **31**, Suppl. 112, 67 pp. (1954).

98. OETS, J., "Electrocardiograms of fishes," *Physiol. Comp. Oecol.*, **2**, 181 (1950).

99. OHUYE, T., "On corpuscles in the body fluids of some invertebrates," *Sci. Rept. Tohôku Imp. Univ.*, Ser. 4, **13**, 359 (1938).

100. OTIS, A. B., "Effects of certain drugs and ions on the oyster heart," *Physiol. Zool.*, **15**, 418 (1942).

101. PANTIN, C. F. A. and SAWAYA, P., "Muscular action in *Holothuria grisea*," *Zoologia S. Paulo*, No. 18, p. 51 (1953).

102. PICKEN, L. E. R., "The mechanism of urine formation in invertebrates. 1. The excretion mechanism in certain Arthropoda," *J. Exp. Biol.*, **13**, 309 (1936).

103. PILGRIM, R. L. C., "The action of acetylcholine on the hearts of lamellibranch molluscs," *J. Physiol.*, **125**, 208 (1954).

104. PROSSER, C. L., "Acetylcholine and nervous inhibition in the heart of *Venus mercenaria*," *Biol. Bull.*, **78**, 92 (1940).

105. PROSSER, C. L., "An analysis of the action of acetylcholine on hearts, particularly in arthropods," ibid., **83**, 145 (1942).

106. PROSSER, C. L., "Single unit analysis of the heart ganglion discharge in *Limulus polyphemus*," *J. Cell. Comp. Physiol.*, **21**, 295 (1943).

107. PROSSER, C. L., "The electrocardiogram of *Arenicola*," *Biol. Bull.*, **98**, 254 (1950).

108. PROSSER, C. L. and JUDSON, C. L., "Pharmacology of haemal vessels of *Stichopus californicus*," *Biol. Bull.*, **102**, 249 (1952).

109. PROSSER, C. L. and WEINSTEIN, S. J. F., "Comparison of blood volume in animals with open and with closed circulatory systems," *Physiol. Zool.*, **23**, 113 (1950).

110. PROSSER, C. L. and ZIMMERMAN, G. L., "Effects of drugs on the hearts of *Arenicola* and *Lumbricus*," ibid., **16**, 77 (1943).

111. RAO, K. P. and BULLOCK, T. H., "Q_{10} as a function of size and habitat temperature in poikilotherms," *Amer. Nat.*, **88**, 33 (1954).

112. ROBERTSON, J. D., "Further studies on ionic regulation in marine invertebrates," *J. Exp. Biol.*, **30**, 277 (1953).

113. SAWAYA, P., "Sôbre a ocorrência da Acetilcolina no tecido cardíaco de *Callinectes danae* e seu efeito sôbre o coração dêste Crustáceo Decápodo," *Zoologia S. Paulo*, No. 7, p. 261 (1943).

114. SEGAL, E., RAO, K. P. and JAMES, T. W., "Rate of activity as a function of intertidal height within populations of some littoral molluscs," *Nature*, **172**, 1108 (1953).

115. SHELTON, G. and RANDALL, D. J., "The relationship between heart beat and respiration in teleost fish," *Comp. Biochem. Physiol.*, **7**, 237 (1962).

116. SIMPSON, W. W. and OGDEN, E., "The physiological significance of urea. 1. The elasmobranch heart," *J. Exp. Biol.*, **9**, 1 (1932).

117. SKRAMLIK, E. VON, "Über den Kreislauf bei den Fischen," *Ergbn. Biol.*, **11**, 1 (1935).

118. SKRAMLIK, E. VON, "Über den Blutumlauf bei Amphioxus," *Pubbl. Staz. Zool. Napoli*, **17**, 130 (1938).

119. SKRAMLIK, E. VON, "Über den Kreislauf bei den Weichtieren," *Ergbn. Biol.*, **18**, 88 (1941).

120. SMITH, R. I., "The action of electrical stimulation and of certain drugs on cardiac nerves of the crab, *Cancer irroratus*," *Biol. Bull.*, **93**, 72 (1947).

121. STAUBER, L. A., "The fate of Indian ink injected intracardially into the oyster *Ostrea virginica*," ibid., **98**, 227 (1950).

122. STEINBACH, H. B., "The sodium and potassium balance of muscle and nerve," in *Modern Trends in Physiology and Biochemistry*, Ed. Barron, E. S. G. (New York, Academic Press, 1952).

123. TAKATSUKI, S., "On the nature and functions of the amoebocytes of *Ostrea edulis*," *Quart. J. Micr. Sci.*, **76**, 379 (1934).

124. TAYLOR, I. R. and WALZL, E. M., "The effect of direct-current stimulation on the electrical and mechanical behavior of the heart of the oyster (*Ostrea virginica*)," *J. Cell. Comp. Physiol.*, **18**, 278 (1941).

125. THORSON, T. B., "The partitioning of body water in Osteichthyes," *Biol. Bull.*, **120**, 238 (1961).

126. TOMPSETT, D. H., *Sepia*, L.M.B.C. Mem. 32 (Liverpool Univ. Press, 1939).

127. TURNER, A. H., "Serum protein measurements in the lower vertebrates. 2. In marine teleosts and elasmobranchs," *Biol. Bull.*, **73**, 511 (1937).

128. WALZL, E. M., "Action of ions on the heart of the oyster," *Physiol. Zool.*, **10**, 125 (1937).

129. WARNER, E. D., BRINKHOUS, K. M. and SMITH, H. P., "Plasma prothrombin levels in various vertebrates," *Amer. J. Physiol.*, **125**, 296 (1939).

130. WEBB, D. A., "Observations on the blood of certain ascidians, with special reference to the biochemistry of vanadium," *J. Exp. Biol.*, **16**, 499 (1939).

131. WELSH, J. H., "Chemical mediation in crustaceans. 1. The occurrence of acetylcholine in nervous tissues and its action on the decapod heart," ibid., **16**, 198 (1939).

132. WELSH, J. H., "Marine invertebrate preparations useful in the bioassay of acetylcholine and 5-hydroxytryptamine," *Nature*, **173**, 955 (1954).
133. WELSH, J. H. and SLOCOMBE, A. G., "The mechanism of action of acetylcholine on the *Venus* heart," *Biol. Bull.*, **102**, 48 (1952).
134. WOLF, H., "Über die Genauigkeit der Herztätigkeit in der Tierreihe," *Pflüg. Arch. ges. Physiol.*, **244**, 181 (1940).
135. WOLF, H., "Über die Beeinflussung der Kreislauftätigkeit bei *Amphioxus lanceolatus* Y," ibid., **244**, 736 (1941).
136. WOOD, F. D. and WOOD, H. E. II, "Autotomy in decapod Crustacea," *J. Exp. Zool.*, **62**, 1 (1932).
137. YEAGER, J. F. and TAUBER, O. E., "On the haemolymph cell counts of some marine invertebrates," *Biol. Bull.*, **69**, 66 (1935).
138. ZUCKERKANDL, E., "Coelomic pressures in *Sipunculus nudus*," ibid., **98**, 161 (1950).
139. ZUNZ, E., "De la teneur en fibrinogène du plasma chez les Poissons," *Bull. Acad. Belg. Cl. Sci.*, **19**, 929 (1933).
140. ZUNZ, E., "Contribution à l'étude de la coagulation du sang chez les Poissons," ibid., **19**, 938 (1933).
141. ZUNZ, E., "La tension superficielle du plasma etc., chez quelques animaux marins," ibid., **19**, 1107 (1933).

CHAPTER 4

RESPIRATION

The properties of the components of the blood are highly adapted to the function of preserving the constancy of the environment of cells and tissues and to the functions of transporting carbon dioxide and oxygen. For example, the buffer action of a mixture of carbonic acid and its salts is unsurpassed as a means of maintaining a nearly neutral reaction through direct neutralization of acid or base. . . . Not less remarkable is the adaptation of the properties of haemoglobin to the transport of oxygen. All of these functions are performed, however, not by the blood alone, but in co-operation with the lungs, the kidneys, and other organs.

L. J. HENDERSON, 1928. *Blood: a study in general physiology*

THE ENVIRONMENT

IN addition to water and salts nearly all marine animals are dependent upon a supply of oxygen. The sole exceptions are certain worms which can live for long periods as facultative anaerobes in oxygen-deficient environments, e.g. intestinal parasites and certain inhabitants of muddy shores. The distribution of oxygen and carbon dioxide in ocean water has been described on previous pages (13, 14). Oxygen levels in most marine environments are adequate to sustain life. As we have already noted, oxygen is depleted in deeper waters of certain enclosed basins and fjords, frequently with production of H_2S, producing lifeless zones. In restricted areas the phytoplankton may accumulate to such a degree that it outstrips herbivores. This material rains upon the bottom, and its gradual decay exhausts the oxygen supply of the water, producing anoxic layers which sometimes occupy a substantial proportion of the water column. Under these conditions heavy mortality of animal life results.

The littoral environment presents certain peculiar conditions. During the night, when the tide is out, the oxygen content of inter-tidal pools may become greatly depleted, depending upon population-density, plant-growth and other factors (117). The subsurface layers of muddy shores and banks are frequently anoxic owing to decay and oxidation of organic matter. Periods of oxygen scarcity are encountered by burrowing littoral animals during tidal ebb, and various devices are employed for coping with such emergency conditions. Certain inhabitants of the littoral region are amphibious, and here also we find a few species of predominantly terrestrial groups, adapted for submergence, and certain species of marine origin adapted for aerial respiration. Various aspects of respiration among animals have been reviewed by Krogh (73) and Guieysse-Pellissier (48).

135

CATEGORIES OF RESPIRATORY EXCHANGE

Respiration in animals embraces three processes, namely gaseous exchange with the external medium at the surface of the body or in internal respiratory passages, transport of gases through the body and exchange of gases between the internal medium and the tissue cells. In all animals these several respiratory processes take place in aqueous media. In aquatic animals, of course, the surface of the body is bathed with water. But even in amphibious and terrestrial species the external bounding surface of the respiratory structures—gills, lungs, tracheae—is kept moist by fluid exudation or secretion. The passage of gas across the external surface is almost invariably accomplished by diffusion. The velocity of diffusion depends upon the power of the liquid to dissolve the gas, and is directly proportional to the absorption coefficient of the gas in the liquid. The direction of diffusion is from the side of the film where pressure of the gas is high to the side where it is low, and the rate of diffusion is dependent on the concentration gradient across the film. The rate of diffusion, or amount of substance crossing a certain area in known time, is given by Fick's law, which states

$$dQ = - DA \frac{du}{dx} dt$$

Here dQ represents amount of substance diffusing in time dt across a plane of area A at right angles to the direction of diffusion, when the concentration gradient is du/dx. D is the diffusion coefficient, and the negative sign appears because diffusion takes place from a region of higher to one of lower concentration.

Diffusion constants of oxygen, determined for a number of substances of biological importance, are as follows—

Substance	Diffusion constant
Water	0·34
Gelatin	0·28
Muscle	0·14
Connective tissue	0·115
Chitin	0·013

The diffusion constant ($10^4 \times$ diffusion coefficient) is defined as the number of cubic centimetres of O_2 (0°C, 760 mm Hg) penetrating per min through 1μ thickness and 1 cm^2 when the pressure difference equals one atmosphere. Diffusion through tissues, whether inert or living material, is obviously slower than through water, other things being equal. Differences exist in the diffusion rates of various gases, CO_2 diffusing through tissues 20–30 times faster than O_2, owing to the higher solubility of the former. The values for the diffusion constant change with shift of temperature, there being a 1 % increase or decrease in the diffusion constant for each degree the temperature is higher or lower than 20°C.

Small organisms and members of primitive phyla secure adequate oxygen by diffusion, without the provision of special respiratory mechanisms. Such include the majority of protozoa, sponges, coelenterates, turbellarians, small nemertines, chaetognaths, the smaller annelids, bryozoans, eggs and embryos. This process is adequate to secure respiratory exchanges across short distances, not exceeding 1 mm. Even among these animals, however, we find mechanisms for moving the external medium and so renewing the oxygen supply of the water layer lying immediately over the surface. Examples are flagellar activity in sponges, and ciliary activity in coelenterates, turbellarians, annelids and echinoderms.

In higher animals, increased oxygen requirements have been met by the evolution of special respiratory structures and mechanisms. These include respiratory organs and appendages; mechanisms for renewing the external medium, whether water or air, over or within these structures; circulation of internal fluids, and respiratory pigments for increasing the oxygen-carrying capacity of the blood. Nevertheless, in the final analysis, gaseous exchange across the external respiratory surface, and between the body fluids and tissue cells, is carried out by diffusion and these distances are usually very short. In gills of decapod Crustacea, for example, the span between the haemolymph and the outside of the gill is narrow, between $3–5\mu$. The internal medium, in turn, bathes all the tissues of the body (62).

RESPIRATORY MECHANISMS

In aquatic animals external respiration takes place across the integument, gills and in specialized portions of the alimentary canal. Aerial respiration takes place across gill surfaces, in lungs and in tracheae. The latter are characteristic of insects, few of which have invaded the sea.

Integument

Some degree of respiratory exchange across the general integument takes place in nearly all marine animals, from the simplest metazoans to fish. For cutaneous respiration to be effective in aquatic animals there must be a current of water over the skin. Respiration is entirely cutaneous in many lower animals—turbellarians, nemertines, many annelids, echiuroids, sipunculoids, chaetognaths, small arthropods, embryos and young larvae—all of which respire through the general body surface. Even when gills are present in aquatic animals, much gaseous exchange still takes place through the general integument. Quantitative information dealing with partition of respiratory function between gills and general integument is scanty. In specimens of sabellid worms (*Bispira, Sabella*), from which the branchial crowns have been removed, respiration through the general body surface continues at around 36% of levels for the whole animal. Similar experiments on *Myxicola* indicate that cutaneous respiration accounts for about one-half of the oxygen requirements of the abdomen (20). The eel (*Anguilla*) respires through skin and gills. The skin of the fins and abdomen is highly vascularized and provides an avenue for respiratory exchange. When the eel is in water about 12 % of the total respiratory exchange occurs through the skin. At 7°C absorption of oxygen through the skin amounts to 1·5 c.c./kg fish/h against a total uptake of 11–14 c.c. (3).

Gills

With increase in the size and efficiency of marine invertebrates, gills have been evolved to promote respiratory exchange. These structures are vascularized outgrowths of the body wall, and they either project freely from the body surface (e.g. sedentary polychaetes), or they are enclosed in special chambers (e.g. crustaceans). In either event a circulation of water must be maintained over them in order that they operate efficiently. This is accomplished by ciliary activity, by movement of the gills, by active pumping movements and, on occasion, by locomotory movements.

Not all gill-like structures are solely respiratory in function, and mere appearance is sometimes deceptive. The elaborate gills of bivalve molluscs, sabellids, protochordates and others are ciliary feeding devices and, as such, are described in Chapter 5; in many of these animals the gills are responsible for only a minor proportion of the total respiratory exchange (Table 4.1). In these forms the respiratory function of the gills seems to be a secondary consequence of their large surface area, and food-trapping their primary function. Well-developed circulatory systems are necessary for respiratory gills to achieve maximal efficiency, and this aspect is discussed in Chapter 3.

In the littoral region animals are encountered in which the gills are adapted for aerial respiration, or are supplemented by other devices. Some crustacea, indeed, have become predominantly terrestrial in habit. As is usual with creatures living in such transitional environments, the multiplicity of functional adaptations which they exhibit, in response to unwonted environmental stresses, demands attention far out of proportion to the numbers of animals concerned.

Respiratory devices are classified in the following sections on the basis of functional morphology. The arrangement adopted necessitates some unavoidable overlap in considering different physiological aspects of external respiratory exchange (Table 4.1).

RESPIRATORY AQUATIC GILLS. **Polychaetes.** Gills exclusively respiratory in function first appear among polychaete annelids. Errant polychaetes such as *Nereis* and *Phyllodoce* possess large vascularized parapodia which undoubtedly augment the respiratory surface, as well as acting as locomotory organs. Specialized branchial structures are found in many families. The lugworm *Arenicola* bears external branchial tufts on segments of the middle region (Fig. 4.1). Gills on anterior segments of terebellids are dichotomously branched outgrowths of the body wall; in amphictenids they are lamelliform and highly differentiated (Fig. 4.2).

Echinoderms. True gills are found in some echinoderms and supplement respiratory exchange in the tube feet. Those of asteroids are papillate evaginations of the body wall (papulae), each of which contains a central cavity communicating with the perivisceral coelom. External cilia maintain a current of sea water over the surface of the animal, and gases are exchanged with the gently circulating coelomic fluid across the walls of the

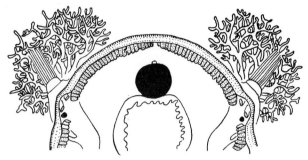

FIG. 4.1. SECTION THROUGH THE DORSAL BODY WALL OF THE LUGWORM *Arenicola marina*, SHOWING BRANCHIAL TUFTS
(From Wells, 1944)

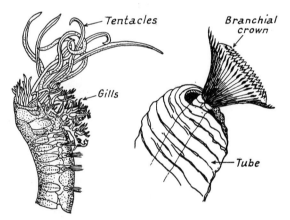

FIG. 4.2. GILLS OF POLYCHAETES

(*Left*) anterior region of the terebellid *Lanice conchilega*, showing feeding tentacles and gills. (*Right*) sabellid worm *Myxicola infundibulum*. Branchial crown protruding from orifice of gelatinous tube. (After McIntosh, 1922.)

gills and tube feet (12). Experimentally it has been shown that the ambulacral system is important in oxygen uptake, which decreases if one or more ambulacral grooves are sealed. About half the respiratory exchange takes place through the tube feet in the normal animal, the remainder occurring through the dermal branchiae. In echinoids the peristomial region is ringed with similar branched gills, which communicate internally with the lantern coelom.

TABLE 4.1

DISTRIBUTION OF GILL STRUCTURE IN RELATION TO FUNCTION

Systematic group	Structure
A. Gills used for feeding and respiration	
Polychaeta	
Sabellariidae ⎫	
Sabellidae ⎬	Cephalic branchial crown
Serpulidae ⎭	
Lamellibranchia	Filter-feeding ctenidia in mantle-cavity
Phoronidea ⎫	Filter-feeding
Polyzoa-Ectoprocta ⎬	lophophore at anterior end
Brachiopoda	Filter-feeding lophophore in mantle-cavity
Tunicata ⎫	Filter-feeding
Cephalochordata ⎬	branchial clefts or basket
B. Branchial and feeding filaments both present but distinct	
Polychaeta	
Terebellidae ⎫	
Cirratulidae ⎬	Cephalic feeding tentacles and branchial
Amphictenidae ⎬	tufts or filaments
Ampharetidae ⎭	
Echinoidea-Spatangoida	Distinct respiratory and feeding tube feet
C. True respiratory gills	
Polychaeta	
Arenicolidae ⎫	
Sternaspidae ⎬	Distinct branchial tufts or filaments
Eunicidae ⎭	
Mollusca	
Amphineura ⎫	
Gastropoda ⎬	Ctenidia in mantle cavity
Cephalopoda ⎭	
Gastropoda—Nudibranchia	Specialized external gills in some species
Crustacea—Malacostraca	Appendages variously modified as gills in different orders; external or enclosed in branchial cavity
Echinodermata	
Asteroidea ⎫	External gills
Echinoidea ⎬	
Pisces	Internal pharyngeal gills

Molluscs. Purely respiratory gills display much diversity in molluscs. In primitive amphineurans, such as *Chiton*, a row of plume-like gills lies in each pallial groove. There is a single ctenidium or a pair of ctenidia in the mantle-cavity of aquatic gastropods, including typical prosobranchs such as whelks and periwinkles, and tectibranchs such as *Aplysia*. The molluscan ctenidium is a respiratory structure consisting of an axis bearing lamellae. The ctenidium has been lost in pteropods and nudibranchs; sea-slugs such as *Doris* possess a tuft of retractile cerata or gills on the posterior dorsal surface.

Cephalopods have one or two pairs of feathery gills located in the posterior region of the mantle cavity, and a special mechanism exists for ventilating these structures. During inspiration the mantle cavity is enlarged, the funnel is closed by a valve, and water is drawn in anteriorly at the sides of the funnel. Expiration results from contraction of the circular muscles of the mantle, and water is driven out through the funnel. When the animal is at rest these respiratory movements are gentle and rhythmical, and circulate water over the ctenidia. In the cuttlefish (*Sepia*) the total branchial area is estimated at 1700–1800 cm².

Pelagic cranchiid squids (*Cranchia*) have acquired another ventilation mechanism. These creatures live at great depths, are neutrally buoyant, and move the mantle only sporadically when swimming. The mantle cavity is divided into upper and lower chambers by a horizontal perforated septum, the gills lying in the lower chamber. An inhalant aperture, guarded by valves, leads into the upper chamber; an exhalant, from the lower. Respiratory movements depend on contractions of the coelom: the wall of the coelom contracts anteriorly, the inhalant valves open and water is sucked into the upper chamber; at the same time the coelom bulges posteriorly, forcing water out of the ventral compartment. The contraction then passes along the coelom, the inhalant valves close, and water is forced into the lower compartment over the gills. The motive force is provided by movement of a plastic plunger which, by virtue of the arrangement of the two chambers, apertures and valves, draws in water above, irrigates the gills, and expels it below (17).

Crustaceans and Xiphosurans. Special respiratory gills are rarely present in the lower crustacea (Entomostraca), and respiration takes place through the general body surface. In the Malacostraca gills occur in connexion with the appendages (modified epipodites). In lower forms they are exposed, but in higher groups, notably the decapods, the gills are enclosed in a branchial chamber. A flow of water over the branchial surfaces is maintained by movements of the appendages. Stomatopods bear gills on the abdominal limbs; euphausiids and some mysids have gills on the thoracic legs. Among isopods the pleopods bear broad respiratory plates, e.g. *Ligia*.

Decapod crustacea, which generally attain larger size than the forms just described, possess well-developed gills which are lodged in a branchial chamber formed by the sides of the carapace. A ventilation current is drawn through the branchial chamber by baling action of the scaphognathite (flattened blade on the maxilla), which keeps up a steady beating. Water enters through inhalant apertures situated between the walking legs and the lower edge of the carapace, passes across the gills and thence to an exhalant aperture which lies in front of the mouth. Average areas of gill surface in various crabs are: *Carcinus maenas*, 7·7 cm²/g body weight; *Cancer pagurus*, 7·8 cm²; and *Portunus* sp., 8·7 cm². Active crabs (portunids) have greater gill areas than sluggish species (*Libinia*). In the lobster (*Homarus vulgaris*) oxygen is mostly taken up through the gills, but the swimmerets play a minor role in respiration, taking up about 3% of total oxygen respired (2, 118).

The branchial apparatus of Xiphosurans (*Limulus* and allies) consists of gill books, lying on the ventral side of the opisthosoma (abdomen) and protected by an operculum. The gill books are built of piles of parallel leaflets attached to plates or appendages of the opisthosoma. Rhythmic movements of the gills cause water to circulate over the gill lamellae. Transection experiments point to the existence of respiratory centres in abdominal and suboesophageal ganglia (123).

Fishes. The branchial apparatus of fishes takes the form of gill filaments which are borne on gill arches lying between the pharynx and branchial chambers. In lampreys the gill filaments are situated in branchial pockets which open to the exterior by separate orifices; water is pumped in and out of the branchial chambers through the external branchial apertures; in hags water is drawn in through the nostril (66). Separate external gill apertures are present in selachians. When resting on the bottom, rays and skates draw in a respiratory current through the spiracles, which are guarded by valves, and expire through the gill openings in the normal manner.

The branchial chamber in teleosts is covered by an operculum. Within, the gill filaments of neighbouring arches meet in such a way that all the respiratory current must pass over the branchial lamellae (Fig. 4.3). Gaseous exchange is facilitated by the counter-current principle by which the blood flows through the lamellae in a direction opposite to that taken by the water passing outside. Consequently, the blood leaving the lamellae comes into equilibrium with the water entering the gills. The respiratory mechanism is such that water flows continuously over the gills. Inspiration is produced by dilatation of the buccal cavity and branchial chambers, while the opercula close and the mouth opens. During expiration the mouth and buccal valves are closed, and the opercula open; water is passed along the gills by reduction of the buccal cavity. In coughing-reflexes the tips of the filaments are separated by contraction of adductor muscles, and accumulated material is ejected.

Variations from type in the structure and functioning of the branchial apparatus are numerous. Very active pelagic fish, notably the mackerel, do not make respiratory movements; rather, ventilation is achieved by swimming through the water with open mouths. Indeed, these animals are condemned to ceaseless locomotion to obtain the oxygen necessary for their metabolic requirements (6, 24).

Estimates of branchial respiratory areas in selachians give values of 0·7 cm²/g body weight in *Cetorhinus* and 1·8 cm² for *Scyliorhinus*. Values for teleosts range from 1 to 18 cm²/g body weight. Active fast-swimming fishes, such as menhaden (*Brevoortia tyrannus*) and mackerel (*Scomber scombrus*) have relatively much greater gill areas than sluggish benthic species such as toadfish (*Opsanus tau*) and flounders (*Pseudopleuronectes americanus*). The respiratory area of the mackerel, for example, is more than five times greater than that of the toadfish (11·58 and 1·97 cm²/g body weight, respectively) (47).

COMBINED FEEDING AND RESPIRATORY GILLS. The extensive feeding-filaments, branchial crowns and baskets of many marine animals are also concerned with respiratory exchange. This is a necessary consequence of their functional morphology, since they present large surfaces past which a current of water is directed externally, while the blood stream circulates within. Tubicolous polychaetes of the families Sabellariidae, Sabellidae and Serpulidae possess extensive branchial crowns which are essentially filter-feeding devices for extracting microscopic organisms from sea water (Chapter 5). The pinnules of the crown (Fig. 5.5) are thin-walled structures,

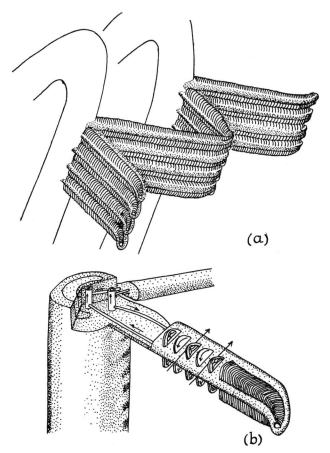

FIG. 4.3. DIAGRAMMATIC REPRESENTATION OF THE STRUCTURE AND DISPOSITION OF GILL LAMELLAE IN TELEOSTS

(a). Gill filaments on two adjacent gill arches. (b). Enlarged view of one gill filament. Large arrows indicate direction of water flow; smaller arrows, course of blood through arteries, arterioles and capillaries. (From van Dam (21).)

each of which contains an axial blood vessel; diffusion distances are about 7μ in *Sabella*.

Extirpation experiments involving removal of the crown provide an estimate of the amount of gaseous exchange occurring across the branchial filaments. Loss of the crown depresses respiratory rate (oxygen consumption) by 63–64% in *Spirographis spallanzanii* and *Bispira volutacornis*. Because the crown is a muscular and strongly ciliated organ its metabolic rate is high, estimated at 26% of the total oxygen consumption of the intact worm. These results indicate that about 38% of the respiratory needs of the body is satisfied by gaseous exchange through the gills. In some species respiration continues when the worm is withdrawn into its tube, as the result of regular irrigation movements (20).

Ciliated tentacles on the lophophore of ectoproct polyzoans and phoronids are functionally similar to those of filter-feeding polychaetes. In both groups they probably subserve respiration as well as feeding. Filter-feeding gills are also found in lamellibranchs and brachiopods (Fig. 5.8). The gills are vascularized and participate in the respiratory exchange, but they are probably of secondary importance compared with the general body surface and mantle lining.

RESPIRATION IN HIND-GUT AND DIVERTICULA. Respiratory mechanisms exist in some species for pumping water into and out of the hind-gut. In an echiuroid worm, *Urechis caupo*, the long hind-gut is employed as a respiratory organ. Water is pumped into the hind-gut and out again by contractions of the muscular cloaca. The thin walls of the hind-gut function as a respiratory surface, and gases are exchanged with the coelomic fluid, which is kept in motion by anti-peristaltic waves passing along the gut wall. A non-feeding animal takes into the hind-gut about half the water pumped through its burrow (51).

Holothurians also possess water-lungs. These are respiratory trees, which form a system of highly ramified tubules originating in the cloaca and extending into the coelom. Water is pumped alternately in and out of this system by rhythmic contractions of the cloaca, and gases are exchanged with coelomic and vascular fluids. The respiratory tree of *H. tubulosa* is responsible for 50–60% of the respiratory exchange of the body. When the water in which it is living becomes stagnant, *Holothuria* raises its posterior end to the surface, and takes air into the cloaca, a behaviour pattern similar to that of *Arenicola* under comparable conditions of oxygen stress (11, 89).

WATER CIRCULATION IN TUBES AND BURROWS. Animals which burrow or live in tubes or galleries must have access to the outside sea water for respiration. Some species, such as burrowing lamellibranchs, extend their siphons to the surface. Cryptocephalous polychaetes protrude cephalic processes. Many other animals possess some means of circulating water through their tenements for respiratory, and often for feeding, purposes.

A burrowing polychaete with a peculiar respiratory mechanism associated with subterranean habits is the sea mouse *Aphrodite*. This animal burrows in muddy sand, while retaining its posterior end at the surface, and in this position maintains a ventilation current of sea water over its body (Fig. 4.4). The dorsal surface bears a series of overlapping scales or elytra, which are covered in turn by a dense feltwork of bristles. By elevation of the ventral surface, water is drawn along the underside of the body from the exposed tail. During inspiration the ventral surface is depressed, the elytra raised, and water streams upwards between the parapodia into a respiratory space lying underneath the elytra. Respiratory exchange takes place over the whole exposed integument. Water is expelled by depressing the scales and driving it out posteriorly over the upper surface of the tail (22).

The heart urchin *Echinocardium* digs burrows some 15–20 cm deep, and maintains a channel open to the surface (Fig. 4.5). Respiratory currents are created by cilia, and tube feet of the aboral surface are enlarged as gills (19).

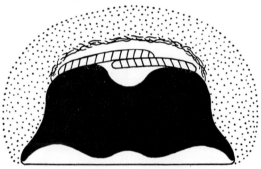

FIG. 4.4. DIAGRAMMATIC CROSS-SECTION THROUGH THE SEA MOUSE *Aphrodite aculeata*, SHOWING RESPIRATORY CHANNELS AND CHAMBERS ABOVE AND BELOW THE BODY WALL

Stipple, sand. Overlapping elytra and feltwork of the chaetae cover the animal. (From van Dam (22).)

Peculiarities of respiratory mechanisms associated with burrowing habits are recorded for many crustaceans (78). The masked crab *Corystes*, for example, forms a siphon with its antennae which extend to the surface of the sand; water is drawn down the siphon into the gill chamber.

Tubicoles usually pump water through their tubes, and such mechanisms are particularly characteristic of polychaetes. *Chaetopterus* inhabits a U-shaped tube which is buried in the substratum and open at both ends to the surface. The worm attaches itself to the wall by modified sucker-like neuropodia and maintains a flow of water through the tube by the coordinated beating of three large fans of the middle region (Figs. 5.3 and 5.4). The water-current serves both for respiration and feeding, and gaseous exchange takes place over the entire integument.

An echiuroid worm *Urechis caupo* creates a feeding and respiratory current through its U-shaped burrow by means of peristaltic contractions of the body wall (Fig. 14.6). Another worm inhabiting a U-shaped burrow is the lugworm *Arenicola marina* found on sandy shores (Fig. 5.23). The tail end of the gallery opens to the surface, while the head shaft is filled with loosened sand which continually settles down as the animal feeds.

Water is pumped through the burrow from the tail to the head shaft by regular waves of contraction which pass anteriorly along the body (headward irrigation, Fig. 4.6). The resultant flow of water provides a respiratory current and also serves to keep the sand in the head shaft loosened. When the tide recedes the burrow may be left exposed and partly filled with stagnant water deficient in oxygen. Under these conditions the lugworm sometimes shows another behaviour pattern, in which the hind-end is coiled and thrust above the surface of the water and is then withdrawn with a trapped bubble of air. This is brought into contact with the gills and replenishes the oxygen supply of the animal.

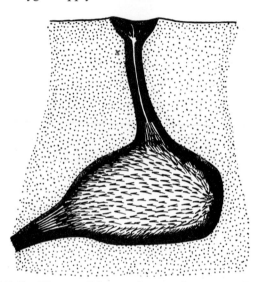

FIG. 4.5. Sea Urchin *Echinocardium cordatum* in its Burrow

Other worms which create respiratory currents through tubes and burrows are nereids, terebellids, maldanids and sabellids. Water is propelled by peristaltic contractions of the body wall (20, 80).

AERIAL GILLS AND ACCESSORY STRUCTURES. Animals of aquatic origin which have moved up the shore towards land have encountered the problem of adapting their gills for aerial respiration. Essentially aquatic forms which are periodically exposed, notably lamellibranchs, shut their valves and retain a supply of water until the tide returns. During this period of anaerobiosis, metabolism is reduced and a temporary oxygen debt is incurred. The oyster *Ostrea virginica*, for example, is able to withstand conditions of anoxia for a week or more. The danger of desiccation is more urgent than temporary anoxia in littoral species.

Aquatic gills are delicate structures unsuitable for aerial respiration, since they collapse in air with consequent reduction of surface area. Progressive adaptation towards terrestrial life is seen in littoral periwinkles

(*Littorina*), which show reduction of branchiae and development of a vascularized mantle epithelium, especially in those species occurring above mid-shore. *Nerita* and *Acmaea* are other littoral prosobranchs which have vascularized mantle-epithelia. Sea-slugs such as *Ancula* found in the tidal zone possess rather rigid branched gills. Some pulmonates have returned to the sea and lead an amphibious existence in the tidal zone. *Siphonaria*, a limpet-like form, is provided with a vascular epithelium in the roof of the mantle cavity, which appears to be used as an aquatic and aerial lung. In *Onchidella* there is a lung chamber which subserves respiration when the animal is in air but is closed off when submerged. Pulmonary respiration is supplemented by gaseous exchange through the dorsal mantle, which bears gills or papillae; this surface is kept moistened by the secretion of pallial glands when the animal is in air.

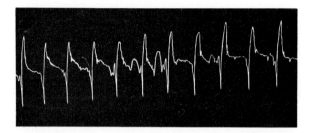

FIG. 4.6. RECORD OF ACTIVITY OF *Arenicola marina* (7-HOUR TRACE)

The worm was feeding actively from the head shaft with its tail towards the float of the recording apparatus. Activity cycles occur about once per 40 min. Each sharp downward peak is due to tailward excursion of the worm and defaecation, the broad second peak (upward) results from vigorous headward irrigation accompanied by gentle headward creeping. (From Wells, 1949.)

Isopods show various respiratory adaptations towards terrestrial conditions. A transitional series is afforded by *Idotea* from the middle shore; *Ligia* at high-tide mark; *Oniscus*, a terrestrial animal which inhabits damp places; and *Porcellio*, which prefers somewhat drier conditions. *Idotea* and *Ligia* shelter in moist niches and become active at night; their pleopods are normal in structure, and act as gills. The pleopods of terrestrial species are thicker than those of aquatic forms, and in some of the former there are capillary grooves for draining water towards the gills and keeping them moist. Littoral barnacles maintain a minute aperture to the exterior between the valves, when exposed to the air, and air is renewed within the mantle cavity by diffusion (45).

Among decapod crustaceans there is a tendency for reduction of the gills as the animals become increasingly terrestrial. This is brought out in Table 4.2, compiled by Pearse, in which species of anomurans and brachyurans are arranged by habitat. Essentially terrestrial crabs (hermit

Coenobita, robber *Birgus*, ghost *Ocypode*) have fewer gills than aquatic species. *Coenobita* tolerates amputation of its gills and in their absence can obtain at least enough oxygen for survival. Reduction in gill area relative to unit body weight is also correlated with migration from sea to land in brachyurans.

Modifications are commonly present in littoral species for retaining water in the gill chamber—by special folds, hairs, etc. (*Sesarma, Uca*). Reduction of gills is compensated by the development of accessory modes of respiration suitable for terrestrial life. The gill chamber is enlarged and used as a lung in terrestrial crabs (*Gecarcinus, Uca*). In *Birgus* it is divided into an upper lung and a lower gill chamber. Vascularized epithelium (protuberances, tufts) in the branchial chamber, supplementing the reduced gills, occur in many species (*Ocypode, Birgus, Uca*). The integument of the anterior ventral surface is very vascular in *Coenobita*, and serves for respiratory exchange in the absence of well-developed gills. Mechanisms

TABLE 4.2

GILL REDUCTION IN CRUSTACEA FROM AQUATIC TO TERRESTRIAL SPECIES

(After Pearse)

Species of Crab	No. of Gills	Body : gill ratio (volumes)[1]	Habitat
Anomura			
Petrochirus bahamensis	26	—	Below low tide
Calcinus tibicen	26	—	Low-tide level
Clibanarius tricolor	18	—	Near high-tide mark
Coenobita clypeatus	14	—	Terrestrial
Birgus latro	14	—	Terrestrial
Brachyura			
Callinectes sapidus	16	23:1	Pelagic, sublittoral
Menippe mercenaria	18	34:1	Sublittoral
Panopeus herbstii	18	36:1	Littoral and sublittoral
Pachygrapsus transversus	18	40:1	Between tides
Uca pugnax	12	46:1	Between tides
U. pugilator	12	49:1	Near high-tide mark
Geograpsus lividus	18	57:1	High-tide mark
Sesarma cinereum	16	63:1	High-tide mark
Ocypode albicans	12	67:1	Beaches and land

[1] Determined from material hardened in chromic acid.

have also been described in various crabs for renewing air in the branchial lungs (92).

Adaptations for aerial respiration are not infrequent among freshwater fish inhabiting waters which are periodically subject to oxygen depletion, but in marine fishes they are limited to some inhabitants of tropical shores. Shore gobies (*Periophthalmus* and allies) are commonly seen in mangrove swamps jumping actively over the mud when the tide is out. In conjunction with their partially terrestrial habits the branchial chamber is enlarged and modified as a gas storage organ for aerating the gills. Gill surface relative to body surface is reduced in littoral gobies compared with aquatic forms. In *Periophthalmus* the gills are supplemented by branchial diverticula, and the mucous epithelium of mouth, pharynx and branchial chambers is well vascularized. By rhythmic movements of the buccal region the air stored in the bucco-pharyngeal cavities can be renewed. Paired pharyngeal sacs are found in the cuchia *Amphipnous*, a brackish- and freshwater fish of tropical Asia. The gills are greatly reduced in this animal, which apparently depends upon aerial respiration (82, 124).

RESPIRATORY EXCHANGE

Apart from anaerobes, animals ultimately require oxygen for oxidizing reactions yielding energy during catabolism. Metabolism embraces the sum total of energy transformations taking place within an organism. In aerobic animals, therefore, the level of oxygen consumption provides an indirect index of metabolic rate (indirect calorimetry). The standard term for describing metabolism is the calorie; direct determination of metabolism involves measuring the heat produced (direct calorimetry). In small organisms metabolism is usually measured by determining the oxygen consumption.

Oxygen Consumption

The metabolic rates of different animals show enormous variation, depending on a complex of interacting intrinsic and extrinsic factors. In aerobic species oxygen available to the cells is delimited by the oxygen content of the surrounding medium, and the rate at which it can be supplied to the tissues. Anaerobes display specialized metabolic economies, and are treated in some detail by Brand (8).

Various factors influencing oxygen consumption include: specific metabolic characteristics of the tissues; intrinsic regulatory mechanisms (nervous and hormonal control); age, size, sex, activity, nutrition, season and temperature. The interrelations of these factors are extremely complex, and some of the data are only suggestive. Our theme will be metabolism and levels of oxygen consumption in relation to the marine environment.

FACTORS INFLUENCING OXYGEN CONSUMPTION. **Specific Differences.** As a rough generalization it may be stated that particular rates of oxygen consumption are characteristic of each species. To be strictly comparable, measurements have to be made under uniform conditions, usually with the animal at rest, and at some temperature of reference. Some selected data for oxygen consumption in marine poikilotherms under approximately normal conditions are presented in Table 4.3. Absolute values available often show great variation, even when secured by one investigator on the same species. Although not strictly comparable, owing to the different temperatures at which the determinations were made and variations in the activity of the animals measured, they give a rough index of oxygen uptake. The figures show no phylogenetic trend but certain conclusions are justified. Very small animals (protozoans, small metazoans) generally

TABLE 4.3

OXYGEN CONSUMPTION OF SOME MARINE POIKILOTHERMS

Animal	Temperature (°C)	Oxygen uptake c.c./kg-hour
Protozoa		
Paramecium caudatum	20–21	500–1,000
Colpidium colpoda	17	2,000
Porifera		
Suberites massa	22	24·1
Coelenterata		
Geryonia proboscidalis	16	4·2–9·03 mean 6·09
Rhizostoma pulmo	16	4·2–11·69 mean 7·21
Aurelia aurita	13–17	3·4–5
Anemonia sulcata	18	12·7
Calliactis parasitica	18	19·9
Ctenophora		
Beroë ovata	16	3·85–7·14 mean 5·04
Cestum veneris	16	1·96–4·34 mean 2·63
Annelida		
Neanthes virens	15	26
Chaetopterus variopedatus	15	8
Arenicola marina	10–12	20–40 mean 31
Spirographis spallanzanii	17	78
Glycera gigantea	16	74·2
Echiuroidea		
Urechis caupo	17	12·6
Bonellia viridis	18	18–29
Sipunculoidea		
Sipunculus nudus	15	49·3
Golfingia elongata	17	19
Mollusca		
Crassostrea virginica	20	15·5
Pecten grandis	20	70
Mytilus edulis	20	22
Aporrhais pes-pelecan	18	4–20
Murex brandaris	18	24–32
Aplysia punctata	18	11·3, 30
A. fasciata	14–15	21–37·8
Tethys leporina	16	11·55
Pterotrachea coronata	16	7·84
Octopus vulgaris	16	86·8
Eledone (Ozaena) moschata	15	226·1
Crustacea		
Talorchestia megalophthalma	12–13	78–180 mean 133
Ligia oceanica	25	179–400
Palaemon serratus	17	123
Pandalus montagui	17	142
Homarus vulgaris	15	68
Palinurus vulgaris	15	44·2
Carcinus maenas	16	51·8–70·7
Emerita talpoida	20	54–144 mean 112·2

TABLE 4.3—Oxygen Consumption of Some Marine Poikilotherms (*continued*)

Animal	Temperature (°C)	Oxygen uptake c.c./kg-hour
Echinodermata		
Asterias rubens	19	32
	15	15·4–68·6
Echinaster sepositus	15	2–12
Ophiura texturata	17	21
Cucumaria sp.	19	12·9
Holothuria impatiens	24–25	17
Tunicata		
Salpa vagina	16	1·2–2·8
		mean 1·92
Cyclosalpa pinnata	16	7·77–9·03
		mean 8·12
Ascidia mentula	24–25	2·9–6·8
Cephalochordata		
Amphioxus lanceolatus	16	35·8
Pisces		
Scyliorhinus sp.	15	54·5
Torpedo sp.	14–15	4·53–48·8
Anguilla sp.	16·5	44·4
Conger sp.	16	75·5
Labrus sp.	19	137
Mugil cephalus	24–25	100–465
Sargus rondeleti	14	185–204
Scorpaena porcus	14	67–71
Serranus scriba	16	116
Fundulus parvipinnis	18–21	130–230
Tautogolabrus adspersus	21	108–126
Syngnathus sp.	18	90
Periophthamus vulgaris	25	145–211
Solea solea	14	74
Scophthalmus maximus	15	80

have high rates of oxygen consumption. Inactive forms tend to show low metabolic rates—namely sponges, lamellibranchs and ascidians—compared with other groups such as decapod crustaceans, cephalopods and teleosts. The former are sedentary ciliary feeders displaying little sustained muscular activity. Data of this kind are amenable to treatment in other ways, which bring out certain fundamental relations.

When compared on the basis of wet weights, the oxygen consumption of species from widely separated groups shows much disparity. Animals differ greatly in water content and therefore in the amount of active protoplasm. Transparent pelagic invertebrates containing much water—e.g. medusae, ctenophores, heteropods and salps—have low rates of oxygen consumption, around 5–15% of those of active solid animals such as octopods and bony fish. When expressed in terms of dry weights, metabolic rates show greater agreement. Respiratory rates in tissues of a wide variety of marine invertebrates, per unit dry weight, approximate those of vertebrates at the same temperature, according to Robbie (102).

A variable proportion of dry weight consists of inactive material, shell, skeleton, etc. In a detailed study Zeuthen (129) has related the oxygen consumption of many marine animals to N-content, and his results are summarized in Fig. 4.7. On this basis the metabolism of lower inverte-brate animals of comparable size (coelenterates, echinoderms, worms, gastropods) shows much correspondence. The curve for *Mytilus* reveals very low values, perhaps correlated with its sedentary habits. Moreover, there is indication of increased respiratory rate per unit-N in animals

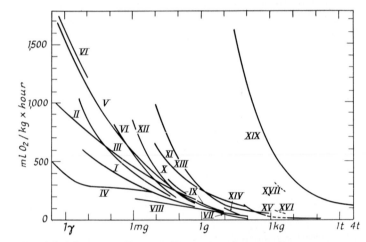

FIG. 4.7. METABOLIC RATE OF DIFFERENT ANIMALS PLOTTED ON THE
BASIS OF BODY WEIGHT

Curves: 1, nematodes and polychaetes; 2, 3, *Littorina* and *Nassarius* (gastropods); 4, 9, *Mytilus* (lamellibranch); 5, 11, crustacea; 6, *Balanus*; 7, *Asterias*; 8, planarians, anne-lids, and echiuroids; 10, gastropods; 12, insects; 13, fish; 14, amphibians; 15, reptiles; 16–19, birds and mammals. (From Zeuthen (129).)

higher up in the phyletic scale, namely crustaceans and fish. These are also more active than the invertebrates previously mentioned, but in addition there appears to be a real difference related to higher metabolism in the more advanced phyla.

Effect of Size. It has long been recognized that rates of oxygen con-sumption are generally lower in larger animals of the same or closely related species. Earlier data are inconsistent, but more recent studies on a wide variety of animals have confirmed this inverse relationship between metabolic rate and body size. The relationship is not linear; rather the rate of oxygen consumption is correlated with body weight as an exponen-tial function,

$$\text{c.c. } O_2 \text{ consumed} = kW^x$$

where k is a species constant, W is body weight and x is an exponent rang-ing from 0·66 to unity. Measurements on a wide variety of marine fish and crustaceans show a decrease in metabolic rate with increase in body size.

Marine forms examined do not conform closely to the surface law ($x =$ 0·66). For many small metazoa (eggs, larvae, small marine crustacea) the value of the exponent relating weight to oxygen uptake lies nearer unity (0·8–0·9). For larger organisms the exponent ranges around 0·7 (98, 110, 112, 118, 129, 137).

Effect of Activity. All body activities are ultimately dependent upon aerobic respiration. Hence, any changes in activity will affect cellular respiration and, if of sufficient magnitude, will result in measurable alterations in oxygen consumption. The condition of standard or basal metabolism derived from human physiology is hardly applicable to lower animals, and recourse sometimes is had to anaesthetics to reproduce non-active metabolism (muscular rest). Such procedures demand a knowledge of the mode of action of the anaesthetic and the optimal dose. Zeuthen (129) makes a brief for relating oxygen consumption to normal activity, i.e. a fair sample of activity characteristic of the animal in nature. In a series of invertebrates he has demonstrated the rise in O_2 consumption which attends greater activity, for example during periods of active swimming as contrasted with periods of rest. Likewise in teleosts swimming activity results in an increase in O_2 consumption of from 35–82%.

Among phyletically related species it is instructive to observe the increased oxygen consumption which attends more vigorous behaviour and habits, for example between active swimming lamellibranchs (Pectinidae) and sedentary or burrowing forms (*Mya, Venus, Ostrea*, etc.); or between active pelagic and sluggish fish (mackerel *versus* puffer fish, for example). These inter-specific differences are also reflected in respiratory rates of isolated tissues, brains of marine teleosts having been used for such comparative experiments (147, 152).

Diurnal, seasonal and other periodic changes in metabolism are probably widespread. In some animals there are regular diurnal variations in O_2 consumption, the maxima of which coincide with periods of heightened muscular activity, e.g. sea pen *Cavernularia obesa*, starfish *Astropecten polyacanthus*. Persistent endogenous rhythms are well marked in certain littoral animals (oyster drill *Urosalpinx*, periwinkle *Littorina* and fiddler crab *Uca*). The oyster drill shows diurnal cyles of O_2 consumption with peaks between 4.30–6.30 a.m. and 7.30–9.30 p.m. (Woods Hole). In addition to diurnal rhythms, there may be persistent tidal and lunar cycles in metabolism, which are maintained for long periods under constant laboratory conditions. These rhythms, although endogenous in nature, must be preset in phase with external conditions, after which they maintain phasic timing for considerable periods without further reinforcement. We shall refer, in a later section, to the existence of seasonal acclimatization in animals dwelling in temperate regions. In the mussel (*Mytilus edulis*), which has been studied through an annual cycle, metabolism shows a pronounced fall during spawning (May–June), and a steady rise during the intervening period (July–March) when reproductive reserves are being built up (52, 87, 88, 105).

Possible endocrinal control of metabolism in lower animals, in a manner analogous to thyroid regulation in mammals, has been a postulate inviting much research. Contrary to expectation, no firm evidence linking thyroid function with respiration has been discovered in fish. Complete thyroidectomy in the dogfish *Scyliorhinus canicula* is without effect on O_2 consumption, and treatment with thyroxine does not increase the consumption of oxygen in fishes (97). Other experiments relate to hormonal control of metabolism in decapod Crustacea. Removal of both eyestalks produces a significant rise in O_2 consumption, which is opposed by injection of eyestalk extracts (*Uca*, *Gecarcinus*). An increase of respiratory rate is characteristic of the premoult period, and moult is attended by an even sharper shift in metabolism. The eyestalks of decapod crustaceans contain endocrine organs, the removal of which deprives the animal of moult-inhibiting and other hormones. Among the functions of the latter may be included regulation of respiration; or the effects produced on respiratory metabolism by interference with the eyestalk-glands may be indirect, consequent upon changes in some other activity (*see* Chapter 15) (35, 54, 69, 85).

Variation during the Life Cycle. Metabolism changes during the life cycle, in correspondence with sequential events of development, differentiation, growth, maturity and senescence. During embryonic life there are often measurable changes in respiratory rates correlated with recognizably distinct developmental stages, namely fertilization, cleavage, vascularization, hatching, etc. In eggs of *Arbacia* (sea-urchin), *Fundulus* (teleost), and some other forms which have been examined, there is a marked increase in oxygen consumption at fertilization. Starfish eggs (*Asterias*), however, show no rise in oxygen consumption at this time, and in *Chaetopterus* (polychaete) and *Cumingia* (lamellibranch) there is a decrease. Following fertilization the metabolic rate increases progressively. Slight fluctuations in oxygen consumption of fertilized eggs (*Psammechinus*, *Urechis*) during cleavage are associated with changes in mitotic activity.

Oxygen consumption in killifish eggs (*Fundulus*) rises progressively during embryogenesis. Subsequent to the increase at fertilization, a rise in O_2 uptake accompanies the establishment of embryonic circulation (third day). Another peak occurs on the ninth day, followed by a decline and subsequent rise at hatching (twelfth day) (Fig. 4.8). These later changes have not been correlated with any noticeable ontogenetic events. Metabolism of developing stages has been investigated in the sea-horse *Hippocampus*. Respiration of embryos in the brood pouch rises gradually and reaches a maximum at birth. Generally, respiration is maximal at time of hatching, and declines in post-natal life. In planktonic stages of benthic animals there may be a further increase in respiratory rate of free-swimming larvae after hatching, but metabolism declines once the animals have settled on the bottom, e.g. *Arbacia*, *Mytilus*, *Teredo* (72, 74, 102, 108, 129, 130, 131, 132).

Observations on a wide variety of animals show that young individuals possess higher respiratory rates than older animals of the same species. This conforms to the relationship between size and metabolism discussed above. Once maturity is reached there may be a decrease in metabolic activity with age, as senescence sets in. Studies on isolated tissues are in agreement with observations made on the whole animal. Thus, tissues from young specimens of the bivalve *Mercenaria mercenaria* have higher respiratory rates than those from older animals (55).

Effect of Temperature. In poikilotherms, oxygen consumption increases with rise in temperature up to some critical value, beyond which deleterious effects become evident and the rate falls off sharply (Figs. 4.9, 4.11). Q_{10} values of 2–3 are usual, but at low temperatures much greater values may be encountered, reaching 10–11 between 0°C and 5°C in some species. Some Q_{10} values for oxygen consumption are given in Table 4.4.

The relationship between temperature and metabolism is linked with many other factors. Seasonal acclimatization takes place in certain animals. It has been noted that smaller animals of a given species show greater

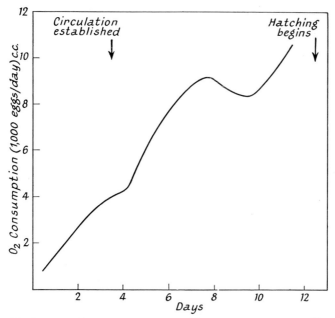

FIG. 4.8. OXYGEN CONSUMPTION DURING EMBRYOGENESIS OF THE KILLIFISH *Fundulus heteroclitus*. (From Amberson and Armstrong, 1933.)

responses to temperature changes than larger ones (beach flea *Talorchestia*, sand crab *Emerita*, killifish *Fundulus*). The interrelations between external oxygen tension and oxygen consumption are also affected by external temperature, since high temperatures raise the metabolic rate (16, 43, 83, 110, 118, 129).

TEMPERATURE ACCLIMATIZATION. Animals are capable of adjusting themselves to altered environmental conditions, a process known as

TABLE 4.4

Q_{10} OF O_2 CONSUMPTION FOR MARINE ANIMALS

(Data from Scholander et al. (110))

Animal	Temperature (°C)							
	0–0.5°C	5°C	10°C	15°C	20°C	25°C	30°C	35°C
Arctic								
Sculpin Myoxocephalus quadricornis	1·7	2	2·1	2·2	—	—	—	—
Polar cod Boreogadus saida	1·9	1·9	1·9	1·9	—	—	—	—
Blackfish Dallia pectoralis	1·7	1·8	1·8	1·0	—	—	—	—
Hermit crab Pagurus spp.	2·6	—	1·4	1·2	—	—	—	—
Spider crab Chinoecetes and Hyas	3	—	1·8	—	—	—	—	—
Amphipod Pseudalibrotus littoralis	4·5	2·5	1·7	1·4	1·2	—	—	—
Amphipod Gammaracanthus loricatus	1·9	2·2	2·5	—	3	—	—	—
Isopod Mesidothea entomon	3·3	2	1·3	1	1	—	—	—
Temperate								
Cunner Tautogolabrus adspersus winter	—	2·5	2·4	2·5	2·4	—	—	—
ditto summer	—	—	3·1	2·7	2·6	2·5	—	—
Sand crab Emerita talpoida winter	—	2·8	2·6	2·2	1·6	1·4	—	—
ditto summer	—	—	5	5·2	2·7	1·6	—	—
Sand flea Talorchestia megalophthalma winter	—	2·4	2·5	2·5	1·9	1·6	—	—
ditto summer	—	2·4	2·5	2·5	1·9	—	—	—
Copepod Calanus finmarchicus	1·8	1·9	2·1	2·2	2·3	—	—	—
Tropical								
Snapper Lutianus apodus	—	—	—	3·2	3·2	2·9	2·3	2
Croaker Haemulon bonariense	—	—	—	—	2·7	2·7	1·7	—
Land crab Sesarma ricordi	—	—	5·8	4·2	2·6	2·2	1·8	1·6
Fiddler crab Uca mordax	—	—	6·8	—	3·1	2·5	2·2	2
Shrimp Penaeus and Angasia	—	—	—	2·4	2·4	2·4	1·7	—
Isopod Rocinela signata (?)	—	—	—	—	3·4	2·6	1·8	1·5

acclimatization. Differences in the physiological responses of individuals of the same species from different latitudes may be due to acclimatization rather than to differences in hereditary constitution. Studies on temperature acclimatization have been carried out on diverse functions: survival at extreme temperatures, rates of many activities, e.g. heart beat, ciliary motility and body metabolism. An instance of the latter is provided from experiments on the goby *Gillichthys mirabilis*, which shows reduced rates of metabolism when exposed for several weeks to high environmental temperatures (9).

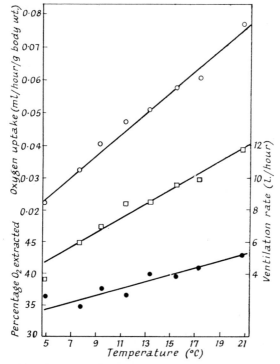

FIG. 4.9. EFFECT OF TEMPERATURE ON THE RESPIRATION OF THE LOBSTER *Homarus vulgaris*

Curves refer to oxygen uptake by the gills, rate of gill ventilation and percentage of oxygen extracted by a lobster weighing 345 g in sea water having an oxygen concentration of 5·3 ml/l. (From Thomas (118).)

Several species of animals are now known to exhibit seasonal acclimatization of metabolism, dependent on temperature changes. *Fundulus parvipinnis* taken from cold water in winter possess a higher rate than specimens measured during the summer (tested at 12°C and 20°C). Moreover, when kept at a constant temperature, these fish still show a seasonal rhythm with higher winter respiration. In the sand crab *Emerita talpoida* oxygen consumption in winter is greater than in summer at temperatures below 20°C; augmentation of winter metabolism is about fourfold at 3°C. Similarly, excised tissues of the bivalve *Mercenaria mercenaria* tend to show higher winter rates of oxygen consumption. These animals become adjusted to seasonal changes in temperature with the result that the metabolic rate is preserved at a relatively high level in winter. Other species become dormant, e.g. beach flea *Talorchestia megalophthalma*, and show no adaptive rise in winter metabolism (55, 110).

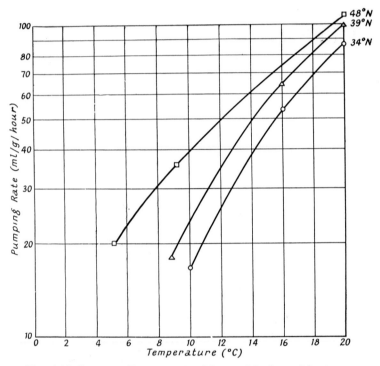

FIG. 4.10. PUMPING RATES OF THE MUSSEL *Mytilus californianus*, AT DIFFERENT TEMPERATURES

Measurements made on three samples of animals from different localities (latitude shown after each curve). Animals weighed 50 g. (From Bullock (13).)

Many instances of temperature compensation or acclimatization involve a shift of the metabolism/temperature curve along the abscissa. Thus in metabolic adaptation to cold, the entire O_2 consumption curve is displaced towards low temperatures. Theoretically, a low temperature-coefficient (Q_{10}) would be advantageous in offsetting the effects of temperature changes, but evidence for such is still equivocal (Table 4.4) (13, 110).

Adaptations to temperature differences associated with geographic distribution are now well established for a series of poikilotherms. Respiratory rates and heart rates of some but not all cold-water polychaetes and crustacea are often higher than those of comparable warm-water forms when measured at the same intermediate temperature; mussels (*Mytilus californianus*) have greater pumping rates in higher than in lower latitudes, other factors being equal (Fig. 4.10) (13, 26).

Among lamellibranchs, Arctic or boreal cold-water species have a higher metabolism than warm-water Mediterranean species, when measured at the same temperature. Thus *Cardium ciliatum* from East Greenland has an oxygen consumption twice that of *C. edule* from the Mediterranean, determined at 5°C. In specimens of one and the same species, *Mytilus edulis*, from different latitudes the same metabolic rate was recorded in the Mediterranean at 15°C as in Danish waters at 5°C. Curves of oxygen consumption *versus* graded temperatures are displaced towards the left in some but not all cold-water as compared with warm-water species. Thus graphs of O_2 uptake for prawns *Pandalus montagui* show that Kristineberg animals have a higher metabolic rate than those from Plymouth, when measured at the same intermediate temperature (10°C) (99).

These relations are brought out in detailed studies on a wide series of arctic and tropical fish and crustaceans investigated in Alaska and Panama. The environmental sea temperatures of the arctic species ranged from $-$ 2°C to 9·4°C (mean 6·8°C). Sea temperatures in the Canal Zone showed a range of 25·6°C to 30°C. In all the arctic aquatic forms (amphipods, isopods, decapod crustaceans, teleosts), the O_2 consumption curves were displaced to the left, toward cold temperatures, when compared with tropical species (Fig. 4.11). The arctic animals, at the normal temperature of their habitat, 0°C, have metabolic rates from three to ten times less than tropical species at a habitat temperature of 30°C. When the corresponding metabolic curves of tropical species are extrapolated to 0°C, the metabolic rates of these animals would be lowered from thirty to forty times (Fig. 4.12). Consequently in the arctic species examined there is a very appreciable amount of metabolic adaptation to low temperatures (110).

Metabolism of isolated tissues sometimes reflects the same temperature influence measurable in the intact animal. In a study of *Mercenaria mercenaria*, excised gills from cold-water animals showed a higher Q_{O_2} than gills from warm-water animals (at 20°C and 25°C). Of the same nature are results obtained from a comparison of the metabolism of brain and liver tissue of the polar cod *Boreogadus saida* and golden orfe *Idus melanotus*. The former is an arctic fish living at environmental temperatures of around 0°C, the latter a freshwater temperate fish having an environmental temperature of 25°C. Polar cod tissues showed a higher respiratory rate over a temperature range of 0°C–25°C, and a relatively much greater rate below 10°C (55, 96).

INTERRELATIONS OF OXYGEN CONSUMPTION AND OXYGEN TENSION. The relations between oxygen consumption and oxygen tension are complex. A convenient generalization divides animals into those which maintain a steady respiratory state over a wide range of external oxygen tensions and those in which the amount of oxygen consumed is directly dependent on the oxygen tension of the environment. Among those factors which determine relative independence are: size of the animal, existence of an efficient circulatory system and magnitude of diffusion distances; degree of locomotory activity and effect of temperature variations; ability to regulate external respiration; existence of respiratory pigments and their physico-chemical characteristics.

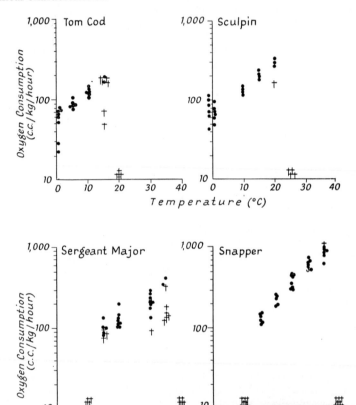

FIG. 4.11. RESPIRATION IN TROPICAL AND ARCTIC FISH

Ordinates in c.c. O_2/kg/hour. Abscissae, temperature (°C). Tropical fish: sergeant major *Abudefduf saxatilis*; snapper *Lutianus apodus*. Arctic fish: tom (polar) cod *Boreogadus saida*; sculpin *Myoxocephalus quadricornis hexacornis*. (From Scholander *et al.* (110).)

Metabolism Directly Dependent on O_2 Tension. In many animals O_2 consumption varies directly with O_2 tension, e.g. *Actinia, Nereis, Calanus, Homarus, Callinectes, Limulus, Asterias*. In *Actinia equina*, for example, oxygen consumption increases threefold when the external tension is raised from 55–220 mm Hg. When the O_2 concentration falls below 2 c.c./l. *Actinia* moves to the surface, and if this is prevented the animal secretes some mucus, closes up and enters upon a period of latent life. In large coelenterates diffusion is a limiting factor in the supply of O_2 to the tissues. In very small animals, larvae and eggs, O_2 uptake remains steady over wide variations in O_2 tension, showing the adequacy of diffusion for supplying O_2 requirements. The oxygen consumption of some animals

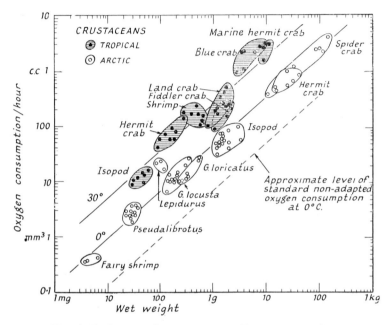

FIG. 4.12. OXYGEN CONSUMPTION OF TROPICAL AND ARCTIC CRUSTACEANS AT THEIR NORMAL HABITAT TEMPERATURES

The tropical forms extrapolated down to 0°C on the basis of Krogh's standard temperature curve would fall along the dotted line, corresponding to a rate 30–40 times lower than at 30°C. Arctic forms show appreciable adaptation in that their metabolic rates are only 4–10 times lower than tropical forms. (Double log plot, regression lines correspond to a weight/rate exponent of 0·85.) (From Scholander *et al.* (110).)

continues to rise at tensions above normal atmospheric pressure, e.g. *Actinia*, *Limulus*, suggesting that the tissues are unsaturated with O_2 under normal conditions.

Relative Independence of External O_2 Tensions. In contrast are those animals in which the respiratory rate remains fairly steady over a wide range of gaseous tensions. Such ability is relative, and critical tensions below which independence ceases differ greatly from one animal to another. Some examples of critical O_2 tensions for various animals at a temperature of 20°C are as follows (mm Hg)—

Arbacia eggs	20	*Fundulus heteroclitus*	16
Loligo pealei	45	*Tetraodon maculatus*	100
Palaemonetes vulgaris	80	*Stenotomus chrysops*	30

Even fairly closely related animals show great differences in this respect, *Callinectes*, for example, being unable to regulate whereas *Palaeomonetes* regulates down to about 50% saturation (80 mm Hg). Sea anemones do not regulate, but jellyfishes, containing a small proportion of dry matter (*Pelagia, Geryonia*), show relative independence of external O_2 tensions. Diffusion in the latter animals is adequate for the small amount of respiring tissue present. Very active animals, because of high levels of oxygen utilization, are more dependent upon high oxygen tensions (e.g. mackerel compared with angler fish). At low temperatures the activity of poikilotherms is reduced, and they are able to tolerate lower O_2 levels, i.e. critical tensions are lowered with fall in temperature.

Aquatic invertebrates differ greatly in their tolerance of abnormal levels of O_2 over long periods. Thus, *Sabella pavonina*, a tubicolous polychaete, will tolerate 100, 21 and 10% dissolved O_2, but succumbs in 4% dissolved O_2 after 4 days. Young *Arenicola marina*, however, tolerates 21, 10 and 4% O_2, but 100% dissolved O_2 is slowly toxic. *Sabella* lives in well-aerated water, whereas *Arenicola* is a burrowing species that encounters periodic anoxia.

Relative independence of external oxygen tensions may result from low levels of metabolism, small size, short diffusion distance and so forth. But many animals possess some degree of control over their respiratory mechanisms, and in these forms low O_2 tensions may stimulate respiratory centres and evoke increased ventilation movements. Frequently, animals with well-developed circulatory systems possess respiratory pigments which, by virtue of their combining power with oxygen and their saturation characteristics, continue to provide the tissues with adequate oxygen in oxygen-deficient environments and confer relative independence of external oxygen concentrations (7, 8, 21, 23, 83, 118).

RESPIRATORY RHYTHMS AND REGULATION
OF VENTILATION

The ventilation patterns of aquatic animals show specific peculiarities and vary in accordance with environmental conditions, including alterations in temperature and levels of oxygen and carbon dioxide. These responses can usually be interpreted as functional adaptations to respiratory stress. Since there is much variation in ventilation patterns of different groups the subject can be reviewed conveniently on phyletic lines. Ventilation volumes for various species are presented in Table 4.5, and should be consulted in conjunction with the following account.

Polychaetes. Tubicolous and burrowing polychaetes show certain characteristic responses to respiratory stress. By an elegant method of recording G. P. Wells has been able to study irrigation by these animals under substantially natural conditions. The lugworm *Arenicola* regularly pumps water headwards, occasionally tailwards, through its burrow. Irrigation is rhythmical and occurs in bursts with definite pauses between successive outbursts of pumping (Fig. 4.6). This rhythmicity is set by an internal pacemaker located in the ventral nerve cord, and the timing of the irrigation cycle is unaffected by reduction of the oxygen tension of the sea water or by accumulation of possible excretory products. Under conditions of oxygen lack, however, the rigour of the outbursts is much reduced. When aerated water is restored after several hours of oxygen deficiency, the worm responds by greatly increased irrigation.

Nereis diversicolor and *Chaetopterus variopedatus* resemble *Arenicola* in showing regular cyclical patterns of irrigation activity (Fig. 5.4). In *Spirographis spallanzanii* pumping movements are nearly continuous under normal conditions; in *Sabella pavonina* pumping is sometimes interrupted by long quiescent periods. Oxygen deficiency has different effects on these species: *Nereis* and *Sabella* respond by decrease or cessation of irrigation; *Chaetopterus* by an increase. In general, tubicolous polychaetes that irrigate their tubes by muscular pulsations utilize 50–60 % of the oxygen. Utilization is lower in worms that irrigate branchial crowns, only about 10 %: much of the pumping activity of the crown serves feeding rather than respiration (20, 21, 51, 73).

Molluscs. Ventilation in some aquatic molluscs is greatly affected by environmental conditions. In *Mya arenaria* the ventilation current is increased after a period of oxygen deficiency (low tide). Following a prolonged period of anaerobiosis (21 hours), normal levels are not restored until 3–4 hours later (Fig. 4.13). The utilization of oxygen is normally low, between 3–10%, but after a period of low tide when the animal has contracted an oxygen debt it rises appreciably (to about 25%). In lamellibranchs the flow of water over the gills shows little variation when the valves are open. When submerged, *Mytilus edulis* keeps its valves open most of the time and pumps almost constantly. In other bivalves the valves are periodically closed and ventilation ceases. The oyster (*Ostrea virginica*), for example, closes its shell, on the average, 7 hours out of 24 (23, 63, 64).

The differential effects of O_2 decrease and CO_2 increase have been distinguished in several species. Ventilation in the oyster (*Ostrea virginica*) is affected by acidity. When HCl is added to sea water so as to lower the pH to 7·0–6·75, the oyster responds by increased pumping activity. In conformity with their more complex organization and physiology, cephalopods show a high degree of respiratory control. Oxygen lack in *Octopus* causes increased ventilation up to ten times normal. Increased CO_2 at tensions below 6 mm also produces an increase, but higher tensions inhibit respiration. Oxygen utilization varies between 50–80%.

Crustacea and Xiphosura. Respiratory control shows much variation in different groups of crustaceans. The respiratory activity of acorn barnacles increases when the oxygen content of the water is reduced, and a rise of acidity produces protracted activity (114). Both decrease in O_2 and increase in CO_2 quicken the rhythm of respiratory movements in *Gammarus locusta* but the effects are transitory. In amphipods and isopods generally, respiratory movements are performed by beating of pleopods, and the rate is accelerated by low O_2 and high CO_2 tensions in most subaquatic species examined (*Cirolana, Cymodoce, Idotea, Melita*).

Ventilation in stomatopods is accomplished both by beating of the pleopods and movements of the thoracic branchiae, and in *Squilla* these

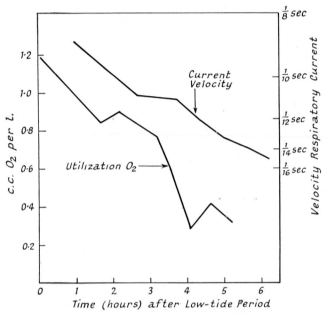

FIG. 4.13. CURVES SHOWING THE COURSE OF OXYGEN UTILIZATION AND VELOCITY OF RESPIRATORY CURRENT AFTER A LOW-TIDE PERIOD OF 20 HOURS IN THE GAPER *Mya arenaria*

Current velocity = 1/streaming time. (From van Dam (1935).)

movements are quickened by lack of O_2 and heightened CO_2. In decapods oxygen lack is generally effective as a stimulus increasing respiratory movements, and increased CO_2 is inhibitory at first but, if prolonged, causes acceleration. Oxygen withdrawal (utilization) in general is rather high, between 25–88% (average value about 50%) (Fig. 4.9). The respiratory centre lies in the suboesophageal ganglion, and is an autonomous pacemaker (73, 75, 91, 118, 119, 122, 128).

Shore crabs (*Carcinus*) pump between 1·5 and 1 c.c./g crab/min (depending on size). Pumping activity and oxygen consumption show a persistent tidal and diurnal rhythm, and ventilation is greatest following a high tide during the daytime (2).

The abdominal appendages in *Limulus* perform ventilation movements at a frequency of 25–50 beats per min. Respiratory movements are controlled by branchial ganglia in the ventral nerve cord, and are influenced by a variety of internal and external stimuli. Anoxia leads to a steady decline in frequency and amplitude of gill movements, resulting in complete arrest after 30 min, with the gills closed. Excess CO_2 causes disorganization of the normal respiratory pattern, and in about 15 min leads to complete stoppage with the gills gaping. The rapidity with which these respiratory changes are effected has prompted the suggestion that exteroceptors are involved (123).

Ascidians. In ascidians ciliary activity produces a more or less continuous current over the gills. Oxygen is taken up by the vascularized test as well as by the branchial and atrial epithelia. Ventilation rates in *Phallusia* are estimated at 825–5,100 c.c./hour. The rhythmical branchial and atrial squirting movements, observed under experimental conditions, are now believed to be concerned with cleansing the branchial basket. Oxygen utilization in solitary sea-squirts is low, around 4–7% (17–20°C) (57).

Fishes. Breathing in fishes is regulated by rhythmically active and relatively autonomous respiratory centres in the medulla. The breathing movements of elasmobranchs continue when the medulla is isolated from anterior and posterior levels of the c.n.s. by cutting through the mid-brain and spinal cord. The respiratory centre lies near the motor regions of the VIIth, IXth and Xth cranial nerves. Additionally, there appears to be reflex control of respiratory movements through afferent pathways from the pharyngeal region in the Vth, VIIth, IXth and Xth cranial nerves. Decreasing the rate of flow of water over the gills depresses the respiratory rate, and when the flow is stopped, breathing ceases. Sectioning the IXth and Xth cranial nerves causes acceleration. Electrical stimulation of these nerves prevents expansion of the pharynx, if delivered when the pharynx is deflated. Nervous activity has been recorded from the vagus nerve when the pharynx is artificially deflated or inflated. The reflex seems to be an inhibitory one, acting to halt the expansion of the pharynx and produce a pause before the onset of the next phase of the cycle.

The respiratory centre of teleosts is also located in the medulla and, in the tench at least, this region can be isolated from the rest of the brain and from the spinal cord without causing any changes in respiratory movements. Electrical activity in rhythm with respiratory movements has been recorded from the medulla: active neurones delimiting the respiratory regions lie near motor nuclei of the VIIth, IXth and Xth cranial nerves. Rhythmic activity in these regions is autonomous, taking place independently of influences from higher nervous centres and of peripheral reinforcement. The respiratory neurones are active during phases of expansion and contraction of the respiratory cycle, suggesting the interaction of opposing groups of neurones in the respiratory regions of the brain. Sectioning cranial nerves IX and X leads to an increase in amplitude of respiratory movements; these experiments give grounds for believing that afferent impulses normally exert an inhibitory influence on the respiratory centre (58).

Ventilation in fishes is very efficient and a large proportion of the oxygen in the inspiratory current is withdrawn. Under normal conditions utilization values for different species range from 46% (*Scyliorhinus, Spheroides*) to as much as 80% (*Anguilla, Salmo, Uranoscopus*). Fishes react to adverse respiratory conditions (low O_2 and high CO_2 tensions) in several ways. Oxygen lack and heightened CO_2 result in more active swimming and struggling in some fishes (*Scyliorhinus, Anguilla, Opsanus*), responses which may have value in promoting escape from an adverse environment. Low O_2 and high CO_2 tensions increase respiratory activity and ventilation. The ventilation volume is altered by changes in depth, or frequency of breathing, or both. In the eel ventilation may be increased fivefold when the O_2 content of the water falls below 4 c.c./l. In selachians (*Mustelus, Squalus*) rhythmic respiratory movements show Q_{10} values of from 1·2–2·4.

Ventilation affects utilization since the faster the animal ventilates, the shorter will be the period of contact of the water with the gill filaments. With the same oxygen content a greater ventilation volume results in decreased utilization. In the eel utilization falls when the O_2 content of the inspired water drops below 2–1·5 c.c./l., but down to a level of about 1 c.c./l. the animal still obtains sufficient oxygen for its needs. Increased respiratory activity causes a rise in metabolism, amounting to 40% in the eel, and 70% in the trout; this is due to increased work by the respiratory muscles. In *Spheroides*, utilization remains approximately the same over a fivefold decrease in tension (at 46% for O_2 levels of from 4·7–1 c.c./l.), and is not altered over a temperature range of from 12–22°C (7, 21, 73).

AERIAL RESPIRATION IN FISHES

Special functional problems are encountered by fish which have occasion to leave the water for short periods, e.g. mud-skippers, flying-fishes, etc. Because their respiratory mechanisms are normally suited to aquatic respiration the fish, during the period of emersion, may suffer some degree of asphyxia and be subject to respiratory stress like the diving vertebrates described in the next section. The freshwater eel sometimes travels overland during migration. In air the oxygen uptake is about half that in water; metabolism is reduced and the gills are ventilated periodically. About a third of the total oxygen is taken up through the gills, and during the first hour oxygen is removed from the air bladder. At 15°C the eel accumulates a substantial oxygen debt in air, but at 7°C it obtains sufficient oxygen for its vital activities, which are proceeding at a reduced rate at the lower temperature (3). The grunion is one of several smelts that spawns at the surf-line on high tide, when it emerges from the water for a few minutes. In air it ceases breathing and develops immediate bradycardia. There is a considerable amount of muscular activity and lactic acid builds up in the muscle but not in the blood. When the grunion returns to water, the lactic acid pours into the blood and the oxygen debt is paid off (107).

TABLE 4.5

VENTILATION AND PUMPING VOLUMES

Animal	Temperature (°C)	Vent./vol. ml/hour
Sponges		
Grantia compressa	17–20°	594–1,148
Sycon ciliatum	17–20°	360
Spinosella sp.	—	3,200
Polychaetes and echiuroids		
Arenicola marina	20·4°	177
Nereis (Neanthes) virens	17–18°	92·7
Sabella pavonina	15°	30
ditto	18–20°	73
Urechis caupo not feeding	—	660
ditto feeding	—	1,740
Molluscs		
Mytilus edulis	17–20°	100–29,500 mean 1,850
ditto	17°	1,900–2,600 mean 2,000
ditto	11·8–14·7°	200–4,600 mean 1,800
Cardium edule	17·3–19·5°	200–2,500 mean 500
M. californianus	20–23°	500–18,100 mean 2,600
ditto	20°	4,000–5,500
Crassostrea virginica	24–26·9°	500–3,900 mean 2,700
ditto	—	1,180
ditto	20°	1,027–212,000
Pecten irradians	21·9–25·8°	3,260–14,720
Tunicates		
Molgula sp.	17–20°	207–513
M. manhattensis	—	600–1,200
Ciona intestinalis	17–20°	552–750
ditto	—	1,800–3,400
ditto	—	2,000 ca.
Phallusia mammillata	14°	825–5,100
Fishes		
Salmo shasta	10–12°	700–9,000
Anguilla anguilla	17–18°	330–3,600

TABLE 4.6

PUMPING RATES OF SPONGES, LAMELLIBRANCHS AND ASCIDIANS

(From Jørgensen (63, 64))

Animal	Average content amino-N (mg)	Pumping rate ml/hour/mg
Grantia compressa	3·3	180
	8·5	135
Sycon ciliatum	2	180
Halichondria panicea	—	65
Mytilus edulis	2	80
	25	36
Molgula sp.	1·8	115–285
Ciona intestinalis	6	92–125

Conclusions

In slow-moving and sedentary animals oxygen consumption and utilization are low. Oxygen withdrawal from the respiratory current is of the order of 20% or less in sponges, lamellibranchs and tunicates. These are all sedentary filter feeders. The magnitude of ventilation currents in such animals is determined primarily by nutritive requirements, and there is usually a very large margin for respiration. Absolute values show very great variation, depending on a complex of environmental and intrinsic factors. Greater regularity is obtained by expressing ventilation volumes in terms of dry weight or amino-N (Tables 4.5 and 4.6). Oxygen utilization in worms with muscular pumping mechanisms stands at a higher level than in filter feeders, ranging from 30–75% in different polychaetes and echiuroids. Utilization depends upon the oxygen content of the inspiratory current, the rate and amplitude of pumping, and the metabolic condition of the animal.

Active cephalopods and fish have high levels of oxygen consumption and utilization. Oxygen lack is generally a more effective respiratory stimulus than rise in CO_2 tension. The CO_2 tension of sea water is very low (free CO_2 around 0·23 mm Hg) and relatively constant, and changes in this factor are probably outside the physiological experience of most marine animals. Responses to temporary oxygen deficiency take a variety of forms: increased ventilation (fish, cephalopods, crustacea, *Chaetopterus*), decrease in activity and lowering of metabolism (sponges, various polychaetes, *Limulus*), utilization of oxygen stores (*Arenicola*), incurrence of oxygen debt (lamellibranchs) and escape responses (fish). In all aquatic poikilotherms (invertebrates, fish) the ventilation rate is directly proportional to the circumambient temperature over normal tolerable ranges (7, 15, 63, 64, 65, 125).

RESPIRATION IN DIVING VERTEBRATES

Three main factors are involved in respiration among air-breathing diving vertebrates, namely accessory aquatic respiration (marine reptiles), adaptation to prolonged submergence in absence of oxygen renewal (homoiotherms) and resistance to pressure and pressure effects (deep-diving whales).

Physiological information is very scanty for all marine reptiles. Sea snakes and turtles are said to survive many hours under water (Table 4.7). Diving marine birds usually stay under for only brief periods, from 1–2 min, but can stand submergence up to 6–12 min (guillemot, penguin, etc.). Seals remain submerged up to 15 min. Compared with these times the duration of dives in some whales is striking: about half an hour in fin and humpbacked whales, and 1–2 hours in Greenland, bottle-nosed and sperm whales (Table 4.7) (49, 106).

Respiration in diving birds and mammals does not differ fundamentally from that in typical air breathers. Adaptations which allow divers to

TABLE 4.7

DURATION OF SUBMERGENCE OF MARINE REPTILES, BIRDS AND MAMMALS

Animal	Submergence time
Reptiles	
Loggerhead turtle *Caretta caretta*	Up to 25 min
Sea snakes Hydrophiidae	Possibly up to 8 hours
Birds	
Razorbill *Alca torda*	52 sec
Black guillemot *Uria grylle*	1–1¾ min
Little auk *Alle Alle*	Up to 68 sec
	6–12 min forced submergence
Puffin *Fratercula arctica*	30 sec or more
	4 min forced submergence
Adélie penguin *Pygoscelis adeliae*	30–45 sec normal; can survive 6 min
	forced submergence
Velvet-scoter *Melanitta fusca*	Up to 51 sec
Mammals	
Sea otter *Enhydra lutris*	4–5 min
ditto	10 min
ditto	15–30 min
Sea elephant *Mirounga angustirostris*	6 min, 48 sec
Common seal *Phoca vitulina*	15 min
Grey seal *Halichoerus grypus*	15 min in net
Sperm whale *Physeter catodon*	20–75 min
Bottle-nosed whale *Hyperoodon rostratus*	2 hours (1 hour wounded)
Common rorqual *Balaenoptera physalus*	1½–9 min normal; up to 20 min
Blue whale *B. musculus*	4–15 min normal; harpooned
	30–49 min
Greenland right whale *Balaena mysticetus*	½ to 1½ hours when harpooned.
	Normal 5–20 min
Black right whale *B. sieboldii*	50 min
Humpback whale *Megaptera nodosa*	15–20 min

remain submerged for long periods are diminished sensitivity to CO_2, shunting of blood to essential organs, and ability to contract a large oxygen debt.

In true diving animals contact of the respiratory openings with sea water reflexly inhibits breathing. During submergence O_2 is used up and CO_2 accumulates in the blood. Compared with terrestrial species divers are relatively insensitive to CO_2. Diving birds (puffins and guillemots) show unusual tolerance to CO_2, up to a concentration of 15%. The low sensitivity to CO_2 results from higher threshold of the respiratory centre in birds and diving mammals. Divers carry a supply of oxygen, but this is insufficient for aerobic respiration during a long dive. The oxygen store of the bladder-nose seal *Cystophora* has been estimated to be sufficient for about 5 min at rest, but the animal is of course highly active when diving and its energy consumption will be much greater than at rest. A seal can remain submerged for 15 min and is enabled to do so by contracting an oxygen debt in addition to depleting its oxygen stores. The gaseous capacity of the lungs of divers is only slightly if at all larger than that of terrestrial mammals of comparable size. Only a small proportion (about a third) of the oxygen store is carried in the lungs. The remainder is carried largely in the blood and to a lesser extent in tissue fluids and in cells. Some divers (seals, ducks) have somewhat larger blood volumes and higher concentrations of blood haemoglobin than terrestrial forms. In addition many divers, especially whales and seals, have large stores of muscle haemoglobin, which surrender their oxygen to the muscle cells during submergence. It appears, then, that oxygen capacity and stores of divers may be somewhat higher than in terrestrial mammals, but still insufficient to account for the fact that they can remain submerged so much longer than the latter. On surfacing after a dive lasting 15 min (suspended respiration) the seal displays deep and continuous respiration, lapsing to normal in 15 min. There is a large increase in gaseous exchange, and around 80% of the oxygen debt is paid off in the first 20 min.

During a dive lasting 15 min the seal carries only enough O_2 for at most a third of its requirements. How is this allocated and utilized? In all divers submergence causes reflex slowing of the heart. In the seal the heart rate falls from a resting value of 80/min to 10/min when the animal has submerged, and the oxygen consumption falls during the first minute of the dive to about one-fifth of resting value (Fig. 4.14). At the same time the peripheral circulation (in the muscle mass and probably the viscera) is largely suspended, and the reduced circulation and oxygen supply are reserved largely for the brain. In whales there seems to be a method for shunting blood through retia mirabilia to the brain. While the peripheral circulation is occluded during a dive, the muscle haemoglobin of the seal provides a local store of oxygen for the muscles, enabling them to carry on aerobically for 5–10 min without recourse to lactic acid formation. Once these stores are depleted, lactic acid accumulates in the muscles (anaerobic respiration). On surfacing, lactic acid appears with a surge in the blood once the peripheral circulation is opened, and is gradually removed over the course of the next half-hour (Fig. 4.14) (59, 60, 61, 106, 111).

Whales can dive deeply, and there is evidence that some species regularly go down to great depths. Harpooned right and fin whales are reported as descending to 500–1,200 metres, and there is a record for the sperm whale of 1,600 metres. How do they tolerate these pressures and escape caisson disease? The lungs of whales are not unusually large in proportion to their size and may not be fully inflated during a dive. The whale takes down only a limited supply of air (including N_2), which is not replenished as in human diving apparatuses. Moreover when the whale makes a deep dive its lungs are compressed and reduced in volume, air is displaced into bronchial and tracheal dead space, and the alveolar surface becomes reduced and thickened, all of which are factors reducing or slowing diffusion of nitrogen into the blood. In addition much of the peripheral circulation is closed off. It is probable then that the limited amount of N_2 available is insufficient to supersaturate the blood seriously, and the limited blood volume exposed to nitrogen at high pressure is diluted with blood from the periphery when the animal surfaces (73, 106).

RESPIRATORY PIGMENTS

The oxygen capacity of water is low (sea water 0.54 vol$\%$ at $20°C$), and is inadequate as an oxygen carrier except for animals having low metabolism. Many animals which possess circulatory systems have blood pigments which serve to increase greatly the oxygen-carrying capacity of

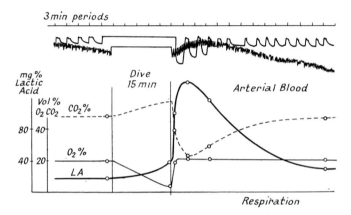

FIG. 4.14. CHANGES IN THE ARTERIAL BLOOD OF THE GREY SEAL *Halichoerus grypus* DURING A DIVE UNDER EXPERIMENTAL CONDITIONS.
(From Scholander (106).)

the blood or haemolymph. Blood pigments are compounds which combine loosely with oxygen. They belong to several different chemical categories but they have this in common that they contain some metal, usually iron or copper, in combination with protein. In the following section we shall examine their role in oxygen transport among marine invertebrates and lower chordates (29, 36, 81).

Occurrence and Chemical Characteristics of Respiratory Pigments in Marine Animals

The distribution of respiratory pigments in marine animals is shown in Table 4.8. The principal categories are haemoglobin, chlorocruorin, haemocyanin and haemerythrin. Several additional pigments, the functional roles of which remain obscure, are also known.

Haemoglobin is a reddish pigment containing an iron-porphyrin complex, widely but sporadically distributed through the animal kingdom. It is found in the blood of all vertebrates, with the exception of certain pelagic transparent fish larvae (Leptocephalus) and certain antarctic teleosts of the family Chaenichthyidae (137). It is the dominant respiratory pigment in annelids (polychaetes, oligochaetes and echiuroids). Elsewhere it is distributed in isolated instances among hemichordates, pogonophores, holothurians, phoronids, arthropods, lamellibranchs and nemertines (53, 104, 115).

In animals with closed circulatory systems haemoglobin occurs in corpuscles (erythrocytes) or dissolved in the plasma. Where haemoglobin is found in the coelomic fluid or haemolymph it is always enclosed in corpuscles. In certain terebellids (*Terebella* and *Travisia*) both conditions coexist: the blood contains haemoglobin in solution, and the coelomic fluid is provided with erythrocytes. Among invertebrates with closed circulatory systems there is a general tendency for haemoglobin to be dissolved in the plasma. Haemoglobin has also been recognized in other tissues. As muscle haemoglobin (myoglobin) it occurs in heart muscle of vertebrates; striated muscle of many fish and homoiotherms; pharyngeal and radular muscles of gastropods (*Busycon*); locomotory muscles of *Arenicola*, *Potamilla* and *Urechis*. It is also found in the nervous system of worms (*Urechis*, *Aphrodite*, nemertines) and lamellibranchs (*Tivela*).

Haemoglobins are complexes made up of a protein globin in combination with a prosthetic haem group. The latter is a metalloporphyrin containing ferrous iron combined with protoporphyrin (p. 471). The haem component of haemoglobin is identical in all species but the protein (globin) fraction shows specific differences. The oxygen-transporting function of haemoglobin is due to haem, which combines loosely with oxygen in the proportion 1 molecule of O_2 to 1 atom of Fe (oxygenation). More than one haem unit is combined with globin, the exact number varying with different species. The iron content of haemoglobins will differ accordingly. When present inside corpuscles, haemoglobin has its own chemical environment which may be of functional significance. Haemoglobins dissolved in plasma have high molecular weights. The large molecular size will tend to retain the haemoglobin in the vessels but increases the viscosity of the blood. The haemoglobin and erythrocyte contents of various bloods are shown in Table 4.9 (37, 38, 39, 41, 46, 67, 94, 109, 116).

Chlorocruorin. This is a greenish respiratory pigment related to haemoglobin. It is confined to certain families of polychaetes—namely Chlorhaemidae, Ampharetidae, Sabellidae and Serpulidae—in which it is dissolved in the plasma, and it may coexist with haemoglobin in the same species. In marine invertebrates the porphyrin-containing blood pigments, haemoglobin and chlorocruorin, are restricted to relatively inactive sedentary species, the majority of which live in tubes, burrows or crevices. Their occurrence in such animals is often related to conditions of temporary or permanent oxygen deficiency.

The prosthetic group of the chlorocruorins is also a haem, but contains a different porphyrin from haemoglobin. The affinity of chlorocruorin for oxygen is on the basis of 1 molecule O_2 per atom of Fe (18, 38, 95).

Haemocyanin. This is a copper-containing pigment which appears light blue in the oxygenated condition. It is found in the blood of some gastropods, in cephalopods and in higher crustaceans, and is the most important respiratory pigment of invertebrates, yielding to haemoglobin in vertebrates. Some gastropods containing haemocyanin have myoglobin as well, e.g. *Busycon*.

The haemocyanins are copper-protein compounds in which the copper is contained in a prosthetic group showing polypeptide characteristics. The oxygen-combining capacity of haemocyanin is dependent upon its copper content, 1 molecule of oxygen combining in proportion to 2 atoms of copper. The haemocyanin and copper contents of the blood of various animals are given in Table 4.10. Haemocyanins differ in their copper content, those of molluscs generally containing more copper than arthropod haemocyanins. Copper in the haemolymph is predominantly located in haemocyanin, and hence is indicative of haemocyanin content. It has been pointed out that the high copper content of animals containing haemocyanin demonstrates remarkable ability to concentrate this element. The copper content of some haemolymphs may be as much as 3×10^5 times greater than that of sea water (1–10 μg Cu per 1.) (10, 56).

Haemerythrin. Another iron-containing respiratory pigment found in invertebrates is haemerythrin, which differs from haemoglobin in the absence of a metallo-porphyrin group. It occurs in the polychaete *Magelona*, in sipunculoids and priapuloids, and in the brachiopod *Lingula*. Haemerythrin is always enclosed in corpuscles, and appears pink when oxygenated. It combines with oxygen in the ratio 3 Fe/O_2; the coloured prosthetic group is not a porphyrin (25, 32).

ADDITIONAL PIGMENTS. Several other pigments of doubtful function have been recognized among invertebrates. These include vanadium chromogens found in blood and body fluids of ascidians; reddish naphthoquinones (echinochromes and related substances), found in tissues and coelomic cells of echinoids (Chapter 11); and pinnaglobin, a manganese-containing pigment found in the haemolymph of the lamellibranch *Pinna*.

Vanadium Chromogens. The presence of surprisingly high levels of vanadium in ascidians has long presented an intriguing problem. Vanadium content varies from 0·04% dry weight in *Ciona intestinalis* to 0·186% in *Ascidia mentula*; nine-tenths of the vanadium is in the blood. Present in the circulation of certain ascidians are large numbers of cells, some of which are green in colour and contain vanadium chromogen. These cells, known as vanadocytes, make up 1·2% of total blood volume in some species of Ascidiidae. Vanadium chromogens occur in the plasma of Cionidae and Diazonidae; and in vanadocytes of the Ascidiidae and Perophoridae.

In view of the low vanadium content of sea water the ability of ascidians to concentrate such large quantities of this element appears remarkable. Tracer studies show that vanadium is taken up at a rate of 0·02 μg/g body weight/day, and enters through the branchial sac possibly in colloidal or adsorbed form on mucus sheets.

Vanadium chromogen (native haemovanadin) contains vanadium and pyrrols, possibly in straight-chain form, linked with sulphate and protein. Vanadium forms about 10–15% of the haemovanadin obtained from haemolysis of the blood cells. Inside the corpuscles (vanadocytes), the vanadium is kept in reduced form by a remarkably high concentration of H_2SO_4, reaching 9% (1·83 N). The physiological characteristics of haemovanadin appear to exclude it as a respiratory pigment: recent studies suggest it may have an oxidation-reduction role in the animal (45).

The oxygen capacity of blood depends on the amount and nature of the respiratory pigment present. In Table 4.9 information is summarized for haemoglobin concentrations and erythrocyte contents of the blood or body fluids of various animals. These figures show certain trends. There is much variance in haemoglobin concentrations and oxygen capacities of divers (birds and mammals); the erythrocytes of some diving mammals show high oxygen capacities (seals, sea lions, porpoises, Table 4.12). Haemoglobin concentrations are lower in poikilotherms, around 5% in most fish, and less in the few invertebrates examined. Highly active pelagic fish have large oxygen capacities and haemoglobin concentrations (menhaden, scombrids), whereas sluggish bottom forms show low haemoglobin values. A series of deep-sea fish examined proved to have average haemoglobin values (Table 4.11) (14, 24, 109).

TRANSPORT OF OXYGEN

Oxygen Capacity and the Dissociation Curve

The effective transporting ability of blood is given by its oxygen capacity, which is a measure of the maximal amount of O_2, in volumes per cent, with which the blood will combine. Oxygen capacities of the blood of most invertebrates are rather low, 3–18% in worms, 1–5% in molluscs and 1–3% in arthropods; levels are higher in fishes, from 5–15%, and very high capacities are shown by some diving mammals, up to 34% (Table 4.12). The oxygen capacity of the blood of diving birds is little greater than that of terrestrial species but, because the total blood volume is proportionately larger in the former, the total oxygen reserve is greater.

Most bloods become saturated with oxygen below atmospheric tension. The affinity for O_2 is characterized by the dissocation curve, connecting degree of saturation of the blood (percentage) with tension of O_2. Standard values, which indicate the nature of the dissociation curve and its useful range, are given by tensions of loading and unloading. Loading tension (t_l) refers to the tension at which the blood becomes 95% saturated with O_2; tension of unloading (t_u) corresponds to half-saturation. Some oxygen dissociation curves for haemoglobins of different animals are shown in Fig. 4.15, and values for tensions of saturation (loading) and half-saturation are listed in Table 4.12.

FUNCTION OF HAEMOGLOBIN. Haemoglobins of different animals often possess quite dissimilar dissociation curves. The tension of half-saturation

TABLE 4.8

Phyletic group	Subgroup or species	Location
	Haemoglobin	
Platyhelminthes		
Turbellaria	*Syndesmis echinorum*	Body fluids
	Derostomum?	ditto
Nemertinea	*Drepanophorus spectabilis*	Blood corpuscles
	Tetrastemma flavidum	ditto
	Amphiporus cruentatus	ditto
	Cerebratulus marginatus	Cephalic ganglia
	C. ehrenbergii	ditto
	Lineus gesserensis	ditto
	L. geniculatus	ditto
Mollusca		
Amphineura	*Chiton*	Pharyngeal muscle
Gastropoda	*Patella, Buccinum, Aplysia*	ditto
	Busycon	Heart, radular muscle
Lamellibranchia	*Ensis, Solen, Arca, Cardita, Glycymeris (Pectunculus), Phaxas, Gastrana, Tellina, Poromya, Astarte*	Blood corpuscles
	Mercenaria mercenaria	Heart, adductor muscle
Polychaeta		
Aphroditidae	*Aphrodite*	Brain and nerve cord
Nereidae		Blood plasma
Glyceridae		Coelomic corpuscles
Eunicidae		Blood plasma
Cirratulidae		ditto
Capitellidae		Coelomic corpuscles
Arenicolidae	*Arenicola*	Blood plasma, muscles
Maldanidae	*Clymene lumbricoides*	Blood plasma
Amphictenidae		ditto
Opheliidae	*Thoracophelia mucronata*	ditto
Terebellidae	*Amphitrite rubra*	ditto
	Pista cristata	ditto
	Polycirrus haematodes	Coelomic corpuscles
	P. aurantiacus	ditto
	Terebella lapidaria	Blood plasma and coelomic corpuscles
	Travisia forbesii	Blood plasma and coelomic corpuscles
Sabellidae	*Potamilla stichophthalmos*	Muscles
	P. reniformis	ditto
Serpulidae	*Spirorbis corrugatus*	Blood plasma
	Serpula vermicularis ⎫ *S. lobiancoi* ⎭	Haemoglobin and chlorocruorin in blood plasma
Echiuroidea	*Urechis caupo*	Coelomic corpuscles, muscles, nerve cells
	Thalassema neptuni	Coelomic corpuscles
	T. erythrogrammon	ditto
	Hamingia arctica	ditto
Phoronidea	*Phoronis, Phoronopsis*	Blood corpuscles

TABLE 4.8—Occurrence of Respiratory Pigments in Marine Animals (*continued*)

Phyletic group	Subgroup or species	Location
	Haemoglobin	
Echinodermata		
Ophiuroidea	*Ophiactis virens*	Vascular corpuscles
Holothuria	*Cucumaria, Thyone, Leptosynapta*	Coelomic corpuscles
	Caudina chilensis and *Molpadia roretzii* }	Corpuscles in coelom and vessels
Pogonophora	All species	Blood Plasma
Arthropoda		
Crustacea		
Copepoda	*Lernanthropus, Clavella, Congericola, Mytilicola*	Haemal vessels
Rhizocephala	*Septosaccus, Peltogaster, Galatheascus*	Blood in external sac
Amphipoda	*Urothoë*	Muscle, blood?
Insecta	*Chironomus*	Blood plasma
Chordata		
Hemichordata	*Discoglossus pictus*	Blood corpuscles
Vertebrata	All classes	Blood corpuscles, heart, striated muscle (many species)
	Chlorocruorin	
Polychaeta	Chlorhaemidae	Blood plasma
	Ampharetidae	
	Sabellidae } many	ditto
	Serpulidae } species	ditto
	Haemocyanin	
Mollusca		
Amphineura	General	Haemolymph
Gastropoda	Prosobranchs	ditto
Cephalopoda	*Loligo, Sepia, Octopus, Eledone, Rossia, Sepietta*	ditto
Arthropoda		
Xiphosura	*Limulus*	ditto
Crustacea	Malacostraca—many species	ditto
	Haemerythrin	
Polychaeta	*Magelona papillicornis*	Blood corpuscles
Sipunculoidea	*Sipunculus, Golfingia, Phymosoma*	Coelomic corpuscles
Priapuloidea	*Priapulus caudatus*	Coelomic corpuscles
	Halicryptus spinulosus	ditto
Brachiopoda	*Lingula unguis*	Blood corpuscles

TABLE 4.9

ERYTHROCYTE AND HAEMOGLOBIN CONTENT OF BLOODS OF MARINE ANIMALS

Species	Fluid	Erythrocytes Vol %	Count 10^6 per mm^3	Haemoglobin g per 100 c.c. blood
Mammals				
Seal *Leptomychotes weddelli*	Blood	60–65	3·6–3·8	22·5–25
Sea lion *Eumetopias stelleri*	Blood	29	—	—
Porpoise	Blood	42–5	8·4–11·2	—
Porpoise *Phocaena phocaena*	Blood	35–6	—	—
Dolphin *Tursiops tursio*	Blood	51·7	—	—
Blue and fin whales *Balaenoptera*	Blood	—	—	9
Birds				
Red-throated diver	Blood	54	3·1	20·7
Red-head and canvasback ducks	Blood	37	3·2	18
Reptiles				
Marine turtle	Blood	—	—	6·94–8·98
Fish				
Sole *Solea solea*	Blood	13	0·7, 1·29	2·2, 3·1
Gar-fish *Belone belone*	Blood	29, 37	—	5·6
Angler *Lophius piscatorius*	Blood	15·5	0·867	—
Toadfish *Opsanus tau*	Blood	19·5	0·585	—
Tautog *Tautoga onitis*	Blood	—	1·5–2·36	5·4–7·5
Shark sucker *Echeneis naucrates*	Blood	—	3·75	11·5
Puffer *Spheroides maculatus*	Blood	17·5	2·28–4·38	7·2–7·5
Scup *Stenotomus chrysops*	Blood	32·6	2·685	—
Lingcod *Ophiodon elongatus*	Blood	21–68	2·094–4·24	—
Sea robin *Prionotus carolinus*	Blood	24	2·49–2·54	7·1
Mackerel *Scomber scombrus*	Blood	37·1	3·0–3·9	14·2
Trout *Salmo trutta*	Blood	—	1·5	—
Eel *Anguilla anguilla*	Blood	—	1·1	—
Eel *A. japonica*	Blood	27–41	2·22–3·13	—
Skate *Raja ocellata*	Blood	20	0·2	—
Skate *R. laevis*	Blood	—	0·21–0·29	3·2–4·0
Skate *R. erinacea*	Blood	11–24 mean 18	—	—
Skate *R. binoculata*	Blood	4–24	—	—
Skate *R. clavata*	Blood	14–25	0·15–0·24	1·3–4·
Stingray *Dasyatis centroura*	Blood	—	0·29	2·3
Stingray *D. pastinaca*	Blood	19–30·5	0·20–0·29	3·1–4·6
Dogfish *Squalus acanthias*	Blood	6–25	—	—
Smooth hound *Mustelus canis*	Blood	—	0·41–0·52	3·7–4·2
Ratfish *Hydrolagus colliei*	Blood	18, 21	—	—
Echiuroidea				
Urechis caupo	Coelomic	18·3–40·3	—	1·4–5·1†
Annelida				
Arenicola marina	Blood	—	—	3·25
Terebella nebulosa (= *johnstoni*)	Blood	—	—	3·31
Lamellibranchia				
Arca inflata	Haemolymph	6·5	—	—
Arca sp.	Haemolymph	—	—	1·06–1·64

† Calculated on basis of 1 vol % O_2 = 0·746 g Hb per 100 c.c. cells.
(Various sources)

TABLE 4.10

HAEMOCYANIN CONTENT AND OXYGEN CAPACITY OF
SOME INVERTEBRATE BLOODS

Species	Cu mg/100 c.c.	Haemocyanin g/100 c.c.	O₂ capacity vol %
Busycon canaliculatum	9·16–16·2	3·7–6·6	2·1–3·35
B. carica	4·94	—	1·36
Sepia officinalis	23·7	—	—
Loligo pealei	18·8–22·8	7·2–8·8	3·8–4·5
Octopus vulgaris	1·48–23·5	5·9–9·1	3·1–4·5
Squilla mantis	6·1	—	—
Homarus vulgaris	4·14–14·8	—	[1·22, 3·1
H. americanus	8·3	4·4	1·95
Palinurus vulgaris	5·34–9·5	—	1·43–1·80
Panulirus longipes	4·3–20·8	—	—
Cancer pagurus	6·0–10·3	—	1·6–2·3
C. irroratus	4·2–6·82	—	1·23–1·69
C. borealis	5·16	—	1·40
Carcinus maenas	3·69–9·0	—	1·14–1·16
Callinectes sapidus	4·5–8·4	—	1·29
Ovalipes ocellatus	7·33	—	1·78
Maia squinado	1·99–7·16	—	0·84–1·75
Limulus polyphemus	1·42–12·6	0·8–7·3	0·74–2·7

Various sources)

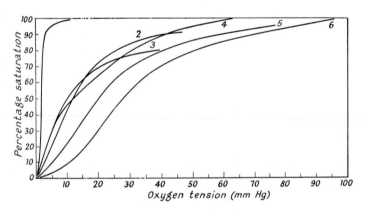

FIG. 4.15. OXYGEN DISSOCIATION CURVES FOR
HAEMOGLOBIN OF SEVERAL MARINE ANIMALS

Curves: 1: *Arenicola marina*, 20°C, pH 7·3; 2: *Anguilla bostoniensis*, 20°C pH 7·3; 3: *Petromyzon marinus*, 20°C, pH 7·4; 4: *Opsanus tau*, 20°C, CO_2 1 mm Hg; 5: skate, 10·4°C, CO_2 1 ± 0·5 mm Hg; 6: *Phoca vitulina*, 38°C, CO_2 46–47 mm Hg. (From various sources.)

TABLE 4.11

HAEMOGLOBIN CONCENTRATION OF THE BLOOD OF MARINE FISHES

(Selected values. Expressed in terms of iron per unit volume)

Fish—Teleosts	mg Fe per 100 c.c. blood
Bonito *Sarda sarda*	45·5
Mackerel *Scomber scombrus*	43·0
Menhaden *Brevoortia tyrannus*	41·0
Cunner *Tautogolabrus adspersus*	27·7
Butter-fish *Poronotus triacanthus*	27·4
Scup *Stenotomus chrysops*	25·3
Rosefish *Sebastes marinus*	24·9
Silver hake *Merluccius bilinearis*	19·4, 24·0
Sea robin *Prionotus carolinus*	23·7
Simenchelys parasiticus	22·0
Puffer-fish *Spheroides maculatus*	21·5
Eel *Anguilla bostoniensis*	20·4
A. japonica	26·0–37·1
Macrourus berglax	16·5
Angler *Lophius piscatorius*	14·7
Toadfish *Opsanus tau*	13·5
Coryphenoides rupestris	11·9
Sand dab *Lophopsetta maculata*	11·5
Fish—Elasmobranchs	
Smooth dogfish *Mustelus canis*	15·4
Electric ray *Torpedo nobiliana*	8·8

indicates the facility with which O_2 is transferred from blood to the tissues: a high value for t_u increases the availability of O_2 to the tissues; a low value indicates that oxygen is available only when supplies in the tissues are nearly exhausted, and tensions are very low. Saturation tension is linked with unloading tension, but does not become functionally significant until oxygen becomes depleted in the external medium, and falls below 100 mm Hg.

The dissociation curve is typically sigmoid in shape, the slope differing greatly from species to species (Fig. 4.15). At one extreme are animals with haemoglobins which possess high t_u values and have a low affinity for O_2, e.g. seal, porpoise, duck; at the other are animals such as eel and lugworm, the haemoglobins of which show high affinity for O_2 and possess low t_u and t_l values. Most aquatic poikilotherms have dissociation curves lying to the left of those of homoiotherms. The oxygen affinities of some invertebrate haemoglobins are very high.

EFFECT OF CO_2 AND TEMPERATURE ON DISSOCIATION CURVE. The oxygen affinities of haemoglobins are affected, sometimes greatly, by temperature, CO_2 and pH. An appreciation of the normal functional role of haemoglobin in a species is best obtained from the dissociation curve determined under conditions of temperature and CO_2 tensions actually existing in the animal and at its respiratory surfaces.

In mammalian blood the addition of CO_2 reduces the affinity for oxygen, and shifts the dissociation curve to the right—the Bohr effect. At low CO_2 tensions, such as encountered in normal sea water, loading tension (t_l) is lower than in the tissues, where CO_2 tensions are high. The Bohr effect therefore raises loading tension and facilitates unloading at sites where O_2 is required. The same results are achieved by varying the pH. The Bohr effect is quite pronounced in certain bloods (Figs. 4.16, 4.17). Haemoglobins of marine teleosts are very sensitive to changes in CO_2 tension and pH. Among invertebrates the O_2 affinities of *Arenicola* and *Thalassema* haemoglobins are increased by CO_2. Other bloods (*Urechis*, *Cucumaria*) show no Bohr effect.

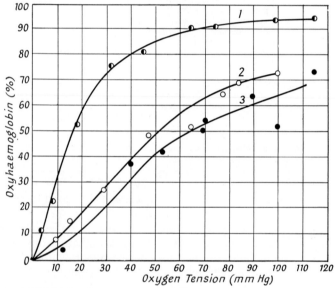

FIG. 4.16. THE EFFECT OF CARBON DIOXIDE ON OXYGEN DISSOCIATION CURVES OF MACKEREL BLOOD (*Scomber scombrus*) AT 20°C
Curve 1 for 1 mm CO_2; curve 2 for 10 mm CO_2; curve 3 for 25 mm CO_2 tension (From Root, 1931.)

A rise in temperature also shifts the haemoglobin dissociation curve to the right, reducing affinity for O_2. In poikilotherms (fish, marine invertebrates), warming raises t_u and t_l values, promoting unloading in the tissues.

Functioning of Haemoglobin in Marine Fishes. Marine fishes live in a fairly constant environment, where the O_2 tension is high (100–160 mm Hg), and the CO_2 tension generally less than 1 mm. The blood in passing through the gills is brought into equilibrium with the sea water in the branchial cavity. The haemoglobins of many teleosts have high values of t_u and t_l at the summer environmental temperatures to which the fish are normally exposed. There is some correlation between habits of the fish and haemoglobin characteristics. Active pelagic teleosts such as mackerel (*Scomber*), which have bloods of relatively high oxygen capacity, possess haemoglobins with low oxygen affinities, whereas sluggish species such as the toadfish (*Opsanus*), with bloods of low oxygen capacities, have haemoglobins with high affinities. Other fish are intermediate in these respects, e.g. scup (*Stenotomus*). The Bohr effect is often quite pronounced, an increase of CO_2 raising loading tension and reducing oxygen affinity

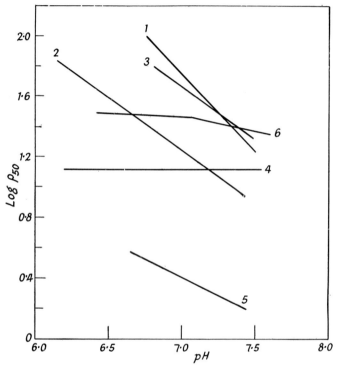

Fig. 4.17. Bohr Effect on Haemoglobins of Various Marine Animals

Ordinates, log p_{50} (O_2 pressure in mm Hg at which Hb is half saturated). Curves: 1: mackerel blood (*Scomber scombrus*), 25°C; 2: lamprey *Petromyzon marinus*, 20°C; 3: porpoise *Phocaena phocaena*, 38°C; 4: echiuroid *Urechis caupo*, 19°C; 5: lugworm *Arenicola marina*, 20°C; 6: skate *Raja ocellata*, 10·4°C (from various sources).

(Figs. 4.16, 4.17). There is, however, considerable interspecific variation in this respect, haemoglobins of sea-robin (*Prionotus*) and mackerel (*Scomber*), for example, being much more sensitive to CO_2 than tautog (*Tautoga*) and toadfish (*Opsanus*). Reduction of O_2 affinity with rise in acidity and CO_2 tension would be advantageous in promoting unloading in the tissues and, owing to the relative constancy of sea water, can but rarely hinder loading in nature. Elasmobranch haemoglobin is less affected by CO_2 than that of teleosts, but there is still a distinct acid effect within physiological ranges of CO_2 tension, namely 1–2 mm Hg.

Haemoglobins of sharks possess higher oxygen affinities than in rays. In the skate *Raja* 66% of the oxygen is utilized or removed from the arterial blood in passing through the tissues (50, 77, 101, 103, 121).

Haemoglobin in Invertebrates. Although restricted in occurrence, the haemoglobins of marine invertebrates are of much theoretical interest and are as variously adapted as those of vertebrates to their diverse functional roles.

Haemoglobin possesses strong affinity for carbon monoxide, which blocks it as an oxygen carrier. In *Nereis diversicolor*, treatment with CO reduces O_2 consumption by 50% at high O_2 tensions (6–7 c.c./l.), and stops O_2 consumption at a level of 3·4 c.c./l. *Nereis*, therefore, is dependent on Hb to a high degree for oxygen transport under normal conditions.

Urechis caupo is a littoral echiuroid which inhabits a U-shaped burrow through which sea water is circulated. Oxygen capacities lie between 3–7 vols%, comparable to those of marine fishes, and oxygen affinity of the haemoglobin is fairly high ($t_u = 12$ mm Hg). *Urechis* haemoglobin is little affected by changes in pH over the physiological range (pH 6·6–7·5). The critical tension, which in this species is 70 mm Hg (17°C), is probably determined by the dissociation characteristics of the blood ($t_l = 80$–90 mm Hg). The haemoglobin of *Urechis* is almost completely saturated when well-aerated sea water is available, and only becomes operative in oxygen transport under conditions of relative anoxia. When there is a shortage of oxygen, it has been calculated that the oxygen requirements of the animal can be met for about 14 min by oxygen dissolved in the coelomic fluid and water of the hindgut (water-lung), whereas the oxygenated blood pigment would permit normal metabolism for another 55 min. This would be of value to the animal during rest periods between pumping, periods which may last as long as an hour. In addition, the burrows of *Urechis* are exposed during tidal ebb and the oxygen pressure in the sea water in the burrow falls to 14 mm Hg (0·06 vols%). At this pressure the haemoglobin of *Urechis* is 60% saturated, and functions effectively as an oxygen carrier.

In *Urechis*, then, blood Hb subserves O_2 transport at low levels (to 14 mm Hg), and probably also provides an oxygen store during temporary periods of oxygen lack. Somewhat similar considerations apply to *Arenicola marina*. The Hb of *Arenicola* is completely saturated at 7 mm Hg and shows high affinity for oxygen (t_u about 2 mm Hg); there is likewise a pronounced Bohr effect (Fig. 4.17). Oxygen stores in the blood are not exhausted, therefore, until the positive pressure of O_2 in the tissues falls below t_u level. During low tide the water in the animal's burrow contains dissolved O_2 at a tension of 13 mm Hg, at which level the Hb is saturated (Fig. 4.18). The blood is depleted of O_2 on passing through the tissues, and on returning to the gills the pressure gradient of O_2 between the external medium and the venous blood permits the latter to be recharged with O_2.

The vascular Hb of *Arenicola* thus functions as an O_2-transporter during periods of tidal exposure when the O_2 supply in its burrow is depleted. A storage function is probably negligible (1).

Nephthys is a burrowing polychaete with both coelomic and vascular haemoglobins. The oxygen affinity of *Nephthys* Hb is low compared with that of *Arenicola*, and the tension of half-saturation is below the oxygen tension of interstitial water in its burrow during tidal ebb (Fig. 4.18). The worm has an O_2-combining potential which would suffice its metabolic needs for only some 10 min, and the Hb is thus inadequate to serve as an oxygen store during exposure. It would seem that the pigment of *Nephthys* serves as a high-tension oxygen transport system only when the sand is

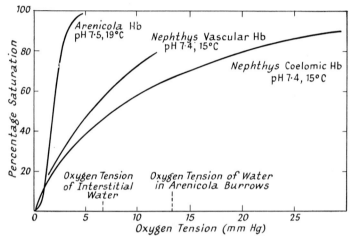

FIG. 4.18. COMPARISON OF OXYGEN DISSOCIATION CURVES OF POLYCHAETE HAEMOGLOBINS, NAMELY VASCULAR AND COELOMIC HAEMOGLOBIN OF *Nephthys hombergi* AND VASCULAR HAEMOGLOBIN OF *Arenicola marina*

The vertical dotted lines above the abscissa show the levels of oxygen tension in the interstitial water from the sand in which *Nephthys* lives, and in the residual water of exposed *Arenicola* burrows (from Jones (1955).)

covered by the sea and when the oxygen tension of the water in its burrow is high.

In *Caudina* and *Anadara* (*Arca*), with corpuscular haemoglobin, O_2 becomes available only at low tensions (8–10 mm). In two closely related holothurians, one, *Cucumaria elongata*, possesses Hb, while another, *C. saxicola*, lacks it. The former is a mud-dweller, the latter lives among rocks, and the presence or absence of Hb appears to be correlated with availability of oxygen.

The possession of haemoglobin is exceptional in arthropods. Among entomostracans it is sometimes limited to parasitic species (parasitic copepods, cirripedes). In the brine shrimp *Artemia salina*, haemoglobin

TABLE 4.12

RESPIRATORY CHARACTERISTICS OF BLOODS OF MARINE ANIMALS
CONTAINING HAEMOGLOBIN

Animal	O_2 capacity, 100 c.c. blood	Vols% 100 c.c. cells	t_u mm Hg	t_l mm Hg	CO_2 tension mm Hg	Temp. (°C)
Mammals						
Sea lion *Eumetopias stelleri*	19·8	67·0	40	—	44	38
Seal *Phoca vitulina*	29·3	61·3	26	40	40	38
Porpoise *Phocaena phocaena*	19·7–22·2	55·4–62·2	31	ca. 105	46	38
Dolphin *Tursiops truncatus*	19·1	—	—	—	—	—
Dolphin *T. tursio*	—	61·5	—	—	—	—
Blue and fin whales						
Balaenoptera	14·1	—	—	—	—	—
Birds						
Murre *Uria aalge*	26·0	—	—	—	—	—
Puffin *Fratercula arctica*	24·0	—	—	—	—	—
Surf scoter *Melanitta*						
perspicillata	22	47	—	—	—	—
Reptiles—Marine turtles						
Chelonia mydas	—	—	19	65	pH 7·4	25·5
Caretta caretta	—	—	28·5	—	pH 7·4	25·5
Fish						
Eel *Anguilla japonica*	13·5	35	2	25	0	17
A. anguilla	—	—	3	10	0·3	17
Trout *Salvelinus fontinalis*	11·0–13·9	—	17	43·5	1–2	15
Salmon *Salmo salar*	12·3	31·6	23	53	1	15
Cod *Gadus callarias*	6·5–7·8	39	15	70	< 0·3	14
Scup *Stenotomus chrysops*	7·3	23	6·4	80	pH 7·38	25
Puffer *Spheroides maculatus*	6·8	39	—	—	—	—
Mackerel *Scomber scombrus*	15·8	43	17	> 100	1	20
Sea robin *Prionotus carolinus*	7·7	32	16	85	1	20
Toadfish *Opsanus tau*	6·2	32	14	49	1	20
Angler *Lophius piscatorius*	5·1	33	—	—	—	—
Plaice *Pleuronectes platessa*	—	—	10	40	< 0·3	15
Smooth hound *Mustelus canis*	5·5–7·8	—	7	—	1	25
Skate *Raja ocellata*	4·2–6·0	30	20	77	1	10·4
Invertebrates						
Arenicola marina polychaete	5·7–9·7	—	1·8	7, 13	0, pH 7·3	17
Glycera gigantea ditto	2·6–3·0	—	—	—	—	—
Nephthys hombergi ditto						
coelomic fluid	0·19–0·49	—	7·5	—	pH 7·4	15
blood	—	—	5·5	—	pH 7·4	15
Urechis caupo echiuroid	2·7–7·2	9·3–17·4	12·0	90–100	7	19
Thalassema neptuni echiuroid	—	—	1·4	—	0	17
Glycymeris (Pectunculus)						
violacea lamellibranch	1–2	—	—	—	—	—
Cardita sulcata lamellibranch	1–2	—	—	—	—	—
Arca inflata lamellibranch	5·1	—	10	40	—	—
Caudina chilensis holothurian	6·1	—	—	—	—	—

functions in oxygen transport when the animals are living in concentrated brines (such media have low oxygen content, about one-third that of sea water when saturated with air). Treatment with CO, leading to formation of carboxyhaemoglobin, significantly reduces oxygen consumption (external medium, salinity 195‰, O_2 2 c.c./l.). *Artemia* is an example of a species that gains or loses haemoglobin in response to low or high oxygen concentrations of the surrounding medium. The haemoglobins of *Chironomus* (tidal-pool and freshwater insects) have remarkably high oxygen affinities ($t_u < 1$ mm Hg), and function in oxygen-deficient environments (44, 76).

TABLE 4.13

RESPIRATORY CHARACTERISTICS OF HAEMOCYANINS

Animal	CO_2 tension mm Hg or pH	Temp. (°C)	t_u	t
Sepia officinalis	1·95 mm	20	12	19
Loligo vulgaris	1·95 mm	20	14	22
L. pealei	2·7 mm	15	42	90
Octopus vulgaris	0·6 mm	25	3	7
Busycon canaliculatum	0 mm	22	12	55
Limulus polyphemus	0 mm	23	11	45
Homarus americanus	pH 7·72	25	22	50
Panulirus interruptus	pH 7·53	15	6·5	25
Cancer irroratus	0 mm	23	12	35

FUNCTION OF CHLOROCRUORIN. The chlorocruorin of sabellids normally functions as an oxygen carrier at high tensions. Oxygen capacity of *Spirographis* blood is 9 vols %, and the dissociation curve is shifted to the right with rise in temperature and increase of acidity. Dissociation constants are high ($t_l = 50$, $t_u = 27$, at pH 7·7 and 20°C), permitting the chlorocruorin to function in O_2 transport under conditions of abundant oxygen supply (Fig. 4.19). Treatment of *Sabella* with CO reduces O_2 consumption over a wide range of O_2 tensions (1·1–5·5 c.c. O_2 per l.), showing that a considerable fraction, up to half of the O_2, is transported by chlorocruorin, the remainder being carried in solution (Fig. 4.20). It is interesting that in *Serpula*, where chlorocruorin and haemoglobin occur together in the blood, both pigments possess equally low oxygen affinities. Chlorocruorin functions as an oxygen transporter under normal conditions and during periods of oxygen depletion (30, 31, 38, 40, 86).

FUNCTION OF HAEMERYTHRIN. Haemerythrins found in sluggish sipunculoids have high oxygen affinities. Unloading tensions are low (8 mm Hg) and the dissociation curves are little affected by acidity and CO_2 (Fig. 4.19). In the coelomic fluid of *Sipunculus* the oxygen tension is 32 mm Hg (animal in sea water), at which level the haemerythrin would remain saturated and oxygen transport would depend on gas carried in solution. However, these animals may be periodically exposed to low O_2 tensions in littoral regions, when the haemerythrin would subserve O_2 transport, as

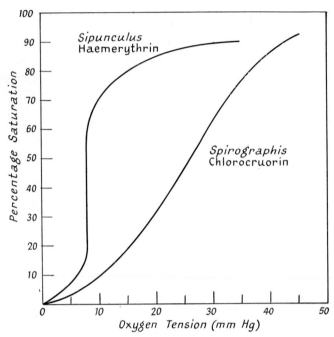

FIG. 4.19. OXYGEN DISSOCIATION CURVES FOR HAEMERYTHRIN OF *Sipunculus nudus* (19°C, CO₂ 0·07–80 MM Hg), AND CHLOROCRUORIN OF *Spirographis spallanzanii* (20°C, pH 7·7)

(Haemerythrin data from Florkin, 1932; chlorocruorin data from H. M. Fox, 1932.)

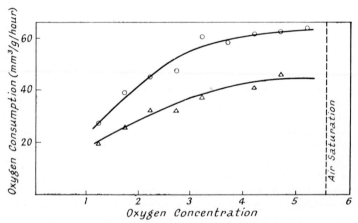

FIG. 4.20. EFFECT OF CARBON MONOXIDE ON OXYGEN CONSUMPTION OF *Sabella pavonina*, A WORM CONTAINING CHLOROCRUORIN

The curves show the rate of O_2 consumption at various concentrations of dissolved O_2 (17°C). Circles, normal animals; triangles, animal with carboxychlorocruorin. (From Ewer and Fox (30).)

in the littoral worms *Arenicola* and *Urechis*, which possess haemoglobins of correspondingly high oxygen affinities. The haemerythrin of the brachiopod *Lingula* likewise shows fairly high oxygen affinity (t_u and t_l, 16 and 60 mm Hg respectively).

FUNCTION OF HAEMOCYANIN. Haemocyanin is the most important blood

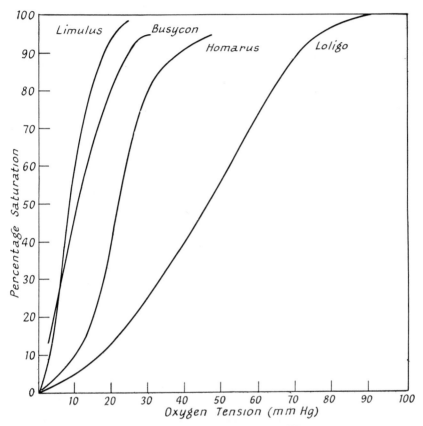

FIG. 4.21. OXYGEN DISSOCIATION CURVES OF HAEMOCYANINS
OF SEVERAL ARTHROPODS AND MOLLUSCS

Limulus polyphemus, pH 7·35, 25°C; *Busycon canaliculatum*, pH 8·35, 25°C; *Homarus americanus*, pH 7·72, 25°C; *Loligo vulgaris*, 5·3 mm CO_2, 20°C (from various sources).

pigment of molluscs and arthropods (representative dissociation curves, Fig. 4.21). Of these the cephalopods show highest levels of blood copper and oxygen capacity, the latter lying around 4–5 vols% in arterial blood. About nine-tenths of the oxygen is removed in passing through the tissues and is made good by oxygenation in the gills. Oxygen affinity appears to be least in the squid, the most active of cephalopods (Table 4.13). Increased CO_2, rise in acidity and elevation of temperature raise unloading tensions (Fig. 4.22). It has been computed that the effect of tissue levels of CO_2 on the dissociation of oxyhaemocyanin would account for about a third of the oxygen exchange in the squid (*Loligo*). Cephalopods, in general, are moderately to highly active animals, living in well-aerated waters, and their haemocyanins function to the full in oxygen transport under such conditions (127).

The oxygen capacities of other haemocyanin-containing bloods are rather low, ranging from 1 to 3 vols% in chitons, gastropods, decapod crustaceans and Limulus. The dissociation curves are similar in shape to those of haemoglobins and are very diverse. On warming there is a marked increase in loading and unloading tensions, but the effects of acidity and CO_2 are variable. In the decapods *Homarus*, *Cancer* and *Maia*, haemocyanin shows minimal affinity for O_2 below pH 7, whereas in *Busycon* (conch) and *Limulus* (king crab) minimal affinity lies above neutrality. The normal reactions of all these bloods lie slightly above pH 7.

The blood of *Limulus* appears reduced under normal conditions when drawn and contains about the same amount of O_2 as ordinary sea water. Oxygen capacities of *Limulus* and *Busycon* blood are 2–6 times that of sea water, indicating maximal amounts of O_2 which can be taken up under optimal conditions. In *Busycon* about 80% of the O_2 is utilized in passage through the tissues, and most of this O_2 is carried by haemocyanin. The increased oxygen affinity which attends rise in CO_2 may be of value in promoting loading in oxygen-deficient environments, but it is otherwise

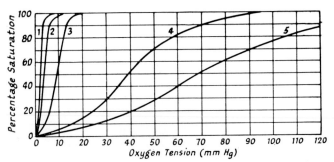

FIG. 4.22. OXYGEN DISSOCIATION CURVES FOR HAEMOCYANIN
IN BLOOD OF THE CUTTLEFISH *Sepia officinalis* AT 14°C

Curves: 1: pH 7·97, CO_2, 0·6 mm; 2: pH 7·85, CO_2, 1·95 mm; 3: pH 7·60, CO_2, 2·8 mm; 4: pH 7·35, CO_2, 9·75 mm; 5: pH 7·24, CO_2, 16·1 mm Hg. (From Wolvekamp *et al.* (127).)

rather difficult to understand. Lobster haemocyanin, like that of *Loligo*, shows fairly high affinity for O_2 in the normal physiological range (t_u *Panulirus* 6·5 mm at 15°C). About 0·5 c.c. of oxygen is delivered to the tissues by 100 c.c. of blood, and haemocyanin accounts for 80–90% of the oxygen exchange in the spiny lobster. It has been observed that the amount of haemocyanin in the blood of the spider crab changes greatly during the moulting cycle, becoming greatest in the premoult period (stage C, p. 632), and small or negligible at other times. The respiratory importance of haemocyanin is highest during the moult. The Bohr effect appears to be of slight significance in the blood of decapod crustacea (73, 100, 128).

To summarize, it appears that haemoglobins and haemerythrins occurring in the body cavities of many invertebrates serve as oxygen stores as well as in oxygen transport. These respiratory pigments have high oxygen affinities, and further oxygen transport under conditions when the ambient oxygen pressure is low. Such animals may be periodically active or be subject to irregular periods of partial anoxia by tidal ebb, etc. Then the respiratory pigment unloads its oxygen, and metabolic activity, normally

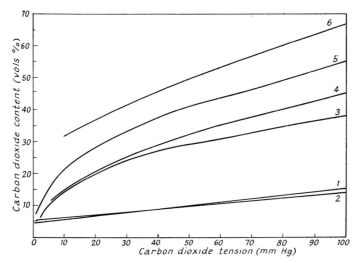

FIG. 4.23. CARBON DIOXIDE DISSOCIATION CURVES FOR SEA WATER
AND DIFFERENT BLOODS

Curves: 1: sea water; 2: *Aplysia fasciata*; 3: *Octopus macropus*; 4: *Palinurus vulgaris*; 5: *Scomber scombrus*; 6: *Phoca vitulina*. (From various sources.)

low, switches to anaerobic pathways. Myoglobins and other tissue haemoglobins function as oxygen-transfer systems, maintaining a steep oxygen gradient between the internal medium and the tissue concerned. Blood pigments in the circulatory systems of active animals (squid, mackerel, etc.) are suited to oxygen transport when the external partial pressures of oxygen are high. Such pigments characteristically have low oxygen affinity and a pronounced Bohr effect. Invertebrate haemoglobins like that of *Nephthys* become functional when levels of ambient oxygen in the environment are high. There is much interesting work showing changes in the nature of haemoglobins during ontogeny, and differences between foetal and maternal haemoglobins (e.g. in ovoviviparous spur dogs), which differences favour oxygen transport and exchange (81).

B.M.A.—7*

TRANSPORT OF CARBON DIOXIDE

Normally sea water contains about 4·8 vols% CO_2 and fluid of similar composition could serve adequately as a transport medium in many sluggish invertebrates. Sea water and body fluids in general contain a surplus of strong cations over strong anions, which combine with CO_2 to make up the alkali reserve. For such fluids carbon dioxide dissociation curves have been obtained (Fig. 4.23).

In vertebrate bloods buffering is provided by bicarbonates, phosphates,

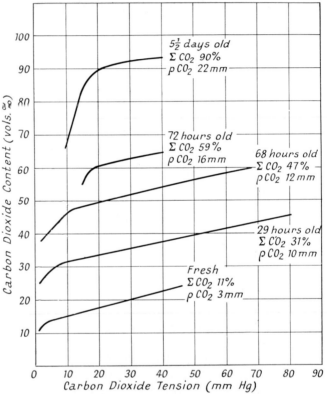

FIG. 4.24. CURVES FOR CARBON DIOXIDE COMBINING ABILITY OF MANTLE FLUID IN *Mercenaria mercenaria* AFTER VARIOUS PERIODS OF EXPOSURE TO AIR.
(From Dugal (28).)

plasma proteins and haemoglobin. Among invertebrates the phosphate content of the blood is usually low, and high buffering capacity, when present, is due to blood protein. In the coelomic fluids of *Aplysia* and *Echinus*, for example, there is little protein and buffering is slight (cf. Table 2.12, p. 64). Protein content is low in *Urechis* plasma, but haemoglobiniferous corpuscles are present and buffering is due largely to the latter. The blood of *Urechis* absorbs CO_2 by chemical combination up to about 20 mm Hg, above which the dissociation curve becomes parallel to that for H_2O and transport capacity is exhausted. In bloods containing haemocyanin most of the CO_2 is combined with this pigment, and such bloods show high buffering capacity. Haemolymphs of *Palinurus*, *Limulus* and *Sepia*, for example, contain from 10–20 vols of CO_2. Usually marine gill-bearing animals are exposed to very low CO_2 tensions (CO_2 0·23 mm Hg) and utilize the steep portion of their dissociation curves (33).

The reaction $CO_2 + H_2O \rightleftharpoons H_2CO_3$ is relatively slow and is often catalysed by an enzyme, carbonic anhydrase, found in tissues and cells. Carbonic anhydrase occurs in vertebrate erythrocytes and in many invertebrate tissues. Variable, often high, concentrations are found in gills of fishes, especially in the pseudobranch; in the gills of *Loligo*, *Limulus*, *Homarus* and *Libinia* (absent, however, in *Palinurus*); in gills of some polychaetes; and in mantle tissue of lamellibranchs and gastropods (34, 42, 79, 113).

In animals with calcareous shells and skeletons, e.g. bivalves, crustacea and starfish, the skeleton is an important source of buffer substance. During periods of anaerobiosis in lamellibranchs, when the valves are shut, the blood and mantle fluids show only a slight increase in acidity, while the CO_2 and calcium content increase greatly, along with CO_2-binding capacity (*Mercenaria*, *Mya*, *Ostrea*). In *Mercenaria mercenaria*, for example, the CO_2 content increases from 6–150 vols% in the mantle fluid of animals kept in air for 15 days (Fig. 4.24). As the result of anaerobiosis, non-volatile acid is produced, and this is buffered by calcium eroded from the shell, resulting in the accumulation of $Ca(HCO_3)_2$ and CaL_2, where the latter represents the buffering of some non-volatile acid such as lactic acid (28).

REFERENCES

1. ALLEN, D. W. and WYMAN, J., JR., "The oxygen equilibrium of hemerythrin of *Arenicola cristata*," *J. Cell. Comp. Physiol.*, **39**, 383 (1952).
2. ARUDPRAGASAM, K. D. and NAYLOR, E., "Gill ventilation in *Carcinus*," *J. Exp. Biol.*, **41**, 209, 309 (1964).
3. BERG, T. and STEEN, J. B., "Physiological mechanisms for aerial respiration in the eel," *Comp. Biochem. Physiol.*, **15**, 429 (1965).
4. BIELIG, H. J., BAYER, E., CALIFANO, L. and WIRTH, L., "Haemovanadin, ein Sulfato-Komplex des 3-wertigen Vanadiums," *Pubbl. Staz. Zool. Napoli*, **25**, 26 (1954).
5. BIELIG, H.-J., JOST, E., PFLEGER, K., RUMMEL, W. and SEIFEN, E., "Aufnahme und Verteilung von Vanadium bei der Tunicate *Phallusia*," *Hoppe-Seyler Z. physiol. Chem.*, **325**, 122 (1961).
6. BIJTEL, J. H., "The structure and the mechanism of movement of the gill-filaments in Teleostei," *Arch. Néerl. Zool.*, **8**, 267 (1949).
7. BLACK, E. C., "Respiration in fishes," *Univ. Toronto Stud. Biol.*, Ser. 59, p. 91 (1951).

8. BRAND, T. VON, *Anaerobiosis in Invertebrates* (Normandy, Missouri, Biodynamica, 1946).
9. BRETT, J. R., "Some principles in the thermal requirements of fishes," *Quart. Rev. Biol.*, **31**, 75 (1956).
10. BROHULT, S., "Hemocyanins of the gastropods," *J. Phys. Chem.*, **51**, 206 (1947).
11. BUDINGTON, R. A., "The normal spontaneity of movement of the respiratory muscles of *Thyone briareus*," *Physiol. Zool.*, **10**, 141 (1937).
12. BUDINGTON, R. A., "The ciliary transport-system of *Asterias forbesi*," *Biol. Bull.*, **83**, 438 (1942).
13. BULLOCK, T. H., "Compensation for temperature in the metabolism and activity of poikilotherms," *Biol. Rev.*, **30**, 311 (1955).
14. BURKE, J. D., "Oxygen capacity in mammals," *Physiol. Zool.*, **26**, 259 (1953).
15. CHIPMAN, W. A. and HOPKINS, J. G., "Water filtration by the bay scallop, *Pecten irradians*, as observed with the use of radioactive plankton," *Biol. Bull.*, **107**, 80 (1954).
16. CLARKE, G. L. and BONNET, D. D., "The influence of temperature on the survival, growth and respiration of *Calanus finmarchicus*," ibid., **76**, 371 (1939).
17. CLARKE, M. R., "Respiratory and swimming movements in the cephalopod *Cranchia*," *Nature*, **196**, 35 (1962).
18. CRESCITELLI, F., "A note on the absorption spectra of the blood of *Eudistylia gigantea* and of the pigment in the red corpuscles of *Cucumaria miniata* and *Molpadia intermedia*," ibid., **88**, 30 (1945).
19. CUÉNOT, L., "Échinodermes," in *Traité de Zoologie*, Ed. Grassé, P. P., Vol XI (Paris, Mason, 1948).
20. DALES, R. P., *Annelids* (London, Hutchinson Univ. Library, 1963).
21. DAM, L. VAN, *On the utilization of oxygen and regulation of breathing in some aquatic animals* (Diss.) (Groningen, Drukkerij "Volharding", 1938).
22. DAM, L. VAN, "On the mechanism of ventilation in *Aphrodite aculeata*," *J. Exp. Biol.*, **17**, 1 (1940).
23. DAM, L. VAN, "On the respiration in scallops," *Biol. Bull.*, **107**, 192 (1954).
24. DAM, L. VAN and SCHOLANDER, P. F., "Concentration of hemoglobin in the blood of deep sea fishes," *J. Cell. Comp. Physiol.*, **41**, 522 (1953).
25. DEHORNE, A., "Le problème des corpuscules du sang vasculaire de *Magelona papillicornis*," *Arch. Zool. Exp. Gén.*, **86**, 41 (1949).
26. DÉMEUSY, N., "Respiratory metabolism of the fiddler crab *Uca pugilator* from two different latitudinal populations," *Biol. Bull.*, **113**, 245 (1957).
27. DOUDOROFF, P., "The resistance and acclimatization of marine fishes to temperature changes. 2. Experiments with *Fundulus* and *Atherinops*," ibid., **88**, 194 (1945).
28. DUGAL, L.-P., "The use of calcareous shell to buffer the product of anaerobic glycolysis in *Venus mercenaria*," *J. Cell. Comp. Physiol.*, **13**, 235 (1939).
29. ELIASSEN, E., "The physiology of the vascular system of invertebrates. 1. A monograph on the blood pigments," *Univ. Bergen Årb.*, 1953, Nr. 11 (1954).
30. EWER, R. F. and FOX, H. M., "On the function of chlorocruorin," *Proc. Roy. Soc. B.*, **129**, 137 (1940).
31. EWER, R. F. and FOX, H. M., "The function of chlorocruorin," *Pubbl. Staz. Zool. Napoli*, **24**, 197 (1953).

32. FÄNGE, R. and ÅKESSON, B., "The cells of the coelomic fluid of Priapulides and their content of haemerythrin," *Ark. Zool.*, Ser. 2, **3**, 25 (1952).
33. FERGUSON, J. K. W., HORVATH, S. M. and PAPPENHEIMER, J. R., "The transport of carbon dioxide by erythrocytes and plasma in dogfish blood," *Biol. Bull.*, **75**, 381 (1938).
34. FERGUSON, J. K. W., LEWIS, L. and SMITH, J., "The distribution of carbonic anhydrase in certain marine invertebrates," *J. Cell. Comp. Physiol.*, **10**, 395 (1937).
35. FLEISCHMANN, W., "Comparative physiology of the thyroid hormone," *Quart. Rev. Biol.*, **22**, 119 (1947).
36. FLORKIN, M., *Biochemical Evolution* (New York, Academic Press, 1949).
37. FOX, D. L., *Animal Biochromes and Structural Colours* (Cambridge Univ. Press, 1953).
38. FOX, H. M., "On chlorocruorin and haemoglobin," *Proc. Roy. Soc. B.*, **136**, 378 (1949).
39. FOX, H. M., "Haemoglobin in Crustacea," *Nature*, **164**, 59 (1949).
40. FOX, H. M., "Oxygen affinities of respiratory blood pigments in *Serpula*," ibid., **168**, 112 (1951).
41. FOX, H. M., "Haemoglobin and biliverdin in parasitic cirripede crustacea," ibid., **171**, 162 (1953).
42. FREEMAN, J. A. and WILBUR, K. M., "Carbonic anhydrase in molluscs," *Biol. Bull.*, **94**, 55 (1948).
43. GAULD, D. T. and RAYMONT, J. E. G., "The respiration of some planktonic copepods," *J. Mar. Biol. Ass. U.K.*, **35**, 447 (1953).
44. GILCHRIST, B. M., "Haemoglobin in *Artemia*," *Proc. Roy. Soc. B.*, **143**, 136 (1954).
45. GRAINGER, F. and NEWELL, G. E., "Aerial respiration in *Balanus*," *J. Mar. Biol. Ass.*, *U.K.*, **45**, 469 (1965).
46. GRANICK, S. and GILDER, H., "Distribution, structure, and properties of the tetrapyrroles," *Advanc. Enzymol.*, **7**, 305 (1947).
47. GRAY, I. E., "Comparative study of the gill area of marine fishes," *Biol. Bull.*, **107**, 219 (1954).
48. GUIEYSSE-PELLISSIER, A., *Les Appareils Respiratoires dans la Série Animale* (Paris, Payot, 1945).
49. GUNTHER, E. R., "The habits of fin whales," *'Discovery' Rep.*, **25**, 113 (1949).
50. HALL, F. G. and MCCUTCHEON, F. H., "The affinity of hemoglobin for oxygen in marine fishes," *J. Cell. Comp. Physiol.*, **11**, 205 (1938).
51. HALL, V. E., "The muscular activity and oxygen consumption of *Urechis caupo*," *Biol. Bull.*, **61**, 400 (1931).
52. HARKER, J. E., "Diurnal rhythms in the animal kingdom," *Biol. Rev.*, **33**, 1 (1958).
53. HETZEL, H. R., "Studies on holothurian coelomocytes," *Biol. Bull.*, **125**, 289 (1963).
54. HOAR, W. S., KEENLEYSIDE, M. H. A. and GOODALL, R. G., "The effects of thyroxine and gonadal steroids on the activity of salmon and goldfish," *Canad. J. Zool.*, **33**, 428 (1955).
55. HOPKINS, H. S., "The influence of season, concentration of sea water and environmental temperature upon the oxygen consumption of tissues in *Venus mercenaria*," *J. Exp. Zool.*, **102**, 143 (1946).

56. HORN, E. C. and KERR, M. S., "Hemolymph protein and copper concentrations of blue crabs," *Biol. Bull.*, **125**, 499 (1963).
57. HOYLE, G., "Spontaneous squirting of an ascidian, *Phallusia mammillata*," *J. Mar. Biol. Ass. U.K.*, **31**, 541 (1953).
58. HUGHES, G. M. and SHELTON, G., "Respiratory mechanisms and their nervous control in fish," *Adv. Comp. Physiol. Biochem.*, **1**, 275 (1962).
59. IRVING, L., SCHOLANDER, P. F. and GRINNELL, S. W., "The respiration of the porpoise, *Tursiops truncatus*," *J. Cell. Comp. Physiol.*, **17**, 145 (1941).
60. IRVING, L., SCHOLANDER, P. F. and GRINNELL, S. W., "Significance of the heart rate to the diving ability of seals," ibid., **18**, 283 (1941).
61. IRVING, L., SOLANDT, O. M., SOLANDT, D. Y. and FISHER, K. C., "Respiratory characteristics of the blood of the seal," ibid., **6**, 393 (1935).
62. JACOBS, M. H., "Diffusion processes," *Ergebn. Biol.*, **12**, 1 (1935).
63. JØRGENSEN, C. B., "Feeding-rates of sponges, lamellibranchs and ascidians", *Nature*, **163**, 912 (1949).
64. JØRGENSEN, C. B., "The rate of feeding by *Mytilus* in different kinds of suspensions," *J. Mar. Biol. Ass. U.K.*, **28**, 333 (1949).
65. JØRGENSEN, C. B., "On the relation between water transport and food requirements in some marine filter-feeding invertebrates," *Biol. Bull.*, **103**, 356 (1952).
66. JOHANSEN, K. and STRAHAN, R., "The respiratory system of *Myxine*," *The Biology of Myxine*, Ed. Brodal, A. and Fänge, R., 352 (Oslo, Universitetsforlaget, 1963).
67. KEILIN, D. and HARTREE, E. F., "Relationship between haemoglobin and erythrocruorin," *Nature*, **168**, 266 (1951).
68. KISCH, B., "Observations on the haematology of fishes and birds," *Exp. Med. Surg.*, **7**, 318 (1949).
69. KNOWLES, SIR FRANCIS G. W., Bt. and CARLISLE, D. B., "Endocrine control in the Crustacea," *Biol. Rev.*, **31**, 396 (1956).
70. KORSHUIEV, P. and BULATOVA, N., "Physiological peculiarities of erythrocytes of cartilaginous fishes," *Dokl. Akad. Nauk S.S.S.R.*, N.S., **70**, 149 (1950).
71. KORSHUIEV, P. A. and NIKOLSKAYA, J. S., "The blood-volume of some marine and fresh water fishes," ibid., **80**, 989 (1951).
72. KRAHL, M. E., "Metabolic activities and cleavage of eggs of the sea urchin, *Arbacia punctulata*," *Biol. Bull.*, **98**, 175 (1950).
73. KROGH, A., *The Comparative Physiology of Respiratory Mechanisms* (Phil., Univ. Penn. Press, 1941).
74. LANE, C. E., TIERNEY, J. Q. and HENNACY, R. E., "The respiration of normal larvae of *Teredo bartschi* Clapp.," *Biol. Bull.*, **106**, 323 (1954).
75. LARIMER, J. L. "Measurement of ventilation volume in decapod crustacea," *Physiol. Zool.*, **34**, 158 (1961).
76. LINDROTH, A., "Die biologische Bedeutung des 'Hämoglobins' (Erythrocruorins) der Wirbellosen," *Ergebn. Biol.*, **19**, 324 (1943).
77. McCUTCHEON, F. H., "Specific oxygen affinity of hemoglobin in elasmobranchs and turtles," *J. Cell. Comp. Physiol.*, **29**, 333 (1947).
78. MACGINITIE, G. E. and MACGINITIE, N., *Natural History of Marine Animals* (London, McGraw-Hill, 1949).
79. MAETZ, J., "L'anhydrase carbonique dans deux Téléostéens voisins. Comparaison des activités anhydrasiques chez *Perca* et *Serranus*," *C.R. Soc. Biol.*, *Paris*, **147**, 204 (1953).

80. Mangum, C. P., "Activity patterns in metabolism and ecology of polychaetes," *Comp. Biochem. Physiol.*, **11**, 239 (1964).

81. Manwell, C., "Blood pigments," *Ann. Rev. Physiol.*, **22**, 191 (1960).

82. Marlier, G., "Considérations sur les organes accessoires servant à la respiration aérienne chez les Téléostéens," *Ann. Soc. Zool. Belg.*, **69**, 163 (1938).

83. Marshall, S. M., Nicholls, A. G. and Orr, A. P., "On the biology of *Calanus finmarchicus*," 6. Oxygen consumption in relation to environmental conditions," *J. Mar. Biol. Ass. U.K.*, **20**, 1 (1935).

84. Martin, A. W., "Some remarks on the blood volume of fish," in *Studies honoring Trevor Kincaid*, Ed. Hatch, M. H. (Seattle, Univ. Wash. Press, 1950).

85. Matty, A. J., "Thyroidectomy of the dogfish, *Scyllium canicula* (L.), and the effect of dogfish thyroid upon the oxygen consumption of rats," *J. Mar. Biol. Ass. U.K.*, **33**, 689 (1954).

86. Mendes, E. G., "On the respiratory function of chlorocruorin," *Pubbl. Staz. Zool. Napoli*, **22**, 348 (1950).

87. Mori, S., "Daily rhythmic activity of the sea pen, *Cavernularia obesa*," *Physiol. Ecol. Kyoto*, **4**, 12 (1950).

88. Mori, S. and Matutani, K., "Studies on the daily rhythmic activity of the starfish, *Astropecten polyacanthus*, and the accompanied physiological rhythms," *Publ. Seto Mar. Biol. Lab.*, **2**, 213 (1952).

89. Newell, R. C. and Courtney, W. A. M., "Respiratory movements in *Holothuria*," *J. Exp. Biol.*, **42**, 45 (1965).

90. Norman, J. R. and Fraser, F. C., *Giant Fishes, Whales and Dolphins* (London, Putnam, 1948).

91. Olthof, H. J., *Die vergleichende Physiologie der Notatmung und verwandter Erscheinungen* (Dissertation) (Groningen, J. B. Wolters, 1941).

92. Pearse, A. S., *The Emigration of Animals from the Sea* (Dryden, N.Y., Sherwood Press, 1950).

93. Penseneer, P., "Sur le degré d'eurythermie de certaines larves marines," *Bull. Sci. Acad. Belg.*, p. 279 (1901).

94. Pérez, C. and Bloch-Raphaël, C., "Note préliminaire sur la présence d'un pigment respiratoire chez le *Septosaccus Cuénoti*," *C.R. Acad. Sci., Paris*, **223**, 840 (1946).

95. Phear, E. A., "Gut haems in the invertebrates," *Proc. Zool. Soc.*, **125** (2), 383 (1955).

96. Peiss, C. N. and Field, J., "The respiratory metabolism of excised tissues of warm- and cold-adapted fishes," *Biol. Bull.*, **99**, 213 (1950).

97. Pritchard, A. W. and Gorbman, A., "Thyroid hormone and oxygen consumption in embryos of the spiny dogfish," *Biol. Bull.*, **119**, 109 (1960).

98. Raymont, J. E. G. and Gauld, D. T., "The respiration of some planktonic copepods," *J. Mar. Biol. Ass. U.K.*, **29**, 681 (1951).

99. Read, K. R. H., "Respiration of the bivalved molluscs *Mytilus* and *Brachidontus*," *Comp. Biochem. Physiol.*, **7**, 89 (1962).

100. Redmond, J. R., "The respiratory characteristics of Chiton hemocyanins," *Physiol. Zool.*, **35**, 304 (1962).

101. Riggs, A., "The oxygen equilibrium of the hemoglobin of the eel, *Anguilla rostrata*," *J. Gen. Physiol.*, **35**, 41 (1951).

102. ROBBIE, W. A., "Respiration of the tissues of some invertebrates and its inhibition by cyanide," ibid., **32**, 655 (1949).

103. ROOT, R. W., IRVING, L. and BLACK, E. C., "The effect of hemolysis upon the combination of oxygen with the blood of some marine fishes," ibid. **13**, 303 (1939).

104. RUUD, J. T., "Vertebrates without erythrocytes and blood pigment," *Nature*, **173**, 848 (1954).

105. SANDEEN, M. I., STEPHENS, G. C. and BROWN, F. A., JR., "Persistent daily and tidal rhythms of oxygen consumption in two species of marine snails," *Physiol. Zool.*, **27**, 350 (1954).

106. SCHOLANDER, P. F., "Experimental investigations on the respiratory function in diving mammals and birds," *Hvalråd. Skr.*, No. 22 (1940).

107. SCHOLANDER, P. F., "Physiological adaptation to diving in animals and man," *Harvey Lectures*, **57**, 93 (1962).

108. SCHOLANDER, P. F., CLAFF, C. L., SVEINSSON, S. L. and SCHOLANDER, S. I., "Respiratory studies of single cells. 3. Oxygen consumption during cell division," *Biol. Bull.*, **102**, 185 (1952).

109. SCHOLANDER, P. F. and VAN DAM, L., "The concentration of hemoglobin in some cold-water arctic fishes," *J. Cell. Comp. Physiol.*, **49**, 1 (1957).

110. SCHOLANDER, P. F., FLAGG, W., WALTERS, V. and IRVING, L., "Climatic adaptation in arctic and tropical poikilotherms," *Physiol. Zool.*, **26**, 67 (1953).

111. SCHOLANDER, P. F., IRVING, L. and GRINNELL, S. W., "Aerobic and anaerobic changes in seal muscles during diving," *J. Biol. Chem.*, **142**, 431 (1942).

112. SMITH, A. H. and KLEIBER, M., "Size and oxygen consumption in fertilized eggs," *J. Cell. Comp. Physiol.*, **35**, 131 (1950).

113. SOBOTKA, H. and KANN, S., "Carbonic anhydrase in fishes and invertebrates," *J. Cell. Comp. Physiol.*, **17**, 341 (1941).

114. SOUTHWARD, A. J. and CRISP, D. J., "Activity rhythm of barnacles in relation to respiration and feeding," *J. Mar. Biol. Ass. U.K.*, **45**, 161 (1965).

115. SOUTHWARD, E. C., "Pogonophora," *Oceanogr. Mar. Biol. Ann.-Rev.*, **1**, 405 (1963).

116. SPILLMANN, J., "Première apparition d'hémoglobine dans le noyau des cellules sanguines primitives de *Discoglossus pictus*," *C.R. Soc. Biol., Paris*, **131**, 607 (1939).

117. STEPHENSON, T. A., ZOOND, A. and EYRE, J., "The liberation and utilisation of oxygen by the population of rock-pools," *J. Exp. Biol.*, **11**, 162 (1934).

118. THOMAS, H. J., "The oxygen uptake of the lobster (*Homarus vulgaris*)," ibid., **31**, 228 (1954).

119. VALENTE, D., "Mecanismo da respiração de *Trichodactylus petropolitanus*," *Zoologia, S. Paulo*, No. 13, 259 (1948).

120. VERNBERG, F. J. and GRAY, I.E., "A comparative study of the respiratory metabolism of excised brain tissue of marine teleosts," *Biol. Bull.*, **104**, 445 (1953).

121. WALD, G. and RIGGS, A., "The hemoglobin of the sea lamprey, *Petromyzon marinus*," *J. Gen. Physiol.*, **35**, 45 (1951).

122. WALSHE-MAETZ, B. M., "Environment and respiratory control in certain crustacea," *Nature*, **169**, 750 (1952).

123. WATERMAN, T. H. and TRAVIS, D. F., "Respiratory reflexes and the flabellum of *Limulus*," *J. Cell. Comp. Physiol.*, **41**, 261 (1953).
124. WILLEM, V. and BOELAERT, R., "Les manoeuvres respiratoires de 'Periophthalmus,' " *Bull. Sci. Acad. Roy. Belg.*, 5 Sér., **23**, 942 (1937).
125. WILLEMSEN, J., "Quantities of water pumped by mussels (*Mytilus edulis*) and cockles (*Cardium edule*)," *Arch. Néerl. Zool.*, **10**, 153 (1952).
126. WITHERBY, H. F., JOURDAIN, F. C. R., TICEHURST, N. F. and TUCKER, B. W., *The Handbook of British Birds*, Vol. 5 (London, Witherby, 1944).
127. WOLVEKAMP, H. P., BAERENDS, G. P., KOK, B. and MOMMAERTS W. F. H. M., "O_2- and CO_2- binding properties of the blood of the cuttlefish (*Sepia officinalis*) and the common squid (*Loligo vulgaris*)," *Arch. Néerl. Physiol.*, **26**, 203 (1942).
128. WOLVEKAMP, H. P. and WATERMAN, T. H., "Respiration," in *The Physiology of Crustacea*, Ed. Waterman, T. H., Vol. 1, p. 35 (New York and London, Academic Press, 1960).
129. ZEUTHEN, E., "Body size and metabolic rate in the animal kingdom with special regard to the marine micro-fauna," *C.R. Lab. Carlsberg, Sér. Chim.*, **26**, 17 (1947).
130. ZEUTHEN, E., "Respiration and cell-division in eggs of the sea urchin, *Psammechinus miliaris*," *Nature*, **160**, 577 (1947).
131. ZEUTHEN, E., "Oxygen consumption during mitosis; experiments on fertilized eggs of marine animals," *Amer. Nat.*, **83**, 303 (1949).
132. ZEUTHEN, E., "Segmentation, nuclear growth and cytoplasmic storage in eggs of echinoderms and amphibia," *Pubbl. Staz. Zool. Napoli*, **23** (Suppl.), 47 (1951).
133. ZEUTHEN, E., "Oxygen uptake as related to body size in organisms," *Quart. Rev. Biol.*, **28**, 1 (1953).

CHAPTER 5

NUTRITION AND FEEDING MECHANISMS

For they shall suck of the abundance of the seas, and of treasures hid in the sand.

Deuteronomy

INTRODUCTION

THE food of all animals in the sea is ultimately derived from marine plants which synthesize carbohydrates, fats, proteins and other compounds such as some vitamins. Plant cells are eaten by animals, or their dead bodies provide a source of dissolved organic material which is utilized by bacteria. Seaweeds become broken down into detritus, which provides food for many shallow-water animals. Bacteria break down waste and dissolved organic matter into forms which can be utilized as food by marine animals, and bacteria are themselves consumed by many animals (125).

The background conditions of nutrition in the sea have been subjected to intensive study during the present century. These investigations have been concerned with the spatial distribution of phyto- and zooplankton, and with variations in abundance, both long-term and seasonal, of planktonic organisms. No less important has been the study of physical conditions—namely temperature, light and nutrient salts—which affect the growth of floating plants and, indirectly, the animals dependent upon them. A knowledge of these interrelated conditions is a necessary prerequisite for a fuller understanding of factors regulating the abundance of marine organisms, the annual turnover of organic matter and the limits of economic exploitation of marine resources. For an extended treatment of this subject, the reader is referred to Harvey (51, 52).

Flagellates, including both green and colourless species, contain various forms that bridge the gap between phototrophic and heterotrophic organisms. Certain flagellates are strictly autotrophic and can subsist on inorganic sources of nitrogen and carbon; others require one or more organic substances which they take from solution. Apart from these flagellates all animals are dependent upon a source of preformed carbohydrates, fats, proteins and certain other essential substances, i.e. they are holozoic (97).

The zooplankton is largely responsible for harvesting the phytoplankton crop in the sea, and in turn provides food for other organisms. Herbivores predominate in the zooplankton and are generally of small size. Chief among them are copepods, especially nauplii and juvenile stages. In the southern oceans the large krill, *Euphausia superba*, sometimes occurs in immense numbers, to the exclusion of all other planktonic

198

animals, and smaller swarms of *Nyctiphanes* are sometimes encountered in the North Atlantic. Along with the permanent plankton occurs a small and variable proportion of larvae of bottom-dwelling forms, especially in shallow waters. Many of the medium-sized planktonic animals are omnivores; the remainder, forming a small proportion of the community, are carnivores. These are generally of fairly large size, e.g. medusae, ctenophores, arrow worms, *Tomopteris*, etc. Adding their depredations to the latter are pelagic fish and various bottom-feeding organisms, particularly in shallow water. At the top of the food chain are carnivorous fish, cephalopods, etc., which feed on the larger benthic and pelagic animals (47).

The population density of zooplankton organisms in a unit volume of sea water provides a measure of their availability as food for other organisms. The average quantity of zooplankton existing below a large unit area of sea is maintained by the phytoplankton in the water below that unit area. The average quantity of organic matter below a unit area of sea surface provides a measure of the amount of food available for pelagic animals in different regions and at different times. Sampling the bottom biomass also reveals the quantity of food available for demersal animals.

This chapter deals almost entirely with the ingestion of insoluble organic material. The student's attention is directed, however, to Pütter's claim that many marine animals obtain a substantial proportion of their dietary requirements by the uptake of dissolved organic substances. Pütter's hypothesis has taken an unconscionably long time in dying (24, 25). Tracer methods have permitted a fresh approach to the problem and it has been found that corals, polychaetes and bivalves can absorb labelled glucose and amino acids across the body wall in quantities that may possibly supplement normal feeding on particulate matter (100).

FEEDING MECHANISMS

Marine animals display most diverse adaptations and specializations for obtaining food; in general, their feeding mechanisms are related to their nutritive habits. Autotrophic, saprozoic and some parasitic animals lack special feeding mechanisms and absorb dissolved substances directly from the medium. In holozoic animals it is possible to recognize definite types of feeding mechanisms determined by common features of the environment and the kinds of food available. Yonge's classification (116) for invertebrates selects three main categories of feeding mechanisms—

1. Mechanisms for dealing with small particles.
2. Mechanisms for dealing with larger particles or masses.
3. Mechanisms for taking in fluid or soft tissues.

Each of these categories includes a variety of different devices for dealing with particular kinds of foodstuffs. Many animals make use of a variety of feeding mechanisms, conjointly, or separately as occasion demands (123).

METHODS OF UTILIZING SMALL PARTICLES

Minute particles, including fine detritus, bacteria and plankton, form the sole nutriment of a great many invertebrates and protochordates. Mechanisms for collecting fine particulate matter are classified as pseudopodial, ciliary, tentacular, mucoid and setous. The filtering apparatus is usually made more efficient by the secretion of mucus or other viscid matter. Selection of particles is usually quantitative, and there is seldom any mastication of the food. Jørgensen (60) has reviewed certain aspects of filter feeding among invertebrates.

Pseudopodial Mechanisms

Feeding by the use of pseudopodial processes is characteristic of rhizopods. In amoebae food is captured by pseudopodia which extend around the food particle and engulf it, together with a certain amount of water. The pseudopodia of foraminifers (Polythalamia) are long-branching and anastomosing filaments. The protoplasm in each filament shows active streaming movements, one stream being directed centrifugally, the other centripetally, and the actual length of a pseudopod is determined by the relative magnitude of the two currents. Food particles encountering the pseudopods adhere to their sticky surfaces, and are either carried directly towards the body with the return stream, or out to the tip and thence back to the body where they are ingested. Feeding is similar in radiolarians, which also entrap food particles on sticky pseudopodia and carry them into the body by protoplasmic streaming movements (Fig. 14.17, p. 605).

Feeding in these groups is largely a passive affair, and depends on chance encounters with food particles. Radiolarians are predominantly floating forms which feed upon fine planktonic materials. The Foraminifera include both pelagic and benthic forms which feed upon fine plankton. *Astrorhiza*, a sublittoral foraminiferan, has sticky pseudopodia to which unfortunate animals adhere; these are subjected to extracellular contact digestion (17).

Among colourless flagellates, some are saprophytic, others holozoic in feeding habits. Holozoic species are frequently amoeboid in habit, and ingest their prey by means of pseudopodia. More specialized is the feeding of *Noctiluca*, which catches small planktonic organisms on a sticky filament. The food particles are aggregated into balls or strands, and conveyed to the cytostome where they are ingested (43, 54).

Ciliary Mechanisms

Ciliary methods of feeding are widespread, especially in sedentary species, and are encountered in various guises in many phyla. Cilia and flagella which primitively possessed a locomotory function, have in these forms become concerned with food-getting. Their activity sets up water currents which carry food particles to the animal, and they are furthermore arranged in definite tracts by which captured material is sorted and transported either towards the mouth, if suitable, or to the region where ejection takes place. Frequently, a viscid mucous sheet is secreted for trapping the particles. Many ciliary feeders appear to exercise mechanical rather than chemical selection of food particles, selecting or rejecting on the basis of particle-size.

Protozoa. In ciliates (Infusoria) the cilia are frequently organized in complex patterns. Some are mouthless endoparasites (Astomata), inhabiting the gut of invertebrates; some of the holotrichs are raptorial. Many species, however, produce a feeding current by means of complex ciliary apparatuses in the cytopharynx, which is a funnel extending into the endoplasm. Food particles which gather in the bottom of the pharynx become incorporated in food vacuoles and are engulfed by the endoplasm.

In particle feeders the cytopharynx is approached by a spiral groove, the peristome, which leads from the anterior end to the pharyngeal opening or cytostome. The peristome, like the pharynx, is ciliated. The ciliary pattern is fairly simple in holotrichs (*Paramecium, Colpoda*); but in higher forms the cilia on the outer edge of the peristome are fused so as to form a row of cirri or membranelles, the adoral wreath, which produces a powerful current. A few characteristic marine forms from different orders may be mentioned. Bottle animalcules *Folliculina* (Heterotricha) have the peristomial area enlarged into paired wing-like extensions. In planktonic tintinnids (Oligotricha) the peristome bearing the adoral wreath and mouth opening occupies the anterior end of the body. In sessile peritrichs such as *Vorticella* the peristome forms a disc at the anterior end. The peristome bears a spiral groove, which is provided with cilia in the form of an undulating membrane and which descends to the vestibule (chamber leading into the cytopharynx in these forms).

Free-living ciliates ingest bacteria, algal cells, diatoms and other protozoa, and probably a certain amount of detrital matter. Littoral sand-dwelling holotrichs appear to derive nourishment from diatoms. In peritrichs the formation and course of food vacuoles have been described in some detail. Food vacuoles, containing bacteria, are constricted off from an oesophageal sac at the bottom of the cytopharynx. This vacuole then passes rapidly on a fixed course through the cytoplasm, while its contents are undergoing digestion, and returns to an anal spot on the wall of the vestibule for discharge (80).

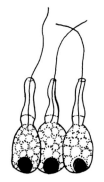

FIG. 5.1. COLLAR CELLS OF A SPONGE, *Leucosolenia coriacea*. (From Minchin, 1909.)

Porifera. Among sponges the feeding water current is created by the lashing of flagella on collar cells or choanocytes which line internal cavities (Figs. 5.1, 5.2). The surface of the sponge is perforated by dermal pores like a sieve, and water drawn through these openings flows past the collar cells. The choanocytes beat in an independent and unco-ordinated manner, and as the water currents sweep past the cell bodies, food particles are caught and ingested in an area near the base of the collar.

The simplest type of sponge structure, the ascanoid type, is realized in Olynthus, a fleeting stage in the development of calcareous sponges. It is

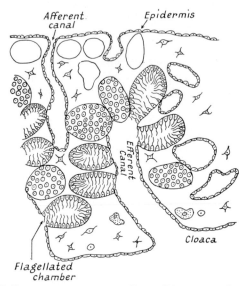

FIG. 5.2. SECTION THROUGH THE BODY WALL OF A CALCAREOUS SPONGE *Leuconia aspera*. (From Vosmaer, 1880.)

a hollow vase-shaped structure in which the internal paragastral cavity is lined with choanocytes. The pores in the body wall are surrounded by porocytes, capable of constriction; the osculum or terminal exhalant opening of the body cavity can also be closed by the action of myocytes. The ascanoid type is found modified to some extent in the calcareous sponges *Clathrina* and *Leucosolenia*, which are colonies made up of branch-

Structure	Estimated number	Aggregate area (cm²)	Velocity (cm/sec)
Afferent canals	81,000	4·2	0·1
Surface of choanocytes	—	200	0·001
Flagellated chambers	2,250,000	52	0·01
Efferent canals	5,200	2·5	0·2
Paragaster	1	0·21	2
Osculum	1	0·03 (diameter 0·20 cm)	8·5

ing ascon tubes. In the syconoid type, found in *Sycon* and *Grantia* (Calcarea), the choanocytes lie in elongated radial canals lying at right angles to the internal surface. Water currents enter incurrent canals via ostia, pass through prosopyles (pores) into the flagellated chambers and from thence into the central cavity or paragaster, which opens to the exterior through an osculum. Most sponges show a leuconoid type of structure in which the choanocytes are restricted to small chambers which communicate with the paragaster by exhalant canals.

The hydraulics of this system have been investigated in *Leuconia*, a calcareous sponge of leuconoid type, from which the measurements on p. 202 were obtained. The total pressure involved in this flow varied from 1 to 3 mm of water.

It appears from these calculations that the maximal surface area and slowest rate of flow are found in the flagellated chambers, especially at the surface of the choanocytes, and this will permit maximal opportunity for capturing food particles. The greatest velocity, on the other hand, is reached at the osculum, from which a jet of water is thrown upwards away from the sponge. Waste materials, released by the sponge, are carried upwards in this jet and then enter a slow circular eddy returning to the sponge. The farther the exhalant current goes, the greater will be the opportunity for waste materials to be dissipated and for water entering the sponge to be renewed by diffusion, or water currents. The size of the osculum determines the pumping rate and the velocity with which the water is expelled. These are conflicting demands which counterbalance each other, and for any particular sponge there is found to be an optimal oscular diameter, which is proportional to the square root of volume of the sponge. The leuconoid type of structure confers certain advantages, which become most apparent in sponges of large size and those living in quiet water. The increase in number of choanocytes brought about by folding of the walls of the sponge results in greater current flow, and frictional resistance is minimized by the smooth surface and absence of choanocytes in afferent and efferent channels. Pumping rates in sponges and other ciliary feeders are summarized in Table 4.5 (p. 167) (14, 97).

Coelenterates. The coelenteron in these animals is usually ciliated, and in certain forms cilia are also employed in transporting food to the mouth. In anemones the cilia may be widespread over the ectoderm (*Protanthea*) or limited to disc, tentacles and stomodaeum (*Metridium*). These ciliated areas transport food particles to the stomach. Likewise in many corals the general ectoderm participates in the capture of food, and ciliary tracts transport particles to the mouth. Normally the cilia on the disc beat outwards, but in the presence of nutritive substances the direction of ciliary beat is reversed and the mucus is drawn inwards. In the scyphomedusa *Aurelia* we also find that cilia on the bell and ventral surface of the arms are concerned with transporting food particles to the mouth (98).

Polychaetes. The tubicolous polychaetes for the most part are plankton or detritus feeders and make use of ciliary mechanisms for obtaining food.

Detritus feeders such as terebellids, cirratulids and ampharetids are provided with long mobile tentacles which extend over the surface of the substratum. Food particles (detritus, small organisms) are picked up from the surface and transported along a ciliated groove in each tentacle towards the mouth (Fig. 4.2, p. 139). Small particles are moved by cilia, larger ones by muscular action (terebellids). Other forms, such as *Sternaspis* and *Pectinaria*, collect detritus beneath the surface (28).

Filter-feeding is carried out by a variety of ciliary mechanisms in chaetopterids, sabellariids, sabellids and serpulids. In *Chaetopterus* water is propelled through the U-shaped tube by rhythmical beating of parapodial

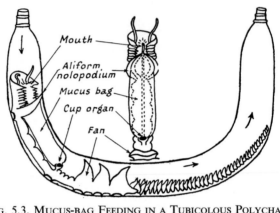

Mouth

Aliform
notopodium

Mucus bag

Cup organ

Fan

FIG. 5.3. MUCUS-BAG FEEDING IN A TUBICOLOUS POLYCHAETE
Chaetopterus variopedatus. (From MacGinitie, 1939.)

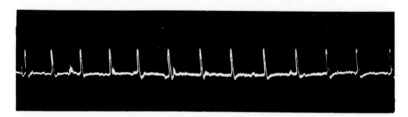

FIG. 5.4. EXTRACT FROM AN IRRIGATION RECORD OF
Chaetopterus variopedatus (DURATION 4 HOURS)

The worm was carrying out mucus-bag feeding and pumping steadily, except for brief pauses at the peaks when the lever returns to null position. The frequency is about 1 fan stroke per sec, too fast for individual strokes to be distinguished on this record. At the pauses, which occur every 18 min, a mucus-bag is passed forwards to the mouth and swallowed. (From Wells and Dales (1951).)

fans (Figs. 5.3, 5.4). Copious quantities of mucus secreted by the aliform notopodia entangle food particles suspended in the water current. Strings of mucus, bearing food material, are carried in ciliated grooves on the aliform notopodia to a median ciliated groove on the dorsal body surface, and thence to the buccal funnel. MacGinitie has also described an alternative mode of feeding by formation of a mucus-bag. This is produced by the aliform notopodia and extends posteriorly to a dorsal cup organ where it is rolled up. All the water which flows through the burrow must traverse this net, which filters out suspended food matter. At intervals the front margin is detached and the net is transported anteriorly to the mouth by reversal of ciliary beat in the dorsal groove. The mucus-bag forms a very efficient straining apparatus, and by feeding proteins of different particle sizes it has been calculated that the mesh openings are about 40 Å in diameter (71, 73).

In cryptocephalous polychaetes exemplified by *Sabella*, feeding is carried out by a branchial crown consisting of a circlet of tentacles (Figs. 4.2, 15.9). These bear lateral pinnules which are ciliated and form a filtering

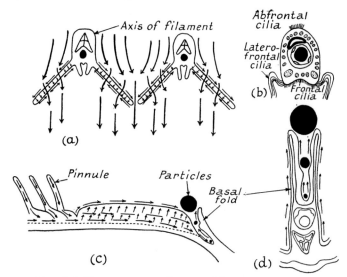

FIG. 5.5. FILTERING AND SORTING MECHANISMS IN THE
BRANCHIAL CROWN OF *Sabella pavonina*

(*a*) Section through two gill filaments, showing direction of flow of water across the filament, and direction of beat of the cilia which produce the current; (*b*) transverse section through a pinnule to show ciliation (× 250); (*c*) lateral lip and base of gill filament, showing ciliated tracts and sizes of particles passing along the basal folds; (*d*) section through basal folds, showing sorting of particles. (From E. A. T. Nicol (1930).)

apparatus. Water is drawn into the branchial funnel by abfrontal cilia on the pinnules and is directed between the latter by latero-frontal cilia (Fig. 5.5). Suspended particles are thrown by the latero-frontal cilia into a ciliated groove running along the inner face of each pinnule, whence they are transported by frontal cilia to the base of the pinnule where there are ciliary tracts running along the filament towards the base of the crown. Here there is a ciliary mechanism in the basal folds by which particles are sorted into three classes on the basis of size: the largest particles are carried to the palps and rejected; medium-sized particles are carried to ventral sacs below the mouth, and are stored there for use in tube formation (p. 647); the finest are carried to the mouth and ingested

Sabellids and serpulids depend on finely divided suspended detritus for food. Some data for filtering rates are listed in Table 4.5 (28).

Echinodermata. Some asteroids such as *Porania, Astropecten* and sand dollars make use of ciliary feeding currents; the exact details of the food-collecting mechanism vary from species to species (40). Ciliary mechanisms are universal in crinoids, in which the ambulacral grooves possess mucous glands and cilia and carry food particles (plankton and detritus) to the mouth. Ophiuroids show great flexibility in feeding, employing both microphagous and macrophagous methods. *Ophiocomina* sometimes employs a mucus-net method of suspension-feeding. Fine material becomes trapped in strands of mucus spread between the spines of the arms, and is transferred to the mouth by the tube feet (34).

Polyzoa and Phoronidea. Polyzoans capture plankton and fine detritus by means of a lophophore or ring of ciliated tentacles surrounding the mouth (Fig. 5.6). In ectoprocts such as *Flustrella* the extended tentacles form a funnel with the mouth at the base. A water current is produced by the beating of lateral cilia on the tentacles, and proceeds straight down the lophophore and outwards between the tentacles. Suspended food particles arriving at the bottom of the funnel are sucked in by the muscular pharynx, which is also provided with inward-beating cilia.

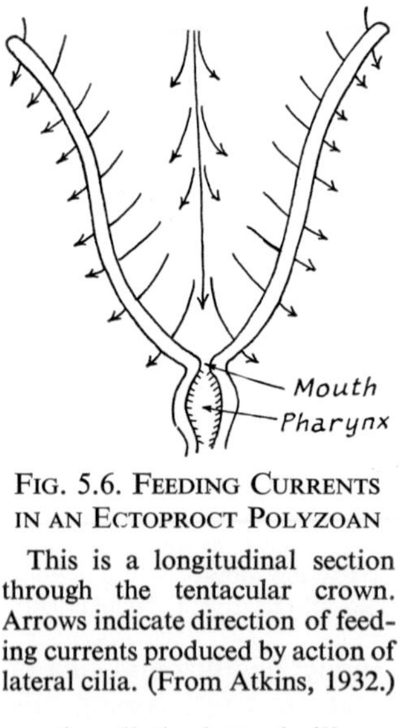

FIG. 5.6. FEEDING CURRENTS IN AN ECTOPROCT POLYZOAN

This is a longitudinal section through the tentacular crown. Arrows indicate direction of feeding currents produced by action of lateral cilia. (From Atkins, 1932.)

In endoprocts a rather different ciliary mechanism prevails (Fig. 5.7). Water is drawn into the tentacular funnel, again by the action of long lateral cilia on the tentacles, but the current proceeds from the outside between the tentacles and upwards away from the animal. Suspended particles in the water passing between the tentacles are thrown by the lateral cilia on to the inner surface whence they are carried by short frontal cilia towards the base. Here they reach a ciliated vestibular groove which leads to the mouth. The lateral cilia, both in ectoprocts and endoprocts, beat intermittently. In *Loxosomella*, for example, all the lateral cilia may suddenly become motionless, and activity is subsequently resumed in a somewhat irregular manner. It may be that the lateral cilia are subject to nervous regulation (5).

The lophophore of *Phoronis* is similarly employed in feeding. The cilia on the two sides of the tentacles beat in opposite directions, towards and away from the mouth. An inhalant current passes downwards between the two circles of tentacles forming the lophophore and outwards between the tentacles. Particles are carried by tentacular cilia towards the mouth and, if not ingested, they are borne outwards by distally-beating cilia to the tips of the tentacles, where they drop off. Phoronids feed on fine plankton and detritus.

Brachiopods. These animals are provided with an internal ciliated lophophore, bearing fringes of filaments, which forms a complicated filtering apparatus. In *Crania*, the lophophore divides the mantle cavity into a lower inhalant and an upper exhalant chamber (Fig. 5.8). An inhalant current enters on either side and is drawn upward through gaps between the filaments into the exhalant chamber. Currents are created by lateral cilia on the lophophore filaments; heavy particles drop down on the lower mantle surface and are rejected by ciliary action, whereas the finer particles become entangled in mucus on the filaments. These trapped food

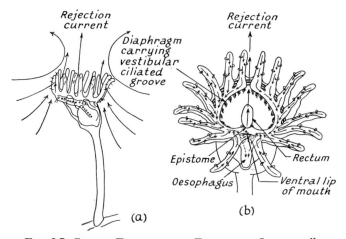

FIG. 5.7. CILIARY FEEDING IN AN ENDOPROCT *Loxosomella*

(*a*) Lateral view of animal, showing direction of feeding currents; (*b*) ciliary currents, and direction of beat of lateral cilia on tentacles (tiny arrows) (from Atkins, 1932.)

particles are carried by frontal cilia to a buccal groove at the base of the filaments, and are thence conveyed by a strong ciliary current to the mouth. From the exhalant chamber the water emerges through three apertures. Feeding mechanisms of other brachiopods are described by Atkins (7).

Molluscs. Ciliary feeding devices are highly developed in lamellibranchs and certain gastropods, in which they have independently evolved. They have been intensively studied, especially in lamellibranchs, and for detailed accounts the reader is referred to papers by Orton, Yonge and Atkins (*see* 123).

Ciliary feeding in prosobranch gastropods has developed independently in at least six families. Of these the Calyptraeidae (*Calyptraea* and *Crepidula*) are the most specialized, and feed by sifting out diatoms and other fine plankton material by means of a modified ctenidium. In the sedentary slipper-limpet *Crepidula fornicata*, the mantle cavity is divided into two lateral chambers, one ventro-lateral, the other dorso-lateral, by a

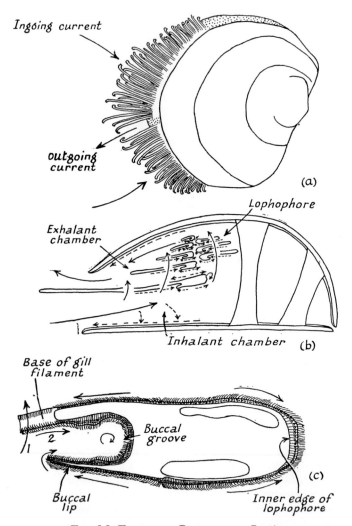

Ingoing current

outgoing
current

(a)

Lophophore

Exhalant
chamber

Inhalant chamber (b)

Base of gill
filament

Buccal
groove

2

1

(c)

Buccal
lip

Inner edge of
lophophore

FIG. 5.8. FEEDING IN BRACHIOPOD *Crania*

(*a*) View of feeding animal. (*b*) Diagram of currents in the mantle cavity (longitudinal section through animal). Larger arrows show the course of the main currents; dotted arrows below represent the course of larger particles falling out of the main stream. (*c*) Section through lophophore to show ciliary currents: 1, direction of beat of current-producing cilia on gill filament; 2, direction of beat of frontal cilia. (From Orton, 1914. See Atkins and Rudwick (8) for a corrected account.)

long filamentous gill. The gill filaments are attached to the left side of the mantle cavity and extend across it so as to form a continuous membrane. On the sides of the filaments are lateral cilia which create a water current; this current enters the ventral chamber, passes through the gill, and leaves the dorsal chamber as an exhalant stream (Fig. 5.9A).

The current entering the mantle cavity passes through a mucus-filter produced by a filter gland. This filter strains out mainly the larger particles, which are carried towards a food pouch near the mouth. Here the particles are worked up into mucous pellets to be eaten or rejected. The gill filaments are covered by mucus, which is secreted by an endostyle at their base. Besides lateral cilia, the filaments bear frontal and abfrontal cilia which beat

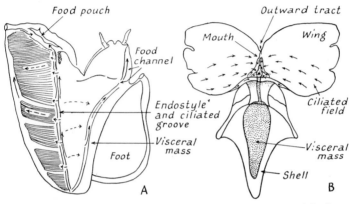

FIG. 5.9A. FEEDING MECHANISM OF THE SLIPPER-LIMPET *Crepidula fornicata*

Animal removed from its shell and mantle turned over to the left. From the endostyle at the base of the gill, mucus and food particles are lashed on to the gill filaments. (From Orton, 1914.)

FIG. 5.9B. FEEDING MECHANISM IN A THECOSOMATOUS PTEROPOD *Cavolinia inflexa* ($\times$ 3$\frac{1}{2}$)

Arrows on wings indicate directions of ciliary currents. (After Yonge, 1926.)

towards their tips. Fine particles in the inhalant stream are caught on the gill filaments, and are transported by frontal cilia across the ventral surface of the gill to a food channel. This is a ciliated groove placed in the left side of the mantle cavity and roofed above by the tips of the gill filaments. In it the collected food particles, embedded in mucous strings, are carried forwards towards the mouth where they are seized by the radula and ingested.

The method of filtering is essentially the same in other ciliary-feeding prosobranchs. Mucus used for entangling food particles is secreted by a pedal gland in *Vermetus*, and by the propodium in *Capulus*. The latter structure is an anterior extension of the foot, to which food particles are conveyed from the mantle cavity and from which they are collected by a grooved proboscis. An interesting variation is the development in

Stephopoma of a sweeping mechanism for supplementing collection of particles within the mantle cavity. The long anterior filaments of the gill are extended and drawn through the water like a sweep-net, and any particles encountered are trapped in the mucus which coats the filaments (60, 85, 116, 121).

Shelled pteropods (opisthobranchs) are another group of gastropods making use of ciliary feeding (Fig. 5.9B). In *Limacina*, for example, feeding currents are created by the beating of cilia in the mantle cavity. Food particles falling out of the stream become entangled in mucus and are carried by ciliary tracts to the mouth. Some collecting is also carried out by the foot. Pallial feeding has been lost in higher pteropods, and feeding is carried out by ciliated fields on the wings and lateral and median lobes of the foot (*Cavolinia, Cymbulia*). These animals feed on smaller members of the plankton, e.g. diatoms, protozoa, crustacean larvae, etc. (79, 86).

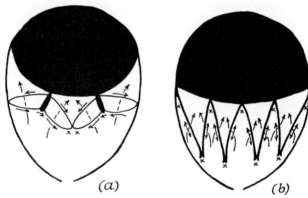

(a)   (b)

FIG. 5.10. DIAGRAMS SHOWING THE ORGANIZATION OF THE MANTLE CAVITY IN (a) A PROTOBRANCH *Nucula*, AND (b) A TYPICAL LAMELLIBRANCH SUCH AS *Ostrea*

Transverse view across the body, with exhalant chamber above, and inhalant chamber below the gills. Direction of water currents indicated by arrows passing through the gills; direction of food streams by arrows on surface of gills; forwardly directed streams to mouth indicated by *x*. (From Yonge, 1928.)

Lamellibranchs. The majority of lamellibranchs feed on particulate matter, which they filter by means of ciliary mechanisms on gills and labial palps. The ctenidia typically take the form of folds of the body wall, which are suspended in the mantle cavity and which divide the latter into two chambers (Figs. 5.10, 5.11). Water currents created by cilia on the gills enter the ventral or inhalant chamber, pass through slits in the gills and proceed posteriorly as an exhalant stream in the dorsal or exhalant chamber. As the current slackens on entering the large inhalant chamber, coarse particles fall out of the stream on to the mantle surface. Fine particles become entangled in a mucus-sheet covering the gill surface. The filtered particles are then carried to food grooves at the bases and free margins of the gills and thence towards the mouth.

In the majority of lamellibranchs (filibranchs, eulamellibranchs) the gills are responsible for collecting food particles. Some species, e.g. *Ostrea* and *Pecten,* are without siphons for regulating the passage of water currents. In *Ostrea* the inhalant current is restricted to a ventral area; in *Pecten* water is drawn into the mantle cavity along the whole ventral and part of the anterior region, but chiefly in two restricted areas (ventral and anterior). Water leaves the body posteriorly in an exhalant

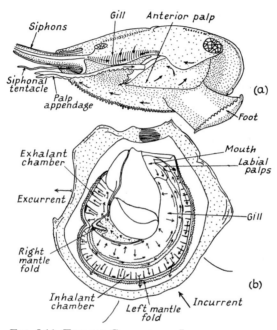

FIG. 5.11. FEEDING CURRENTS IN LAMELLIBRANCHS

(*a*) A protobranch *Yoldia,* with right valve and mantle fold removed. Arrows added to indicate directions of ciliary currents. (*b*) *Ostrea,* right valve and mantle fold removed. Within the shell plain arrows denote ingoing currents, and feathered arrows outgoing currents. ((*a*) after Kellog, 1915; (*b*) after Yonge, 1926.)

region (Fig. 5.11 (*b*)). In many other lamellibranchs, in- and excurrents enter and leave the mantle cavity by way of siphons at the posterior end of the body, elsewhere the mantle folds being largely fused.

Water currents are created by the lashing of lateral cilia on gill filaments or leaflets, as illustrated in Fig. 5.12. In protobranchs the gills consist of a series of flat leaflets on either side of the body. In other lamellibranchs the gills on either side usually consist of two lamellae or demibranchs, each of which is made up of a series of ascending and descending filaments united at their free extremities. The lateral cilia cause a current to flow through the narrow slits between the gill filaments or leaflets, from the inhalant into the exhalant chamber. On the outer surface of the filaments are frontal

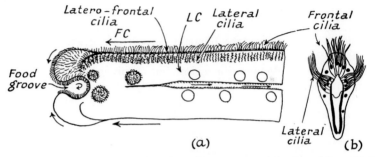

FIG. 5.12. (a) LATERAL VIEW OF A GILL FILAMENT OF *Mytilus edulis*. LC, FC, DIRECTIONS IN WHICH LATERAL CILIA AND FRONTAL CILIA LASH. (b) GILL FILAMENT OF *Heteranomia squamula* IN TRANSVERSE SECTION. ((a) from Orton, 1912; (b) from Atkins, 1936.)

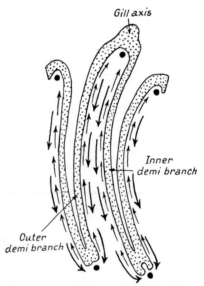

FIG. 5.13. TRANSVERSE SECTION THROUGH GILL FILAMENTS OF *Pteria hirundo*

Solid circles, orally directed currents. The arrows indicate directions of currents created by frontal cilia: ventral currents are due to coarse cilia; dorsal currents to fine cilia. (From Atkins, 1936.)

cilia which are chiefly responsible for collecting food particles. In proto-branchs the frontal cilia transport particles to the mid-line, whence they are conveyed anteriorly in two streams towards the mouth. In other lamellibranchs the frontal cilia usually beat towards the lower free margin of the lamellae where there is a food groove in which particles move anteriorly towards the mouth (Figs. 5.12, 5.13). In addition, the gill filaments of many lamellibranchs possess large latero-frontal cilia, which strain the feeding currents and throw particles on to the frontal face of the filaments where they come under the influence of the frontal cilia.

A certain amount of mechanical selection of food particles takes place on the gills. In *Pecten* the gill lamellae are thrown into folds, and the frontal cilia in the grooves between the folds beat towards the base of the lamellae, where there are forwardly-directed ciliary tracts. On the ridges of the folds the frontal cilia beat normally towards the free extremities of the filaments, again provided with ciliated tracts. But when particulate matter becomes very heavy it evokes a profuse secretion of mucus, and the mucous strings which result are conveyed by frontal cilia on the ridges to the ventral ends of the lamellae, to be dropped off on the mantle wall. Muscular movements of the gills are also used in getting rid of large or irritant particles. Such movements cause the gill grooves in *Ostrea* and *Pecten* to contract, and throw their contained particles upon the ridges, whence they drop upon the mantle surface. Heavy particles also tend to fall out of the ventral food grooves upon the surface of the mantle, whence they are removed.

In protobranch bivalves the gills are relatively small and function chiefly in the creation of a water current, food being collected principally by the large labial palps (Fig. 5.11 (*a*)). These are provided with a long appendage or *proboscis* which is grooved and ciliated; as this moves over the substratum it collects fine particles which are carried along the ciliated groove to the base. Here they are subjected to sorting by the palp lamellae, suitable material being carried by cilia to the mouth.

In other lamellibranchs the labial palps sort out food material passed to them from the gills. There is a pair of palps in front of the gills on either side of the mouth. The inner surface of the palps is ridged and ciliated, and conveys food particles from the ciliated tracts on the demibranchs to the mouth (Fig. 5.14). The ciliation of the palps is complicated, the whole forming an extremely efficient sorting mechanism. A tract of especially large cilia on each labial fold drives small particles across the palps towards the mouth. Large particles or mucous masses tend to be drawn down into furrows on the palps by other ciliary tracts. The cilia in the furrows beat towards the upper or anterior margins of the palps, where there are posteriorly directed ciliated tracts carrying material to the mantle to be rejected. Muscular action is also of importance in the degree of sorting which takes place, retraction of the palps, for example, opening up the furrows and causing particles to fall into the outwardly directed ciliary tracts.

Habits and modes of feeding of lamellibranchs are many and varied.

Most are dependent upon fine detritus, bacteria and plankton. *Mytilus* and *Ostrea* filter particles down to a lower limit of about 2μ. The optimal particle size for most efficient filtering is $7–8\mu$ in *Mytilus*, and particles of that size can be completely retained or let through at will. An estimated diet sheet for bivalves (*Tivela*, *Mytilus*) is given in Table 5.1, and data for filtering rates are listed in Tables 4.5 and 4.6 (p. 167). Quantities of water pumped by bivalves are surprisingly large, up to 34 l./hour in the oyster, for example. Under suitable conditions the oyster feeds almost continuously, and stomachs are nearly always found to contain food (6, 10, 23, 37, 60, 66, 67, 87, 106, 116, 120, 122).

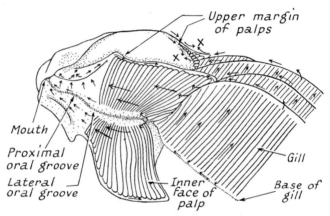

FIG. 5.14. VIEW OF LABIAL PALPS AND JUNCTION WITH THE GILLS
IN THE OYSTER *Ostrea edulis* ($\times$ 5⅓)

Arrows indicate directions taken by particles; *X*, point where material is rejected from the palps. (From Yonge, 1926.)

Protochordates. Besides the groups we have just examined, ciliary feeding mechanisms are widely utilized by protochordates. Although pharyngeal gills are often involved, considerable diversity exists in the functional patterns concerned with feeding in these forms.

Pharyngeal gill-bars form a straining apparatus in *Amphioxus* and other cephalochordates. These animals lie buried in sand, with the oral region at the surface, and draw a feeding current into the mouth, over the gill-bars and out through the atrium. Large particles are strained off by buccal cirri and smaller particles by the gills (Fig. 5.15). The feeding current is created by lateral cilia on the pharyngeal bars, where particles become entangled in mucus secreted by the ventral endostyle, and these mucous masses are driven dorsally by frontal cilia on the pharyngeal surfaces of the gill-bars. In the dorsal wall of the pharynx the food material enters a dorsal ciliated groove and is moved posteriorly to the oesophagus and stomach. There is also some minor collecting of food in the buccal cavity

TABLE 5.1

MATERIALS INGESTED BY CILIARY-FEEDING LAMELLIBRANCHS

	Ingested	Digested	
		Living	Dead (as detritus)
a. Phytoplankton			
1. Dinoflagellates, 32,000 per l., 12 g*	+	−	+
2. Diatoms, 32,000 per l., 1·5 g*	±	±	+
3. Bacteria, 45,000,000 per l., 0·05 g*	+	+	+
4. Other unicellular and multicellular algae	±	−	+
5. Zoospores and other reproductive cells	+	±	+
b. Zooplankton and Nekton			
1. Flagellates	+	±	+
2. Rhizopods and ciliates (including tintinnids)	±	±	+
3. Reproductive products of invertebrates			
Ova and larvae	±	−	+
Spermatozoa	+	+	+
4. Invertebrates and vertebrates	−	−	+
c. Benthic algae and eelgrass	−	−	+
d. Benthic invertebrates	−	−	+
e. Inorganic and refractory	±	0	0

Sign + indicates generally; ± commonly, but only small individuals or species; − rarely or not at all.
* Quantity of dry organic matter potentially ingested by one adult animal per year. Based on computations for a single mussel (*Mytilus californianus*) 70 mm in length, filtering 2·5 l. of water per hour. (From Coe (23).)

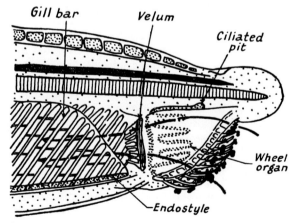

FIG. 5.15. ORAL HOOD AND ANTERIOR REGION OF AMPHIOXUS, SHOWING FEEDING CURRENT (INDICATED BY ARROWS). PARTICLES OF DETRITUS ARE TRAPPED ON THE ORAL CIRRI. (From Dennell (30).)

by the ciliated wheel organ and Hatschek's pit, where particles become entangled in mucus and whence they are carried to the dorsal groove via peripharyngeal ciliated bands (30).

In balanoglossids the anterior end of the body consists of a proboscis and collar which together form a simple ciliary mechanism for collecting particulate matter and detritus. The proboscis secretes mucus which traps particles and the resultant mucous strings are moved towards the mouth under the impetus of cilia on the proboscis. A respiratory current created by pharyngeal cilia assists in drawing in the mucous strings. Most entero-pneusts are burrowers (e.g. *Saccoglossus, Balanoglossus*), inhabiting muddy sand, and appear to ingest the surrounding soil for the sake of contained organic matter without much selection. Some species are said to protrude their proboscis from the burrow on occasion, and gather up detritus from the surface of the substratum. In any event, the gut of freshly collected animals is swollen with sand and the casts consist largely of sand grains. The pharynx is perforated by gill slits and the pharyngeal bars bear strongly developed lateral cilia which create an outwardly directed respiratory and feeding current. Particles are prevented from passing through the gill-slits by the action of a sorting mechanism dependent upon latero-frontal cilia, which carry such particles ventrally into the lumen of the pharynx. Ciliary tracts lining the pharynx move particulate matter and mucous strings posteriorly into the oesophagus, while surplus water is strained off by the gill-slits and oesophageal pores (12, 62).

In *Cephalodiscus* all parts of the body and stalk are covered with cilia which transport food particles to the arms. These bear short cilia which carry some particles distally to be discharged, and they are also provided with a broad and shallow groove containing longer cilia which move food particles basally towards the mouth. Tentacles arising from the arms are ciliated as well, and exhibit active jerking movements which may be concerned with procuring and selecting food particles.

Ascidians are provided with a branchial sac perforated by many small apertures. By the beating of cilia on the sides of the gill-bars, sea water is drawn into the branchial siphon and passes through the fine meshwork of the pharyngeal basket on which fine particles are caught. These food particles are collected by cilia on the pharyngeal surface of the gill-bars and on their papillae, and are carried across the branchial surface towards the dorsal lamina. In simple ascidians this process is aided by transverse waving of the longitudinal bars. The filtering process is assisted by the production of mucus-sheets, which are secreted by the endostyle and transferred to the inner surface of the pharynx by endostylar cilia. On reaching the dorsal lamina the food-laden mucous masses are carried towards the posterior end of the branchial cavity and thence to the oesophagus.

Ascidians feed on plankton and detritus. On exposed shores the food consists almost entirely of plankton, often enriched by a considerable quantity of gametes and algal spores. But in protected waters and estuaries it is made up largely of suspended matter and detritus, together with some unicellular algae. *Ciona intestinalis* is capable of filtering off particles down to $1–2\mu$ in size, and this is in large part due to the fine porosity of the mucus-sheets produced, since when mucus secretion is in abeyance, small particles of this size are no longer retained.

In solitary ascidians ciliary activity is augmented by rhythmical squirting, caused by quick contractions of the body wall. The steady ciliary current of *Phallusia mammillata* amounts to 60 c.c. per hour, while spontaneous squirting moves some 300 c.c. of sea water per hour in a fasting animal. In a hungry animal, rhythmic squirting increases greatly in frequency, whereas the addition of food restores the frequency to normal (Fig. 5.16).

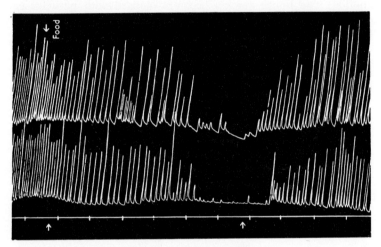

FIG. 5.16. SPONTANEOUS SQUIRTING BY AN ASCIDIAN *Phallusia mammillata*

The animal was starved for 14 hours, and given food (flagellate culture) continuously for 6 hours. Food added at first arrow, and stopped at second arrow. Time scale in hours. (From Hoyle (55).)

Squirting renews the sea water in branchial and atrial chambers, brings a fresh lot of food particles into the branchial sac and periodically renews the water about the animal (*cf.* p. 165) (55, 60, 72).

In thaliacians (*Salpa, Doliolum*) the endostyle secretes a mucous net of entangling threads into the pharyngeal cavity. Food particles caught in the mucus are transported to the dorsal pharynx by peripharyngeal cilia, and thence to the oesophagus by other ciliary tracts. In doliolids the through-current is produced by cilia of the branchial stigmata; in salps, by rhythmic contractions of circular muscles of the body wall (19, 60).

The small appendicularians (Larvacea) have a most remarkable method of feeding. These animals are pelagic in habit and dwell in a gelatinous house which is secreted by the animal and forsaken from time to time, when a new one is formed (Fig. 5.17). The house is essentially a filtering apparatus for straining off fine particles and nannoplankton on which the animal depends for food. Water currents, created by lashing of the animal's tail, enter through a pair of dorsal funnels provided with a fine grating for excluding larger particles ($> 30\mu$ in *Oikopleura*). Within the cavity of the house is an elaborate collecting apparatus containing paired wings divided into dorsal and ventral chambers. Water enters the ventral division on each side, and on passing through the dorsal division it is strained of all suspended matter by many fine septa. This collected food material is sucked into the pharynx by ciliary action. When the pressure inside the house rises sufficiently, it forces open a spring door at the posterior end. Ejection of water through this opening propels the animal forward, but the main function of the house and water current is feeding and not locomotion. The house quickly becomes clogged with particles and is abandoned in the matter of a few hours; a new one is constructed in 15–30 min.

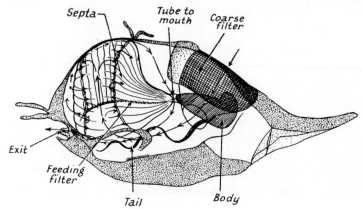

FIG. 5.17. *Oikopleura albicans* IN ITS HOUSE
The arrows show the feeding currents. (From Lohmann.)

CILIARY FEEDING BY LARVAE. Free-swimming planktonic larvae of many animals feed by ciliary devices, often quite different from those of the adults. Among such larvae are numbered the pilidium of nemertines, the trochophore of annelids, veliger of molluscs and successive larval stages of echinoderms. A veliger larva—that of the oyster for example—bears a conspicuous ciliated disc or velum, which is used for feeding and locomotion (Fig. 5.18(*a*)). Arising from the velum is a crown of large cilia which collect and throw particles on to a ciliated tract around the base, where they become entangled in mucus and are carried back to the mouth (29).

In echinoderm larvae, such as the auricularia and bipinnaria of star-fishes, food particles are collected by longitudinal ciliated bands bordering grooves or sulci, along which they are conveyed to the dorsal border of the stomodaeum. The great extension of the longitudinal ciliated band which results from folding and development of the larval arms greatly increases the effective food-collecting area.

The feeding process in tornaria larvae of enteropneusts is remarkably similar to that of echinoderm larvae. The planktonic tornaria likewise possesses longitudinal bands of cilia bordering a system of sulci which lead to the mouth (Fig. 5.18(*b*)). The cilia beat transversely, sweeping particles into the gutters, along which they are conveyed to the mouth opening. The adoral bands of echinoderm larvae are represented in the tornaria by ciliary patches above and below the mouth: the sub-oral appears to be inhalant, driving particles inwards over the ventral lip; the supra-oral is exhalant, driving surplus water outwards. Echinoderm and hemichordate larvae are generally regarded as showing phyletic affinities (39).

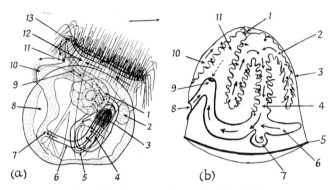

FIG. 5.18. FEEDING DEVICES OF LARVAE

(*a*). Veliger larva of the oyster. Large arrow above shows direction of movement; smaller arrows in figure show direction of ciliary feeding currents; 1: digestive diverticula; 2: adductor muscle; 3: stomach; 4: style sac; 5: midgut; 6: rectum; 7: anus; 8: mantle cavity; 9: oesophagus; 10: foot; 11: mouth; 12: ciliated tract at base of velum; 13: velum (from Yonge, 1926). (*b*). Tornaria larva showing fields and furrows on surface, and paths taken by feeding currents; 1: apical plate; 2: antero-dorsal sulculus; 3: mid-dorsal field; 4: lateral sulcus; 5: locomotive girdle; 6: sub-dorsal sulculus; 7: lateral bay; 8: oral sulcus; 9: mouth; 10: pre-oral sulculus; 11: pre-oral field (from Garstang (39).)

Tentacular Methods

A few animals depend largely or entirely upon freely movable tentacles for collecting fine food particles. The best examples are provided by certain holothurians, such as *Cucumaria*, *Thyone* and *Psolus*. These animals, which live in crevices or buried in mud, bear a crown of sticky tentacles about the mouth. When extended they entangle plankton and other fine particles. At intervals the tentacles are thrust one after another into the mouth and adhering material is wiped off and ingested. There are also many tubicolous and burrowing polychaetes (terebellids, spionids, etc.) possessing extensile cephalic tentacles, which move over the surface of the bottom, collecting particles and small organisms. This material is transferred to the mouth by ciliary action (p. 203).

Mucus-traps

Secretion of mucus-sheets for entangling food particles is commonly associated with ciliary feeding, as we have seen, and we have instanced one form in which a mucus-bag is used as an alternative mode of feeding. This animal, *Chaetopterus*, produces a mucous sieve, and draws water through it by the pumping action of parapodial fans (p. 204). Very similar is the feeding habit of the echiuroid worm *Urechis caupo*. This animal inhabits a U-shaped burrow through which it pumps water by means of peristaltic movements of the body wall (Fig. 14.6, p. 584). Near the anterior end of the worm there is a ring of girdle-glands, which secrete a mucus-bag or funnel. The mouth of this bag is fastened to the wall of the burrow, while the lower end remains attached to the body wall. Water flowing along the burrow passes through this net, which filters out particles down to 40 Å in diameter. Periodically, when the net becomes clogged, it is slipped over the head, caught by the muscular proboscis and swallowed.

Urechis feeds intermittently, periods of pumping alternating with long periods of quiescence lasting from 20–60 min. During pumping periods the animal is not always feeding, and a shift to feeding activity is accompanied by an increase in ventilation rate, from 11 to 29 c.c./min. Observations show that a worm produces a new feeding bag about once per hour, and that the time spent in feeding amounts to 13 min in each hour (average values). The metabolic rate of *Urechis* is known, but observations are not at hand to relate these data (pumping rate and O_2 consumption) to actual food intake under normal environmental conditions. Feeding funnels, produced by parapodial glands, are also used by *Nereis diversicolor* in filter-feeding (44, 48, 71, 73).

An interesting example of a mucus-trap is provided by a sessile gastropod *Vermetus gigas*. By means of a large pedal gland this animal secretes long mucous strings, which extend up to 30 cm away from the shell, and which entangle fine plankton material. At intervals these threads are drawn back towards the mouth, to be seized by the radula and swallowed. In addition *Vermetus gigas* is able to capture small organisms which come within range of its radula. The ctenidia are small and the ciliary current slight in this form, and are of minor importance in securing food. Certain other filter-feeding gastropods also possess a supplementary mode of feeding by means of thread-like mucus-traps (4, 85, 124).

Feeding Mechanisms Involving Setae

Crustacea, in common with other arthropods, lack cilia, but many species nevertheless feed on minute particles which they strain from the surrounding sea water with the aid of fine setae occurring on appendages. Feeding by copepods, the most important members of the zooplankton, will be described first, before considering other filter-feeding crustaceans.

Copepods. When swimming slowly and steadily, pelagic copepods such as *Calanus finmarchicus* often feed automatically by straining off phytoplankton, although they are capable of selecting larger food items. Swimming movements are due to rapid vibrations of the anterior appendages, and some of the water drawn towards the animal is caught in a vortex created by the activity of the maxillipeds and maxillules (Fig. 5.19). This current passes through the stationary maxillae which bear long setous filters, and food particles which are filtered off are passed to the mandibles.

Because of their importance in the economy of the sea, copepods have been studied intensively, particularly *Calanus finmarchicus*, which is widely

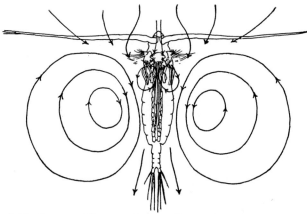

FIG. 5.19. VENTRAL VIEW OF *Calanus finmarchicus*, TO SHOW WATER CURRENTS WHEN THE ANIMAL IS SWIMMING SLOWLY

Large incoming whirls to right and left; smaller feeding whirls on ventral surface. Other arrows indicate direction of water currents towards and away from the animal. (From Cannon, 1928.)

distributed and often abundant. *Calanus* feeds upon the microplankton; its food includes diatoms, flagellates and other unicellular algae, protozoa and small crustaceans. The filtering apparatus is very efficient, straining off minute flagellates from the nannoplankton down to a few micra in size.

The actual food intake varies somewhat with the habits of the animal. The majority of the *Calanus* at the surface are feeding at all hours of the day. At deeper levels the proportion of individuals containing food is distinctly less, in correlation with decrease in density of phytoplankton. There is some evidence for a diurnal feeding rhythm with greater activity at night, which may be significant in terms of daily movements to and from the surface. When the animals execute vertical diurnal migrations, feeding takes place mostly at the surface and during the hours of darkness (77, 78).

Ostracods. There is much variety in the feeding habits of different ostracods, some like *Asterope* and *Cytherella* being purely filter feeders, others like *Cypridina* feeding on detritus and large food masses. While feeding, *Asterope* remains buried in the mud and abstracts minute food particles from the feeding-current which it passes through its burrow. In feeding, a current of water is drawn through the valves of the shell by the vibratory activity of the maxillae, while the first trunk limbs bear valves which allow the passage of water in an antero-posterior direction only. Food particles are caught in a setous filter on the maxillule, are combed off by the maxilla and are transferred to the mouth by long setae on the maxillules. The mechanisms of filter-feeding are essentially the same in other filter-feeding ostracods, although the various processes may be carried out by different limbs (18).

Cirripedes feed largely on small marine crustacea which they garner by means of casting movements of cirri. These are really the thoracic legs which terminate in a pair of rami armed with long hairs. The food collected by the cirri is deposited on the mouth parts, where it is ground up by the mandibles and worked into small masses to be swallowed.

Amphipods. Several benthic amphipods are particle feeders. *Ampelisca* lives in tubes or pockets of sand grains and mucus. When feeding, the pleopods are kept in constant motion, drawing in water over the head and mouth parts, and driving it outwards over the telson. Food particles brought in by this current are seized by the gnathopods and mouth parts; setae on these structures probably serve for straining and selecting minute particles.

A rather different method of feeding is used by *Haustorius*. This animal is found on sandy beaches, where it burrows into the sand. It possesses a filter-mechanism by which it feeds on small food particles suspended in the water in the sand. The maxilla acts as a pump, producing an anteriorly directed current, and also performs the function of a sieve plate, filtering off food particles. These are removed by the maxillipeds and passed on to the mouth parts.

Mysids such as *Hemimysis* and *Praunus* have two methods of feeding, one for dealing with large food masses and another for filtering off suspended particles. We are here concerned with the latter process. Water currents responsible for locomotion and feeding are produced by rotary movements of the thoracic limbs (Fig. 5.20). As these whirl around they draw water towards them from all directions and pass it into an area of low pressure near the base of the limb. The separate water streams join to form a forwardly directed current beneath the mid-ventral body wall. Anteriorly the food stream is sucked forwards by vibration of the maxillae. Food particles are collected by setous combs on the maxillae and are pushed on to the mandibles, where the food mass is ground up and sucked into the oesophagus by peristalsis. Less palatable material is thrown out laterally by the mouth parts. Food may be filtered directly from the sea water as the animals swim about, but when live plankton is sparse the animals swim to the bottom where they stir up particles from bottom deposits. In this way mysids are able to increase the amount of material in suspension and can feed upon it (107).

Euphausiids are pelagic in habit and feed upon detritus and small planktonic organisms. The chief food of the antarctic krill *Euphausia superba* consists of diatoms. That of *Meganyctiphanes norvegica* is predominantly organic detritus, supplemented by diatoms, flagellates and small crustaceans. Euphausiids appear to feed in a manner similar to mysids (q.v.). The filtering apparatus or food basket is formed by the thoracic limbs which are provided with fringes of setae. Feeding currents are created by lateral movements of the thoracic limbs and by beating of pleopods. Food particles caught in the thoracic basket are transferred to the mandibles to be triturated and swallowed. *Meganyctiphanes* has also been observed to feed upon suspended matter on the bottom, which is stirred up by the pleopods (69).

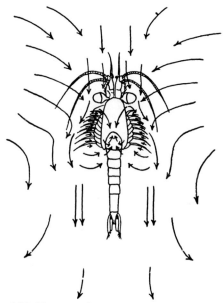

FIG. 5.20. FEEDING CURRENTS PRODUCED BY *Hemimysis*
Dorsal view of an animal swimming freely in the water (× 4.8). (From Cannon and Manton, 1927.)

Decapods. These animals are typically omnivores or carnivores, feeding on large food masses, but filter-feeding has been adopted by a few forms, often in conjunction with specialized habits. The peculiar gall crabs *Hapalocarcinus* and *Cryptochirus* live in chambers within corals and are dependent upon plankton and suspended matter drawn into the chamber with the respiratory and feeding current (p. 653). The oral region in these animals is screened by a sieve of setae fringing the maxillipeds, while the mandibles, apparently, are also used for sifting food and creating water currents. Spider crabs (*Inachus*) also consume fine particles. Essentially deposit feeders, they pick up fine material in their chelae and hold it in front of the mouth where it is brushed over the maxillipeds.

Filter-feeding has been acquired by several groups of anomurans. The hermit crab *Eupagurus* feeds to a large extent upon bottom detritus and small organisms which are swept up by a terminal brush of setae on the third maxillipeds. In addition the small chela is used to scrape bottom deposits and pick up small masses which are passed to the maxillipeds and thence to the mouth parts. Feeding methods are essentially the same in *Galathea* which collects finely-divided material from the substratum by sweeping movements of the maxillipeds, but larger pieces of food may also be seized by the chelae and maxillipeds and passed to the mandibles. *Porcellana* is a particulate feeder and possesses a filter in the form of a fringe of long hairs on the third maxillipeds (Fig. 5.21). These perform

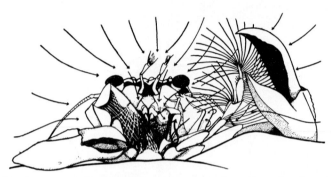

FIG. 5.21. ANTERIOR VIEW OF PORCELAIN-CRAB *Porcellana longicornis* WHILE FEEDING, TO SHOW THE DIRECTION OF THE WATER CURRENTS DRAWING FOOD IN SUSPENSION TOWARDS THE ANIMAL (from E. A. T. Nicol (1932).)

regular casting movements, thus entangling suspended particles which are transferred by the second maxillipeds to the mouth.

Another method of filter-feeding is used by the mud shrimp *Upogebia*. This animal lives in a burrow through which it draws a feeding current by fanning its swimmerets. The first two pairs of limbs are heavily fringed with hairs so as to form a basket, and as water passes through this filter, detritus and plankton are strained off. The collected food material is brushed off the basket by the maxillipeds and transferred to the mouth. Finally, we may mention here the parasitic pea crabs (*Pinnotheres*), some of which inhabit the mantle cavity of lamellibranchs. These animals collect mucous food-strings from the gills of their hosts with the aid of setous fringes on their claws (70).

Efficiency of Filter-feeding among Invertebrates

The food available to filter feeders consists of minute zooplankton, phytoplankton, protozoa, bacteria and organic detritus. This organic matter varies greatly in particle size, from several hundred micra in certain algal cells to sub-microscopic colloidal dimensions in the case of detrital matter. Animals probably differ in the efficiency of their straining apparatuses: those with structural sieves—namely sponges, bivalves, copepods and ascidians—retain particles down to 1 μ in size; mucous net feeders, on the other hand, filter out material down to 40 Å in size. The food intake is a function of the efficiency of the filter, amount of food present in the surrounding sea water and pumping rate. Absolute filtering rates, of course, vary greatly—from less than 100 ml/day in *Calanus finmarchicus* to 10 l./hour in *Ostrea virginica*. Jørgensen, however, finds that filtration rates of different animals are of about the same order when expressed as litres of sea water per millilitre O_2 consumed. Calculated values are as follows—

Sponges	*Grantia compressa*	13 l./ml O_2
	Halichondria panicea	14, 31 l./ml O_2
Echiuroid	*Urechis caupo*	20 l./ml O_2
Lamellibranchs	*Ostrea virginica*	16 l./ml O_2
	Mytilus edulis	14–15 l./ml O_2
Copepods	*Calanus finmarchicus*	8 l./ml O_2
	Centropages hamatus	8 l./ml O_2
Ascidians	*Ciona intestinalis* ⎱ *Molgula manhattensis* ⎰	10–20 l./ml O_2

It is interesting to test the calculated values against actual measurements of food stuffs available. One ml of O_2 will burn about 0·8 mg of organic matter. For an animal filtering 15 l./ml O_2, this is equivalent, in terms of energy consumption, to 0·05 mg of organic matter per litre. Allowing two-thirds of the energy absorbed for growth, the total food requirements for growth and respiration are about 0·15 mg of organic matter per litre. Only part of the organic matter ingested is utilized, however; in *Calanus finmarchicus*, for example, it is estimated that half the nitrogen ingested is lost in the faeces. Actual amounts of organic matter, in detritus and phytoplankton from different waters, range from 0·14–2·8 mg/l. These values appear to be of about the order necessary to satisfy the nutritional requirements of the filter-feeding animals concerned. (52, 60, 67).

Data are now available for various species, for example *Calanus helgolandicus*. It respires 31 μl. O_2/mg dry weight/day in winter and 79 μl. O_2 in summer (8°C). Metabolism is lower during the winter and when animals are not feeding. Sea water contains 0·95–2·5 mg insoluble organic matter/l. *Calanus* filters 135 ml sea water and removes 135–415 mg organic matter/ mg dry weight/day, of which 80% is digested. The average amount of food digested is equivalent to an average respiration rate of 170 μl. O_2, and an increase in dry weight of 25%. The average concentration of amino-acid N is 7·7% of dry body weight; in sea water amino-acid N is 11·9 μg/l. Starving *Calanus* loses 1·8% and 2·1% of body weight as amino acid/day in winter and summer, respectively. To replenish this daily loss filtering rates of 90 and 315 ml sea water/mg dry weight/day, winter and summer, respectively, are required (24, 27).

Filtering Devices in Vertebrates

Despite great disparity in size, certain adult vertebrates utilize filtering methods of feeding fundamentally not unlike those already described in certain invertebrate forms. In all these cases, whether they concern fish, fowl or whale, there is some form of filter or sieve which strains off plankton from the sea water. These animals really by-pass one or several intermediate links in the food chain by feeding on planktonic crustaceans; because of their size and food requirements they must clear large volumes of water to obtain sufficient food organisms, and at least for feeding purposes they are restricted to areas of high planktonic density.

Fish. Various pelagic fish are plankton feeders. Huge basking sharks *Cetorhinus* and whale sharks *Rhineodon* are provided with numerous closely set gill-rakers, which strain off the myriads of small crustaceans from the water which enters the mouth (83). *Cetorhinus* feeds on plankton in spring and summer, and on bottom organisms in deep water during the winter (when the gill rakers disappear) (90).

Among teleosts, mackerel and herring possess large thin gill-rakers

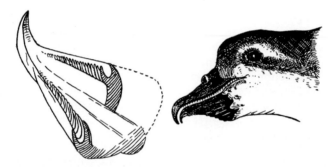

FIG. 5.22. HEAD AND BILL OF THE BROAD-BILLED PRION *Pachyptila forsteri*
(*Left*) a palatal view of the upper mandible, showing the baleen-like maxillary lamellae. (*Right*) view of the head, showing the extensible pouch. (From Murphy (88).)

which project across the pharyngeal openings and prevent the escape of planktonic organisms. Clupeids are part filter-feeders, part carnivores; ocpepods predominate in the food of young herring; adults feed largely on a non-crustacean diet in spring (mostly sand eels) and shift to a crustacean diet in summer (15).

Birds. Although many marine birds feed on plankton (*see* p. 56), there is only one group which is anatomically specialized for sifting out floating animals, namely prions or whale birds (*Pachyptila*). In certain species the upper mandible bears two rows of comb-like lamellae, strikingly analogous to the baleen plates of whalebone whales (Fig. 5.22). The resemblance is heightened by the presence of a large fleshy tongue. Whale birds are denizens of subantarctic waters. They feed from the surface on crustacea by submerging the head, and scooping up food with the laminated bill (88).

Whalebone Whales (Mystacoceti). These animals show highly specialized adaptations for securing plankton. The filtering apparatus consists of whalebone or baleen, which is a collective term for horny plates attached to the roof of the mouth and hanging down into the buccal cavity. The plates are arranged transversely to the long axis of the jaws and are very numerous, over 300 having been counted in the right whales. On the inner side the plates bear fine hair-like fringes which form an efficient filtering apparatus. As the whale swims about at or near the surface, with mouth open, planktonic organisms are strained off by the hair-like fringes of whalebone and the water escapes through the sides of the mouth. When the lower jaw is raised and the tongue elevated, water is forced out of the mouth cavity. The planktonic organisms which have been filtered off are left stranded on the tongue and are swallowed.

The principal food of whalebone whales consists of larger species of plankton (krill). In the Antarctic, blue, fin and humpback whales (*Balaenoptera* and *Megaptera*) feed heavily and almost exclusively on the immense shoals of *Euphausia superba* which abound there; this is in the summer season. The majority of whales eat little in the winter, when they draw upon their reserves of fat. These are supplemented by small quantities of crustacea and fish, captured in warmer waters of the Southern Hemisphere during the winter months. The staple food of blue and fin whales (*Balaenoptera*) in the Northern Hemisphere is *Meganyctiphanes norvegica* during the summer. During the winter, fin and humpback whales consume some fish (clupeids (75)).

MECHANISMS FOR DEALING WITH LARGE PARTICLES OR MASSES

In this section are described methods for dealing with inactive food; for seizing prey, and mechanisms for scraping and boring in connexion with feeding.

Ingestion of Inactive Food

There are many benthic animals which swallow, with little selection, sand, mud or other bottom deposits, from which they extract organic material for nourishment. Such animals possess gullets, tentacles and similar structures which can be pushed through the ground, whereas organs of mastication are absent.

Annelids. Many polychaetes fall into this group, such as *Arenicola, Ophelia, Notomastus* and others. *Arenicola* prefers muddy sand in which it forms a U-shaped burrow. This consists of head-shaft, gallery and tail-shaft (Fig. 5.23). Usually only the latter is open to the surface, while the head-shaft is blocked by loosened sand. When the worm finds a suitable location it may stay there for weeks on end, showing a very regular pattern of activity, at least when the tide is in. Sand is loosened in the head-shaft by regular irrigation movements, and is swallowed by the muscular proboscis which is frequently extended and withdrawn. Feeding activity is rhythmic, showing a periodicity of about 7 min in *A. marina* (Fig. 4.6, p. 147) (28). Sipunculoids also ingest sand and mud by means of a muscular introvert and utilize the contained organic material.

Food consumption and energy expenditure have been worked out for the benthic polychaete *Clymenella torquata*. Ingested sediment amounts to 0·4 c.c./worm/day; the organic matter in the sediment contains 10·2 potential calories; and the worm expends 1·1 calories/day. Even if food is assimilated with low efficiency, there seems to be ample for its requirements (76).

Echinoderms include many benthic and burrowing species which feed on bottom deposits. Holothurians push mucus-bound aggregations of bottom materials into the mouth with the buccal tentacles. Heart urchins (spatangoids) burrow in sand or mud and maintain communication with

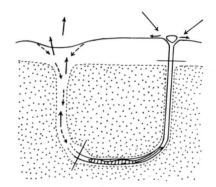

FIG. 5.23. LUGWORM *Arenicola marina* IN ITS BURROW

The cross-lines lie at the boundaries between head shaft (*left*), gallery (*below*) and tail shaft (*right*). Yellow sand above, black sand below. Solid arrows show water movements through burrow; broken arrows, settling of sand in the head shaft. (After Wells, 1945.)

the surface by a mucus-lined canal (Fig. 4.5, p. 146). Through the latter a respiratory current is drawn, while small rosette feet of the buccal region collect sand and food particles, the small circumoral spines pushing the food into the gut. Somewhat similar habits are displayed by burrowing ophiuroids (*Amphiura*, *Ophiopsila*, etc.), which move particles and detritus along the arms to the mouth by means of tube feet.

Crustacea. Many littoral amphipods feed on organic detritus, largely vegetable matter. *Corophium*, a burrowing form, sometimes filters off fine particulate matter, but to a much greater extent feeds by selecting particles from the mud in which it lives. When behaving as a selective deposit feeder, *Corophium* scoops up and sifts small quantities of mud with the gnathopods. Larger particles are conveyed to the mandibles, where they are crushed by molar processes and swallowed. Smaller particles are retained by a fringe of setae on the gnathopods, sifted and then transferred to the mandibles to be swallowed.

The Cumacea are small burrowing animals which employ filter-feeding or which feed on small micro-organisms occurring in the soil detritus. *Cumopsis* collects food by cleaning off sand grains and other small objects. These are picked up by the first pereiopods and manipulated and cleaned by the maxillipeds. The food is then passed to the mouth parts (32).

Scraping and Boring

Here are included devices which enable animals to bore into hard materials, the fragments of which are swallowed and digested; or to scrape off encrusting material and organisms; or to rasp and bore into living prey or dead animals. Invertebrates which feed in this manner include various echinoderms, molluscs and crustacea. Certain fishes are also included in this category.

Echinoderms. Sea urchins possess a set of strong teeth forming a biting and scraping apparatus known as Aristotle's lantern. With this structure, rock-dwelling forms such as *Echinus* are able to scrape off and masticate encrusting organisms; bottom material is also conveyed to the mouth by tube feet.

Molluscs. Especially suitable for scraping is the radula of chitons and gastropods. This is a horny ribbon covered with many rows of small recurved teeth (Fig. 5.24). The radula lies on the ventral side of the buccal cavity and frequently works in conjunction with the palatal plate or jaws. Growth of the radula is continuous during the life of the animal and takes place in a ventral diverticulum known as a radular sac, in which proliferating tissue gives rise to transverse rows of cells (odontoblasts), forming new teeth, and other cells forming the horny base of the ribbon. As a result of posterior growth the radula is pressed forwards and a new surface constantly replaces that worn away.

The radula is supported by cartilaginous masses providing attachment for protractor and retractor muscles by which the odontophore apparatus is protruded from, or withdrawn into, the buccal cavity. Rasping movements of the radula are brought about by action of another set of protractor and retractor muscles, by which it is drawn backwards and forwards over its supporting cartilage, as over a pulley. Since the radular teeth slope backwards the effective stroke is executed on withdrawal, and this accords with the greater size of the radular retractor.

In herbivorous chitons and gastropods radular teeth are well developed. Representative browsing forms are *Chiton* and *Patella*, which scrape encrusting algae and other small organisms off rocks. Pieces of seaweed are also eaten, being seized with lips and palate and scraped with the radula. *Aplysia* (an opisthobranch) browses on green algae, which are grasped by lips and jaws and rasped by the radula. Eolids feed on hydroids and sea anemones, breaking off pieces with the jaws and passing them back with the radula. They appear to be physiologically specialized in some manner for inactivating the nematocysts of their prey. Many of the dorids browse on sponges, using the radula as rasp and scoop. Others, such as *Acanthodoris*, attack ascidians and polyzoans: they cut into their prey with

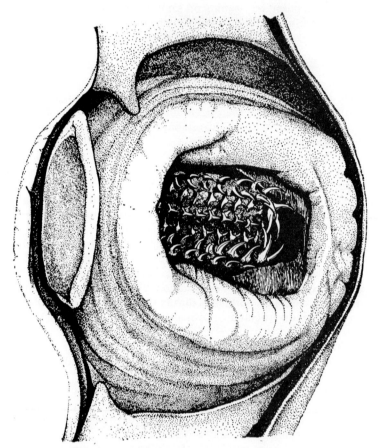

FIG. 5.24. PROBOSCIS OF A CARNIVOROUS GASTROPOD *Natica millepunctata* Radula in mouth opening, boring gland below. (From Ankel (4).)

the radula and suck out semi-liquid food by means of a buccal pump (36, 99).

In many carnivorous gastropods the radular apparatus is carried on the end of a long extrusible proboscis which can be inserted into the prey. Thus *Cerithiopsis* feeds on siliceous sponges by thrusting its long proboscis into the osculum, or through adventitious apertures, to reach the softer parts within. *Sycotypus* attacks oysters by stealth, waiting until the latter opens up, when it thrusts its shell between the oyster's valves and pushes its proboscis into the soft parts. Whelks (*Buccinum*, *Busycon*) force open the valves of lamellibranchs and remove the soft parts of the prey with the aid of the proboscis (Fig. 5.25). Other gastropods bore through the shells of lamellibranchs by mechanical or chemical means. *Urosalpinx* and *Nucella* drill an opening with the radula; *Natica* liberates a certain amount of free acid (H_2SO_4) from a gland on the proboscis for dissolving a hole in the shell of the prey (Fig. 5.24). In either event the proboscis is pushed through the aperture so made and extracts the soft parts of the prey (20, 21, 38, 41, 59).

Shipworms Teredinidae obtain much of their nourishment from the wood in which they bore. The wood is rasped away by movements of the shell valves and the scrapings are carried into the mouth by ciliary action

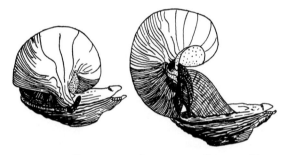

FIG. 5.25. *Sycotypus*, A GASTROPOD, OPENING AN OYSTER. (From Ankel (4).)

(p. 651). In addition a certain amount of plankton is collected by gills and palps. Analyses of amino-acids show that *Teredo* acquires its dietary-N from both the wood and suspended nannoplankton (42, 64).

Crustacea. The gribble *Limnoria* is an isopod which tunnels into wood and feeds on wood particles. Pure wood has a very low protein content, and wood-destroying fungi contribute much amino-N to the diet of the gribble (95). The habits of these marine borers are further described in Chapter 15 (p. 651). *Ligia*, the sea slater, browses on sea weeds which are cut up by the mandibles; *Idotea*, another isopod, is an omnivorous scavenger and scrapes and bites food masses with the mouth parts (89). Some of the littoral gammarids feed on sea weeds, tearing off pieces with the maxillipeds and crushing them with the mouth parts. Caprellids, often found clinging to stems of hydroids, possess large palm-like claws, with which they scrape off diatoms and debris or even attack living hydroid zooids.

Fishes. The majority of fishes are active carnivores and relatively few species feed upon plants or organic debris. Some exceptions are the grey mullet *Mugil* and *Mulloides*, which feed upon sea weeds, bottom mud and detritus. The gill-rakers of the mullet form a sieve-like apparatus preventing fine particulate matter from reaching the gills. The jaw teeth are micro-scopic, pharyngeal grinding teeth are present in *Mulloides*, and both animals possess strong pyloric gizzards. Some of the parrot-fishes (Scaridae) feed on vegetation or pieces of coral. In these animals the jaw teeth are fused into shearing plates and the pharyngeal teeth form a flat grinding pave-ment. Trunk fishes (Ostraciidae) also feed on bottom algae (1, 50, 65).

Methods for Seizing Prey

In this section we shall be dealing with feeding mechanisms principally of carnivores which seize and devour living prey, but we shall have occasion to refer to certain omnivores which are partially scavenging in habit. Yonge shows how such mechanisms may be classified into those concerned with seizing, with seizing and masticating, and with seizing followed by external digestion. These are considered together on a phyletic basis.

Protozoa. Many protozoa are raptorial, feeding on other protozoans, phytoflagellates, diatoms and even small crustaceans. Amoebae capture small, slow-moving prey which they engulf in a food-cup formed by pseudopodia. In raptorial ciliates the mouth is usually located at the an-terior end and can be widely distended for engulfing large prey. Some species possess special devices for seizing prey, such as proboscides, scoops formed of undulatory membranes and suctorial tentacles. The latter are found in certain parasitic holotrichs which use them to suck out the con-tents of epithelial cells of their host. In suctorians, which feed upon other protozoa, the prey is captured by sticky tentacles which release a paralysing secretion and suck out the contents of the prey (61).

Coelenterates and Ctenophores. Members of these groups are carnivores, apart from those sedentary species dependent on symbiotic algae (p. 605). With the exception of species making use of ciliary feeding currents, coelenterates usually capture their prey by means of tentacles armed with cnidae capable of discharging adhesive and penetrating filaments. The latter are capable of paralysing small animals. Both hydroids and medusae (Hydrozoa) feed on small crustacea, worms, eggs, larvae and small fish. In the feeding reaction of tubularians, for example, the proximal tentacles bearing food bend towards the mouth while the manubrium, in turn, bends to meet them. In colonial forms the food is shared among the mem-bers of the colony. The individual polyps initiate digestion of the prey which they capture, and a constriction at the entrance to the stalk allows only the smallest particles and dissolved material to gain ingress into the branches and common stem of the colony, where absorption takes place. *Corymorpha*, a solitary hydroid living on soft bottoms, feeds on detrital matter and has characteristic feeding movements which are repeated in quiet water about twenty times a minute. When feeding, the stalk bends over, mouth and distal tentacles touch the mud, after which the stalk straightens out and food material adhering to the tentacles is conveyed to the mouth.

In hydromedusae, food is grasped by the marginal tentacles which respond to chemical and tactile stimuli. In the subsequent feeding reaction the stimulated margin bends towards the manubrium (*Phialidium*) or, when the manubrium is long, the latter structure bends towards the margin (*Stomatoca*). The food is seized by the lips of the manubrium and swallowed. Some species display a fishing behaviour in which they swim to the surface and then float downwards with tentacles fully extended (56).

Siphonophores are colonial animals, entirely oceanic and pelagic in habit. Special polyps known as dactylozooids, bearing long tentacles, capture and digest the prey. As the animals drift through the water, their long trailing tentacles act like nets, capturing animals which strike against them. The tentacles are muscular and highly contractile, and when the prey is paralysed by nemotocyst-action it is drawn up to the mouths of the gastrozooids by contraction of the tentacles (13, 74, 112).

Feeding behaviour in Scyphomedusae differs in detail but usually involves stinging and manipulating the prey with tentacles and manubrium, after which the food is transferred to the mouth. The food consists of small planktonic animals—small crustacea, worms, small medusae and the like. In *Chrysaora* the tentacles, laden with food, contract and the food particles are swept off by the lips which form a temporary receptacle beneath the stomach. Food material collected by the bell of *Aurelia* is licked off by the oral arms and conveyed by cilia to the mouth and gastric pouches. Experiments have shown that the arms respond to mussel juice, proteins, peptones and amino-acids but not to carbohydrates. *Cassiopeia*, a sedentary form, lies on the bottom with oral surface upwards. Pulsations of the bell produce a current of sea water from which planktonic organisms are seized by the oral arms. The food, entangled in mucus, is swept by ciliary action into the numerous mouths which lie along the arms (98).

Actinians (sea anemones and corals) are exclusively carnivorous. In less specialized corals the collection of food is reserved for the tentacles. These paralyse their prey with nematocysts and convey it to the mouth by muscular action. In some other corals, however, the general ectoderm participates in the capture of food, and ciliary tracts transport particles to the mouth (118, 119).

In sea-anemones the presence of suitable food evokes an orderly series of feeding reactions. When a piece of meat is placed on the tentacles there is first a discharge of cnidae. The tentacles then clasp the food and bend towards the mouth, which turns towards the food and opens. The food is gradually thrust in and swallowed, and the tentacles subsequently return to their normal feeding position. The feeding response is initiated by both mechanical and chemical stimuli. Owing to rapid adaptation mechanical stimuli rarely induce a complete response, but the intervention of proper chemical stimuli usually results in acceptance of foodstuffs. Of a range of chemical substances tested, the most active are proteins and their derivatives, including peptones and various amino-acids. Certain lipoid extracts are also effective, but not carbohydrates. This selective sensitivity is obviously closely related to the purely carnivorous habits of these animals (92).

All ctenophores are carnivorous in feeding habits. Tentaculate forms, exemplified by *Pleurobrachia* and young *Mnemiopsis*, capture small plankton organisms with their tentacles. These are provided with sticky lasso cells known as colloblasts, which hold on to the food. After making a successful capture the tentacle contracts and conveys the food to the mouth. In adult *Mnemiopsis* a complex ciliary and tentacular mechanism is employed. Extending along the sides of this animal are four auricular grooves into which food particles are carried by beating cilia. At the bottom of a groove the particles become entangled on small tentacles: these bend over into a labial trough and food particles are conveyed down the latter channel to the mouth. Non-tentacular beroids capture their prey by means of the extensible mouth rim and can ingest relatively large animals such as crustaceans and other ctenophores.

Turbellaria. These animals possess a muscular pharynx, which can be protruded for capturing food. This consists of a variety of small animals—protozoa, nematodes and small crustaceans. *Cycloporus* (a polyclad) feeds on colonial tunicates, and sucks out zooids individually (58).

Nemertines are entirely carnivorous when adult, feeding on a variety of prey. Immature and small animals feed on protozoa. Larger benthic and littoral species capture small crustacea, worms, molluscs and even small fish, living or dead; pelagic nemertines subsist on small crustacea. Food is captured with the aid of a muscular proboscis which can be everted for some distance in front of the head, and in some species it is actually as long as or longer than the animal's body. When the proboscis is shot forth it entwines itself around the prey, which is retained by tenacious mucus or quietened by means of immobilizing secretions. Moreover in some species the proboscis is armed with sharply pointed stylets (Hoplonemertea, e.g. *Amphiporus*). The food is then conveyed to the mouth to be swallowed entire. A large *Cerebratulus*, for example, can swallow an annelid nearly equal to its own diameter. An aberrant form, *Malacobdella*, is commensal in the mantle cavity of bivalves (*Seliqua*), where it feeds on plankton filtered off by the host (22).

Annelids. Many polychaetes have muscular introverts armed with small teeth, e.g. *Aphrodite, Lumbriconereis, Nephthys, Glycera*, etc. The introvert is used for capturing prey, which consists usually of living animals such as worms, molluscs and small crustaceans. *Nereis virens*, an errant carnivore, also feeds on dead animals and algae. *Tomopteris*, a voracious planktonic form, swallows entire *Sagitta* and larval herrings. Certain syllids, e.g. *Autolytus edwardsi*, attack hydroids. They cut off the tentacles or penetrate the coelenteron by means of pharyngeal teeth, and suck in hydroid tissue and fluids through a protrusible proboscis (91).

Crustacea. Excluding the filter-feeders these animals are generally omnivorous, although many species are chiefly dependent on living prey or carrion. Food material is grasped by head or thoracic appendages and masticated by the mouth parts before being swallowed. Some species capture large particles and prey to supplement filter-feeding. Mysids, for example, seize small animals (crustaceans, arrow worms) with thoracic limbs and tear them up by means of mandibles and maxillules. Isopods are frequently carnivorous or scavenging in habit. *Chiridotea*, for example, seizes carrion with its gnathopods and bites off pieces with the mandibles (107).

Chelae and chelipeds are used by decapods for seizing, manipulating and shredding food. In the prawn *Palaemon* the chelipeds convey pieces of food to the maxillipeds, which hold them while fragments are torn off by the mandibles and other mouth parts. In lobsters (*Nephrops, Palinurus*) food is held by the mandibles, while it is torn up by the action of the third maxillipeds prior to being swallowed. Similarly in the shore crab *Carcinus maenas* the food is shredded and torn before it is swallowed. Pieces seized by the chelae are transferred to the mandibles, which hold them while they are being torn into fragments by the other mouth parts. Algae have little or no food value for larval prawns (*Palaemonetes*), which need animal food for survival (16).

Molluscs. Many gastropods are carnivorous in habits, feeding on living prey or carrion. Some species swallow their prey whole. Tectibranchs, such as *Scaphander* and *Bulla*, swallow entire lamellibranchs, which they grind up in a muscular gizzard. Special predatory habits are also encountered among nudibranchs. *Calma*, for example, feeds on the eggs of shore fishes, which are slit open with the radula and the egg contents extracted. Other gastropods masticate the food to some extent before swallowing it. Thus *Pleurobranchus* grasps pieces of carrion with its muscular proboscis and rasps off bits by means of the radula. It is likely that many of the carnivorous gastropods secrete protease from salivary glands and this assists the radula in breaking up the food. Gymnosomatous pteropods are also carnivorous in habit and feed largely on thecosomes. These animals possess an eversible proboscis provided with various devices for seizing prey, namely hooks, suckers and sticky secretions. Supplementing these devices are jaws and powerful radulae (79).

Among bivalves one group, the septibranchs, have become carnivorous in habits. *Cuspidaria* and *Poromya* are burrowing forms which keep the siphonal openings at the surface. In this position they draw in small animals, living or dead, which chance to be in the vicinity, through the large inhalant siphon. This is accomplished by aspiratory movements of a transverse muscular septum which replaces the branchiae of other lamellibranchs, and which divides the mantle cavity into upper and lower chambers (Fig. 5.26). Perforating the septum are small pores provided with valves and sphincters. Normally the septum lies quiescent with open pores, through which a slight current is maintained by lateral cilia. Several times each minute, however, the septum is lowered slowly, pores are closed, then the septum is quickly lifted, causing water to be expelled through the exhalant siphon and water and food to be sucked in through the inhalant siphon. The food is retained in the infra-septal cavity by a large valve guarding the opening from the inhalant siphon and is pushed into the mouth by small muscular palps. Cilia are greatly reduced and are concerned with the removal of fine particles from the mantle cavity (117).

Cephalopods capture prey by means of arms and tentacles bearing sucking discs. Cuttlefish and octopus feed on fish and decapod crustacea. The prey is conveyed to the mouth by the appendages, torn by the horny

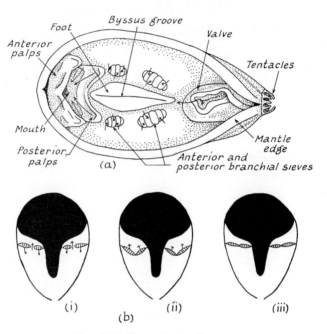

FIG. 5.26. SEPTIBRANCH BIVALVES

(a) Ventral view of *Poromya granulata* with mantle lobes drawn back to expose the septum. Large arrows indicate direction of food; small arrows, water currents through the branchial sieves. (b) Movements of septum in *Cuspidaria*, (i) position of septum at rest and prior to descending; current of water through pores indicated by upward arrows; downward arrows indicate initial septal movement; (ii) position of septum at end of downward movement, pores closed; septum now moves upwards as indicated by arrows; (iii) position at completion of upward movement, pores still closed. (From Yonge, 1928.)

jaws and rasped by a radula. Several salivary glands discharge into the mouth region, namely the sublingual, anterior and posterior salivary glands. The latter two are generally regarded as poison glands. The secretions contain nerve poisons capable of paralysing prey, and a proteolytic enzyme (p. 251) (109, 111).

Chaetognaths are small voracious carnivores, chiefly planktonic in habits. They are provided with a pair of chitinous hooks on either side of the mouth, and with these they seize their prey, usually swallowing it whole. *Sagitta* feeds on copepods, young fish and other arrow worms. *Spadella* is a bottom-dwelling chaetognath which attaches itself to the substratum and lunges at passing prey (93).

Echinoderms. Ophiuroids are omnivorous feeders, sometimes using filtering methods; at others using their mouth-parts to browse on algae or sessile animals, capturing large particles with their tube feet or active animals with the arms (35). Their prey consists of small polychaetes, molluscs and crustaceans: these are captured by the arms and transferred to the mouth to be swallowed whole. Asteroids show diversified carnivorous habits. Those with pointed tube feet, such as *Astropecten*, live in sand and feed upon small lamellibranchs. Others, with sucker tube feet, attack larger bivalves, which they pull open and devour, e.g. *Asterias, Pisaster*. Snails, barnacles, echinoids, even decapod crustacea are attacked. Starfish have the remarkable habit of everting their stomach over the prey if this be too large to be swallowed whole, and digesting the prey before swallowing it (3, 46).

Carnivorous Habits in Vertebrates

Marine vertebrates are predominantly carnivorous and display much variety in feeding habits, enabling them to exploit manifold sources of food.

Fishes. Cyclostomes are scavengers semiparasitic in habits. Lampreys fasten themselves to the bodies of other fish by means of a funnel-shaped sucker which surrounds the mouth. Thus attached, they suck the blood and rasp off the flesh of their prey with horny teeth which are borne on a piston-like tongue. As the teeth wear away, they are replaced by new ones which form underneath. Hagfishes feed on dead or dying fishes and inactive invertebrates. They have a powerful tongue and teeth and bite into their food (105).

Among gnathostome fishes there is great diversity in food and feeding habits. The kind of prey captured by a fish is dependent upon the structure and habits of the fish, as well as the predatory species available. We classify carnivorous fish into pelagic and benthic feeders, and note various methods of locating and seizing prey in these two categories.

Pelagic foragers hunt by sight, scent or touch. These animals are usually provided with a well-developed strong dentition of pointed, cutting or sometimes grinding teeth, which are renewed as they age or wear. In sharks the older teeth in front of the jaw are shed and are replaced by forward movement of more posterior teeth. In teleosts new teeth are formed at the bases of the old, or in the spaces between. As examples of active pelagic foragers which depend upon sight for hunting other fish, we may mention mackerel, tunny, bluefish (*Pomatomus*) and barracudas (*Sphyraena*). The jaws are armed with sharp teeth but are otherwise unspecialized, and agility and speed are used in pursuing the prey. Herring and other clupeids feed by sight, and snap at plankton animals and small fish. Food taken into the mouth is selected by texture and taste (15). Many sharks sight their prey and some have peculiar feeding habits, such as the thresher shark (*Alopias*) which herds shoals of small fishes into compact masses by threshing the water with its tail, before rushing in to devour them. The rough dogfish *Scyliorhinus* hunts chiefly by scent, mostly but not exclusively near the bottom, and feeds on anything which comes its way (57, 101).

Fishes from deeper pelagic waters are frequently much modified in connexion with feeding, but naturally the habits of these animals are subject to inference. Teeth are often long and fang-like and the jaws flexible and distensible, so that very large prey can be captured (*Chauliodus*, *Chiasmodon*, etc., Fig. 5.27). The mechanics of these distensible jaws are described in some detail by Tchernavin (108). Conditions of feeding are certainly peculiar in the dark, sparsely populated waters of the deep sea. Anglers (ceratioids), which have a luminous fishing lure, are believed to attract their prey within reach by this device (Fig. 13.6, p. 542). Long barbels, occurring for example in *Eustomias*, may provide tactile appreciation of prey (Fig. 13.16, p. 551). Very large gape and distensible stomach are significant adaptations to few and infrequent meals.

Carnivorous fishes living on or near the sea bottom may be classed as active foragers, stalkers and purely sedentary forms which sit and wait for prey to come near. Active foragers which depend on sight hunt only by day, at least in shallow waters. The cod, for example, is a roving fish which snaps at anything within its reach on or near the bottom. Foraging is largely visual but is aided by a barbel which is employed as a tactile or gustatory organ. A strictly bottom dweller is the dragonet *Callionymus*. This fish swims along near the bottom and comes to rest at intervals with the body poised on the large pectoral fins. In this manner it explores a wide area of the sea floor and captures such slow-moving bottom forms as crustacea, echinoids and worms. The lemon dab *Microstomus kitt* hunts mainly tubicolous polychaetes. Coming to rest at intervals with head raised, it scans its neighbourhood with movable eyes and, sighting a worm, suddenly pounces upon it.

Certain other bottom fish depend largely on tactile sense when foraging. The sole *Solea solea*, for example, has a dense mass of tactile villi on the lower cheek. When feeding it creeps slowly over the bottom, exploring with its snout and feeling objects in its path with the sensitive cheek villi. Its food consists of errant polychaetes, small crustaceans, molluscs and ophiurans. The gurnard *Trigla lineata* is another form which crawls over the bottom by means of long pectoral filaments (Fig. 5.28). As the fish creeps along, the filaments are kept in constant movement, exploring the bottom: whenever anything promising is encountered, the fish suddenly whirls along and swallows it or subjects it to further examination. The filaments are richly provided with sensory cells acting as taste receptors. Rays are thought to feed largely by scent. On encountering small fish and crustacea they dart over it, cover it with body and pectoral fins, and devour it at leisure (50, 96, 101, 102).

Fishes which stalk their prey are often provided with peculiar mouth parts. In tube-mouthed fishes the snout is prolonged in the form of a tube with a small mouth at the end. Pipe-fishes (Syngnathidae), for example, feed largely on small crustacea, which they actively seek in crevices,

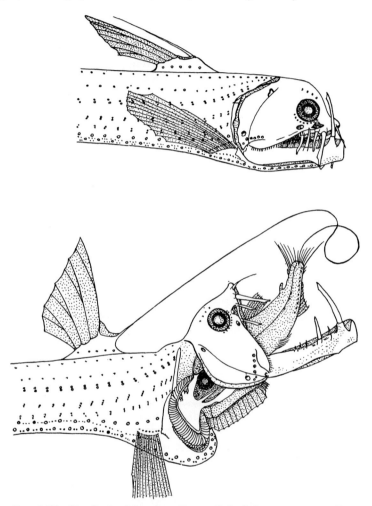

FIG. 5.27. *Chauliodus* (*above*) AT REST; (*below*) SWALLOWING A FISH.
(From Tchernavin (108).)

among vegetation, etc. The tube-like beak is used after the manner of a syringe, small crustaceans being sucked in by inflating the cheeks. The John Dory *Zeus* is provided with a protractile mouth and stalks small fish. Gradually approaching its victim, it shoots its jaws forward with great rapidity and engulfs the prey.

Finally we may note a few examples of sedentary benthic forms which lie and wait for prey to approach. Perhaps the best-known is the angler-fish *Lophius piscatorius*, which simulates the bottom on which it lies remarkably closely in shade and pattern. The first dorsal spine of the angler consists of a movable spine with a bait-like tag at the end, and this can be erected as a fishing lure. When a fish is attracted by the lure, this is cast down in front of the mouth, and as the fish follows it the angler opens its mouth and takes in its victim with a sudden gulp. Angler-fish feed preferably on gadoids, clupeoids and other soft-finned fishes. Of a similar nature are the habits of stargazers *Uranoscopus*. The mouths of these creatures open towards the dorsal surface of the head and they bury themselves to a large extent in the sand, with only the mouth and eyes at the surface. At intervals a small

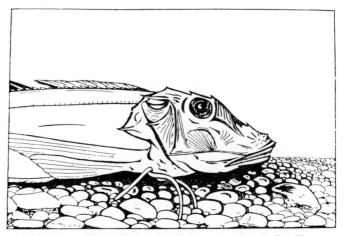

FIG. 5.28. *Trigla lucerna* FEELING ITS WAY ALONG THE SEA FLOOR BY MEANS OF LONG PECTORAL FILAMENTS. (From Steven (101).)

lure is protruded from the mouth and caused to wriggle on the sand so as to simulate a worm or other small invertebrate, and thus attract small prey to within reach of the stargazer's jaws. The electric fish *Torpedo*, which is an inactive benthic form, is believed to stun or kill other fish by means of electric shocks. This animal captures round fishes, some of them of fair size. Individuals, observed in captivity, respond only to living prey. At the approach of a fish the electric ray leaps upwards and attempts to envelop it with its pectoral fins and snout. Galvanometer recordings obtained during this manoeuvre show that the ray discharges an electric shock at the moment that it folds its head and wings over the prey. The shock apparently is used to stun the prey while it is being swallowed (110, 117).

Marine Birds. Marine birds can be grouped into several communities: as littoral species confined to shores and beaches, e.g. plover, sandpipers; inshore species which do not range beyond sight of land, e.g. cormorants, ducks, the majority of gulls and terns; offshore species which range out to the continental edge, e.g. gannets, auks, certain gulls; and pelagic species, notably the tubinares (petrels, shearwaters, albatrosses) and penguins. The food of the various species is determined by availability in the regions frequented but each species has its own inherent feeding habits (Fig. 5.29).

Along shores the sandpipers and plovers feed on small crustacea, insects, worms and molluscs secured at the surface, by turning over stones or weed or by probing into the ground. Curlews, willets and phalaropes have

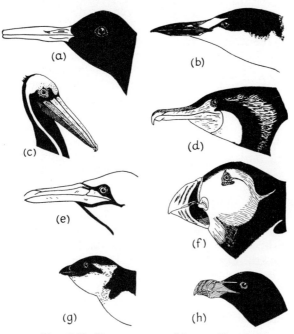

FIG. 5.29. HEADS OF SOME MARINE BIRDS

(*a*) Oyster catcher *Haematopus*; (*b*) sooty tern *Sterna fuscata*; (*c*) brown pelican *Pelecanus occidentalis*; (*d*) cormorant *Phalacrocorax*; (*e*) gannet *Sula bassana*, (*f*) puffin, *Fratercula*; (*g*) dovekie *Alle alle*; (*h*) razor-billed auk *Alca torda*.

long thin bills which serve for probing in sand and mud. Oyster-catchers (*Haematopus*) and turnstones (*Arenaria*) use their chisel-like bills for jabbing shellfish or knocking limpets off rocks.

In high latitudes of the southern hemisphere are found peculiar littoral birds known as sheath-bills (Chionididae). The sheath-bill is an omnivorous scavenger but also feeds in the inter-tidal zone on small fishes and invertebrates. Another antarctic scavenger is the giant fulmar (*Macronectes giganteus*). At sea it feeds on crustacea and squid, but it spends much time on land, where it eats offal and attacks other birds.

Gulls have varied feeding habits. They gather shellfish, worms, crustacea, etc., on the shore when the tide is out, and also fish and play the role of scavengers in coastal waters. Terns are mainly coastal birds of warmer waters, although some species migrate far north to breed, notably the arctic tern *Sterna paradisea*. Their food is mainly small fish which they secure by plunging from the wing into the sea. To a minor extent small cuttlefish, crustacea and pelagic molluscs are also taken.

Conspicuous fishers in coastal waters are cormorants and shags (Phala-crocoracidae). Their food consists chiefly of fish and crustacea, obtained by diving from the surface. Cormorants possess hooked mandibles, and employ feet and wings for propulsion under water. Pelicans (Pelicanidae) frequent coasts and estuaries, where they dive for fish in shallow waters. Frigate-birds (*Fregata*) are tropical and completely aerial in habits. They feed on fish, molluscs, jellyfishes, etc., picked up from the surface, and they also force other birds such as gulls and terns to release their catch.

Characteristic coastal and offshore birds of the continental shelf in the northern hemisphere are the auks, guillemots and puffins (Alcidae). Their food consists of planktonic crustacea and fish, which are captured by diving from the surface. Gannets and boobies (Sulidae) are also fish eaters, which plunge from the wing and pursue their prey beneath the surface. These birds generally have lance-shaped bills suited for catching fish and larger crustaceans.

In the southern hemisphere the role of the Alcidae is filled by penguins and diving petrels. Some penguins are pelagic in the non-breeding season, others sedentary in habits. Their food consists almost entirely of fish, cuttlefish and crustacea, obtained by diving. King penguins consume squid and fish; smaller penguins, such as the Adélie and Gentoo, feed extensively on krill, especially *Euphausia*. The diving petrels of the southern hemisphere (Pelecanoididae) are usually found in coastal regions, although some species are partly pelagic in habits. Their food consists largely of small fish and crustacea, obtained by diving.

Among the characteristic pelagic birds are the Tubinares—petrels, shearwaters, fulmars and albatrosses. Most of these birds spend much of their lives far beyond sight of land. Their food consists to a large extent of surface plankton, including crustacea, jellyfish, molluscs, as well as squid and small fish. They frequently glean their food from the surface as they skim over the waves, but they sometimes settle to swim about and feed when food is concentrated, or dive short distances below the surface. With the large-scale exploitation of marine resources now practised by man, namely whaling and trawling, some sea birds, notably fulmars, obtain a substantial amount of their food from the offal thus afforded. Indeed Fisher (34) advances evidence for the thesis that the phenomenal increase in numbers of the fulmar (*Fulmarus glacialis*) in the North Atlantic during the past three centuries is the result of the additional food provided for these birds by the activities of whalers and, later, steam trawlers. Other pelagic birds have diets as follows: penguins (fish and plankton feeders); kittiwakes and swallow-tailed gulls (fish, crustacea, molluscs, offal); tropic birds (fish and squid) (26, 31, 34, 49, 63, 68, 84, 88, 103, 104, 114, 115).

Mammals. Carnivorous marine mammals include whales, seals, sea otters and even bats.

The toothed whales (Odontoceti) are hunters and exploit many forms of nekton. The sperm whale *Physeter* feeds on fishes and especially cephalopods. It is believed that squid are caught during deep dives. Porpoises and dolphins are voracious feeders on small fish. The killer whales (*Orca*) are powerful rapacious animals and are the only whales that attack other cetaceans. They eat whole porpoises, seals, and kill walruses and large whales.

Seals differ greatly in feeding habits. Some seals are planktonic feeders. Ringed seals (*Phoca hispida*) and harp seals (*P. groenlandica*) in the Canadian Arctic eat mostly planktonic crustacea, at least in summer. Crab-eating seals (*Lobodon carcinophagus*) of the Antarctic are selective feeders, consuming krill. Fish plays an important part in the diet of eared seals (*Callorhinus ursina*). Elephant seals (*Mirounga leonina*) of South Georgia capture cephalopods; walruses (*Odobenus*) dive after bivalves. In antarctic waters the large leopard seal, besides eating fish and cephalopods, attacks penguins and other seals (33, 45, 81, 82).

Among other carnivorous marine mammals we may note the interesting sea-otter (*Enhydra lutris*), colonies of which occur off the west coast of North America. Their food consists of hard-shelled invertebrates—bivalves, sea-urchins, abalones, etc.—which they collect on the bottom (11). A curious return to the sea has been made by certain peculiar piscivorous bats (*Noctilio, Pizonyx*) which fly offshore and capture fish at the surface, using their hind legs for that purpose (2).

MECHANISMS FOR TAKING IN FLUIDS OR SOFT TISSUES

These mechanisms are especially characteristic of parasites.

Some parasitic polychaetes are described in Chapter 14. *Ichthyotomus sanguinarius* is a blood-sucker, attacking eels (*Myrus*). It cuts into the flesh of the fish by means of a pair of stylets and pumps in blood with its pharynx. An anticoagulant is secreted by glands near the mouth (Fig. 14.8, p. 589). Marine leeches, such as *Pontobdella* which attacks rays, also have piercing jaws and secrete an anticoagulant hirudin from salivary glands.

Certain gastropods, free-living and parasitic, fall into this category, There are nudibranchs, such as *Hermaea*, which slit open algae (*Codium.* etc.) with their radulae, and suck in the fluid contents of the cells. *Dendrodoris* attacks compound ascidians, sucking in the soft tissues. Among parasites may be mentioned ectoparasitic Aglossa with well-developed suctorial proboscides (p. 590). There is also a semiparasitic lamellibranch *Entovalva*, which lives in *Synapta*, and which apparently depends on fluid matter for nutriment.

Parasitic crustaceans often depend upon piercing and sucking to obtain nourishment. Parasitic copepods found in fish and invertebrates usually have suctorial mouth parts which allow only liquid or semiliquid food to be ingested. Ectoparasitic Epicaridea possess stylet-like mandibles enclosed in a suctorial oral cone.

Pycnogonids are partially sucking, partially raptorial in habit. They are armed with a complicated proboscis for sucking in soft tissues and fluids. They show a preference for hydroids and anthozoans, but also attack many other soft-bodied animals, including tunicates, holothurians, etc. Hydranths are seized with the chelae and gradually forced into the mouth. When feeding on larger animals, e.g. actinians, the proboscis is thrust into the host and the tissue juices sucked out. In the hind part of the proboscis there is a filter of chitinous hairs which strain out coarse matter so that only juice and fine particles reach the mid gut (53).

Finally, we may mention those endoparasites, which have lost both feeding mechanisms and alimentary canal, and absorb circumambient nutrient fluids through the general body surface. Examples are cestodes, endoparasitic gastropods (Entoconchidae) and rhizocephalans (9).

REFERENCES

1. AL-HUSSAINI, A. H., "On the functional morphology of the alimentary tract of some fish in relation to differences in their feeding habits," *Quart. J. Micr. Sci.*, **90**, 109 (1949).
2. ALLEN, G. M., *Bats* (Cambridge, Harvard Univ. Press, 1940).
3. ANDERSON, J. M., "Studies on the cardiac stomach of the starfish, *Asterias forbesi,*" *Biol. Bull.*, **107**, 157 (1954).
4. ANKEL, W. E., "Erwerb und Aufnahme der Nahrung bei den Gastropoden," *Verh. dtsch. zool. Ges.*, **40**, 223 (1938).
5. ATKINS, D., "The ciliary feeding mechanism of the entoproct Polyzoa, and a comparison with that of the ectoproct Polyzoa," *Quart. J. Micr. Sci.*, **75**, 393 (1932).
6. ATKINS, D., "On the ciliary mechanisms and interrelationships of lamellibranchs," *Quart. J. Micr. Sci.*, **84**, 187 (1943).
7. ATKINS, D., "The ciliary feeding mechanism of the Megathyridae (Brachiopoda)," *J. Mar. Biol. Ass. U.K.*, **39**, 459 (1960).
8. ATKINS, D. and RUDWICK, M. J. S., "The lophophore and ciliary feeding mechanisms of the brachiopod *Crania,*" *J. Mar. Biol. Ass. U.K.*, **42**, 469 (1962).
9. BAER, J. G., *Le Parasitisme* (Lausanne, F. Rouge & Cie, Librairie de l'Université; Paris, Masson, 1946).
10. BALLANTINE, D. and MORTON, J. E., "Filtering, feeding and digestion in the lamellibranch *Lasaea rubra,*" *J. Mar. Biol. Ass. U.K.*, **35**, 241 (1956).
11. BARABASH–NIKIFOROV, I. I., *The Sea Otter*. Translated from the Russian (U.S. Dept. of Commerce, Office of Technical Services, 1962).
12. BARRINGTON, E. J. W., "Observations on feeding and digestion in *Glossobalanus minutus,*" *Quart. J. Micr. Sci.*, **82**, 227 (1940).
13. BERRILL, N. J., "On the occurrence and habits of the siphonophore, *Stephanomia bijuga,*" *J. Mar. Biol. Ass. U.K.*, **16**, 753 (1930).

14. BIDDER, G. P., "The relation of the form of a sponge to its currents." *Quart. J. Micr. Sci.*, **67**, 293 (1923).

15. BLAXTER, J. H. S. and HOLLIDAY, F. G. T., "The behaviour and physiology of herring and other clupeids," *Adv. Mar. Biol.*, **1**, 261 (1963).

16. BROAD, A. C., "The relationship between diet and larval development of Palaemonetes," *Biol. Bull.*, **112**, 162 (1957).

17. BUCHANAN, J. B. and HEDLEY, R. H., "A contribution to the biology of *Astrorhiza limicola* (Foraminifera)," *J. Mar. Biol. Ass. U.K.*, **39**, 549 (1950).

18. CANNON, H. G., "On the feeding mechanism of certain marine ostracods," *Trans. Roy. Soc. Edinb.*, **57**, 739 (1933).

19. CARLISLE, D. B., "Alcune osservazioni sulla meccanica dell'alimentazione della *Salpa*," *Pubbl. Staz. Zool. Napoli*, **22**, 146 (1950).

20. CARRIKER, M. R., "On the structure and function of the proboscis in the common oyster drill, *Urosalpinx cinerea*," *J. Morph.*, **73**, 441 (1943).

21. CARRIKER, M. R., "Observations on the penetration of tightly closing bivalves by *Busycon* and other predators," *Ecology*, **32**, 73 (1951).

22. COE, W. R., "Biology of the nemerteans of the Atlantic coast of North America," *Trans. Conn. Acad. Arts Sci.*, **35**, 129 (1943).

23. COE, W. R., "Nutrition, environmental conditions, and growth of marine bivalve mollusks," *J. Mar. Res.*, **7**, 586 (1948).

24. CORNER, E. D. S., "On the nutrition and metabolism of zooplankton. I. Preliminary observations on the feeding of the marine copepod, *Calanus helgolandicus*," *J. Mar. Biol. Ass. U.K.*, **41**, 5 (1961).

25. CORNER, E. D. S. and COWEY, C. B., "Some nitrogenous constituents of the plankton," *Oceanogr. Mar. Biol. Ann-Rev*, **2**, 147 (1964).

26. COTTAM, C. and HANSON, H. C., "Food habits of some arctic birds and mammals," *Zool. Ser. Field Mus. Nat. Hist.*, **20**, 405 (1938).

27. COWEY, C. B. and CORNER, E. D. S., "On the nutrition and metabolism of zooplankton," *J. Mar. Biol. Ass. U.K.*, **43**, 495 (1963).

28. DALES, R. P. *Annelids* (London, Hutchinson Univ. Library, 1963).

29. DAVIS, H. C., "On food and feeding of larvae of the American oyster, *C. virginica*," *Biol. Bull.*, **104**, 334 (1953).

30. DENNELL, R., "Note on the feeding of *Amphioxus* (*Branchiostoma bermudae*)," *Proc. Roy. Soc. Edin. B.*, **64**, 229 (1950).

31. DEWAR, J. M., "Identity of specialized feeding habits of the turnstone and oyster-catcher," *Brit. Birds*, **34**, 26 (1940).

32. DIXON, A. Y., "Notes on certain aspects of the biology of *Cumopsis goodsiri* and some other cumaceans in relation to their environment," *J. Mar. Biol. Ass. U.K.*, **26**, 61 (1944).

33. DUNBAR, M. J., "On the food of seals in the Canadian eastern arctic," *Canad. J. Res.*, D, **19**, 150 (1941).

34. FISHER, J., *The Fulmar* (London, Collins, 1952).

35. FONTAINE, A. R., "The feeding mechanisms of the ophiuroid *Ophiocomina nigra*," *J. Mar. Biol. Ass. U.K.*, **45**, 373 (1965).

36. FORREST, J. E., "On the feeding habits and the morphology and mode of functioning of the alimentary canal in some littoral dorid nudibranchiate mollusca," *Proc. Linn. Soc.*, **164**, 225 (1953).

37. FOX, D. L., "Comparative metabolism of organic detritus by inshore animals," *Ecology*, **31**, 100 (1950).

38. FRETTER, V., "Observations on the life history and functional morphology of *Cerithiopsis* and *Triphora*," *J. Mar. Biol. Ass. U.K.*, **29**, 567 (1951).

39. GARSTANG, W., "*Spolia bermudiana*. 2. The ciliary feeding mechanism of Tornaria," *Quart. J. Micr. Sci.*, **81**, 347 (1939).

40. GOODBODY, I., "The feeding mechanism in the sand dollar *Meletta*," *Biol. Bull.*, **119**, 80 (1960).

41. GRAHAM, A., "Form and function in the molluscs," *Proc. Linn. Soc.*, **164**, 213 (1953).

42. GREENFIELD, L. J., "Observations on the nitrogen and glycogen content of *Teredo*," *Bull. Mar. Sci. Gulf Caribbean*, **2**, 486 (1953).

43. GROSS, F., "Zur Biologie und Entwicklungsgeschichte von *Noctiluca miliaris*," *Arch. Protistenk.*, **83**, 178 (1934).

44. HALL, V. E., "The muscular activity and oxygen consumption of *Urechis caupo*," *Biol. Bull.*, **61**, 400 (1931).

45. HAMILTON, J. E., "The leopard seal *Hydrurga leptonyx*," '*Discovery*' *Rep.*, **18**, 241 (1939).

46. HANCOCK, D. A., "The feeding behaviour of starfish on Essex oyster beds," *J. Mar. Biol. Ass. U.K.*, **34**, 313 (1955).

47. HARDY, A. C. and GUNTHER, E. R., "The plankton of the South Georgia whaling grounds and adjacent waters, 1926–1927," '*Discovery*' *Rep.*, **11**, 1 (1935).

48. HARLEY, M. B., "Occurrence of a filter-feeding mechanism in the polychaete *Nereis diversicolor*," *Nature*, **165**, 734 (1950).

49. HARTLEY, C. H. and FISHER, J., "The marine foods of birds in an inland fjord region in West Spitsbergen. 2. Birds," *J. Anim. Ecol.*, **5**, 370 (1936).

50. HARTLEY, P. H. T., "The Saltash tuck-net fishery and the ecology of some estuarine fishes," *J. Mar. Biol. Ass. U.K.*, **24**, 1 (1940).

51. HARVEY, H. W., *Recent Advances in the Chemistry and Biology of Sea Water* (Cambridge Univ. Press, 1945).

52. HARVEY, H. W., "On the production of living matter in the sea off Plymouth," *J. Mar. Biol. Ass. U.K.*, **29**, 97 (1950).

53. HELFER, H. and SCHLOTTKE, E., "Pantapoda," *Bronn's Klassen*, **5**, IV Abt., 2 Buch (1935).

54. HOPKINS, D. L., "The relation between food, the rate of locomotion and reproduction in the marine amoeba, *Flabellula mira*," *Biol. Bull.*, **72**, 334 (1937).

55. HOYLE, G., "Spontaneous squirting of an ascidian, *Phallusia mammillata*," *J. Mar. Biol. Ass. U.K.*, **31**, 541 (1953).

56. HYMAN, L. H., "Observations and experiments on the physiology of medusae," *Biol. Bull.*, **79**, 282 (1940).

57. IFFT, J. D. and ZINN, D. J., "Tooth succession in the smooth dogfish, *Mustelus canis*," ibid., **95**, 100 (1948).

58. JENNINGS, J. B., "Studies on feeding, digestion, and food storage in free-living flatworms," ibid., **112**, 63 (1957).

59. JENSEN, A. S., "Do the Naticidae drill by mechanical or by chemical means?" *Nature*, **167**, 901 (1951).

60. ØRGENSEN, C. B., "Quantitative aspects of filter feeding in invertebrates," *Biol. Rev.*, **30**, 391 (1955).

61. KITCHING, J. A., "On suction in Suctoria," *Colston Papers* (*Proc. 7th Symp. Colston Research Soc.*), **7**, 197 (1954).

62. KNIGHT-JONES, E. W., "Feeding in *Saccoglossus* (Enteropneusta)," *Proc. Zool. Soc.*, **123**, 637 (1953).

63. LACK, D., "The ecology of closely related species with special reference to cormorant (*Phalacrocorax carbo*) and shag (*P. aristotelis*)," *J. Anim. Ecol.*, **14**, 12 (1945).

64. LASKER, R. and LANE, C. E., "The origin and distribution of nitrogen in *Teredo bartschi*," *Biol. Bull.*, **105**, 316 (1953).

65. LONGLEY, W. H. and HILDEBRAND, S. F., "Systematic catalogue of the fishes of Tortugas, Florida," *Publ. Carneg. Instn.* No. 535 (Papers Tortugas Lab. **34**, 331, 1941).

66. LOOSANOFF, V. L. and ENGLE, J. B., "Effect of different concentrations of micro-organisms on the feeding of oysters," *Fish. Bull.*, *U.S.*, **51**, 31 (1947).

67. LOOSANOFF, V. L. and NOMEJKO, C. A., "Feeding of oysters in relation to tidal stages and to periods of light and darkness," *Biol. Bull.*, **90**, 244 (1946).

68. LUMSDEN, W. H. R. and HADDOW, A. J., "The food of the shag (*Phalacrocorax aristotelis*) in the Clyde Sea Area," *J. Anim. Ecol.*, **15**, 35 (1946).

69. MACDONALD, R., "Food and habits of *Meganyctiphanes norvegica*," *J. Mar. Biol. Ass. U.K.*, **14**, 753 (1927).

70. MACGINITIE, G. E., "The natural history of the mud shrimp *Upogebia pugettensis*," *Ann. Mag. Nat. Hist.*, Ser. 10, **6**, 36 (1930).

71. MACGINITIE, G. E., "The method of feeding of *Chaetopterus*," *Biol. Bull.*, **77**, 115 (1939).

72. MACGINITIE, G. E., "The method of feeding of tunicates," ibid., **77**, 443 (1939).

73. MACGINITIE, G. E., "The size of the mesh openings in mucous feeding nets of marine animals," ibid., **88**, 107 (1945).

74. MACKIE, G. O. and BOAG, D. A., "Fishing, feeding and digestion in siphonophores," *Pubbl. Staz. Zool. Napoli*, **33**, 178 (1963).

75. MACKINTOSH, N. A., "The natural history of whalebone whales," *Biol. Rev.*, **21**, 60 (1946).

76. MANGUM, C. P., "Activity patterns in metabolism and ecology of poly-chaetes," *Comp. Biochem. Physiol.*, **11**, 239 (1964).

77. MARSHALL, S. M. and ORR, A. P., "The production of animal plankton in the sea," *Essays in marine biology: Elmhirst Memorial Lectures*, p. 122 (Edinburgh, Oliver and Boyd, 1953),

78. MARSHALL, S. M. and ORR, A. P., *The Biology of a Marine Copepod* (Edinburgh, Oliver and Boyd, 1955).

79. MASSY, A. L., "Mollusca; Gastropoda Thecosomata and Gymnosomata," '*Discovery*' *Rep.*, **3**, 267 (1932).

80. MAST, S. O. and BOWEN, W. J., "The food-vacuole in the Peritricha, with special reference to the hydrogen-ion concentration of its content and of the cytoplasm," *Biol. Bull.*, **87**, 188 (1944).

81. MATTHEWS, L. H., "The natural history of the elephant seal with notes on other seals found at South Georgia," '*Discovery*' *Rep.*, **1**, 235 (1929).

82. MATTHEWS, L. H., "The sperm whale, *Physeter catodon*," ibid., **17**, 93 (1938).

83. MATTHEWS, L. H. and PARKER, H. W., "Notes on the anatomy and biology of the basking shark (*Cetorhinus maximus*)," *Proc. Zool. Soc.*, **120**, 535 (1950).

84. MOORE, H. B., "The biology of *Purpura lapillus*. 3. Life history and relation to environmental factors," *J. Mar. Biol. Ass. U.K.*, **23**, 67 (1938).

85. MORTON, J. E., "The structure and adaptations of the New Zealand Vermetidae," *Trans. Roy. Soc. N.Z.*, **79**, 1 (1951).

86. MORTON, J. E., "The biology of *Limacina retroversa*," *J. Mar. Biol. Ass. U.K.*, **33**, 297 (1954).

87. MORTON, J. E., BONEY, A. D. and CORNER, E. D. S., "The adaptations of *Lasaea rubra*, a small intertidal lamellibranch," ibid., **36**, 383 (1957).

88. MURPHY, R. C., *Oceanic Birds of South America*, 2 vols. (New York, Amer. Mus. Nat. Hist., 1936).

89. NAYLOR, E., "The diet and feeding mechanism of *Idotea*," *J. Mar. Biol. Ass. U.K.*, **34**, 347 (1955).

90. NIKOLSKY, G. V., *The Ecology of Fishes*, translated by Birkett, L. (London and New York, Academic Press).

91. OKADA, YÔ K., "Feeding organs and feeding habits of *Autolytus Edwarsi* St. Joseph," *Quart. J. Micr. Sci.*, **72**, 219 (1929).

92. PANTIN, C. F. A. and PANTIN, A. M. P., "The stimulus to feeding in *Anemonia sulcata*," *J. Exp. Biol.*, **20**, 6 (1943).

93. PARRY, D. A., "Structure and function of the gut in *Spadella* and *Sagitta*," *J. Mar. Biol. Ass. U.K.*, **26**, 16 (1944).

94. RICHTER, R., "Einiges über die Lebensweise des Eissturmvogels (*Fulmarus glacialis*)," *J. Orn. Lpz.*, **85**, 187 (1937).

95. SCHAFER, R. D. and LANE, C. E., "Some preliminary observations bearing on the nutrition of *Limnoria*," *Bull. Mar. Sci. Gulf Caribbean*, **7**, 289 (1957).

96. SCHARRER, E., "Die Empfindlichkeit der freien Flossenstrahlen des Knurrhahns (*Trigla*) für chemische Reize," *Z. vergl. Physiol.*, **22**, 145 (1935).

97. SCHEER, B. T., *Comparative Physiology* (London, Chapman and Hall, 1948).

98. SOUTHWARD, A. J., "Observations on the ciliary currents of the jelly-fish *Aurelia aurita*," *J. Mar. Biol. Ass. U.K.*, **34**, 201 (1955).

99. STEHOUWER, H., "The preference of the slug *Aeolidia papillosa* for the sea anemone *Metridium senile*," *Arch. Néer Zool.*, **10**, 161 (1952).

100. STEPHENS, G. C., "Uptake of organic material of aquatic invertebrates. II. Accumulation of amino acids by the bamboo worm *Clymenella torquata*," *Comp. Biochem. Physiol.*, **10**, 191 (1963).

101. STEVEN, G. A., "Bottom fauna and the food of fishes," *J. Mar. Biol. Ass. U.K.*, **16**, 677 (1930).

102. STEVEN, G. A., "Rays and skates of Devon and Cornwall. 2. A study of the fishery; with notes on the occurrence, migrations and habits of the species," ibid., **18**, 1 (1932).

103. STEVEN, G. A., "The food consumed by shags and cormorants around the shores of Cornwall," ibid., **19**, 277 (1933).

104. STOTT, F. C., "The marine foods of birds in an inland fjord region in West Spitsbergen. 1. Plankton and in-shore benthos," *J. Anim. Ecol.*, **5**, 356 (1936).

105. STRAHAN, R., "The behaviour of *Myxine* and other myxinoids," *The Biology of Myxine*, Eds. Brodal, A. and Fänge, R., p. 22 (Oslo, Universitetsforlaget, 1963).

106. TAMMES, P. M. L. and DRAL, A. D. G., "Observations on the straining of suspensions by mussels," *Arch. Néerl. Zool.*, **11**, 87 (1955).

107. TATTERSALL, W. M. and TATTERSALL, O. S., *The British Mysidacea* (London, Ray Soc., 1951).

108. TCHERNAVIN, V. V., *The Feeding Mechanisms of a Deep Sea Fish Chauliodus sloani* (London, Brit. Mus. (Nat. Hist.), 1953).

109. TOMPSETT, D. H., *Sepia*, L.M.B.C. Mem. 32 (Univ. Liverpool Press, 1939).

110. WILSON, D. P., "The habits of the angler-fish, *Lophius piscatorius*," *J. Mar. Biol. Ass. U.K.*, **21**, 477 (1937).

111. WILSON, D. P., "A note on the capture of prey by *Sepia officinalis*," ibid., **26**, 421 (1946).

112. WILSON, D. P., "The Portuguese man-of-war, *Physalia physalis* L., in British and adjacent seas," ibid., **27**, 139 (1947).

113. WILSON, D. P., "Notes from the Plymouth aquarium. 2," ibid., **32**, 199 (1953).

114. WITHERBY, H. F., JOURDAIN, F. C. R., TICEHURST, N. F. and TUCKER, B. W., *The Handbook of British Birds*, Vols. 3 and 4 (London, Witherby, 1944).

115. WYNNE-EDWARDS, V. C., "On the habits and distribution of birds on the North Atlantic," *Proc. Boston Soc. Nat. Hist.*, **40**, 233 (1935).

116. YONGE, C. M., "Feeding mechanisms in the invertebrates," *Biol. Rev.*, **3**, 21 (1928).

117. YONGE, C. M., "Structure and function of the organs of feeding and digestion in the septibranchs, *Cuspidaria* and *Poromya*," *Phil. Trans. Roy. Soc. B.*, **216**, 221 (1928).

118. YONGE, C. M., "Studies on the physiology of corals. 1. Feeding mechanisms and food," *Sci. Rep. Gr. Barrier Reef Exped.*, **1**, 13 (1930).

119. YONGE, C. M., "A note on *Balanophyllia regia*, the only Eupsammiid coral in the British fauna," *J. Mar. Biol. Ass. U.K.*, **18**, 219 (1932).

120. YONGE, C. M., "On the habits and adaptations of *Aloidis gibba*," ibid., **26**, 358 (1946).

121. YONGE, C. M., "On the habits of *Turritella communis*," ibid., **26**, 377 (1946).

122. YONGE, C. M., "Marine boring organisms," *Research*, **4**, 162 (1951).

123. YONGE, C. M., "Alimentary canal, food, and feeding of invertebrates," *Tabul. Biol.*, **21**, Pts. 3 and 4 (1954).

124. YONGE, C. M. and ILES, E. J., "On the mantle cavity, pedal gland, and evolution of mucous feeding in the *Vermetidae*," *Ann. Mag. Nat. Hist.*, Ser. 11, **3**, 536 (1939).

125. ZOBELL, C. E. and FELTHAM, C. B., "Bacteria as food for certain marine invertebrates," *J. Mar. Res.*, **1**, 312 (1938).

CHAPTER 6

DIGESTION

For many divisions there are in the stomack of severall animals: what number they maintain in the *Scarus* and ruminating Fish, common description, or our own experiment hath made no discovery. But in the Ventricle of *Porpuses* there are three divisions. In many Birds a crop, gizzard, and little receptacle before it; but in Cornigerous animals, which chew the cudd, there are no less than four of distinct position and office.

SIR THOMAS BROWNE, *Garden of Cyprus*

INTRODUCTION

IN the preceding chapter we have reviewed various feeding methods encountered among marine animals and we now turn to a consideration of how foodstuffs are digested and absorbed. The earliest holozoic denizens of the seas were probably unicellular forms that ingested their food by phagocytic action. This level of organization is represented by marine rhizopods and flagellates among the protozoa. In this group there is diverse specialization within the boundary of a single cell-equivalent, and intracellular digestive mechanisms are present. Digestion in sponges is essentially the same as in protozoans, since they lack a true gut and capture food particles by means of flagellated choanocytes, which resemble choano-flagellate protozoans. In metazoans a true gut is present, except in certain degenerate and parasitic forms, and it is here that the food is processed and broken down preparatory to assimilation by the animal. In the following account attention will be focused on digestive processes in invertebrate metazoans and lower chordates. Comparative reviews of digestion in these animals have been prepared by Yonge (66), Vonk (61) and Barrington (8).

FUNCTIONAL DIVISIONS OF THE GUT

The foodstuffs utilized by animals and the digestive mechanisms which deal with the ingested food show extraordinary diversity throughout the animal kingdom. Every conceivable kind of organic food is exploited and consumed in the sea. In general it may be said that the form of the alimentary canal and the nature of the digestive process are correlated with the mode of feeding and character of the food. From a functional viewpoint Yonge (66) has proposed a classification recognizing the following five regions in the gut: (*a*) reception; (*b*) conduction and storage; (*c*) digestion and internal trituration; (*d*) absorption; (*e*) formation and transport of faeces.

250

INGESTION, STORAGE AND TRITURATION OF FOOD

Reception

The region of reception includes the mouth, buccal cavity and pharynx, together with those diverse ancillary structures employed in feeding— for example, ciliated fields, biting mouth parts, radulae, jaws and sucking apparatuses. The work of these structures in gathering or seizing food has already been described (Chapter 5). Digestion of foodstuffs takes two forms: the food particles are taken in by cells and broken down intracellularly; or they are attacked by digestive enzymes in the gut cavity and the soluble products are absorbed. Food material has to be selected of a size that can be swallowed; or, if of excessive size for the gape, it must be reduced to suitable dimensions. The food of filter and detritus feeders is preselected and consists of fine particles. Scrapers and borers, by means of mechanical aids, obtain their food in particulate condition. Carnivores and omnivores break down prey or food masses by tearing them apart with appendages or mouth parts; grinding them up in the mouth or gizzard; or by subjecting them to chemical action. In any event the food has to be rendered particulate in order to permit phagocytosis, or to provide maximal surface for enzymatic action.

In the anterior gut region there are teeth in the buccal cavity of vertebrates; radulae and jaws in chitons, gastropods and cephalopods; and jaws on the eversible pharynx of certain errant and carnivorous polychaetes. The muscular pharynx of the polychaete *Aphrodite* serves as a gizzard for crushing the food.

In some animals preliminary chemical action is used to attack and break down large food masses preparatory to swallowing. Carnivorous nemertines (*Lineus*) kill ingested prey by means of an acid secretion in the foregut (37). Certain carnivorous gastropods which lack a gizzard—e.g. *Dolium, Cassis*—secrete free acid from the buccal glands and use it for dissolving calcareous matter in their food (consisting of other molluscs and echinoderms). A poisonous secretion is produced by the buccal glands of certain gastropods (Toxiglossa) and by the posterior salivary gland of the octopus. In the latter animal the gland produces amines having powerful effects on the nervous system, such as tyramine, octopamine and hydroxytryptamine. These toxic secretions are used to immobilize the prey (6, 27). Equally specialized are the salivary glands of blood-sucking ectoparasites such as leeches and the polychaete *Ichthyotomus*, which produce an anticoagulant (p. 588). The secretion of the salivary or sublingual glands of lampreys also prevents coagulation of the blood of fishes on which the lamprey feeds.

Proteolytic secretions are poured over the food in some instances to reduce it to semi-liquid form, a process termed extra-intestinal digestion. To cope with large food masses starfish evert the stomach and pour proteases over the food, and Portuguese men-of-war discharge ferments through the gasterozooids which adhere to the prey. A polyclad *Leptoplana* initiates digestion outside the body by exuding protease through the everted pharynx over the food mass. The enzyme in these instances is secreted by the stomach or coelenteron. The octopus predigests its prey by discharging a protease into it. This is said to arise in the posterior salivary gland, along with toxic substances (27, 36).

Salivary glands are frequently present in the anterior gut region. The glands are given topographical names according to their location, e.g. buccal glands opening into the buccal cavity, sublingual glands discharging under the tongue or radula and pharyngeal glands opening into the pharynx. The primitive function of these glands is that of secreting mucus for lubricating the food—for example in triclad turbellarians, gastropods such as *Patella*, and cephalopods. Unicellular mucus glands are of general occurrence in the gut epithelium as well. In certain animals which have acquired extracellular digestion, the salivary glands secrete digestive ferments. The kinds of enzymes produced by the salivary glands differ according to the animal's diet. Thus, in many carnivorous gastropods the secretion effects a preliminary digestion of protein, and in herbivorous opisthobranchs it attacks carbohydrates. Secretion of special substances for use outside the body has been mentioned (*vide supra*).

Conduction and Storage

Food is conducted to the digestive chambers by the oesophagus. In certain animals the oesophagus is dilated into a crop for storage purposes. In leeches, for example, which depend upon large meals of blood at infrequent intervals, the crop forms a large part of the gut. A crop is present in herbivorous gastropods such as *Patella*, *Aplysia* and *Haliotis*. The large gastric cavity in fishes may be considered a storage as well as a digestive chamber; when a stomach is wanting, the anterior intestinal region is similarly enlarged (e.g. *Chimaera*, *Fundulus*). Some preliminary digestion often takes place in the crop, by enzymes regurgitated from more posterior regions (herbivorous gastropods).

Trituration in Gizzards

Following the oesophagus, the anterior region of the gut is frequently specialized as a grinding organ or gizzard for reducing food to particles small enough to be further manipulated by the digestive apparatus. A gizzard lined with chitinous teeth is present in various opisthobranchs (e.g. *Aplysia*) and pteropods. It is particularly well developed in *Scaphander* (Bullidae), where it contains several tough plates capable of crushing shells which are swallowed whole. Septibranchs (Lamellibranchia) are scavengers, and possess a powerful crushing gizzard capable of breaking up large food masses into particles small enough to be ingested by cells of the digestive diverticula. The pyloric stomach of certain bottom-feeding fishes which ingest sand and mud is bulbous and highly muscular (e.g. *Mulloides*). Trituration is aided by sand taken in with the food (1, 24, 30, 34, 50).

The stomach of crustacea is a capacious organ, ectodermal in origin and lined with chitin. Here the food is broken up and mixed with digestive enzymes secreted in the midgut. The stomach is relatively simple in the Entomostraca. In the Malacostraca, especially in decapod crustaceans, a powerful gastric mill is present, provided with calcareous teeth which grind up the food.

Sorting Mechanisms

The stomach is often the site of special mechanisms for sorting out the finely divided food and passing it on to other regions where digestion is completed. In many crustacea these filtering mechanisms are very complex, and guard the entrance to the hepatopancreas in which absorption of

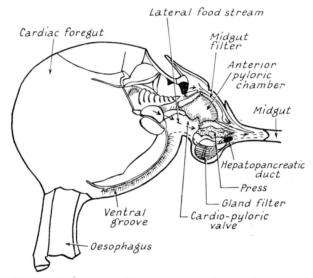

FIG. 6.1. MEDIAN VIEW OF THE FOREGUT OF *Nephrops* (after Yonge (1924).)

digested foodstuffs takes place. The foregut of *Ligia* bears a series of chitinous cushions and lamellae furnished with spines and bristles. These are arranged so as to form a filter for separating the liquid portion of the food from the solid particles. When the foregut contracts, liquid food is squeezed through the filter, carrying with it very fine particles. Secretions from the hepatopancreas are discharged into the gut cavity and attack the food. Filtered fluids enter the hepatopancreas; more solid portions of the food, mixed with digestive enzymes, pass into the intestine, where further digestion occurs.

In the Norway lobster (*Nephrops*) the cardiac gizzard is succeeded by a pyloric chamber. The two chambers are separated by a cardio-pyloric valve (Fig. 6.1). Dorsally, there is a channel termed the midgut filter which opens into the midgut. Behind the valve the walls of the pyloric foregut are thickened to form a press, and beneath this is a gland filter made of

B.M.A.—9*

chitinous plates and rods (Fig. 6.2). Hepatopancreatic secretion passes into the cardiac foregut by way of the gland filter and ventral channels. Food is ground up in the gastric mill and attacked by enzymes. Finely-divided material passes back into the pyloric chamber by the midgut filter and lateral channels; dissolved material passes back to the hepato-pancreas through the gland filter and ventral channels. The filters prevent all but the finest matter from reaching the hepatopancreas; larger particles are passed on to the midgut.

Among filter-feeding lamellibranchs the stomach is concerned with the final sorting of finely divided food. The wall of the stomach is ciliated and

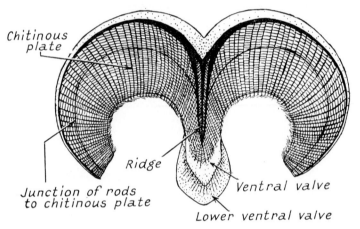

Chitinous plate

Ridge

Junction of rods to chitinous plate

Ventral valve

Lower ventral valve

FIG. 6.2. GLAND-FILTER IN THE PYLORIC FOREGUT OF *Nephrops* (× 13)
(From Yonge (1924).)

bears a caecum, a cuticular gastric shield and several sorting areas (Fig. 6.3). The ducts of the digestive gland open into the stomach, as does a style sac containing a rod-like structure termed the crystalline style, which bears against the gastric shield. Food material on entering the stomach is carried by ciliary action into the caecum where sorting occurs: heavy particles fall into a groove which conducts them across the floor of the stomach to the intestine; lighter particles are carried outwards by a ciliary tract in the caecal wall. The ciliary fields on the stomach wall transport fine particles, sorted out in the caecum and elsewhere, towards the ducts of the digestive gland, into which they are directed by inwardly beating cilia; while cilia on the opposite sides of the ducts beat outwards, thus maintain-ing a circulation within the diverticula. The style itself is kept revolving by the action of cilia in the style sac, and its motion assists in mixing particles in the stomach cavity. Coarse particles and mucous masses are carried across ridges in the stomach wall to the midgut. The whole ciliary mechanism is one which allows only fine particles and liquid matter to enter the digestive diverticula. Carbohydrases released from the crystalline style attack cellulose and starch, but digestion of other foodstuffs is mainly intracellular, following phagocytosis in the digestive gland (29).

Similar sorting mechanisms occur in the stomach or anterior intestine of many herbivorous and microphagous gastropods (*Vermetus, Struthiolaria, Aplysia,* etc.). In cephalopods (*Sepia, Loligo,* etc.) the stomach is a digestive chamber. Connected with the stomach by a vestibule is a caecum, which receives the ducts of the digestive glands. The caecum contains an elaborate mucous and ciliary collecting mechanism, the function of which is to

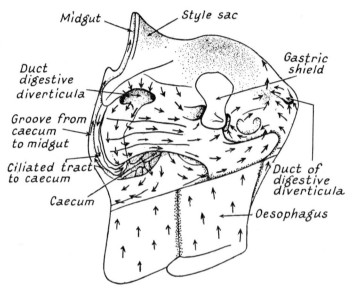

FIG. 6.3. STOMACH OF THE OYSTER, OPENED OUT TO SHOW CILIARY CURRENTS (× 7.6). (From Yonge (1926).)

clear the nutrient fluid of all solid particles. Soluble material is absorbed, while particles and mucus are carried to the intestine (14, 28, 34, 46).

In most fishes the initial phases of digestion are completed in the stomach, where food is reduced to a semi-liquid chyme. A strong sphincter muscle closes the lower end of the stomach until the food reaches the proper fluid condition for further treatment by the intestine, when the valve periodically relaxes and allows some of the chyme to pass through.

DIGESTION

Chemical breakdown or digestion of foodstuffs may be intracellular or extracellular. Among holozoic protozoans and sponges, prey or particulate matter is ingested, and digestion takes place inside the cell. In the metazoa intracellular digestion is found in coelenterates, ctenophores and turbellaria, and also occurs in certain higher groups of animals in correlation with their manner of feeding.

Intracellular Digestion

In the coelenterates and probably the ctenophores extracellular digestion is largely limited to the preliminary digestion of proteins; the digestion of carbohydrates, fats and the final breakdown of polypeptides to amino-acids are accomplished intracellularly. Turbellaria, like coelenterates, are carnivorous animals. In triclads and polyclads there is some preliminary digestion of proteins extracellularly, reducing the foodstuffs to a condition in which they can be ingested by phagocytic cells lining the alimentary canal, and a similar process obtains in the nemertine *Lineus* (35, 36, 37, 39).

More advanced forms retaining intracellular digestion include poly-chaetes, brachiopods, molluscs, with the exception of cephalopods, echinoderms and *Limulus* and pycnogonids among arthropods.

Intracellular and extracellular modes of digestion coexist in the lugworm *Arenicola*. Food particles are engulfed by the epithelial cells of the stomach and are passed to amoebocytes in which digestion is completed. Indigest-ible material is deposited in the coelom or gut lumen (38).

Brachiopods are ciliary feeders and their food consists of finely divided material. It appears that no digestive enzymes are secreted into the gut; the food particles are ingested and broken down by the cells of the digestive diverticula.

Most lamellibranchs are ciliary feeders, and have sorting mechanisms for selecting fine particles on gills, palps and the stomach wall. In lamelli-branchs such as *Ostrea*, *Ensis* and *Mytilus*, some digestion of carbo-hydrates takes place in the gut lumen through the action of an amylase set free by dissolution of the crystalline style. Fluids and fine materials enter-ing the tubules of the digestive diverticula are taken up by the epithelial cells in which digestion is completed. The cells of the digestive diverticula have been shown to contain protease, lipase and amylase. Small amounts of proteolytic and lipolytic enzymes occurring free in the lumen of the stomach and intestine result from the breakdown of phagocytes and cyto-lysis of the distal ends of cells in the digestive diverticula (7, 17, 49, 68). In septibranch bivalves, which have secondarily become carnivorous, ingested food masses are triturated by a muscular gizzard but, like other members of the class, septibranchs continue to digest protein intracellularly in the digestive diverticula.

The gastropods show feeding and digestive mechanisms of great diversity which permit exploitation of varied food resources. Primitively digestion is intracellular but there is a tendency for this to be replaced by enzymatic digestion within the gut cavity. In herbivorous prosobranchs conditions are somewhat similar to those in lamellibranchs. An extracellular amylase is secreted—by foregut diverticula in *Patella*, and from the style in *Crepi-dula* and *Vermetus*—but digestion of fats and proteins takes place intracel-lularly within cells of the digestive diverticula. Intracellular digestion occurs in the digestive gland of carnivorous prosobranchs (*Natica*, *Murex*), in opisthobranchs (*Pleurobranchus*, *Hermaea*) and in gymnosomatous pteropods. Proteases and sucrases are secreted into the gut in other gastropods (*vide infra*) (45).

Limulus and pycnogonids among arthropods retain a degree of intracellular digestion. The food of *Limulus* consists of polychaetes and lamellibranchs which are torn up by the gnathobases of the walking legs before being swallowed. Enzymes, including proteases, are released into the stomach cavity but the breakdown of proteins is completed intracellularly, within the cells of the digestive gland, by an intracellular dipeptidase. The food of pycnogonids consists of fluids, soft tissues and fine particles. Secretory cells in the midgut release extracellular enzymes, while absorptive cells in the same region ingest materials and complete digestion, especially of proteins, intracellularly.

In addition to the gut epithelium proper, phagocytic amoebocytes also ingest and decompose food particles in certain animals.

INTRACELLULAR DIGESTION BY AMOEBOCYTES. Intracellular digestion of food particles by wandering amoebocytes takes place in lamellibranchs

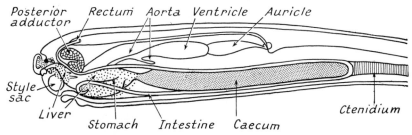

FIG. 6.4. INTERNAL ANATOMY OF THE SHIPWORM *Bankia gouldi*. ANTERIOR HALF OF THE BODY, WITH LEFT VALVE, MANTLE AND GILL REMOVED (after Sigerfoos, 1907.)

and echinoderms. Amoebocytes are numerous about the stomach, digestive diverticula and midgut of bivalve molluscs, and it has been observed that these cells pass through the epithelium of the gut into the lumen, where they ingest food particles, and then return to the tissues to digest this material. Under abnormal conditions the amoebocytes may pass through the gill membranes and absorb food material from the mantle cavity.

Digestive amoebocytes occur in the gut of filter-feeding lamellibranchs but are absent in protobranchs and carnivorous septibranchs. The digestive capacity of amoebocytes has been investigated in *Ostrea*, *Ensis* and other bivalves: they are known to contain proteolytic, lipolytic and sucroclastic enzymes, and are capable of absorbing glucose (26). *Teredo* and *Bankia* (Teredinidae) are wood-borers, and the particles of wood swallowed by the animal are passed into a specialized region of the digestive diverticula: here they are taken up by amoeboid cells and attacked by an intracellular cellulase (Figs. 6.4, 6.5). The tridacnids are peculiar in that their amoebocytes house symbiotic zooxanthellae which are ultimately digested by the host (p. 607). Yonge (66) has pointed out the important role amoebocytes play in the digestive processes of lamellibranchs by permitting the utilization of diatoms and other food particles which are too large to gain access to the tubules of the digestive diverticula.

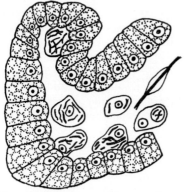

Extracellular digestion is well developed in echinoderms, but there is also some evidence for the co-existence of intracellular digestive mechanisms. Amoebocytes in the gut epithelium and lumen of echinoids and holothurians participate in digestion to greater or lesser degree by ingesting particles and absorbing dissolved nutriment. Phagocytes in the pyloric and intestinal caeca of asteroids have a similar role (58).

FIG. 6.5. SECTION THROUGH A LIVER TUBULE OF A SHIPWORM, SHOWING PHAGOCYTIC CELLS CONTAINING PARTICLES OF WOOD (after Potts, 1923.)

Extracellular Digestion

Intracellular digestion is the more primitive mechanism from which extracellular digestion has developed as a specialization, notably in the annelids, crustacea, cephalopods and chordates, all groups containing active forms. Extracellular digestion has certain apparent advantages in that it breaks down food substances and eliminates indigestible material rapidly and also permits a compact and reduced alimentary canal. Various specializations of structure and function have appeared in conjunction with the secretion of digestive enzymes into the gut lumen. There is regional differentiation for secretion of enzymes, absorption of digestive products and elimination of faeces. Special digestive enzymes are developed to meet particular needs, secretion is regulated and the enzymatic environment is controlled with apparent nicety.

Digestive enzymes are secreted by unicellular glands lining the digestive tract or localized in special diverticula and by compound glands of many sorts. In coelenterates secretory cells are dispersed through the endoderm in hydrozoa, localized in gastric filaments in scyphozoa or in mesenterial filaments in anthozoa. A protease is secreted which initiates the breakdown of proteins, the final conversion of polypeptides to amino-acids taking place intracellularly. Digestive enzymes (proteases) are secreted into the stomach and intestine of nemertines and in the stomach of bryozoa. In most polychaetes enzymes are secreted by unicellular glands in the stomach and intestine (terebellids, sabellids and serpulids). Enzymes identified in the gut fluids of sabellids and terebellids include a protease, lipase and amylase (18). A protobranch *Nucula* differs from most bivalves in that digestion is extracellular, taking place in the stomach lumen into which enzymes (protease, lipase and amylase) are secreted (54). The stomach of the starfish (*Asterias*) produces a strong proteolytic secretion, and proteases and amylases have been found in the stomach and intestine of sea-urchins. The stomach is also the region of secretion in some tunicates (*Ciona*).

The majority of fishes possess a stomach in which enzymes are secreted and the breakdown of foodstuffs commences. As in higher vertebrates the stomach juices are acid, and a proteolytic enzyme (pepsin) and acid are produced by special cells in gastric glands. These, known as *chief glands*, are largely limited to the descending limb of the stomach, termed the *corpus* (10, 13).

In many marine animals the gut is provided with various kinds of digestive diverticula, which increase the surface available for secretion and absorption and in some instances permit a differentiation of function. These structures show much diversity in different groups and need separate consideration. The digestive diverticula of most polyclad turbellaria, brachiopods, lamellibranchs and certain gastropods (in which they are also termed liver, hepatopancreas or digestive gland) are concerned exclusively with intracellular digestion of food particles. They are the loci both of secretion and intracellular digestion in many gastropods; of secretion and absorption in *Aphrodite* (a polychaete) and in crustaceans; and of secretion alone in squid (hepatopancreas) and certain ascidians (liver diverticulum). Adnexa of the gut (liver, pancreas) in fishes and higher vertebrates secrete digestive fluids, among their other functions.

Digestive caeca are a conspicuous feature of the anatomy of *Aphrodite*. At the bases of the caeca there are little sieves, so that when fluid is forced from the intestine into the caeca all but the finest particles are filtered off. Food undergoes partial digestion in the intestine, and within the caeca digestion is completed and nutrient matter absorbed (20). The pyloric caeca of starfish (*Asterias*) function in a somewhat similar manner. Particulate and partially digested food is transported from the stomach into the caeca by special tracts of flagellated cells, while centripetal currents stream back into the stomach, and thus a constant circulation of fluid and materials is maintained; digestion is completed and absorption takes place in the caeca. Nutrient substances (sugar, amino acids) are stored in the latter organs, from which they are slowly released, to be conveyed in the circulating coelomic fluid to other tissues (2, 19).

In simpler crustaceans, exemplified by *Calanus*, secretion and absorption take place in the large midgut and digestive diverticula are rudimentary. With the appearance of diverticula in Malacostraca (isopods, decapods) secretion becomes limited to this region. In the latter forms we have already noted how hepatopancreatic secretions are discharged into the foregut where foodstuffs are triturated and filtered. In this process enzymes are mixed with the food and enzymatic degradation of nutrient material takes place. Carbohydrates, fats and proteins are attacked (33).

Gastropods show much specific variation in the matter of extracellular secretion. We have seen how amylases and proteases are liberated from buccal glands or diverticula of the foregut in certain genera (p. 252).

Extracellular enzymes are produced by the digestive diverticula of carnivorous prosobranchs and some opisthobranchs, and are discharged into the stomach (Fig. 6.6). An amylase and, in some forms at least, a cellulase are found in the crystalline style of particle-feeding lamellibranchs and gastropods (*Crepidula, Pterocera*). This is a hyaline rod extending into the stomach where it undergoes dissolution, thereby releasing its enzymes (22, 34, 47).

The midgut gland of cephalopods (*Loligo, Alloteuthis*) produces digestive

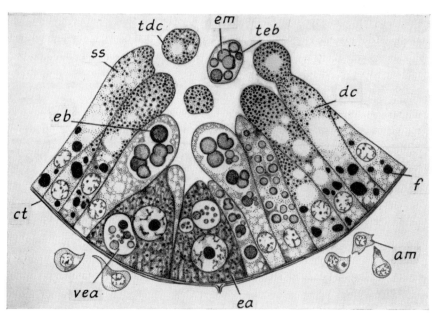

FIG. 6.6. SECTION THROUGH A TUBULE OF THE DIGESTIVE GLAND
OF *Philine quadripartita*, AN OMNIVOROUS TECTIBRANCH

Enzymes are secreted by the digestive gland, and digestion is completed intracellularly. *am*, amoebocyte; *ct*, connective tissue; *dc*, digestive cell; *ea, eb*, excretory cells; *em*, excretory masses from excretory cells; *f*, fat droplet; *ss*, secretory spherules; *tdc, teb*, tips of digestive cells cut off from the epithelium; *vea*, vacuole with excretory material. (From Fretter (24).)

enzymes. The gland consists of two recognizably distinct parts known as liver and pancreas, both of which discharge into the caecum by a hepato-pancreactic duct. In structure they present the appearance of ramifying tubules; histologically, the secreting cells are distinctly different in the two regions. Proteolytic, amylolytic and lipolytic enzymes are produced by the gland. Preliminary digestion of foodstuffs takes place in the stomach, into which hepatopancreatic secretions are passed from the caecum, and digestion is completed in the latter. The digested food is absorbed in the caecum and intestine. In *Octopus* enzyme secretion and absorption both take place in the liver (14, 15).

Digestive diverticula are present in some of the lower chordates. Secretion is confined to the stomach in some tunicates, e.g. *Ciona*, but in *Boltenia* and *Tethyum* the gut diverticula are the primary organs of secretion. Enzymes are produced which attack proteins, fats, starch and sugars. In balanoglossids (*Glossobalanus*) the intestine and intestinal diverticula are concerned with secretion and absorption. Studies of digestive ferments have involved extracts of whole animals or gross regions: these digest proteins, fats and carbohydrates. The digestive secretions of *Amphioxus* are produced by the midgut and its diverticulum (liver). Extracts show proteolytic, amylolytic and lipolytic activity. Digestion takes place initially in the gut lumen and is completed intracellularly (8, 9, 43).

Digestion in fishes, which is initiated in the stomach, is completed in the intestine through the action of intestinal and pancreatic secretions. The intestinal mucosa of selachians and teleosts secretes protease, amylase and lipase. Opening into the anterior intestine of teleost fishes there is usually a variable number of pyloric caeca, which secrete a complement of digestive enzymes similar to those of the intestine. The pancreas, discharging into the duodenum, secretes a powerful proteolytic enzyme, trypsin, and lipolytic and amylolytic enzymes which supplement those of the intestine. Digestion and absorption take place in the lumen of the intestine, and in the pyloric caeca when present (4, 11, 12, 57, 59, 65).

Digestive Enzymes

From the scattered information available, dealing with many groups, it is possible to recognize some correlation between the enzymatic complement produced and the nature of the diet. Omnivorous animals, such as many polychaetes, echinoderms and decapod crustacea, secrete proteolytic, lipolytic and amylolytic enzymes and digest corresponding categories of foodstuffs with equal facility. Secretions with strong proteolytic action occur in carnivorous coelenterates, turbellaria, gastropods, cephalopods and stomatopods, but other kinds of food materials are not necessarily attacked with equal ease. Coelenterates, for example, appear to have little or no ability to digest starch and sugars, and stomatopods lack an amylase and invertase (sucrase). In herbivorous animals, on the other hand, extracellular proteoclastic secretions tend to be deficient or weak in action— for example in cirripedes, lamellibranchs, herbivorous prosobranchs and tunicates.

TYPES OF ENZYMES. During the course of digestion proteins are broken down into their component amino-acids, carbohydrates hydrolysed into monosaccharides, and fats hydrolysed into fatty acids and alcohol. Enzymatic degradation of proteins and carbohydrates usually proceeds in step-wise sequence, involving a number of enzymes, and we have noted instances in which digestion may be initiated by secretions, later steps being completed intracellularly. Special enzymes are present in certain animals, e.g. cellulase, permitting exploitation of particular categories of food, and ancillary substances may be produced in conjunction with the working of special enzymes, e.g. bile salts.

Lipases. Neutral fats are absorbed and hydrolysed intracellularly, or they are digested in part in the gut lumen by secreted lipases, which have been detected in a wide variety of animals. Lipases are secreted by the hepatopancreas of cephalopods, the hepatic diverticula of decapod crustacea and the liver of ascidians. In fishes, fat digestion takes place in the intestine through the agency of lipases secreted probably by both pancreas and intestinal mucosa.

The bile of vertebrates contains bile salts, such as those of glycocholic acid and taurocholic acid, which facilitate hydrolysis and absorption of fats. Bile salts reduce surface tension at fat and water interfaces, and so permit emulsification of the fats. A larger surface area is thus presented upon which the digestive lipases can act. Very little is known about the physiological conditions of fat hydrolysis and absorption in lower animals, but it has been shown that the digestive secretion of decapod crustaceans is capable of emulsifying fats, and in this respect resembles liver bile of vertebrates (66).

Proteases. Earlier studies on protein digestion were often concerned with mixtures of proteolytic enzymes, and it is only comparatively recently that different kinds of proteases have been recognized in lower animals. Proteases are classified according to effective substrate, optimal pH, and effects of activating and inhibiting agents.

Peptidases split proteins and complex polypeptides. In this group are included endopeptidases which attack central peptide bonds, e.g. trypsin, pepsin and kathepsins; and exopeptidases which attack terminal peptide bonds.

Endopeptidases. Trypsin acts in an alkaline medium, from about pH 7–9. It is secreted by the vertebrate pancreas as trypsinogen which is activated by an intestinal enzyme, enterokinase. Proteolytic secretions having trypsin-like properties have been identified in *Maia* (crustacean) and *Murex* (gastropod), and possibly other forms. Extracts which show proteolytic activity over an optimal pH range of 4·5–6·5 have been noted in a great many invertebrates and have been vaguely characterized as intracellular and extracellular kathepsins. Instances are gastropods, lamellibranchs and echinoderms. Crystallized pepsin has been prepared from fishes as well as mammals, and its properties studied (Fig. 6.7). It is secreted as pepsinogen and becomes converted to pepsin in the acid medium of the stomach. Pepsin is not known among invertebrates (52, 53).

Exopeptidases, including carboxypeptidases and aminopeptidases, attack terminal peptide bonds, and dipeptidases act on dipeptides. These enzymes have been identified in various invertebrates, those which have been studied including *Limulus, Maia, Murex, Octopus,* etc.

Sequential digestion by different proteases takes place to a limited extent in vertebrates where distinct peptidases are secreted in the stomach (pepsin) and intestine (trypsin), but in many invertebrates the enzymes are poured into a single chamber and attack the foodstuffs concurrently. Endopeptidases split the proteins into peptide fragments; carboxypeptidases and aminopeptidases continue the hydrolysis, attacking the polypeptides from the ends until dipeptides are formed; and the latter are split into their amino-acid components by dipeptidases. In some instances the secreted enzymes carry hydrolysis only as far as polypeptides, and further degradation takes place intracellularly.

Carbohydrases. Amylases capable of hydrolysing starch and glycogen probably occur in most animals, either extracellularly or intracellularly. Starches are broken down to dextrins and finally to maltose. Disaccharides,

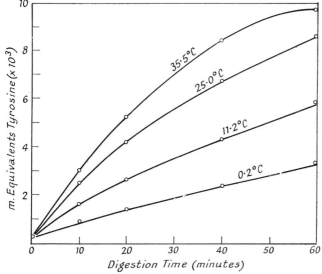

FIG. 6.7. DIGESTION OF 2% HB AT pH 2·0 BY CRYSTALLINE SALMON PEPSIN AT VARIOUS TEMPERATURES

Ordinates represent the tyrosine equivalent liberated in 6 ml of digest. (From Norris and Elam (52).)

especially maltose and sucrose, are broken down by sucrases (maltase and sucrase or invertase), which have been identified in many species.

Of special interest are those enzymes attacking other complex carbohydrates, notably cellulose and chitin. These are both chain compounds, cellulose consisting of β-glucoside (cellobiose) units, and chitin of acetyl-glucosamine units. Cellulases capable of digesting cellulose are widely distributed among marine invertebrates, including polychaetes, echiuroids, sipunculoids, brachiopods, crustacea, gastropods, lamellibranchs, and sea urchins. Noteworthy are the wood-boring shipworms *Teredo* and gribbles *Limnoria*. In *Teredo* and its relative *Bankia*, wood particles are passed to a specialized region of the gut diverticula, where they are attacked by an intracellular cellulase. Similarly, the digestive diverticula of *Limnoria* produce a cellulase capable of hydrolysing cellulose in the wood eaten by this animal. The cellulase of gastropods which crop algae, e.g. *Strombus*, breaks down cell walls and releases an additional source of glucose. Cellulase, occurring in the crystalline style of bivalves attacks the walls of unicellular algae filtered from the sea water (64).

The seaweeds found on the shore and in shallow waters contain an abundance of polysaccharides other than cellulose, and these form a considerable proportion of the diet of many littoral animals. A hemicellulase (lichenase) is widespread among invertebrates, and is known to

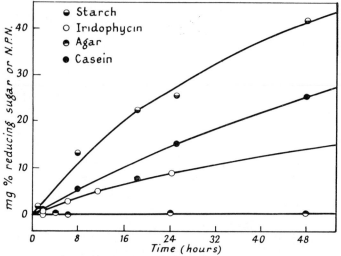

FIG. 6.8. RATES OF DIGESTION OF VARIOUS SUBSTRATES BY INTESTINAL EXTRACTS FROM THE SEA URCHIN *Strongylocentrotus purpuratus*

Substrates: 1% casein at pH 6·8 and 30°C; 1% boiled starch, 0·1% agar, and 0·02% iridophycin at pH 6·8 and 30°C. (From Lasker and Giese (40).)

occur in sponges, annelids, echinoderms, molluscs, arthropods and ascidians. Lichenase hydrolyses hemicelluloses (xylans, arabans, mannans, galactans, etc.). There is some doubt whether the hemicellulases and cellulases of some animals may not be identical. The ormer or abalone *Haliotis* (a prosobranch gastropod) is said to possess enzymes capable of digesting agar and alginic acid found in the brown algae on which it feeds. Another herbivore, the urchin *Strongylocentrotus*, produces enzymes breaking down the complex polysaccharides and proteins of the brown and red algae on which it feeds; agar, however, is attacked by the intestinal flora (Fig. 6.8). Kelp (*Macrocystis*) is digested with an efficiency of 80%, and labelled mannitol from the alga soon becomes dispersed through the perivisceral fluid. Red coelomocytes of the perivisceral fluid carry the digested products about the body (16).

A digestive chitinase has not been reported for marine animals, although it is known to occur in terrestrial pulmonates and arthropods (31, 40, 41, 46, 50, 55, 67).

Conditions affecting Digestion

Hydrogen Ion Concentration. Intracellular digestion in general involves two main phases, a preliminary acid phase when the food organism is killed and some digestion takes place, and a succeeding alkaline phase during which digestion of the food is carried to completion. The activity of extracellular digestive enzymes is affected by the hydrogen ion concentration of the medium, and such enzymes show a narrow or broad pH range of optimal activity. Much attention has been given to determining both the hydrogen ion concentration of gut regions where the digestive enzymes act and the pH optima of different categories of enzymes in lower animals.

The acidity of the alimentary tract depends on the kind of food eaten, and on whether the animal is fasting or has eaten; it varies during the course of digestion, as the result of secretion and resultant breakdown of foodstuffs; and it tends to change in some regular manner in successive regions of the gut. Sometimes the acidity actually found in a given region of the gut cavity (the physiological pH) approximates the optimal pH for the enzyme or enzymes secreted into it, but this is not invariably so.

In coelenterates (Scyphozoa, Anthozoa), the pH in the coelenteron falls during digestion, when secretion is taking place and proteins are being broken down. Thus, the pH in the coral *Fungia*, about 7·8 when fasting, drops to 7·0 after feeding. This latter value is optimal for the extracellular proteinase of *Fungia*. When digestion is completed and the coelenteron evacuated, the pH rises once more. In the nemertine *Lineus* acid is secreted into the foregut, and extracellular digestion is initiated within the intestine in an acid medium (pH 5–5·5) (37). In starfishes (*Patiria, Asterias*) the acidity in the pyloric caeca appears to be regulated at about pH 6·7; this level is optimal both for ciliary viability and proteolytic action. An acid secretion from the lips and pharynx of *Echinus* lowers the pH to 5·9, whereas the acidity in succeeding gut regions gradually rises to pH 6·8 (58).

Molluscs, we have already seen, present much variety in digestive mechanisms. In those lamellibranchs and gastropods possessing a crystalline style, the entire gut shows an acid reaction and the style, moreover, modifies the pH of the gut. Average pH values for the oyster (*Ostrea edulis*) are: mantle cavity, 6·9; oesophagus, 5·8; stomach, 5·5; style, 5·2; digestive diverticula, 5·8; midgut, 5·8; rectum, 5·9. The low pH of the stomach results from continuous dissolution of the head of the crystalline style, which rotates against the gastric shield, and the acid reaction so produced is about optimal for the amylase which is also released by the style (Fig. 6.9). In the herbivorous tectibranch *Aplysia punctata* the pH drops from

6·2 in the buccal cavity to 4·9 in the gizzard, and rises to 7·6 in the posterior intestine; in the octopus the pH also falls from about 6·8 in the gullet to 5·5–5·8 in the stomach (34).

It is not uncommon among invertebrates with a well-differentiated gut to find the anterior region (of reception) nearly neutral, stomach and midgut acid, and intestine more alkaline, but this is not invariably the case. In any event enzyme activity is confined to certain regions where the pH becomes significant for that particular enzyme, e.g. amylolytic action in the stomach and digestive diverticula of bivalve molluscs. Conditions in fishes are somewhat peculiar, since the stomach produces a highly acid secretion (containing free HCl) with a variable pH that may drop to 3 or less in different teleosts and selachians. Pepsinogen (the precursor of pepsin) and acid are apparently produced by the same gastric cell, and the pH optima for pepsin lie well on the acid side of neutrality (from 1·5

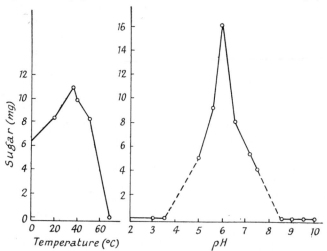

FIG. 6.9. DIGESTION OF STARCH BY THE STYLE AMYLASE OF
Ensis siliqua

(*Left*) Effect of temperature on digestion. Digest, pH 6, duration of experiment five hours. (*Right*) effect of hydrogen ion concentration on digestion. Temperature 22°C; time of digestion 18 hours. Ordinates, milligrammes reducing sugars liberated. (From Graham (1931).)

to 2·9 depending on the source and substrate) (Fig. 6.10). On passing into the duodenum the gut contents become alkaline (pH 7–9), in which range pancreatic trypsin shows maximal activity (pH 7·5–8·5). In stomachless fish, such as *Fundulus*, the foodstuffs pass directly from the oesophagus into the alkaline duodenum and neither pepsin nor acid is secreted (10).

Some other effects of hydrogen ion concentration may be noted briefly. The acidity of the vertebrate stomach has a bactericidal action and is also responsible for decalcification of skeletal structures in the food. The changing pH values in different gut regions may be of importance in altering the viscosity of mucus, especially in ciliary-feeding animals. The isoelectric point of mucus in lamellibranchs approximates the pH actually measured in the stomach, and resultant changes in mucus-viscosity may influence speed of digestion.

Temperature. Like most chemical reactions the enzymatic hydrolysis of foodstuffs is influenced by temperature, the reaction rate increasing with rise in temperature and decreasing with fall in temperature. But enzymes, being proteins, are subject to thermal inactivation, and the higher the temperature at which digestion is occurring the more rapidly the enzyme is destroyed. At low temperatures, therefore, hydrolysis proceeds more slowly but the enzyme lasts longer; at high temperatures hydrolysis is rapid but the enzyme is more rapidly inactivated. For any given set of

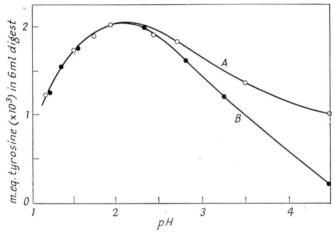

FIG. 6.10. DIGESTION OF HB BY CRYSTALLINE PEPSIN. DEPENDENCE OF INITIAL RATE OF DIGESTION ON PH

Curve A, salmon pepsin. Curve B, Northrop's swine pepsin. (From Norris and Elam (52).)

experimental conditions it is possible to determine the optimum temperature at which digestion proceeds most rapidly.

Much attention has been devoted to determining optimal temperatures for digestive enzymes of invertebrates. The curve in Fig. 6.9, for example, shows that the optimal temperature for style amylase of *Ensis* is about 35°C for a digestion time of 5 hours. Style amylase, however, is rapidly destroyed at temperatures above 38°C and the optimum temperature depends on the incubation time. If the incubation time is short at high temperatures, little enzyme is destroyed and the reaction rate is high; if the incubation time is long, much more enzyme is inactivated and the reaction rate is reduced. The optimal temperature for an enzyme, consequently, is high over short periods, and falls as digest time of the experiment is prolonged. This effect is brought out nicely in a study of the effect of temperature on the digestive proteinase of the sea-squirt *Tethyum* (Fig. 6.11), in which it has been shown that the optimum temperature of the enzyme is about 50°C over a period of 2 hours but only about 20°C over 55 hours. In cold-blooded marine animals environmental temperatures generally lie below 30°C and temperature optima above such a figure have no physiological significance. Food passes through the gut slowly, and the time thus consumed may correspond to the period for maximal enzymatic action at the normal environmental temperature. In *Tethyum* food takes 35 hours to pass through the alimentary canal at 15°C. Purified pepsin,

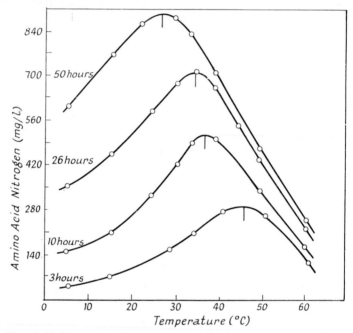

FIG. 6.11. EFFECT OF TEMPERATURE ON DIGESTION BY THE PROTEASE OF *Halocynthia* (=*Tethyum*). (From Berrill (1929).)

which has now been obtained from several species of fish, still shows appreciable activity at the low temperatures which the fish encounter in nature (Fig. 6.7). Since food remains for a long time in the stomach (some 18 hours in *Pleuronectes*), there is opportunity for prolonged pepsin hydrolysis (52).

Temperature certainly influences other processes besides enzyme hydrolysis, and thus affects total digestion time. A rise in temperature increases gut motility and probably influences rates of secretion and absorption.

Factors controlling Secretion

The secretion of enzymes is concerned with the digestion of food and it is not surprising to find that the mode of secretion is related to feeding habits. In lamellibranchs, as we have noticed, feeding is continuous while the valves are open, and depends on ciliary mechanisms. The best-known extracellular enzyme is an amylase, which is continuously released by dissolution of the crystalline style. There is always enzyme present, therefore, to deal with the constant food intake. Fabrication of the style, however, ceases under adverse conditions.

In other animals we find that secretion is elicited by the presence of food. The principal extracellular enzyme of coelenterates is a proteinase. There is little digestive action in a fasting animal, while the presence of animal material (meat) stimulates secretion. In several groups (gastropods, intertidal lamellibranchs, decapod crustacea) digestive secretion is a rhythmical process, which is accelerated by the presence of food. Secretion is holocrine (*Potamobius*) or merocrine (*Atya*). In the former condition the individual cells are sacrificed, and periodic replacement takes place by cell division at the ends of the diverticula. Merocrine secretion involves discharge of cellular granules (39, 49, 62).

Secretion in cephalopods is markedly different from that in other molluscs and is related to the active predatory habits of these animals. In the squid, pancreatic secretion accumulates in the caecum between meals and passes into the stomach during gastric digestion. When this occurs, the caecal valve is held open and contractions of the caecal sac drive out the stored fluids. The hepatic secretion, on the contrary, is liberated only during digestion, and control is effected by the hepatic sphincter (14).

The factors which regulate discontinuous secretion—which evoke it prior to, and during the course of, a meal—have rarely been subjected to any precise analysis in invertebrates, and the situation in fishes is not less obscure. There is a continuous secretion of small amounts of gastric juice in fasting selachians. But in contradistinction to the situation in tetrapods, gastric secretion is not subject to nervous control. It is true that stimulation of the sympathetic nervous system and injection of adrenaline in rays may produce inhibition of normal secretion, but this can be ascribed to vasoconstriction and the attendant drop in blood flow. Even less is known about the situation in teleosts, where gastric secretion is certainly discontinuous and depends on the presence of food. The secretion of pepsin under the influence of pilocarpine has, however, been detected in intact plaice (*Pleuronectes*).

In fasting fish the intestinal fluids contain little trypsin, but this increases greatly when food enters the duodenum. Secretin (a hormone provoking pancreatic secretion) has been detected in the fish gut, and it is found that injection of secretin or the introduction of HCl into the duodenum of the ray causes the pancreas to secrete. Consequently, there appears to be a hormonal regulation of pancreatic secretion in fish, mediated by secretin and comparable to that found in mammals. Passage of acid chyme into the stomach excites this mechanism and results in pancreatic secretion into the duodenum (3, 5, 10, 11, 13, 51).

TRANSPORT OF FOOD THROUGH THE GUT

Ciliary action and muscular contractions propel the foodstuffs and fluids along the alimentary canal while they are being comminuted, digested and absorbed. Ciliary beating alone is responsible for the manifold mechanical processes occurring in the lamellibranch gut—moving food particles, separating fine from coarse particles in the stomach, mixing the food with enzymes, rotating the crystalline style, transporting digestible matter to the diverticula and driving the mucous string through the intestine. Both ciliary and muscular peristaltic movements act co-operatively in gastropods, e.g. *Aplysia*. Peristaltic waves push food into the crop and gizzard, and fluids are driven backwards and forwards into the anterior gut from the digestive diverticula and stomach by contraction and dilatation of the latter structures. Larger particles reaching the intestine are moulded into a faecal rod with mucus, and propelled to the anus by a combination of ciliary and muscular action (34, 46).

Among polychaetes there is much variation in the way in which the gut contents are transported. In particle-feeding sabellids and serpulids, cilia alone are used; in *Clymenella* cilia transport food through the oesophagus and muscular contractions move food through the stomach; regular peristaltic waves occur in the intestine of *Tomopteris;* terebellids propel food through the gut mainly by muscular action. Such examples could be multiplied (18, 32, 38, 60).

There are no cilia in crustacea and movement of food through the gut depends on muscular contraction. In *Nephrops*, for example, food is pushed through the oesophagus into the cardiac foregut by the action of constrictor and dilator muscles. Anterior and posterior gastric muscles actuate the gastric mill, while rhythmical contraction and expansion of the hepatic tubules (which bear circular and longitudinal muscles) cause secretion to be forced out and dissolved materials to be taken in. Peristaltic and antiperistaltic waves occur in the midgut, and pronounced peristalsis takes place in the hindgut. In smaller crustacea, such as prawns, there is regular intake of water at the anus, and this seems to stimulate antiperistalsis, followed by defaecation. The muscles of the intestine appear to be under the control of an autonomous internal plexus, but can be regulated by extrinsic nerves originating in the nerve cord (23, 53).

In fishes the intrinsic musculature of the gut wall likewise propels the food bolus, churns and breaks up the food mass and thoroughly mixes it with digestive secretions. The musculature of the oesophagus is striated and food is pushed into the stomach by peristaltic waves. The walls of the stomach and intestine contain circular and longitudinal smooth muscle, and nervous plexi which are responsible for autonomous activity of the gut wall. Movements take the form of local contractions, peristaltic waves, waving of the pyloric caeca, etc. A strongly-developed sphincter at the junction of the pylorus and duodenum regulates the passage of chyme from the stomach into the intestine. The gut plexi receive extrinsic nerves from the c.n.s. via autonomic pathways, and these regulate and modify activity of the alimentary canal. Stimulation of the visceral vagus causes the oeso-phagus to contract, and evokes local contractions and peristalsis of the stomach in both selachians and teleosts. Stimulation of the sympathetic (splanchnic) nerves produces gastric and intestinal activity. Both para-sympathetic and sympathetic systems are excitatory, and their effects are additive in the regions where they overlap (12, 51).

ABSORPTION

When an extensive complement of digestive enzymes is secreted, foodstuffs are broken down into their component units before absorption takes place. In that event carbohydrates are absorbed as monosaccharides, proteins as amino-acids, and fats as fatty acids and glycerol. Emulsification is aided by the presence of bile salts and monoglycerides, and when small-enough particles are produced they are absorbed directly. Products of digestion have been detected in the body fluids after feeding. In *Strongylocentrotus*, for example, reducing sugars and non-protein nitrogen increase in the coelomic fluid as digestion proceeds. Digestion has also been followed histologically by looking for uptake of iron saccharate and fat spherules. Physiological studies on absorption in marine animals are rather meagre, however.

Regions of absorption coincide with digestion in many instances. Absorption takes place in the intestine of polychaetes (*Sabella*) and sea-urchins, intestine and caeca of *Aphrodite*, intestine and caecum of squid, pyloric caeca of starfish, and intestine and pyloric caeca of fish. In lower crustaceans (*Calanus*) absorption takes place in the midgut, but with the development of the hepatopancreas, absorption becomes limited to that organ (decapods). Absorptive cells are usually distinct from glandular secretory cells. In other groups the reader will recall instances in which particles are ingested to be followed by intracellular digestion, e.g. coelen-teron of sea-anemone, digestive diverticula of lamellibranchs and many gastropods, and so forth.

ELIMINATION OF FAECES

Faeces contain the undigested and indigestible residues of food, together with water, salts, mucus, bacteria, desquamated cells, etc. In gastropods and lamellibranchs, indigestible particles and chlorophyll break-down products, extruded by the digestive cells of the midgut gland, are eliminated in the faeces. Bile pigments, the breakdown products of haemoglobin metabolism, are discharged into the intestine of vertebrates and pass into the faeces after undergoing modification. In some animals the intestine participates in ionic regulation. The gut of fish is relatively impermeable to magnesium and sulphate, which pass out in the faeces (p. 73), and studies with marine molluscs (*Acanthodoris*, *Mytilus*) have shown that radioactive strontium is excreted in part by cells of the digestive gland (25).

Special means of dealing with the faeces occur in certain animals. Thin peritrophic membrances of chitin are formed about the faeces in some crustaceans (shrimps, barnacles, etc.). In gastropods and lamellibranchs the intestinal contents are consolidated with mucus and moulded by ciliary and muscular action into a faecal cord. From this cord firm faecal pellets are constricted off and these can be eliminated without fouling the mantle cavity. Tubicolous animals have special means of keeping their burrows clean. Lugworms in sand move back to the surface of the tail shaft at regular intervals to defaecate outside the burrow, and sabellids possess a longitudinal ciliated groove which carries the faecal pellets from the anus to the head, where they are shot forth from the mouth of the tube (21, 30, 63).

REFERENCES

1. AL-HUSSAINI, A. H., "The feeding habits and the morphology of the alimentary tract of some teleosts, etc.," *Publ. Mar. Biol. Sta. Ghardaqa*, No. 5 61 pp. (1947).
2. ANDERSON, J. M., "Histological studies on the digestive system of a starfish, *Henricia*," *Biol. Bull.*, **119**, 371 (1960).
3. BABKIN, B. P., "Further studies on the pancreatic secretion in the skate," *Contr. Canad. Biol.*, **7**, 1 (1931).
4. BABKIN, B. P. and BOWIE, D. J., "The digestive system and its function in *Fundulus heteroclitus*," *Biol. Bull.*, **54**, 255 (1928).
5. BABKIN, B. P., CHAISSON, A. F. and FRIEDMAN, M. H. F., "Factors determining the course of gastric secretion in elasmobranchs," *J. Biol. Bd Can.*, **1**, 251 (1935).
6. BACQ, Z. M. and GHIRETTI, F., "Physiologie des glands salivaires postérieures des Céphalopodes octopodes isolées et perfusées *in vitro*," *Pubbl. Staz. Zool. Napoli*, **24**, 266 (1953).
7. BALLANTINE, D. and MORTON, J. E., "Filtering, feeding, and digestion in the lamellibranch *Lasaea rubra*," *J. Mar. Biol. Ass. U.K.*, **35**, 241 (1956).
8. BARRINGTON, E. J. W., "The digestive system of *Amphioxus (Branchiostoma) lanceolatus*," *Phil. Trans. Roy. Soc. B.*, **228**, 269 (1937).
9. BARRINGTON, E. J. W., "Observations on feeding and digestion in *Glossobalanus minutus*," *Quart. J. Micr. Sci.*, **82**, 227 (1941).
10. BARRINGTON, E. J. W., "Gastric digestion in the lower vertebrates," *Biol. Rev.*, **17**, 1 (1942).
11. BATTLE, H. I., "Digestion and digestive enzymes in the herring (*Clupea harengus* L.)," *J. Biol. Bd Can.*, **1**, 145 (1935).
12. BAYLISS, L. E., "Digestion in the plaice (*Pleuronectes platessa*)," *J. Mar. Biol. Ass. U.K.*, **20**, 73 (1935).
13. BERNARD, F., "La digestion chez les poissons," *Trav. Lab. Hydrobiol. Grenoble*, Ann. 43–4, p. 61 (1952).
14. BIDDER, A. M., "The digestive mechanisms of the European squids *Loligo vulgaris, Loligo forbesi, Alloteuthis media,* and *Alloteuthis subulata*," *Quart. J. Micr. Sci.*, **91**, 1 (1950).
15. BIDDER, A. M., "Evidence for an absorptive function in the 'liver of *Octopus vulgaris*," *Pubbl. Staz. Zool. Napoli*, **29**, 139 (1957).

16. BOOLOOTIAN, R. A. and LASKER, R., "Digestion of brown algae and the distribution of nutrients in the purple sea urchin *Strongylocentrotus purpuratus*," *Comp. Biochem. Physiol.*, **11**, 273 (1964).

17. COE, W. R., "Nutritional, environmental conditions, and growth of marine bivalve mollusks," *J. Mar. Res.*, **7**, 586 (1948).

18. DALES, R. P., "Feeding and digestion in terebellid polychaetes," *J. Mar. Biol. Ass. U.K.*, **34**, 55 (1955).

19. FERGUSON, J. C., "Nutrient transport in starfish," *Biol. Bull.*, **126**, 33 (1964).

20. FORDHAM, M. G. C., *Aphrodite aculeata*, L.M.B.C. Mem. 27 (Liverpool Univ. Press, 1925).

21. FORSTER, G. K., "Peritrophic membranes in the Caridea," *J. Mar. Biol. Ass. U.K.*, **32**, 315 (1953).

22. FOX, D. L., "Comparative metabolism of organic detritus by inshore animals," *Ecology*, **31**, 100 (1950).

23. FOX, H. M., "Anal and oral intake of water by crustacea," *J. Exp. Biol.*, **29**, 583 (1952).

24. FRETTER, V., "The structure and function of the alimentary canal of some tectibranch molluscs," *Trans. Roy. Soc. Edinb.*, **59**, 599 (1939).

25. FRETTER, V., "Experiments with radioactive strontium (^{90}Sr) on certain molluscs and polychaetes," *J. Mar. Biol. Ass. U.K.*, **32**, 367 (1953).

26. GEORGE, W. C., "The digestion and absorption of fat in lamellibranchs," *Biol. Bull.*, **102**, 118 (1952).

27. GHIRETTI, F., "Les excitants chimiques de la sécrétion salivaire chez les Céphalopodes octopodes," *Arch. Int. Physiol.*, **61**, 10 (1953).

28. GRAHAM, A., "On the structure of the alimentary canal of style-bearing prosobranchs," *Proc. Zool. Soc. Lond.*, Ser. B, **109**, 75 (1939).

29. GRAHAM, A., "The molluscan stomach," *Trans. Roy. Soc. Edinb.*, **61**, 737 (1949).

30. GRAHAM, A., "Form and function in the molluscs (Symposium)," *Proc. Linn. Soc. Lond.*, **164**, 213 (1953).

31. GREENFIELD, L. J. and LANE, C. E., "Cellulose digestion in Teredo," *J. Biol. Chem.*, **204**, 669 (1953).

32. HANSON, J., "Transport of food through the alimentary canal of aquatic annelids," *Quart. J. Micr. Sci.*, **89**, 47 (1948).

33. HASLER, A. D., "The physiology of digestion in plankton crustacea. 2. Further studies on the digestive enzymes of *Daphnia*, etc.," *Biol. Bull.*, **72**, 290 (1937).

34. HOWELLS, H. H., "The structure and function of the alimentary canal of *Aplysia*," *Quart. J. Micr. Sci.*, **83**, 357 (1942).

35. HYMAN, L. H., "Observations and experiments on the physiology of medusae," *Biol. Bull.*, **79**, 282 (1940).

36. JENNINGS, J. B., "Studies on feeding, digestion, and food storage in free-living flatworms," ibid., **112**, 63 (1957).

37. JENNINGS, J. B., "Observations on the nutrition of the rhynchocoelan *Lineus*," ibid., **119**, 189 (1960).

38. KERMACK, D. M., "The anatomy and physiology of the gut of the polychaete *Arenicola marina*," *Proc. Zool. Soc. Lond.*, **125**, 347 (1955).

39. KRIJGSMAN, B. J. and TALBOT, F. H., "Experiments on digestion in sea anemones," *Arch. Int. Physiol.*, **61**, 277 (1953).

40. LASKER, R. and GIESE, A. C., "Nutrition of the sea urchin, *Strongylocentrotus purpuratus,*" *Biol. Bull.*, **106**, 328 (1954).
41. LAVINE, T. F., "A study of the enzymatic and other properties of the crystalline style of clams: evidence for the presence of a cellulase," *J. Cell. Comp. Physiol.*, **28**, 183 (1946).
42. MANSOUR-BEK, J. J., "The digestive enzymes in Invertebrata and Protochordata," *Tabul. Biol.*, **21**, Pt. 3, p. 75 (1954).
43. MILLAR, R. H., *Ciona,* L.M.B.C. Mem. 25 (Liverpool Univ. Press, 1953).
44. MILLER, R. C. and NORRIS, E. R., "Some enzymes of the Northwest shipworm, *Bankia setacea,*" *Proc. Sixth Pac. Sci. Congr.*, **3**, 615 (1940).
45. MILLOTT, N., "On the morphology of the alimentary canal, process of feeding and physiology of digestion of the nudibranch mollusc *Jorunna tomentosa,*" *Phil. Trans. Roy. Soc. B.*, **228**, 173 (1938).
46. MORTON, J. E., "The ecology and digestive system of the Struthiolariidae (Gastropoda)," *Quart. J. Micr. Sci.*, **92**, 1 (1951).
47. MORTON, J. E., "The role of the crystalline style," *Proc. Malac. Soc. Lond.*, **29**, 85 (1952).
48. MORTON, J. E., "The biology of *Limacina retroversa,*" *J. Mar. Biol. Ass. U.K.*, **33**, 297 (1954).
49. MORTON, J. E., "The tidal rhythm and action of the digestive system of the lamellibranch *Lasaea rubra,*" ibid., **35**, 563 (1956).
50. NEWELL, B. S., "Cellulolytic activity in the lamellibranch crystalline style," ibid., **32**, 491 (1953).
51. NICOL, J. A. C., "Autonomic nervous systems in lower chordates," *Biol. Rev.*, **27**, 1 (1952).
52. NORRIS, E. R. and ELAM, D. W., "Preparation and properties of crystalline salmon pepsin," *J. Biol. Chem.*, **134**, 443 (1940).
53. NORRIS, E. R. and MATHIES, J. C., "Preparation, properties and crystallization of tuna pepsin," *J. Biol. Chem.*, **204**, 673 (1953).
54. OWEN, G., "Observations on the stomach and digestive diverticula of the Lamellibranchia," *Quart. J. Micr. Sci.*, **97**, 541 (1956).
55. RAY, D. L. and JULIAN, J. R., "Occurrence of cellulase in *Limnoria,*" *Nature*, **164**, 32 (1952).
56. SAWAYA, P., "Contribuição para a fisiologia do aparelho de apreensão dos alimentos e da glândula do intestino médio de Ostrácodo," *Bol. Fac. Filos. Ciênc. S. Paulo, Zool.*, No. 6, p. 107 (1942).
57. STERN, J. A. and LOCKHART, E. E., "A study of the proteolytic enzyme activity of the pyloric caeca of redfish," *J. Fish. Res. Bd Can.*, **10**, 590 (1953).
58. STOTT, F. C., "The food canal of the sea urchin *Echinus esculentus* and its functions," *Proc. Zool. Soc. Lond.*, **125**, 63 (1955).
59. TAKESUE, K., "Studies on the change of the digestive enzyme systems with growth of the fish, *Plecoglossus altivelis,*" *J. Shimonoseki Coll. Fish.*, **3**, 89 (1954).
60. ULLMAN, A. and BOOKHOUT, C. G., "The histology of the digestive tract of *Clymenella torquata,*" *J. Morph.*, **84**, 31 (1949).
61. VONK, H. J., "The specificity and collaboration of digestive enzymes in Metazoa," *Biol. Rev.*, **12**, 245 (1937).
62. WEEL, P. B. VAN, "Processes of secretion, restitution, and resorption in gland of midgut of *Atya spinipes,*" *Physiol. Zool.*, **28**, 40 (1955).

63. WELLS, G. P., "Defaecation in relation to the spontaneous activity cycles of *Arenicola marina*," *J. Mar. Biol. Ass. U.K.*, **32**, 51 (1943).
64. YOKOE, Y. and YASUMASU, I., "The distribution of cellulase in invertebrates," *Comp. Biochem. Physiol.*, **13**, 323 (1964).
65. YONGE, C. M., "Digestive processes in marine invertebrates and fishes," *J. Cons. Int. Explor. Mer*, **6**, 175 (1931).
66. YONGE, C. M., "Evolution and adaptation in the digestive system of the metazoa," *Biol. Rev.*, **12**, 87 (1937).
67. YONGE, C. M., "Recent work on the digestion of cellulose and chitin by invertebrates," *Sci. Progr.*, **32**, 638 (1938).
68. ZACKS, S. I. and WELSH, J. H., "Cholinesterase and lipase in the amoebocytes, intestinal epithelium and heart muscle of the quahog, *Venus mercenaria*," *Biol. Bull.*, **105**, 200 (1953).

CHAPTER 7

EXCRETION

Les corps ammoniacaux sont toxiques, ils doivent être éliminés rapide-
ment, ou être transformés en corps moins toxiques (urée, acide urique)
pour éviter leur accumulation dans l'organisme.

H. Delaunay, 1931

INTRODUCTION

Excretion, in general, refers to the elimination of waste or poisonous
substances from the organism. In this sense it obviously embraces a
multiplicity of processes and functions and requires closer definition. On
occasion the loose use of the term has resulted, at best, in loss of precision
and, at worst, in much confusion in zoological literature. This is apparent
in treatment both of excretory organs and excretory processes. As with
many other functions, excretion is best known among vertebrates, especially mammals. Among invertebrates our knowledge of excretion is
still fragmentary. Reviews of certain aspects of the subject are available,
notably that of Baldwin (3).

As the result of processes of growth, metamorphosis, tissue maintenance
and metabolism, an animal periodically or continually produces and
accumulates waste materials, obsolete tissue and metabolic end-products
which are eliminated in various ways. The nature and amount of these
products depend upon the animal's way of life, its diet, activities and
environmental conditions. Let us consider these first in terms of materials
which are eliminated.

The foodstuffs taken in by the animal contain a certain amount of
indigestible material, and this is eliminated in the faeces, together with
mucus and any other products which may be discharged into the alimentary canal.

All animals, except possibly in some instances of suspended animation,
are engaged in metabolizing organic materials, either breaking them down
to provide energy, or building them up into specific products or tissues.
Of the foodstuffs which are metabolized by the animal, carbohydrates
and fats are oxidized to water and carbon dioxide, and are readily eliminated as such. The nitrogenous compounds, predominantly proteins and
nucleic acids, are degraded into various nitrogenous end-products, which
are eliminated in several ways according to the species. A large part of the
nitrogen (about 90%) is derived from the α-amino-N of amino-acids
which are split off from proteins through the action of proteolytic enzymes.
Amino-acids are deaminated for the most part to ammonia. Other
nitrogenous waste products from protein catabolism include unchanged

276

amino-acids, and urea, uric acid and trimethylamine oxide. Nucleic acid metabolism yields purines, which may be excreted in this form, or undergo further deamination leading to uric acid, urea or finally ammonia. Porphyrin metabolism yields still further nitrogenous end-products, which are sometimes conspicuous because of their coloration.

Nearly all animals show some degree of ionic regulation, and maintain the internal milieu constant by processes of differential absorption and excretion of specific ions. Most marine invertebrates are isosmotic with sea water, but in estuarine environments species with hyperosmotic body fluids may have to pump out excess water which tends to flow into the organism, in addition to that produced by the oxidation of foodstuffs. Marine vertebrates are usually hypo-osmotic to sea water (except elasmobranchs), and can utilize some of this metabolic water to reduce anisosmotic hazard. Animals are normally efficient in conserving monosaccharides produced by the hydrolysis of more complex carbohydrates.

There are instances in which the animal casts off part of its body at intervals. In the Polyzoa the polyp periodically degenerates, forming a compact brown body which is evacuated through the anus when a new polyp is regenerated. Although sometimes considered a device for getting rid of accumulated excretory products, it must be confessed that the significance of this behaviour is unknown.

Crustacea moult at intervals, casting off their exoskeleton, with resultant loss of chitin.

NITROGEN EXCRETION

In this chapter we shall be concerned chiefly with nitrogen excretion. The principal nitrogenous end-product among marine invertebrates is ammonia, a highly toxic substance which must be eliminated rapidly. In these animals the problem of nitrogenous excretion is greatly simplified by the existence of an abundant circumambient medium for carrying away waste materials. In littoral invertebrates which are partially terrestrial in habit, and in fishes whose phyletic history has involved a return to salt water, specialized mechanisms have developed in conjunction with osmotic stress.

In aquatic animals some part of the excretory nitrogen is lost across the general body surface, especially through thin gill membranes where these are present. Part is discharged through special excretory organs, kidneys and nephridia, which often have other important functions as well as nitrogen excretion, namely ionic regulation and osmoregulation.

Nitrogen excretion presents three facets: the way in which end-products are produced (biochemistry); the manner in which excretory products are discharged to the exterior (physiology); and the relation between the mode of nitrogen excretion and the environmental conditions in which the animal lives (ecologic aspects).

Survey of Nitrogenous End-products among Marine Animals

Ammonia is formed by deamination of amino-acids, and sometimes of purines. To avoid toxaemia ammonia must be excreted rapidly or converted into a less toxic compound. Ammonia is very soluble in water, diffuses rapidly and is eliminated readily by aquatic animals. Ammonia tolerance varies among animals but the concentration in the blood is always low. Some recorded values (as mg NH_3-N per 100 c.c. or 100 g blood) are: crustaceans, 0·4–2·5; cephalopods, 1·4–4·8; selachians, 1·4–2·5; and teleosts, 0·3–5·5 mg%) (Table 7.1).

Animals which eliminate a high proportion of nitrogenous waste as ammonia are termed ammonotelic (Needham). These include actinians, polychaetes, sipunculoids, crustaceans, sublittoral gastropods, lamellibranchs, cephalopods and echinoderms. Teleost fishes also excrete much ammonia (Table 7.2).

Bacterial oxidation of ammonia in the sea is discussed by Spencer (60).

Urea is derived from amino compounds, namely amino-acids and purines. Like ammonia it is very soluble and diffusible but much less toxic. Urea forms a much smaller proportion of the total nitrogenous excretion than ammonia in marine invertebrates. It is excreted in small and variable amounts in all the major groups examined, namely coelenterates (actinians), annelids, sipunculoids, molluscs, crustaceans and echinoderms (Table 7.2). Animals in which the principal excretory end-product is urea are termed ureotelic and are found among vertebrates; ureotelism seems never to have been exploited by an invertebrate group. Marine elasmobranchs are highly ureotelic and excrete more than four-fifths of non-protein nitrogen as urea.

Uric acid is a relatively non-toxic substance of low solubility, which can be excreted in solid form. It is an important excretory product in birds, reptiles, insects and possibly certain gastropods. In some of these animals the ammonia produced by degradation of proteins is largely converted into uric acid, and such forms are termed uricotelic. Uric acid is also formed by the oxidative deamination of purines and is excreted in traces or small amounts by many marine invertebrates and fishes. The occurrence of ureotelism and uricotelism has special significance in conjunction with environmental conditions and breeding habits, and is discussed in a later section.

Purines: when nucleic acids are hydrolysed in the organism, purine and pyrimidine groups are liberated. The purine bases so formed are adenine and guanine. These substances are excreted unaltered by some animals, whereas others degrade them to a greater or lesser extent and excrete them as uric acid, allantoin, allantoic acid, urea or ammonia, depending on the degree of breakdown of the purines. Guanine or guanine-like substances are utilized by certain animals (crustacea, fish) as reflecting agents in chromatophores, sometimes in association with pterines (66). Little is known about the fate of pyrimidine bases.

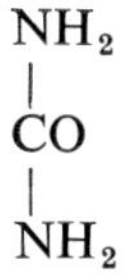

NH$_2$ NH—CO   CH$_3$
|
CO   CO   C—NH   CH$_3$—N=O
| | ‖   >CO
NH$_2$ NH—C—NH   CH$_3$

UREA 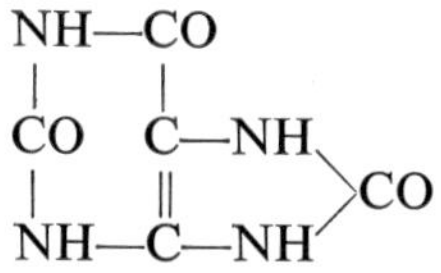   URIC ACID 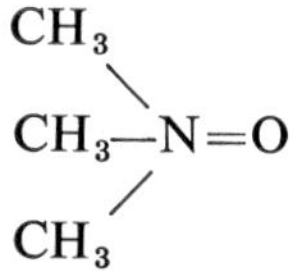   TRIMETHYLAMINE OXIDE

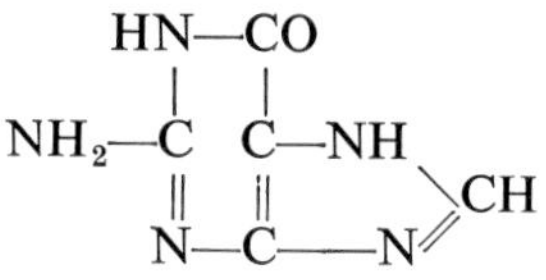

HN—CO   N=C—NH$_2$

NH$_2$—C   C—NH   HC   C—NH
‖   ‖   >CH   ‖   ‖   >CH
N—C——N   N—C——N

GUANINE 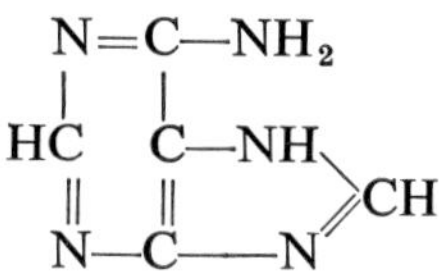   ADENINE

NH$_2$ NH$_2$ NH$_2$
| | |
CO   CO—NH   CO   COOH   CO
| | >CO | | |
NH—CH—NH   NH—CH——NH

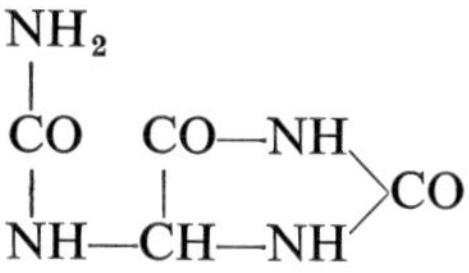

ALLANTOIN 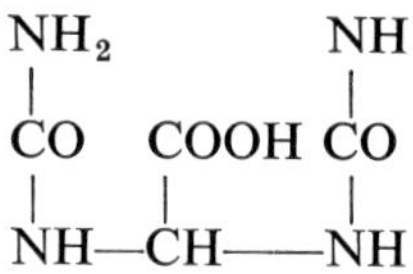   ALLANTOIC ACID

Trimethylamine oxide is a nitrogenous base found in marine teleosts, elasmobranchs and in several invertebrate groups, especially molluscs and crustaceans. Levels in blood and tissues of these animals are shown in Table 7.3. The characteristic odour which arises from marine fish after death is due to the liberation of trimethylamine from the oxide as the result of bacterial activity. Trimethylamine oxide is a soluble non-toxic substance with neutral reaction. It forms a considerable proportion of the waste nitrogen excreted by marine teleosts (30% or more), and smaller amounts are excreted by selachians (Table 7.2). Trimethylamine oxide is possibly produced by methylation of ammonia, but the process is poorly understood. Mammalian experiments have shown that trimethylamine can be converted into urea (1).

Creatine and creatinine: creatine (as creatine phosphate) plays an important role in muscle metabolism of vertebrates and also occurs in some protochordates and echinoderms (Chapter 9). It is always present in small amounts in the excreta of vertebrates, and is an important constituent of urinary nitrogen in some teleosts (Table 7.2). Some creatine may be converted into creatinine, and both occur in the urine of some species (64).

Nitrogenous pigments are produced by breakdown of haemochromogens and other substances. The metabolism of haem in vertebrates gives rise to bile pigments which are excreted in the urine and faeces. Little precise information is available about the transformation of nitrogenous pigments among invertebrates. Bile pigments occurring in wandering connective tissue cells of the leech *Pontobdella* are derived from breakdown of ingested

TABLE 7.1

Distribution of Non-protein-N in the Body Fluids of Marine Invertebrates
(mg N per 100 c.c. body fluid)

Animal	Non-protein-N	NH₃-N	Urea-N	Uric-acid-N	Amino-acid-N	Purine-N	Undetermined and other
Coelenterates							
Anemonia sulcata (tissues)	—	—	—	+	—	—	—
Annelids, Sipunculoids							
Arenicola marina	4·50	0·06	0·35–2·53	traces	1·60	—	1·75
Aphrodite aculeata	—	—	0·50	0·05	—	—	—
Chaetopterus variopedatus	—	—	—	0·24	—	—	—
Amphitrite ornata	—	—	—	0·0	—	—	—
Nereis pelagica	—	—	—	0·0	—	—	—
Sipunculus nudus	11·20	1·30	0·60	0·0	1·30	—	7·23
Golfingia gouldii	—	—	—	0·0	—	—	—
Crustacea, Xiphosura							
Palinurus vulgaris	26·50	2·50	5·50	0·30	8·00	2·10	8·10
Homarus	12·5–13·5	—	—	0·66–0·80	—	—	—
Cancer productus	18·0	1·05	5·15	1·56	—	—	creatine 0·06 creatinine 0·20
C. pagurus	15·0	0·80	0·90	0·08	6·70	0·30	6·22
Carcinus maenas	37·5	2·10	2·70	0·40	12·0	—	20·30
M. ... squin...	4·2–24·6	0·4–2·4	0·4–1·5	0·1–0·3	1·6–8·4	0·27	—

Aplysia fasciata	5·16	0·67	0·20	0·12	1·60	0·20	—
Haliotis rufescens	2·20	0·18	0·05	0·07	0·70	0·09	—
	21·0	0·40	5·60	—	—	—	—
	23·3	0·13	2·27	traces	—	—	—
	15·0	0·29	1·11	—	—	—	—
Mya arenaria (mantle fluid)	10·0	0·48	0·50	0·12	3·00	—	—
Crassostrea angulata (ditto)	6·22	0·45	0·20	0·01	0·82	—	—
Saxidomus nuttalli	13·00	0·95	9·05	—	—	—	—
Schizothaerus nuttalli	10·0	—	—	traces	8·00	—	NH₃+urea 3·3
	14·0	0·66	2·94	—	—	—	—
Ensis directus	—	—	—	0·0	—	—	—
Mercenaria mercenaria	—	—	—	0·0	—	—	—
Sepia officinalis	26·0	4·8	1·9	0·4	9·2	1·8	8·3
	14·8	2·8	1·2	0·1	7·1	—	3·6
Octopus vulgaris	14·0	1·6	1·2	traces	—	—	—
	9·6	1·4	0·8	—	—	—	—
Echinoderms							
Asterias rubens	1·95	0·40	0·09	0·14	0·80	—	0·66
A. forbesii	—	—	—	—	—	—	—
Pisaster ochraceus	4·4	—	—	—	—	—	—
Paracentrotus lividus	3·74	0·24	0·12	0·07	2·40	0·23	creatinine 0·30
Strongylocentrotus franciscanus	8·6	0·08	0·92	traces	—	—	NH₃+urea 1·0 / 0·79
Holothuria tubulosa	1·10	0·14	0·07	0·0	0·40	0·04	creatinine 0·27
Thyone briareus	—	—	—	0·14	—	—	0·06

(Various sources.)

TABLE 7.2

Nitrogenous Excretion in Marine Animals

(Expressed as percentage of total non-protein nitrogen for various compounds listed)

Animal	NH₃	Urea	Uric-acid	Amino-acid	Purines	Creatine	Creati-nine	Trimethyl-amine oxide	Other
Coelenterates									
Actinians	53	4	—	—	—	—	—	—	—
Polychaete, Sipunculoid									
Aphrodite aculeata	80	0·2	0·8	—	—	—	—	—	—
Sipunculus nudus	50	9·7	0·0	16·6	4·1	—	—	—	19·4
Molluscs									
Aplysia fasciata	37·0	7·4	9·2	13·0	16·7	—	—	—	16·7
ditto	30·0	10·0	traces	—	15·0	—	—	—	45·0
Littorina littorea s	39·9	12·6	0·8	6·7	28·7	—	—	—	—
ditto w	61·1	1·9	1·1	9·6	15·9	—	—	—	—
Mya arenaria	21·5	4·5	traces	18·0	5·0	—	—	—	51
Mytilus edulis	10·8	traces	0·0	35·5	16·0	—	—	—	37·7
Sepia officinalis urine	64·4	2·1	2·2	8·4	4·9	—	—	—	18
Octopus vulgaris urine	33·3	—	1·4	12·5	25·0	—	—	—	27·8
ditto urine	12·5	5·2	—	—	—	—	—	—	—
ditto sp? water	50·0	15·0	1	20	—	—	—	—	14
Crustacea									
Gammarus locusta	80	1	0	7	—	—	—	—	non-dialysable 3; unaccounted 9
G. zaddachi	83	1	0	3	—	—	—	—	ditto 3; ditto 9
Marinogammarus marinus	87	0	—	4	—	—	—	—	ditto 7; ditto 2
M. pirloti	87	1	0	2	—	—	—	—	ditto 2; ditto 9
Orchestia sp.	70	1	0	11	—	—	—	—	ditto 8; ditto 10
Ligia oceanica	83	0	0	6	—	—	—	—	ditto 4; ditto 9
Carcinus maenas urine	71·4	2·2	0·6	7·7	3·9	—	—	—	14·2
ditto water	67·8	3·0	0·7	8·7	3·2	—	—	—	17·3

Holothuria tubulosa		39·0	6·0	0·0	18·0	12·0	—	—	—	25·0
Fishes										
Mustelus canis	urine	1·9–7·3	80·7–89·0	0·2	—	—	—	—	—	—
Torpedo sp.	water	3·8	91·4	—	0·8	—	—	—	—	—
ditto	urine	1·7	85·3	—	1·7	—	—	—	—	—
Gadus callarias	urine	0·0	11·3	1·7	14·8	—	51·0	2·2	—	19·0
Pseudopleuronectes americanus	urine	2·6	13·5	1·3	8·2	—	—	26·1	—	48·3
	urine	1·8	21·2	1·2	9·7	—	—	15	—	51·1
Solea solea	water	53·0	16·6	—	—	—	—	—	—	—
Hippocampus europeus	water	63·1	8·9	0·8	13·8	—	—	—	—	—
Spheroides maculatus	urine	5·2	2·5	1·1	—	—	56·4	2·2	—	32·9
ditto	urine	6·2	19·1	0·2–0·4	20·5	—	38·8	5·0	—	9·3
Lophius piscatorius	urine	2·0	28·0	0·7–3·5	5·0	—	27·9–61·7	2·1–4·1	—	65·0
ditto	urine	0·3–0·5	0·1–0·7	0·02	5·3–14·3	—	21·0–55·5	0	28–36	—
ditto	urine	0·8–5·4	0·8–3·6	0·1	2·9–34·0	—	34·3	2·9	—	—
ditto	urine	12·9	1·1	0·7	3·0	—	16·8	0·8	28·4	—
ditto	urine	2·7	14·4	0·7	—	—	—	—	—	—
Myoxocephalus octodecimspinosus	urine	2·0	14·1	—	4·0	—	—	25·0	23·1	31·1
ditto	urine	1·3	15·3	—	4·4	—	—	22·4	23·1	32·8
Reptile										
Chelonia mydas	urine	17·7	45·1	19·1	—	—	9·7	1·6	—	allantoin 13·63; hippuric acid 13·85; undetermined 12·2
ditto	urine	16·1	38·1	16·5	7·53	—	2·6	0·9	—	—
ditto	urine	43·0	0·0	2·23	—	—	6·04	1·54	—	—
ditto	urine	14·5	31·1	14·0	—	—	2·6	0·9	—	—
Mammals										
Balaena mysticetus	urine	1·5	90·0	3·0	—	—	—	—	—	—
Phoca vitulina	urine	10	73	—	—	—	7	11	—	—
ditto	urine	15	73	—	—	—	5	8	—	—

(Various sources.)

s, summer; w, winter.

haemoglobin, and contribute to the external coloration of the animal. A protoporphyrin is found in the integument of starfish (*Asterias*), and is regarded as a by-product of chlorophyll excretion. Porphyrins (uroporphryin and coproporphyrin) are deposited in the shells of testaceous molluscs; in species without shells or with uncalcified shells (*Duvaucelia* and *Aplysia*), uroporphyrin occurs in the integument (33, 34).

MODES OF NITROGEN EXCRETION

Ammonotelism

Aquatic animals are usually ammonotelic, and produce ammonia as the major end-product of protein catabolism. Small amounts of ammonia may also arise from the breakdown of purines and pyrimidines. No species is restricted entirely to one excretory product, however, and as Table 7.2 shows, ammonotelic animals excrete other nitrogenous compounds, sometimes in traces, often in relatively large amounts. Actinians, for example, are predominantly ammonotelic but they also excrete a little urea, and small amounts of uric acid and tetramine (tetramethyl ammonium chloride) are found in the tissues of some species, the latter substance probably being formed by the methylation of ammonia (63). The principal nitrogenous excretory product of polychaetes is ammonia, but *Aphrodite* gives off small amounts of urea and uric acid, and small quantities of urea and uric acid have been reported in the coleomic fluid of *Arenicola*, and uric acid in *Chaetopterus* (Tables 7.1 and 7.2).

Other predominantly ammonotelic groups are sipunculoids, amphipods, isopods, decapod crustaceans, echinoderms, brachiopods, lamellibranchs, cephalopods, many marine gastropods and ascidians. Nearly all species examined excrete small quantities of urea, and frequently uric acid as well. Concentrations of urea and uric acid in the blood and body fluids of various species are given in Table 7.1. The small amounts of urea and uric acid produced by ammonotelic animals are derived largely from degradation of nucleic acids (14, 20, 22, 23, 38, 65).

Some species, although predominantly ammonotelic, excrete considerable quantities of amino-acids. Thus, echinoderms (starfish, urchins and cucumbers) lose amino-acids in quantities that may equal the ammonia excreted. Crustacea excrete surprisingly large amounts of amino-acids, up to 10% of total non-protein nitrogen in some species. Part of the amino-acid nitrogen is discharged through the excretory organs proper, but there is a certain amount of leakage across the body surface as well. Excretion of amino-acids represents loss of potentially useful metabolites, and points to inefficiency of conservation mechanisms (2).

Uricotelism in Vertebrates

Uric acid is the main nitrogenous end-product of protein metabolism in two groups of higher vertebrates, namely Squamata (lizards and snakes) and birds. This mode of excretion is a specialization adapting these animals to dry terrestrial conditions both in the egg stage (they lay enclosed, cleidoic eggs) and after hatching. Because of its low solubility, uric acid in solution does not cause toxaemia, and by excreting it in solid form water is conserved for other metabolic functions. The same factors favour uric acid as an excretory product in embryonic stages, when it can be stored as solid material until the time of hatching. Uricotelism must have proved advantageous to those species of birds which have re-invaded the seas. Pelagic maritime birds, of course, have no access to fresh water for drinking purposes. Since the salt content of their blood is only about one-third that of sea water, maintenance of water balance is an important factor in their physiology and, for all practical purposes, presents demands as acute to maritime avian species as those obtaining in arid desert regions. Uricotelism, by reducing the water required in excretion, has been a favourable character under conditions of overt or concealed water scarcity.

The osmotic relationships obtaining in marine reptiles probably can be bracketed with those found in birds but, unfortunately, very little is known of the physiology of those forms. Among sea-snakes (Hydrophiidae), some are oviparous (Laticaudinae), others viviparous (Hydrophiinae), and one species, *Pelamis platurus*, is wholly pelagic in habit. Presumably these forms, of recent evolutionary origin, have retained the uricotelism of terrestrial ophidians. The green turtle *Chelonia mydas* excretes both urea and ammonia as major nitrogenous end-products, and possibly has undergone little alteration in its mode of nitrogen excretion during progression towards a maritime existence (Table 7.2). Terrestrial forms, on the other hand, appear to be in the process of evolving towards uricotelism at the present time, and crocodiles are ammono-uricotelic. Marine turtles bury their eggs on sandy shores and during development the production of urea predominates over uric acid, as in the adult. Total nitrogen actually diminishes, and it appears that the turtle egg absorbs water from the moist sand in which it lies and gives off end-products of nitrogen metabolism through the shell (35, 41, 44).

Ureotelic Fishes and Excretion of Trimethylamine Oxide

A second mode of nitrogen excretion which has appeared among vertebrates is ureotelism. Teleosts tend to be ammonotelic but many species produce appreciable quantities of urea, amounting to a tenth or a fifth of total excretory nitrogen in some marine forms. A striking peculiarity of marine teleosts is found in the large amounts of nitrogen excreted as trimethylamine oxide (TMO). Trimethylamine oxide is found in muscles, blood and other tissues: concentrations are highest in marine species, and much smaller amounts occur in freshwater teleosts. It also occurs in molluscs and crustacea (up to 300 mg % in muscles of the lobster *Homarus*), but marine teleosts alone excrete it as an important nitrogenous end-product (Tables 7.2, 7.3). Variations in concentration of TMO are reported in different species of teleosts. Several factors affect TMO content, among which may be enumerated environment, season, size, age, etc. Thus arctic species of teleosts tend to have higher concentrations of TMO than species from the North Sea, and seasonal changes have been noted in the herring (56).

The blood of marine teleosts has an osmotic pressure which is much less than that of sea water. This condition imposes a strong osmotic gradient which the fish must combat to maintain physiological homeostasis, and it is reasonable to suppose that the synthesis of TMO, by substituting a highly soluble non-toxic substance for ammonia, is an adaptation linked with the existence of osmotic stress and the necessity of conserving water. Part of the trimethylamine oxide possibly arises from detoxication of NH_3, but a certain amount is exogenous in origin, originating in food. Chinook salmon (*Oncorhynchus tshawytscha*), for example, lack TMO when in fresh water, although it is present in sea-run adults. Salt water does not influence deposition of TMO but feeding *Pecten* muscle (which contains TMO) causes rapid accumulation of the substance in salmon flesh. It has also been suggested that the trimethylamine oxide occurring in the blood and tissues of marine teleosts may have osmoregulatory significance, but the small quantities present in the blood and the ease with which it crosses the gill membranes show that its osmotic effect must be small (5, 46).

Elasmobranchs are peculiar in that they combine a high level of uraemia with ureotelism. Urea levels in the blood of selachians lie around 2–2·5% (Table 2.7), and this substance forms the principal nitrogenous excretory product (80–90% of the total nitrogen excreted). The gills are relatively impermeable to urea and the kidneys regulate the amount of urea excreted so as to maintain the blood concentration at a high level. As a consequence of the high urea content, the blood of marine elasmobranchs is slightly hypertonic to sea water although the salt content is actually less than that of the outside medium (Chapter 2).

The regulation of osmotic pressure during development in selachians is achieved in one of two ways, depending on the method of reproduction in the species. Oviparous forms lay cleidoic eggs which are impermeable to urea. The ammonia which is produced by the embryo during development is converted into urea, and its accumulation provides a source of osmoregulatory material for the young fish on hatching as well as solving its major excretory problem.

In viviparous forms, on the other hand, the urea requirements of the embryo are met by the mother fish which provides the necessary quantities of urea.

In addition to urea, considerable quantities of trimethylamine oxide occur in the blood and tissues of elasmobranchs, ranging from 0·25–1·43% (Table 7.3).

It has been reported that the concentration of TMO in the urine of

TABLE 7.3—CONCENTRATION OF TRIMETHYLAMINE OXIDE IN BLOOD AND TISSUES OF SOME MARINE ANIMALS

(mM per 1,000 g moist tissue or 1,000 c.c. fluid†)

Group and Animal	Tissue	Content TMO
Sea anemones: Hexactiniae	Entire animal	5·7–27·0
Polychaeta		
Terebellidae and Nereidae	ditto	nil
Brachiopoda		
Terebratalia transversa	ditto	negligible
Echinodermata		
Asterias vulgaris	ditto	14·2
Strongylocentrotus franciscanus	ditto	negligible
Cucumaria miniata	ditto	ditto
Mollusca		
Cryptochiton stelleri	ditto	ditto
Littorina sitkana	ditto	ditto
Ostrea japonica	ditto	ditto
Mytilus edulis	ditto	ditto
Macoma inquinata	ditto	ditto
Cardium californiense	ditto	11, 13
C. corbis	ditto	23
Pecten hericius	Muscle	32–52
P. hericius	Entire animal	2·2–4·6
Octopus apollyon	ditto	17
Loligo opalescens	ditto	107, 111
Arthropods		
Copepods, mixture of species	Entire animals	45
Balanus nubilus	ditto	42–71
Amphipods, sand-fleas	ditto	2·2
Pandalus danae	ditto	28–63
Homarus vulgaris	Muscle	40
Pagurus ochotensis	Entire animal	47
Cancer productus	ditto	46
Cyclostomes		
Myxine glutinosa	ditto	45
Fish		
Squalus acanthias	Muscle	88, 135
ditto	Blood serum	64
ditto	Liver	8
ditto	Muscle press juice	190·4†
Scyliorhinus stellaris	Blood serum	101†
Raja laevis	Muscle press juice	166†
Hydrolagus colliei	Muscle	121, 134
ditto	Blood serum	6·5, 7·5
Sebastodes sp.	Muscle	16–48
ditto	Heart	21
ditto	Blood serum, etc.	negligible
Scorpaenichthys marmoratus	Muscle	46
ditto	Blood serum	negligible
Pseudopleuronectes americanus	Muscle	50
ditto	Blood serum	negligible
Gadus callarias	Muscle	30
Clupea harengus	Muscle press juice	64†
Scomber scombrus	ditto	35†
Gadus virens	ditto	64†
ditto	Muscle	39
Oncorhynchus tshawytscha (s.w.)	ditto	7·1, 8·3

Sources: Hoppe-Seyler and Schmidt (31); Hoppe-Seyler (29, 30); Kutscher and Ackermann (37); Beatty (4); Norris and Benoit (47); Dyer (15). s.w., sea water

elasmobranchs is only 10% of that in the blood, and this suggests that it is actively retained by the fish, presumably as an osmoregulatory agent (15, 17, 27, 36).

Conditions in Littoral Invertebrates

As previously noted the mode of nitrogen excretion has adaptive significance in connexion with osmotic stress and the water relations of the organism. Littoral animals might be expected to show specialized trends in nitrogen excretion corresponding to the degree of exposure and desiccation to which they are subjected, but unfortunately only a few species have been investigated. Gastropods show some tendency for gradation from ammonotelism to uricotelism when species are ranked from aquatic to terrestrial forms. At the one extreme are sublittoral and lower littoral marine gastropods, such as *Aplysia*, which excrete much ammonia and little uric acid. At the other are the strictly terrestrial snails and slugs, the excreta of which contain more uric acid. Terrestrial and freshwater gastropods show a tendency to uricotelism. The excretion of uric acid in lieu of ammonia is of value to animals living under conditions of restricted water supply and producing cleidoic eggs.

The uric acid content of the nephridia of a long series of molluscs examined by Needham shows nice correlation with habitat (Table 7.4.) Uric acid levels, low in sublittoral and low-littoral lamellibranchs and gastropods, are higher in littoral periwinkles and show maximal values in terrestrial snails and slugs. Further analyses of the partition of non-protein-N in the excreta of marine molluscs are required to substantiate these correlations (cf. Table 7.2).

The different species of periwinkles listed in Table 7.4 show marked zonation on the shore. Two species, the flat periwinkle *Littorina littoralis* and the common periwinkle *L. littorea*, are found on the lower half of the shore. Occurring at higher levels, from the middle shore to high-tide mark, is the rough periwinkle *L. saxatilis*, while the small periwinkle *L. neritoides* inhabits crevices above high-tide mark. In apparent agreement with the degree of exposure which these different species encounter is an increase in the amount of uric acid excreted, which reaches its maximum in *L. neritoides*, the species subjected to greatest exposure. There appears to be no correlation between breeding habits and uric acid excretion, as has been suggested, however. Thus, both *L. neritoides* and *L. littorea* produce free-swimming larvae; *L. littoralis* produces large eggs in which the larvae develop to the crawling stage; whereas *L. saxatilis* retains eggs and larvae in a brood pouch.

A pulmonate *Onchidella celtica*, which has returned to the sea and which seeks shelter in moist crevices during low tide, contains little uric acid. *Potamopyrgus jenkinsi*, an estuarine species which has invaded fresh water during recent historic times, produces little uric acid (Table 7.4).

Aquatic and terrestrial amphipods and isopods are essentially ammonotelic, and more than 50% of the total non-protein-N of the excreta consists of NH_3. The level of nitrogen excretion is considerably lower in terrestrial than in freshwater, littoral and marine species (Table 7.5). Urea and uric acid, at most, form trivial end-products, and amino-acids seldom

TABLE 7.4
URIC ACID CONTENT OF NEPHRIDIA OF SNAILS AND SLUGS
(mg/g dry weight)

Terrestrial		High littoral	
Helix pomatia	700	Onchidella celtica 1·7	
H. aspersa	64, 167	Estuarine and freshwater	
Limax maximus	205		
L. flavus	31	Potamopyrgus jenkinsi 0·1	
Littoral		Lower littoral and sublittoral	
Littorina neritoides	25	Buccinum	4
L. saxatilis	5	Gibbula	2
L. littoralis	2·5	Nucella	4·5
L. littorea	1·5	Monodonta	0·56, 2·8
	26 summer	Nassarius	2·9
	44 winter		

TABLE 7.5
NITROGEN EXCRETION IN ISOPODS AND AMPHIPODS
Mean values for total non-protein nitrogen excreted

Species	Habitat	mg N/10g/24 hours
Gammarus locusta	Marine littoral	4·9
Marinogammarus marinus	Marine littoral and estuarine	1·1
M. pirloti	Marine littoral	2·9
Gammarus zaddachi	Estuarine	6·0
Orchestia sp.	Semi-terrestrial	2·0
Ligia oceanica	ditto	1·3
Oniscus asellus	Terrestrial	0·3
Gammarus pulex	Freshwater	2·3
Asellus aquaticus	ditto	2·6

(From Dresel and Moyle (14))

exceed 10%. In these groups excretory adaptation to terrestrial conditions has taken the form of reduction of nitrogen metabolism rather than of transformation of NH_3 to other less toxic products (13, 14).

Among decapod crustaceans the shore crab *Carcinus maenas* shows no increase in the relative amounts of urea and uric acid excreted over sub-littoral species. Excretion in high-littoral and terrestrial species has not been investigated.

ENZYMES INVOLVED IN NITROGEN EXCRETION
Protein Degradation
Protein degradation and synthesis of particular excretory products are catalysed by enzymes at all stages. Amino-acids are deaminated with the formation of ammonia by enzymes known as deaminases. However, as we

have seen, not all groups excrete the nitrogenous end-products of protein metabolism as ammonia; some species convert the latter into urea or uric acid. In mammals, ammonia is synthesized into urea by the Krebs (ornithine) cycle, according to the following schema.

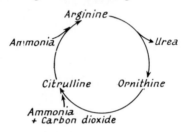

In this process arginine is converted into ornithine and urea through the catalytic action of arginase present in the liver. The resulting ornithine interacts with ammonia and carbon dioxide, and is reconverted into arginine in a repetition of the cycle. Urea may also be formed directly from dietary arginine by the action of arginase.

Among elasmobranch fishes a high degree of uraemia is a natural condition and an ornithine cycle operates. Arginase occurs in many tissues, the liver being especially rich. The liver also contains ornithine transcarbamoylase catalysing the step ornithine → citrulline. Some urea may be formed extrahepatically from blood arginine by tissue arginase (11). Teleost fishes show much specific variation in liver-arginase content, but this never attains the high level of selachians. The ornithine cycle is reported to be absent from bony fishes, and the urea excreted is probably formed from dietary arginine.

The ornithine cycle does not appear to be present in any invertebrate group. Most marine invertebrates are ammonotelic, and in these animals arginase is absent or occurs only in very small quantities. Thus in a series of marine molluscs investigated by Baldwin, the hepatopancreas (liver) was found to be free of arginase (2).

Purine Metabolism

From studies of excretory products and enzyme complements, certain tentative conclusions have been drawn about the course of purine metabolism in invertebrates. Purine bases which are released by the hydrolysis of nucleic acids are sometimes excreted unaltered. But some animals possess specific enzymes, adenase and guanase, which deaminate the purine bases adenine and guanine, converting them to hypoxanthine and xanthine. These, in turn, may be oxidized to uric acid by xanthine oxidase. Some or all of these compounds are excreted in various proportions by different groups of animals. Various invertebrates possess a further complement of enzymes capable of breaking down uric acid through a series of steps to ammonia. An outline for the course of purine degradation is as follows—

Purine Bases

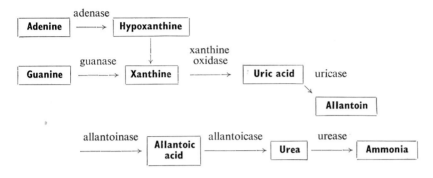

In the few flatworms and annelids which have been examined, enzymes capable of deaminating purines are lacking, and purines are excreted. Ascidians accumulate and store uric acid and purines. These substances seem to be the end-products of purine metabolism because uricolytic enzymes are generally wanting (23). Many other invertebrates possess uricolytic enzymes, namely actinians, sipunculoids, molluscs, crustaceans and echinoderms. All four enzymes capable of decomposing uric acid to ammonia—uricase, allantoinase, allantoicase and urease—have been identified in certain species: such include *Sipunculus*, *Mytilus* and *Homarus*. A small but significant proportion of the excretory products shown in Table 7.2 is derived from purine as distinct from protein metabolism. Data relating to processes of purine deamination among invertebrates are very fragmentary, and more biochemical information is desirable.

Fish degrade purines part or all of the way to urea. The livers of selachians (*Raja*) and of certain teleosts (scombrids *et al.*) contain uricase, allantoinase and allantoicase; others (salmonids, anguillids, pleuronectids) lack allantoicase. Urea is the final end-product of protein degradation in selachians and it forms a significant proportion of the nitrogenous excreta in some teleosts. Now urease converts urea into ammonia, and its absence in marine fish in conjunction with the conservation of urea in selachians and excretion of urea in teleosts, is significant for osmotic reasons which have already been discussed.

It has been pointed out by Florkin that the degradation of amino-acids and purines in many animals tends to terminate in a common end-product. In crustaceans, for example, the end-product of both protein and purine catabolism is ammonia; and in elasmobranchs, urea. Uricolytic enzymes show a rather patchy distribution among animals. Many invertebrates, including some relatively simple groups, possess the full complement of enzymes capable of degrading purines to ammonia. This appears to be a primitive condition, and in the course of evolution certain groups of animals have dropped various enzymes in the series.

ELIMINATION OF NITROGENOUS EXCRETA:
RENAL AND EXTRARENAL ROUTES

Invertebrates. Primitive invertebrate groups, including the protozoa, sponges and coelenterates, possess no specialized excretory organs and excretion takes place across the general body surface. Owing to simple organization no tissue in these animals is far removed from the external medium. Ammonia is the principal end-product of protein catabolism and is readily eliminated by diffusion. Echinoderms and tunicates are other groups lacking excretory organs.

Most metazoans, however, possess some kind of tubular structures which discharge fluids to the exterior, and on the basis of their morphological appearance such structures are termed excretory organs. Several types can be distinguished, the simplest and most primitive being nephridia. These are found in flatworms, nemertines, certain annelids and cephalochordates. A nephridium consists of a hollow flame-cell or solenocyte lying in the parenchyma and a tubule leading from the solenocyte to the exterior (Fig. 7.1). In the intracellular cavity of the solenocyte there are cilia or flagella, the apparent function of which is to drive fluid to the exterior by the creation of a gradient of hydrostatic pressure. In some instances the nephridium may open into the coelom by a ciliated funnel (nephridiostome).

Another tubular structure encountered in many metazoans is the coelomoduct. This is a duct which opens into the coelom by a ciliated funnel (coelomostome) and leads to the exterior of the body. The nephridium is regarded as an excretory organ, whereas the coelomoduct, primitively, is a genital duct. In many polychaetes nephridia and coelomoducts become fused in various ways so as to form a conjoint mixonephridium with excretory and genital functions (Fig. 7.1).

Molluscs and crustaceans possess kidneys of more specialized structure. In gastropods and lamellibranchs there are one or two excretory organs, derived from coelomoducts, which open into the pericardium by ciliated reno-pericardial apertures (Fig. 7.2). The central portion of the tubule is usually enlarged as a renal sac, often very extensive and bearing lamellations and diverticula. Distally a renal duct leads to the pallial cavity. In addition there are pericardial glands surrounding the auricles in lamellibranchs. These structures are believed to move waste material from the haemolymph into the pericardial fluid. The renal apparatus of cephalopods is similar to that of other molluscs, and consists of a multi-chambered renal sac, connected by small apertures with the viscero-pericardial coelom, and opening to the exterior by paired renal papillae.

The excretory organs of crustaceans consist of two pairs of antennal and maxillary glands, which open at the bases of the corresponding appendages. Usually only one pair is functional in the adult, and in the Malacostraca it is the antennal gland. The kidney of decapods arises in an end-sac (coelomic sac), which communicates with an enlargement known as the labyrinth by reason of its convoluted structure. From the latter an excretory duct leads to a bladder which opens to the exterior. There is much specific variation in the structure of these organs. The bladder is sometimes greatly enlarged and the excretory duct very short in marine forms (Fig. 7.3).

The nephridia of lower animals participate in voiding nitrogenous excreta, although much excretory nitrogen is often discharged extrarenally. Other functions are ionic regulation and osmoregulation.

In marine gastropods and lamellibranchs ammonia is an important constituent of nitrogen excretion, but various species, notably *Mytilus*, have an appreciable amino-acid fraction (Table 7.2). No urine analyses are

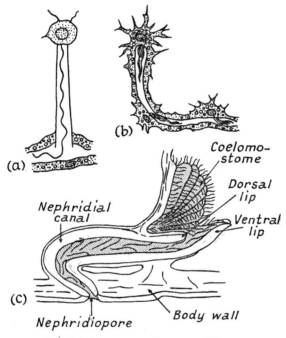

FIG. 7.1. EXCRETORY DUCTS OF WORMS

(*a*) Typical solenocyte of a polychaete; (*b*) inner end of a nephridial canal of a polyclad turbellarian, with flame cell at extremity; (*c*) metanephromixium of *Odontosyllis*. Dorsal and ventral lips pertain to the nephridiostome. (From Goodrich.)

available but it seems likely that some fraction of the total excretory-N is discharged in the urine. There is evidence that fluid is filtered across the heart wall into the pericardium and then enters the kidneys, where glucose is resorbed, and other substances are actively secreted (25). By producing a urine hypotonic to the blood the kidneys of freshwater species participate in the maintenance of a hyperosmotic internal *milieu*.

The total output of non-protein nitrogen in a medium-sized octopus amounts to about 25 mg/day. Half of this is ammonia, but there are appreciable amounts of urea and amines, amounting to 15 and 20% respectively. Since the data are not related to body weight, it is impossible to partition nitrogen excretion by renal and extrarenal routes. The urine of cephalopods contains up to 140 mg non-protein-N per 100 c.c., of which from one-third to two-thirds is NH_3-N. The relative proportions of ammonia are higher in the water surrounding the animal than in the urine, indicating that some ammonia is lost extrarenally. However, there is a possibility of bacterial action affecting the ammonia concentration of the surrounding sea water during the lengthy periods in which the animals were immersed. Concentrations of non-protein-N, especially NH_3, are

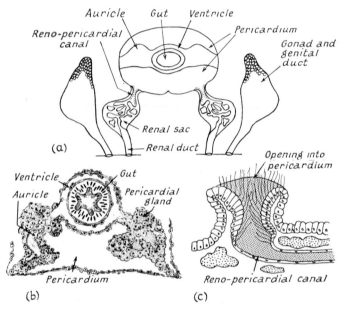

FIG. 7.2. (*a*) DIAGRAMMATIC REPRESENTATION OF THE RENAL ORGANS OF A LAMELLIBRANCH; (*b*) PERICARDIAL GLANDS OF *Mytilus*; (*c*) RENO-PERICARDIAL APERTURE OF *Patella*. ((*a*), (*c*) after Goodrich; (*b*) from Fretter.)

always greater in the urine than in the blood, whereas NH_2-N is less concentrated in the urine. Tests with various substances have produced evidence for a mechanism by which blood is filtered across the wall of an appendage of the branchial heart into the pericardial cavity. The filtrate goes through a renopericardial canal, in which glucose is resorbed, and passes into the renal sacs where urea and other substances are actively secreted. Ammonia, also, is secreted into the filtrate, and amino-acids are selectively resorbed (26). Inorganic constituents are also differentially treated by the kidney, for resorption of K^+, Ca^{++}, Mg^{++} and Cl^- takes place, while $SO_4^=$ and Na^+ are secreted into the renal fluid. These ionic displacements form part of the mechanism of ionic regulation (p. 72) (26, 51).

The urine of marine crustaceans appears to be formed as a blood ultra-filtrate. In the lobster (*Homarus*), levels of injected inulin, creatinine and glucose are the same in blood and urine, thus indicating that these particular substances, at least, are neither secreted nor absorbed in the kidney. When the animals are retained in normal sea water, the urine formed is isotonic with the blood. The hydrostatic pressure of the blood is about 13 cm H_2O in *Carcinus*, and the difference in colloid osmotic pressure between blood and urine is 9·6 cm, leaving a surplus pressure to produce filtration into the coelomic sac of the kidney. Inorganic crystalloids, however, are

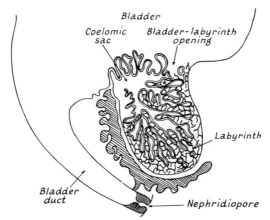

FIG. 7.3. EXCRETORY ORGAN OF *Palinurus*.
(From *Winterstein's Handbuch*)

differentially treated by the kidney as part of the mechanism of ionic regulation. Crustacean blood tends to have low levels of Mg^{++} and $SO_4^=$, and the kidneys act so as to eliminate these substances from the blood, and conserve Na^+ and K^+. Blood glucose is excluded from the urine. In dilute media the rate of urine production is markedly increased (*Carcinus*, *Palaemonetes*).

Ammonia is the principal constituent of total excretory-N in crustaceans, forming some 60–85% of the total. Copepods (*Calanus finmarchicus*) excrete 7 to 12 mg N/g dry weight/day, and the amount varies positively with food intake (12). In decapods most of the excretory-N is eliminated extrarenally. The gills of *Eriocheir* are highly permeable to ammonia, which is lost at the rate of about 40 mg NH_3-N/kg/day, and there is little change in ammonia excretion when the antennary glands are closed. Urea, injected into lobsters, is eliminated through the gills. Nitrogen excretion in *Carcinus maenas* occurs at the rate of 44 mg total N or 38 mg NH_3-N/kg/day, and it is increased by injury and high protein diet. Amino-acids are excreted in amounts which constitute 10–20% of total excretory-N in some species. In *Maia squinado* urine is produced at the rate of 30 c.c./kg/day, and contains only 5·4–10 mg non-protein-N/100 c.c. These nitrogen concentrations are about twice those in the blood, and the kidney, accordingly, appears to concentrate excretory-N. In some crabs (*Cancer, Carcinus*) ammonia represents a large part of non-protein nitrogen in the urine; in *Maia*, however, it forms only some 10% of the total, leaving a substantial fraction unaccounted for (10, 43, 47, 48, 49, 52).

Marine Fish. Most of the waste nitrogen in bony fishes is excreted across the gills, probably by diffusion, only a small amount escaping in the urine. Homer Smith was able to separate the excretory output of the gills and the kidney by means of an experiment in which a fish was encircled with a rubber dam, whereby the fluid in the anterior branchial region could be collected separately from the urine. In freshwater carp the total excretory-N during fasting amounted to about 50 mg/kg/day. The majority of this nitrogen escaped via the gills, in amounts six to nine times as great as that discharged through the ureters. Branchial excretion consisted of readily diffusible substances, ammonia, urea and amines. Together these substances account for about three-quarters of all the nitrogen lost across the gills. Ammonia-N forms some 50–60% of the total, urea-N and amine-N some 5% each. The remaining nitrogen is present in trimethylamine oxide. Less diffusible substances are excreted by the kidneys, namely creatine, creatinine and uric acid. Since only a small amount of nitrogen is lost by this route, however, these substances form only a minor proportion of the total excretory-N.

Similarly, in marine teleosts, a large proportion of the total nitrogen excreted is lost through the gills, as ammonia (some 60–70% in the sculpin *Leptocottus*). Ammonia forms 50–60% and urea 10–20% of the total excretory nitrogen of marine species. In the urine, however, ammonia levels tend to be low (around 1–2%), while creatine and TMO together may constitute two-thirds of the nitrogen lost by this route (8).

The chief excretory end-product in selachians is urea. In the freshwater sawfish *Pristis* the total output of urea together with ammonia-N amounts to 450 mg/kg/day, of which three-quarters is urea. The branchial membranes, it has been noted, are relatively but not absolutely impermeable to urea, and about 75% of the total urea is excreted extrarenally, across the gills. The gills are readily permeable to ammonia, most of which (about 90%) escapes through this route. In selachians as in teleosts, therefore, most of the excretory-N is discharged extrarenally. Nitrogen output in the urine of selachians is relatively low, about 150 mg/kg/day. Most of this can be accounted for as urea (some 80–90%), the remainder being represented by low levels of ammonia, creatine, etc. Both urea and TMO are conserved by the kidney (57, 58).

In vertebrates the coelomoducts have given rise to a specialized kidney. The unit of the vertebrate kidney is the nephron consisting of a corpuscle and tubule leading to the ureter. The corpuscle is made up of a Bowman's capsule into which projects a glomerulus of blood capillaries. This is essentially a filtration unit for filtering off blood plasma free of proteins. The governing factor in filtration is arterial pressure. All dissolved substances in the blood—salts, glucose, amino-acids and nitrogenous end-products—are likewise passed into the capsule. The tubule, especially the proximal convoluted section, alters the composition of the glomerular filtrate, resorbing useful metabolites and salts and excreting other substances, processes which govern the composition of the urine.

Hagfishes (which have mesonephric kidneys) form urine by glomerular filtration. Glucose but not sodium or water is resorbed by cells of the mesonephric ducts. As in teleosts (*vide infra*) the kidney is concerned with ionic regulation, and potassium, magnesium, sulphate and phosphate are secreted into the filtrate. Urea is discharged in the urine and seems to be concentrated. Urine (isosmotic with the plasma) is produced at a rate of 1–8 c.c./kg/day (*Myxine*) (16, 40, 42).

In marine teleosts a large proportion of nitrogenous waste is excreted by extrarenal routes, across the gills. The volume of urine formed by marine teleosts is relatively small, around 2–4 c.c./kg/day, as compared with 60 c.c. or more in freshwater species. In addition to dealing with a fraction of nitrogenous excretion, the kidney of marine fish also plays an important role in ionic regulation by excreting magnesium, calcium and sulphate. In elasmobranchs, which possess a high osmotic pressure by virtue of uraemia, the glomeruli are large and the kidney conserves urea. The urine flow of the dogfish (*Mustelus canis*) amounts to 15 c.c./kg/day.

The subject of kidney excretion has been repeatedly reviewed and we shall confine ourselves to certain problems posed by marine fish (54). Kidney function can be partitioned into two aspects, glomerular filtration and tubular activity. Some substances, such as glucose, which are carried out into the glomerular filtrate, are reabsorbed in the proximal convoluted tubule and appear in the urine only when the concentration in the blood exceeds a certain value, i.e. when the rate at which they enter the tubule exceeds the rate at which they can be absorbed. The glomerular filtration rate is measured by using some substance such as xylose or inulin which is not absorbed or excreted by the tubule. The glomerular filtration rate (xylose) in marine teleosts is rather low, 14 c.c./kg/day in the sculpin *Myoxocephalus*. Some water and salts are resorbed by the tubules since only 3 c.c./kg/day are evacuated. On entering salt water the silver eel reduces its urine flow to a fifth of that produced in fresh water (*ca* 80 c.c./kg/day) (55).

Tubular function is measured by comparing the rate of excretion of inulin or xylose with other substances. The rate of excretion of a substance is expressed as clearance, which refers to the volume of blood cleared of a particular substance in a given time. Since a small amount of xylose is resorbed, inulin clearance rates slightly exceed those of xylose. In dogfish (*Mustelus, Squalus*), for example, the clearance of magnesium, phosphate and creatinine exceeds that of xylose or inulin, while clearance of water, urea and glucose is less. Experiments of this nature show that magnesium, phosphate and creatinine are actively secreted by the tubules, whereas water, glucose and urea are resorbed. The proportion of filtered urea which is taken up by the tubules varies with the concentration in the blood plasma and ranges from 70–99·5%. TMO is also conserved in elasmobranchs by tubular resorption.

In some marine teleosts glomeruli are reduced or absent, the urine being formed by tubular secretion—toadfishes (Haplodoci), anglers (Pediculati) and pipefishes (Lophobranchii). The aglomerular kidney seems to be a secondary specialization, correlated with a regime of low urine output.

The kidney of aglomerular fish has proved a very useful organ for investigating tubular excretion. When aglomerular and glomerular fish are compared, the tubule of the aglomerular kidney shows striking capacity for excretion of certain substances by active secretory processes. There is little difference in the rate of urine formation in the two types of kidneys and under normal conditions marine teleosts appear to be functionally aglomerular. The aglomerular kidney is capable of developing a secretion pressure greater than that existing in the aorta, and of excreting and concentrating a wide variety of plasma constituents. There are, however, marked differences in the relations of the two kidneys to certain substances. The aglomerular kidney is unable to excrete glucose, xylose, sucrose and inulin. Glucose is reabsorbed by the tubules of glomerular kidneys, xylose and sucrose to a small extent, and inulin not at all. Magnesium, calcium, phosphate, phenol red, creatine and creatinine are excreted by both glomerular and aglomerular kidneys of fish. Excretory-N is concentrated several-fold, and teleost urine contains about 80 mg/100 c.c. Levels of ammonia are very low; urea forms some 10–20% of total urinary nitrogen in fish such as the flounder and sculpin, but only about 1% in *Lophius*. A large part of the total nitrogen consists of TMO and creatine or creatinine, which are concentrated by the kidney tubules (6, 7, 8, 9, 18, 19, 24, 32, 45, 50, 62).

Some of the physiological information available concerning the osmotic pressure and the composition of the body fluids and urine of marine vertebrates has been used to support the thesis that modern fishes have had a freshwater ancestry. In particular, it has been argued that the low osmotic pressure of teleost blood (about half that of sea water) and the glomerular kidneys are devices for reducing the osmotic gradient in fresh water and for getting rid of excess water by filtration. It has been supposed that selachians developed ureotelism as a device for countering the osmotic gradient when they invaded the sea; on the other hand, marine teleosts were considered to have lost kidney glomeruli, thereby reducing urine flow. A contrary view for a marine origin of vertebrates is being emphasized, however. Hagfishes, which are the most primitive marine vertebrates, have a blood which is isosmotic with sea water. The kidney, primitively concerned with ionic regulation and elimination of waste, developed a faculty for absorbing sodium ion and producing a hypo-osmotic urine; nitrogen excretion remained largely extrarenal. On entering fresh water the kidney opened up and developed a much greater urine flow. Germane to these ideas is the viewpoint one adopts concerning the ionic and osmotic composition of Ordovician seas (53).

REFERENCES

1. BACH, S. J., "Biological methylation," *Biol. Rev.*, **20**, 158 (1945).
2. BALDWIN, E., *An Introduction to Comparative Biochemistry* (Cambridge Univ. Press, 1952).
3. BALDWIN, E., *Dynamic Aspects of Biochemistry* (Cambridge Univ. Press, 1952).
4. BEATTY, S. A., "Studies of fish spoilage. 3. Trimethylamine oxide content of the muscles of Nova Scotia fish," *J. Fish. Res. Bd Can.*, **4**, 229 (1939).
5. BENOIT, G. J. JR. and NORRIS, E. R., "Studies on trimethylamine oxide. 2. The origin of trimethylamine oxide in young salmon," *J. Biol. Chem.*, **158**, 439 (1945).
6. BRULL, L. and CUYPERS, Y., "Blood perfusion of the kidney of *Lophius piscatorius* L. 2. Influence of perfusion pressure on urine volume," *J. Mar. Biol. Ass. U.K.*, **33**, 733 (1954).
7. BRULL, L. and CUYPERS, Y., "Blood perfusion of the kidney of *Lophius piscatorius*," ibid., **34**, 637 (1955).
8. BRULL, L. and NIZET, E., "Blood and urine constituents of *Lophius piscatorius* L.," ibid., **32**, 321 (1953).
9. BRULL, L., NIZET, E. and VERNEY, E. B., "Blood perfusion of the kidney of *Lophius piscatorius* L.," ibid., **32**, 329 (1953).
10. BURGER, J. W., "The general form of excretion in the lobster," *Biol. Bull.* **113**, 207 (1957).
11. CAMPBELL, J. W., "Studies on tissue arginase and ureogenesis in the elasmo-branch, *Mustelus*," *Arch. Biochem. Biophys.*, **93**, 448 (1961).
12. CORNER, E. D. S., COWEY, C. B. and MARSHALL, S. M., "On the nutrition and metabolism of zooplankton," *J. Mar. Biol. Ass. U.K.*, **45**, 429 (1965).
13. DRESEL, E. I. B. and MOYLE, V., "Nitrogenous excretion of amphipods and isopods," *Biochem. J.*, **46**, xxxiii (1950).
14. DRESEL, E. I. B. and MOYLE, V., "Nitrogenous excretion of amphipods and isopods," *J. Exp. Biol.*, **27**, 210 (1950).
15. DYER, W. J., "Amines in fish muscle. 6. Trimethylamine oxide content of fish and marine invertebrates," *J. Fish. Res. Bd Can.*, **8**, 314 (1952).
16. FÄNGE, R., "Structure and functions of the excretory organs of myxinoids," in *The Biology of Myxine*, Eds. Brodal, A. and Fänge, R., p. 516 (Oslo, Universitetsforlaget, 1963).
17. FLEURY, F., "Note sur l'urémie et la glycémie physiologiques des Selaciens trygoniformes," *Bull. Soc. Sci. Arcachon*, N.S., No. 3 (1951).
18. FORSTER, R. P., "A comparative study of renal function in marine teleosts." *J. Cell. Comp. Physiol.*, **42**, 487 (1953).
19. FORSTER, R. P. and TAGGART, J. V., "Use of isolated renal tubules for the examination of metabolic processes associated with active cellular transport," *J. Cell. Comp. Physiol.*, **36**, 251 (1950).
20. FOX, D. L., *Animal Biochromes and Structural Colours* (Cambridge Univ. Press, 1953).
21. GOLDSTEIN, L., FORSTER, R. P. and FANELLI, F. M. JR., "Gill blood flow

and ammonia excretion in the marine teleost *Myoxocephalus*," *Comp. Biochem. Physiol.*, **12**, 489 (1964).

22. GOODBODY, I., "Nitrogen excretion in Ascidiacea. I," *J. Exp. Biol.*, **34**, 297 (1957).
23. GOODBODY, I., "Nitrogen excretion in Ascidiacea. II," *J. Exp. Biol.*, **42**, 299 (1965).
24. GRAFFLIN, C. L. and GOULD, R. G. JR., "Renal function in marine teleosts. 2," *Biol. Bull.*, **70**, 16 (1936).
25. HARRISON, F. M., "Some excretory processes in the abalone, *Haliotis*," *J. Exp. Biol.*, **39**, 179 (1962).
26. HARRISON, F. M. and MARTIN, A. W., "Excretion in the cephalopod, *Octopus dofleini*," *J. Exp. Biol.*, **42**, 71 (1965).
27. HARTMAN, F. A., LEWIS, L. A., BROWNELL, K. A., SHELDEN, F. F. and WALTHER, R. F., "Some blood constituents of the normal skate," *Physiol. Zool.*, **14**, 476 (1941).
28. HEIDERMANNS, C., "Exkretion und Exkretstoffwechsel der Wirbellosen," *Tabul. Biol.*, **14**, p. 209 (1937).
29. HOPPE-SEYLER, F. A., "Die Bedingungen und die Bedeutung biologischer Methylierungsprozesse," *Z. Biol.*, **90**, 432 (1930).
30. HOPPE-SEYLER, F. A., "Trimethylaminoxyd und andere Stickstoffbasen in Krebsmuskeln," *Hoppe-Seyl. Z.*, **221**, 45 (1933).
31. HOPPE-SEYLER, F. A. and SCHMIDT, W., "Ueber das Vorkommen von Trimethylaminoxyd," *Z. Biol.*, **87**, 59 (1927).
32. KEMPTON, R. T., "Studies on the elasmobranch kidney. 2. Reabsorption of urea by the smooth dogfish, *Mustelus canis*," *Biol. Bull.*, **104**, 45 (1953).
33. KENNEDY, G. Y. and VEVERS, H. G., "The biology of *Asterias rubens* L. A porphyrin pigment in the integument," *J. Mar. Biol. Ass. U.K.*, **32**, 235 (1953).
34. KENNEDY, G. Y. and VEVERS, H. G., "The occurrence of porphyrin in certain marine invertebrates," ibid., **33**, 663 (1954).
35. KHALIL, F. and HAGGAG, G., "Nitrogenous excretion in crocodiles," *J. Exp. Biol.*, **35**, 552 (1958).
36. KROGH, A., *Osmotic Regulation in Aquatic Animals* (Cambridge Univ. Press, 1939).
37. KUTSCHER, F. and ACKERMANN, D., "The comparative biochemistry of vertebrates and invertebrates," *Annu. Rev. Biochem.*, **2**, 355 (1933).
38. LUM, S. C. and HAMMEN, C. S., "Ammonia excretion of *Lingula*," *Comp. Biochem. Physiol.*, **12**, 185 (1964).
39. MOLLITOR, A., "Beiträge zur Untersuchung des Exkretstoffwechsels und der Exkretion von *Eriocheir sinensis*," *Zool. Jb. Abt. 3, allg. Zool. Physiol.*, **57**, 323 (1937).
40. MORRIS, R., "Studies on salt and water balance in *Myxine*," *J. Exp. Biol.*, **42**, 359 (1965).
41. MOYLE, V., "Nitrogenous excretion in chelonian reptiles," *Biochem. J.*, **44**, 581 (1949).
42. MUNZ, F. W. and MCFARLAND, W. N., "Regulatory function of a primitive vertebrate kidney," *Comp. Biochem. Physiol.*, **13**, 381 (1964).
43. NEEDHAM, A. E., "Factors affecting nitrogen-excretion in *Carcinides maenas*," *Physiol. Comp.*, **4**, 209 (1957).
44. NEEDHAM, J., *Chemical Embryology*, Vol. 2 (Cambridge Univ. Press, 1931).

45. NIZET, E. and WILSENS, L., "Quelques aspects de l'anatomie du rein de *Lophius piscatorius* L.," *Pubbl. Staz. Zool. Napoli*, **26**, 36 (1955).
46. NORRIS, E. R. and BENOIT, G. J. Jr., "Studies on trimethylamine oxide. 1. Occurrence of trimethylamine oxide in marine organisms," *J. Biol. Chem.*, **158**, 433 (1945).
47. PARRY, G., "Ionic regulation in the palaemonid prawn *Palaemon* (=*Leander*) *serratus*," *J. Exp. Biol.*, **31**, 601 (1954).
48. PARRY, G., "Urine production by the antennal glands of *Palaemonetes varians*," ibid., **32**, 408 (1955).
49. PROSSER, C. L., GREEN, J. W. and CHOW, T. J., "Ionic and osmotic concentrations in blood and urine of *Pachygrapsus crassipes* acclimated to different salinities," *Biol. Bull.*, **109**, 99 (1955).
50. PUCK, T. T., WASSERMAN, K. and FISHMAN, A. P., "Some effects of inorganic ions on the active transport of phenol red by isolated kidney tubules of the flounder," *J. Cell. Comp. Physiol.*, **40**, 73 (1952).
51. ROBERTSON, J. D., "Ionic regulation in some marine invertebrates," *J. Exp. Biol.*, **26**, 182 (1949).
52. ROBERTSON, J. D., "Further studies on ionic regulation in marine invertebrates," ibid., **30**, 277 (1953).
53. ROBERTSON, J. D., "The habitat of early vertebrates," *Biol. Rev.*, **32**, 156 (1957).
54. SHANNON, J. A., "Renal tubular excretion," *Physiol. Rev.*, **19**, 63 (1939).
55. SHARRATT, B. M., JONES, I. C. and BELLAMY, D., "Water and electrolyte composition of the body and renal function of the eel," *Comp. Biochem. Physiol.*, **11**, 9 (1964).
56. SHEWAN, J. M., "The chemistry and metabolism of the nitrogenous extractives in fish," *Biochem. Soc. Symp.*, No. 6 (The biochemistry of fish), p. 28 (1951).
57. SMITH, H. W., "The absorption and excretion of water and salts by the elasmobranch fishes. 1. Freshwater elasmobranchs," *Amer. J. Physiol.*, **98**, 279 (1931).
58. SMITH, H. W., "The absorption and excretion of water and salts by the elasmobranch fishes. 2. Marine elasmobranchs," ibid., **98**, 296 (1931).
59. SMITH, H. W., "The composition of urine in the seal," *J. Cell. Comp. Physiol.*, **7**, 465 (1936).
60. SPENCER, C. P., "The bacterial oxidation of ammonia in the sea," *J. Mar. Biol. Ass. U.K.*, **35**, 621 (1956).
61. SPITZER, J. M., "Physiologisch-ökologische Untersuchungen über den Exkretstoffwechsel der Mollusken," *Zool. Jb. Abt. 3, allg. Zool. Physiol.*, **57**, 457 (1937).
62. WASSERMAN, K., BECKER, E. L. and FISHMAN, A. P., "Transport of phenol red in the flounder renal tubule," *J. Cell. Comp. Physiol.*, **42**, 385 (1953).
63. WELSH, J. H., "On the nature and action of coelenterate toxins," *Deep-Sea Research*, **3** (Suppl.), 287 (1955).
64. WHITE, F. D., "The occurrence of creatine in the muscle, blood and urine of the dogfish, *Squalus sucklii*," *Contr. Canad. Biol.*, **6**, 341 (1931).
65. WILBER, C. G., "Uric acid in marine invertebrates," *J. Cell. Comp. Physiol.*, **31**, 107 (1948).
66. ZIEGLER-GÜNDER, I., "Pterine: Pigmente und Wirkstoffe im Tierreich," *Biol. Rev.*, **31**, 313 (1956).

CHAPTER 8

SENSORY ORGANS AND RECEPTION

Sense which abroad doth bring
The colour, taste, and touch, and scent, and sound,
The quantity and shape of everything.
Sir John Davis, *Nosce Teipsum*, 1599

INTRODUCTION

All animals are sensitive to certain environmental changes which act as stimuli, influencing the behaviour of the organism as a whole, or of its component parts. Although sometimes directly exciting effector elements, external stimuli usually act on sensory structures, which in turn feed into the nervous system the information received. The relative importance of the several sensory modalities in the economy of animals varies greatly. In the euphotic and littoral regions of the sea, light, as an environmental stimulus, has an importance equal to that of other sensory cues in regulating the behaviour of animals. But nocturnal animals of those regions, and those found in aphotic zones of the ocean, may depend largely or exclusively upon other sensory avenues for information about changes in the external world.

Irritability is a generalized property of protoplasm, as seen in the responses of protozoa and sponges to various kinds of stimuli. In metazoans effective stimulation involves excitation of the nervous system. The stimuli may affect free nerve endings in the skin, or may act on peripheral receptor cells. The epidermis of primitive animals contains undifferentiated primary sense cells, probably responsive to a wide range of stimuli (Figs. 8.1, 8.2). Frequently, however, the receptors are differentiated so as to possess maximum sensitivity to some particular kind of stimulus. This process of differentiation and specialization reaches its apogee in image-forming eyes and in the ear of higher vertebrates.

PHOTORECEPTION

In lowly-organized forms, such as amoebae, the general protoplasm is photosensitive. Higher animals frequently possess specific photoreceptors which take the form of scattered light-sensitive cells, or more highly constructed multicellular organs of varied grades of complexity. These, according to the level of intrinsic organization and the complexity of central nervous pathways, are utilized for detecting intensity differences, direction of light rays, quality of light (spectral composition), form and pattern, the latter by ocular organs of considerable complexity. More than any other sensory guide, light regulates the orientation of animals, their diurnal migrations and rhythmic activities. In animals with highly organized nervous centres, it influences other still more complex behaviour patterns.

Photoreception and photosensitivity in animals can be studied at several

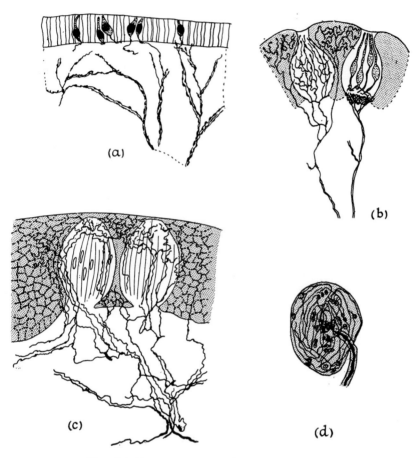

FIG. 8.1. RECEPTORS IN THE SKIN OF CHORDATES

(a) Sensory cells in the skin of *Amphioxus*; (b) end knobs, with sense cells and nerve supply, in the skin of the sturgeon (*Acipenser*); (c) free nerve endings in the epithelium of the fin of the sturgeon; (d) terminal body in the pectoral fin of *Squatina*. (All after Bolk *et al.*, 1934, from various authors.)

levels. Usually some overt reaction or physiological response of the animal constitutes the signal for photosensitivity. In any animal it is usually possible to select some one or few behavioural responses which can be utilized as a sign of the existence and the degree of photosensitivity. These often involve locomotory changes or movement of some structure. At a higher level, where ocular structures for form-vision exist, experiments have been devised for evaluating the importance of shape and pattern in behavioural responses (arthropods, cephalopods, vertebrates). These experiments frequently utilize the learning capacity of animals and their ability to form conditioned reflexes. From a purely physiological approach, photoreception can be studied by recording the electrical signs of ocular activity. This method reveals the photosensitive capabilities of the eye and the mechanisms involved in the conversion of photic stimuli into nerve impulses. Before proceeding to a consideration of the behaviour of animals under photostimulation and the physiology of photoreceptors, we shall examine

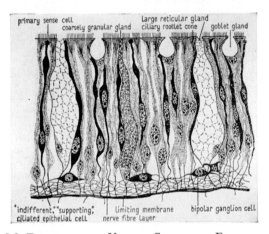

FIG. 8.2. DIAGRAMMATIC VIEW OF SKIN OF AN ENTEROPNEUST
(*Saccoglossus*) (from Bullock, 1946.)

briefly the range of structure encountered in the light receptors of marine animals.

Structure of Photoreceptors

All gradations of complexity exist in the structure of photoreceptors among invertebrates and lower vertebrates, from simple pigmented spots bearing a photosensitive surface to the complex camera eyes of cephalopods and vertebrates. In some cases sufficient experimental data are available to permit the characteristics of photoreception to be correlated with the structure of a given photoreceptor.

Simple Photoreceptors

The general integument of many lower animals is sensitive to light, although light organs as such may be wanting. By studying the behaviour of echinoderms under varying conditions of illumination it has been found that the entire surface of the animal is light-sensitive. Similarly, when the pigmented eye-spots or eyes of flatworms and polychaetes are removed, there is still a residual and generalized light-sensitivity. In these and other instances photoreception may involve stimulation of general unicellular sensory elements distributed over the whole body surface. Alternatively, the nervous system itself may be photosensitive and act as a primary receptor. Simple unicellular photoreceptors are found in the general epidermis of annelids, siphons of lamellibranchs, etc. (Fig. 8.3) (98).

STIGMATA AND OCELLI. Stigmata and ocelli are small cups containing a light-sensitive surface backed by pigment, and often enclosing a lens-like body. Simple structures of this kind are found in certain flagellates. Multicellular ocelli range in complexity from a simple sensory surface with intermingled sensory and pigmented cells to cup-shaped organs provided with cornea and lens. Among medusae pigmented eye-spots are often present at the bases of the tentacles. In *Sarsia*, for example, the photosensitive surface forms a cup containing a hyaline lens-like body. The receptor elements in this ocellus are bipolar primary neurones separated from one another by pigmented supporting cells.

FIG. 8.3. OPTIC ORGANELLE (UNICELLULAR PHOTO-RECEPTOR) IN THE SIPHON OF *Mya arenaria* (from Light (1930).)

Similar cup-shaped ocelli occur in members of many other phyla, e.g. flatworms, nemertines, larval and adult polychaetes, molluscs, chaetognaths and tunicates (Fig. 8.4). In some polychaetes the eye-spots contain a lens which concentrates light on the retinal surface. A wide variety of ocelli is found in gastropods and lamellibranchs. The eye-spot of *Patella* is a simple sensory pit lying at the base of the tentacle; in *Murex* the eye is cut off from the epidermis and encloses a large spherical lens. The scallop (*Pecten*) possesses numerous pallial eyes, each of which is a small sphere with cornea, lens, retina and chorioid backing. The retina consists of two layers, one behind the other: the two layers are supplied by separate rami of the optic nerve and are covered by ganglion cells.

The median eye of crustaceans is essentially a group of three ocelli, one central and two lateral. Each ocellus is a pigmented cup containing a lens and lined with retinal cells from which nerve fibres proceed to the brain. A median eye develops in the nauplius larva and is found in many adult entomostracans.

Limulus possesses two pairs of eyes, two lateral and two median. The lateral eyes, known as facet eyes, are aggregates of ocelli. Each ocellus contains a lens-like thickening of the cuticle, forming a conical projection extending into the interior of the eye. Beneath this is the photosensitive surface, containing several kinds of cells. Among them are retinular cells arranged about the central axis: these are pigmented externally and differentiated at the axial border into a hyaline rod (the rhabdome). Each ocellus also contains a so-called eccentric receptor cell, distinguished by being bipolar and non-pigmented. From both kinds of cells nerve fibres run proximally into the optic nerve. The median eyes are lens-eyes and each consists of a vesicular ocellus containing a large cuticular lens. Receptor elements in the retina are organized as groups of sensory cells (retinulae). Each group can be regarded as a distinct ocellus made up of primary sensory neurones which give rise to optic nerve fibres (64).

COMPOUND EYES. These are composite structures made up of many distinct units, each of which acts as a directional photoreceptor. The units are separated from one another in some degree by pigmented screens, and possess fixed focusing devices (Figs. 8.5, 8.7). Each unit is stimulated by light coming from some particular direction, and the entire lighted area to which the eye is exposed is thus divided into a large number of separate fields, corresponding to the number of receptor units. The total image thus formed by a compound eye consists of a patchwork or mosaic of light and dark, corresponding to intensity differences in the visual field.

Compound eyes occur in some polychaetes, lamellibranchs and are especially characteristic of arthropods.

The typical compound eye of crustaceans is composed of units called ommatidia, each of which consists of photoreceptors and dioptric structures. Externally the eye is divided into facets, corresponding in number to the underlying ommatidia. The facets are biconvex cuticular plates which in sum form the cornea of the eye. Underneath the facet is a crystalline cone which serves as a lens and which is secreted by vitrellae or crystal cells. Below the lens is the retinula which consists of a set of from four to eight cells around a central refractive rod known as a rhabdome. The retinular cells are the photosensitive elements and proximally they give rise to nerve fibres which form an optic nerve and extend to the optic ganglion.

Each ommatidium is demarcated from its neighbours by retinal pigments. These consist of a proximal retinal pigment localized in the retinular cells, and a distal retinal pigment contained in distal pigment cells which surround the crystalline cone and part of the rhabdome. In addition there is a reflecting substance contained in reflecting cells lying basally between the ommatidia; when exposed this substance forms a reflecting layer or tapetum. Pelagic species of decapod crustaceans show much variation in the distribution and amounts of retinal pigments. Eyes of deep-water species from the aphotic zone, such as *Sergestes grandis* and *S. tenuiremis*, are rich in reflecting pigments. Others, such as *S. arcticus* and *Petalidium obesum* from the photic zone, lack reflecting pigment but have a large amount of proximal retinal (screening) pigment (36, 134, 135).

CAMERA EYES. These eyes possess a lens capable of focusing an image on the retina. The most highly organized camera eyes among invertebrates are those of cephalopods. The eye of *Nautilus* is a simple cup-shaped depression with an opening through the integument. In dibranchiate cephalopods the eye has an external cornea, closed over in some forms,

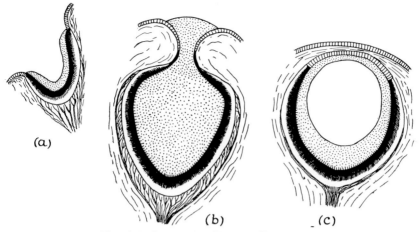

(a)

FIG. 8.4. Ocelli and Eyes of Gastropods
(a) *Patella*; (b) *Haliotis*; (c) *Murex*. (After Plate (1924).)

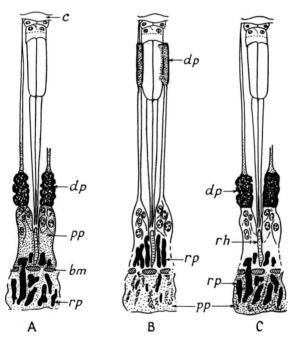

FIG. 8.5. Position of Eye-pigments in Ommatidia of
Palaemonetes under Various Conditions

A, from an eye in the light-condition. B, from a dark-adapted eye. C, from an experimental animal which, after being adapted to darkness, was injected with eye-stalk extract prepared from light-adapted specimens. *bm*, basement membrane; *c*, cornea; *dp*, distal pigment; *pp*, proximal pigment; *rh*, rhabdome; *rp*, reflecting pigment. (From Kleinholz (1936).)

a lens, iris-folds and retina (Fig. 8.6). Enclosing the eye is a cartilaginous sclera perforated by fine holes through which pass the optic nerve fibres. The visual cells of the retina bear long rods and contain retinal pigment.

Numerous small muscles are attached to the exterior of the eyeball and can move the eye to some extent in all directions. In some forms, e.g. *Sepia* and *Octopus*, there is an external eye-fold which closes the eye. There are many peculiarities in the eyes of pelagic cephalopods, the significance of which is poorly understood. One of these, the telescopic eye, found in *Toxeuma* for example, is an adaptation for weak illumination.

A mechanism exists for accommodation in the eye of the cuttlefish (*Sepia*). In accommodating for distant vision the ciliary muscles contract

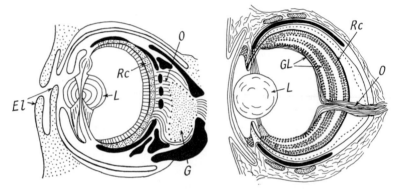

FIG. 8.6. CAMERA EYES

(*Left*) *Sepia*. (*Right*) a teleost. *L*, lens; *G*, optic ganglion; *O*, optic nerve; *El*, eyelid; *Rc*, retinal cells; *GL*, ganglion layers. (After Plate (1924).)

and draw the lens towards the retina. It has been found that stimulation of the sclerotic muscles causes the lens to be displaced forwards, and this displacement may be a means of accommodating for very near vision.

VERTEBRATE EYES. These are all built on the same fundamental pattern and, except when degenerate, are provided with a lens capable of throwing an image upon the photosensitive retina (Fig. 8.6). The latter is inverted and from front to rear shows the following layers: a feltwork of optic nerve fibres; two layers of ganglion cells (tertiary and secondary), separated by a synaptic layer; a basal layer of rods and cones, the photoreceptors proper.

The rods and cones, by virtue of their inherent sensitivities or nervous connexions, are adapted for photoreception over different intensities of illumination. Rods are highly sensitive visual cells, functioning at low intensities, whereas the cones operate in bright light. Corresponding to these differences in function are differences in photosensitive substances (p. 325). Neural connexions in the retina are very complex. Cones are connected to one or a few nerve fibres, arrangements which promote visual acuity. In contrast, many rods feed via secondary neurones into a single fibre. The latter arrangement, which results in a high degree of summation of the more sensitive photoreceptors, enhances sensitivity at the expense of visual acuity.

Probably no other organ in the vertebrate body shows such fine adaptations to the functional needs of the animal as does the eye. Only a few factors relating to vision in marine fishes can be considered, and for fuller treatment the reader is referred to Walls (129).

The eye in most elasmobranchs and teleosts possesses the normal vertebrate structure. Some deep-water selachians and teleosts have degenerate eyes and are blind, e.g. *Benthobatis* (ray) and *Ditropichthys* (teleost). The majority of bathypelagic and bathybenthic fishes, however, have functional eyes and this is probably due to the widespread occurrence of luminescence in deep-water animals (Chapter 13). The eyes of deep-sea fishes are believed to be the most sensitive in existence and contain enormous numbers of rods per unit area of retinal surface (95).

Pure rod retinas are found in most elasmobranchs and deep-sea teleosts. This factor, combined with a high degree of summation, makes for increased visual sensitivity. The former animals are largely nocturnal in habits, and the latter live in dimly-lit or dark waters below the photosynthetic zone. A few selachians are known to possess cones, e.g. *Mustelus*, which is diurnal, and *Myliobatis*, which is pelagic in habits. Retinae with rods and cones are characteristic of teleosts from well-lighted waters.

The eyes of mesopelagic fishes are often relatively large and have wide pupils and large lenses, factors related to the dim light of the regions which they inhabit. Some species—e.g. the hatchet-fish *Argyropelecus*—have tubular (so-called telescopic) eyes, in which the lens is enlarged relative to the size of the eye. The retina in the equatorial region appears thin and degenerate, and the functional retinal surface is confined to the fundus. Because of these optical features a small, bright image is thrown on the retina.

In lower vertebrates accommodation is usually accomplished by displacement of the lens. The lens at rest is adjusted for near vision (myopia) or distant vision (hypermetropia), according to the animal. In a myopic eye, movement of the lens backwards adjusts for distant objects by advancing the image and bringing it into focus on the retina. A converse process takes place in hypermetropic eyes capable of accommodation.

Teleosts are myopic and the eyes at rest are set for near vision. Attached to the lens ligament is a small retractor lentis muscle (campanula Halleri), which is capable of displacing the lens backwards and accommodating to some extent for distant objects. Nervous control is mediated by the oculomotor nerve. In the tubular eyes of deep-sea teleosts little or no lens movement is possible. Such eyes possess an accessory retina lying on the cylindrical walls near the lens, whereas the main retina lies at the back of the fundus. The accessory retina takes care of distance vision, and the main retina perceives near objects. The eyes of selachians are hyperme-tropic at rest but are capable of some accommodation for near vision. The ciliary body bears a small protractor lentis muscle, which is so oriented that it moves the lens outwards towards the cornea on contracting, and so focuses for near objects (16, 42, 129).

Regulation of Light falling upon the Retina

Devices exist in various animals for controlling the intensity of light reaching the retinal cells. This may be achieved at the pupillary entrance by movable lids or iris; or by movement of retinal and chorioidal pigments. Migration of pigments in the eye, as will be noted later, has other physio-logical consequences.

Cephalopods. The iris of the cephalopod eye is pigmented and highly muscular, and by contraction and dilation it regulates the amount of light entering through the pupil (*Sepia*, *Octopus*). Strong illumination causes the pupil to close, darkness produces opening. The two pupils react to light independently of each other. The pupillary reaction to illumina-tion is a reflex whose centre lies in the suboesophageal ganglion. Afferent and efferent pathways pass through the optic peduncle, section of which pro-, duces maximal dilation. The reflex is susceptible to control by higher centres as revealed by the fact that when an octopus is excited the pupil becomes dilated. An additional pathway, in the superior ophthalmic nerve, inhibits closure of the pupil.

The retinal sensory cells contain a dark pigment making excursions in light and darkness (*Loligo*, *Sepia*, *Eledone*). After the animal has been in the dark for 24–48 hours, the pigment becomes densely concentrated at the base of each retinal cell. On exposing the animal to light, some of the pigment remains in a basal position while the remainder becomes scattered through the retinal cell and accumulates also at its distal end. Thus, there is a movement of retinal pigment proximally in darkness, and distally in the light.

Crustacea. The position of crustacean eye-pigments differs in the light- and dark-adapted eye, and shows a pattern characteristic of each condition. In the light-adapted eye of *Palaemonetes*, for instance, the distal retinal pigment envelops the ommatidium and extends inwards as far as the basal retinal pigment, which is dispersed outwards under illumination. The extent of migration depends on the level of incident illumination. In the dark-adapted eye the distal pigment migrates peripherally, while the basal pigment moves inwards and assumes a position below the basement membrane. In the light-adapted eye, therefore, each ommatidium is enclosed in a light-absorbing sleeve of retinal pigment, the separate ommatidia are screened from each other and the retinular cells are stimu-lated only by light entering that ommatidium (appositional eye). But in the dark-adapted state, as the result of pigment dispersion away from the centre of the ommatidium, the separate elements attain optical continuity and may become exposed to light rays passing through neighbouring ommatidia as well (superpositional eye) (Fig. 8.5). The reflecting white pigment bordering the retinular cells migrates proximally beneath the basement membrane in daylight, and extends distally about the retinular elements in darkness. In the latter arrangement it forms a functional tapetum or reflecting layer (*Palaemonetes*). The positional changes which the retinal pigments undergo show much variation in different species. In *Palaemonetes*, as noted, all three pigments migrate, whereas migration is limited to the proximal retinal pigment in the lobster *Homarus* (85, 103).

In addition to pigment movements evoked directly by changes in

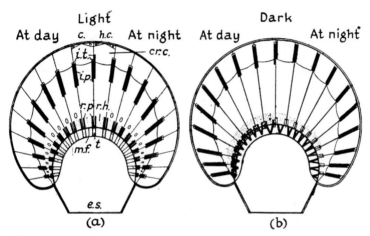

FIG. 8.7. INFLUENCE OF DIURNAL RHYTHM ON THE POSITION OF IRIS (RETINAL) PIGMENTS IN THE COMPOUND EYE OF A DECAPOD CRUSTACEAN

(*a*) Shows the pigment systems in light-adaptation during the day and during the night, respectively; (*b*) shows the migration of the pigment in the dark-adapted eye under the influence of the diurnal rhythm in daytime and at night. *c.*, cornea; *h.c.*, hypodermis cell; *cr.c.*, crystal cone; *i.t.*, iris tapetum; *i.p.*, iris pigment; *rh.*, rhabdome; *r.p.*, retinal pigment; *m.f.*, membrana fenestra; *t.*, tapetum; *e.s.*, eye-stalk. (From Henkes (65).)

environmental illumination, there are rhythmically occurring diurnal migrations which take place independently of any changes in light intensity, and persist even when environmental conditions remain constant (Figs. 8.7, 8.8). The occurrence of persistent diurnal rhythms in the migration of eye pigments has been noted in many crustacea (*Palaemonetes*, *Portunus*, *Homarus*, etc.). In *Palaemonetes* the diurnal rhythm continues for months in animals which are kept under conditions of constant darkness and temperature. Persistent rhythmical movements of retinal pigment can also be observed under conditions of constant illumination, but are of much smaller magnitude (65, 104, 115, 133).

It has been discovered that the eye-stalks of various decapod crustaceans contain substances capable of influencing the position of the eye-pigments.

One of these substances is a pigment-dispersing principle or hormone. When extracts prepared from the eye-stalks of light-adapted prawns (*Palaemonetes*) are injected into dark-adapted animals retained in darkness, the distal and reflecting eye-pigments move proximally into the positions characteristic of the light-adapted state (Fig. 8.9). Eye-stalk extracts taken from light-adapted animals are more effective in causing pigment migration than extracts prepared from dark-adapted specimens (Fig. 8.5). This result indicates a higher content of pigment-dispersing hormone in the sinus glands of light-adapted animals (*vide* p. 443). A pigment-

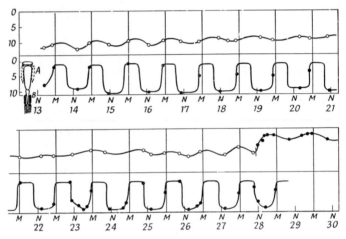

FIG. 8.8. DIURNAL MOVEMENTS OF EYE-PIGMENTS OF A
NOCTURNAL SHRIMP *Anchistioides antiguensis*

Records of the movements of distal pigment cells of four animals kept in constant illumination (hollow circles), except for the last two days, and of four animals kept in constant darkness (solid circles). N, M, noon and midnight. In the sketch of an ommatidium (*left*), A is the extreme peripheral or night position of the distal pigment cells; B, the inner or day position, in constant darkness. Plotted points refer to distance from cornea to outer boundary of the pigments (each unit = 10 μ). (From Welsh (1963).)

dispersing principle has also been recognized in the eye-stalks of many brachyurans (*Cancer, Uca, Libinia*, etc.).

Even a brief exposure to light (5 min for *Palaemonetes*) suffices to release enough stored dispersing-hormone to produce light-adaptation of the distal pigment cells. Light-adaptation continues for a further 10 min after the animal is returned to darkness, indicating continued release of dispersing-hormone during that period, and its accumulation in the blood. Other work points to the existence of a second hormonal factor involved in dark-adaptation.

It appears that some controlling centre is activated by photic stimulation, and the degree of activation, in turn, determines the relative proportions of the two retinal pigment hormones which are secreted. The persistent periodicity in retinal pigment migration, observed in many crustaceans, depends upon regular rhythmicity in the release of the regulatory hormones. In *Palaemonetes* the production of the dark-adapting hormone reaches its maximum about midnight, and is minimal at dawn; during the daylight hours the hormone is stored in preparation for the nocturnal phase of the cycle.

In *Palaemonetes* the eye-stalks are the chief source of the retinal pigment-dispersing hormone, but lesser amounts occur elsewhere in the c.n.s. (brain, connectives and ventral ganglia). Similarly, stores of dis-

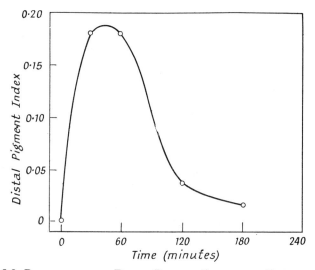

FIG. 8.9. RESPONSE OF THE DISTAL RETINAL PIGMENT OF DARK-ADAPTED PRAWNS (*Palaemonetes*) TO INJECTION OF EYE-STALK EXTRACTS

Maximal dispersion of pigment (light-adaptation) occurs 30–60 min after injection. (From Brown *et al.* (12).)

persing hormone have been found in the brain, optic ganglia and other nervous centres of grapsoid crabs (9, 10, 11, 12, 13, 84, 85, 86, 115, 119, 131).

Photomechanical Changes in Fishes. In fishes three mechanisms are concerned in regulating the amount of light which reaches the retina, namely alteration of pupillary aperture, migration of retinal pigment and movement of visual cells. These adaptations are found in diurnal species of the neritic zone.

PUPILLARY MOVEMENT. According to their habits, three groups of selachians can be distinguished. These are diurnal (day-feeding) sela-chians such as *Mustelus*, having pupils wide open in the daytime; nocturnal (night-feeding) forms, e.g. *Scyliorhinus*, *Raja*, whose pupils close almost completely in daylight; and deep-sea forms such as *Spinax*, with large eyes having wide pupils and weak iris musculature. The sphincter iris muscle contracts in direct response to illumination and is not under nervous control, but the movement is much more marked in nocturnal species (Fig. 8.10). The dilator muscle is under control of the oculomotor nerve, stimulation of which causes the pupil to open.

Pupillary responses occur in some benthic teleosts (eel, star-gazer, angler fish, flat fishes), but are the exception rather than the rule, since the iris shows little movement in the majority of teleosts. The pupil of the eel (*Anguilla*) is capable of wide changes in diameter, but control is mainly by direct response of the sphincter muscle to incident light. The pupil of the isolated eye constricts when illuminated and re-expands in darkness.

The action spectrum for the response has a maximum at 500 mμ, and is

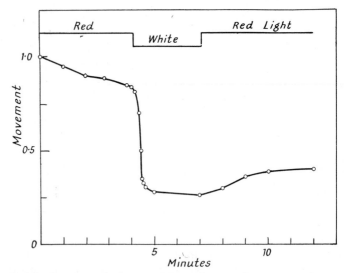

Fig. 8.10. Movement of the Dorsal Margin of the Pupil in the Isolated Eye of *Scyliorhinus stellaris*, in Response to Illumination (from Young (1933).)

not unlike that of eel rhodopsin (117). The well-developed pupillary reaction of other teleosts (*Uranoscopus, Lophius*) is reflexly controlled by antagonistic nerves. Sphincter muscles are supplied by the sympathetic system, stimulation of which causes constriction of the pupil. Dilator fibres originate in the ciliary ganglion, and stimulation of the oculomotor nerve produces dilatation of the pupil (16).

Retinal Photomechanical Changes. In elasmobranchs (selachians and chimaeroids) there is a tapetum lucidum in the inner region of the chorioid. The tapetum may extend entirely over the back of the eye (e.g. pelagic and benthic sharks), or may be absent in a ventral segment occupied by a black field. The pigment epithelium inside the tapetum lucidum is without pigment. The tapetum lucidum contains a layer of plate-like reflecting cells enclosing crystals of guanine (Fig. 8.11). These cells lie parallel to the surface of the retina in the centre of the eye, and slope at increasing angles to the surface of the retina towards the periphery of the eye (Fig. 8.12). Because the iris acts as a stop cutting off some of the light entering the lens at the margin of the pupil, this change of orientation of the plates results in an arrangement whereby light always strikes them approximately normal to their surfaces. About half the light is absorbed on passing through the retina, the tapetum reflects back 85% of that which reaches it, and half this reflected light is absorbed in its second passage through the

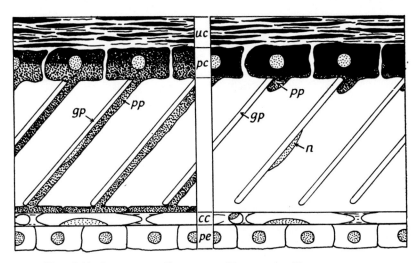

FIG. 8.11. OCCLUSIBLE CHORIOIDAL TAPETUM OF ELASMOBRANCHS

(*Left*) Section through chorioid of light-adapted eye, showing pigmented processes expanded on external surfaces of guanin plates, shielding them from light which has passed through the retina. (*Right*) dark-adapted condition, showing pigmented processes retracted, whereby the guanin can reflect light back through the visual cells. *gp*, reflecting cell; *cc*, chorioidal capillaries; *n*, nucleus of reflecting cell; *pc*, layer of migratory chorioidal pigment cells; *pe*, pigment epithelium of retina (devoid of pigment); *uc*, unmodified chorioid; *pp*, process of chorioid pigment cells. (Diagram based on *Mustelus*, from Walls (129), after Franz. Distally (*i.e.* towards the inside of the eye) the pigmented process of each chorioid pigment cell should extend only towards the left, i.e. towards the fundus.)

receptor layer. Some selachians such as the rough hound (*Scyliorhinus*) prevent the tapetum lucidum from being visible during the daytime (as eyeshine) by closing the pupil; others, such as the spur dog (*Squalus*), by moving pigment from melanophores over the inner surfaces of the reflecting plates (Fig. 8.11) (38, 107).

In the eyes of some teleosts there occur photomechanical changes consisting of migrations of retinal pigment and movements of the visual cells. These changes are most conspicuous in duplex retinae (provided with rods and cones) and are concerned with light- and dark-adaptation of the retina.

In teleost eyes provided with retinal photomechanical mechanisms, the retina is backed by a layer of pigmented epithelium having long processes which extend between the visual cells. When the fish is exposed to bright light, pigment granules migrate down these processes, forming sleeves about the visual cells and shielding them from oblique rays. In dim light the pigment migration is reversed. The cones and rods of many teleosts are also contractile. In the light-adapted condition the cones lie outside the pigmented region or migrate away from it, while the rods move in the

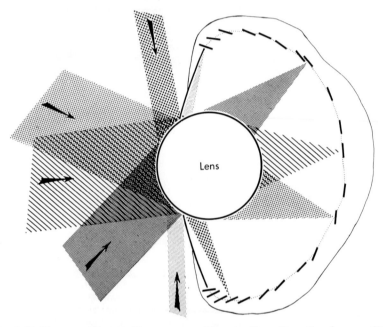

FIG. 8.12. VERTICAL SECTION THROUGH THE EYE OF A SPUR DOG *Squalus acanthias*, SHOWING THE ORIENTATION OF THE REFLECTING PLATES WITH REFERENCE TO THE LIGHT THAT CAN REACH THEM (38)

direction of the pigment and are partially shielded. In darkness the rods shorten and draw their sensitive portions away from the pigment towards the exterior.

When mechanical changes are performed extensively and expeditiously, as described above, they are doubtless of great value in adjusting the retina to changes of external illumination. In the light-adapted condition the cones are exposed to stimulation, while the rods are partially or entirely shielded from strong light. In the dark-adapted state the rods, functional in dim light, are fully exposed, while the cones are displaced out of the way. Examples of fishes whose retinae show photomechanical changes are eels (*Anguilla*), scorpion-fish (*Scorpaena*), top-minnows (*Fundulus*), sticklebacks (*Gasterosteus*), etc.

Retinal pigment is abundant in many pelagic teleosts (mackerels, tunnies, mormyrids, etc.), but it is uncertain to what extent the eye pigment is migratory and whether the guanin forms a functional tapetum. In bathypelagic species, such as *Evermanella*, the pigment epithelium contains guanin but no dark pigments, and the tapetum is therefore non-occlusible (16, 42, 129).

Kinds of Light Responses

Since photic stimuli are utilized as sensory cues in so many forms of behaviour it is possible to select only certain types of photic responses for particular consideration. A well-marked category of photic responses includes orientation reflexes controlled either by intensity differences or the directional properties of light. Many animals show special behavioural responses to sudden changes in light intensity. Tubicolous polychaetes (sabellids, serpulids), gastropods (*Onchidella*, *Chromodoris*), cirripedes and others respond by contraction to a sudden decrease of intensity. Hagfishes (*Myxine*), some anemones (*Cerianthus*), *Mya*, *Ciona* and the enteropneust *Saccoglossus* contract under sudden increase in intensity. Still other species react to either decrease or increase of intensity, e.g. sea-urchin *Diadema*.

Allied to such responses are shadow reflexes and reactions to moving objects. The former occurs even in the absence of image-forming eyes, and then depends on successive temporal stimulation of photosensory cells, either dispersed or aggregated into ocelli. Other responses, non-muscular, evoked by photic stimuli are colour changes and luminescence (*Pyrosoma*) (16, 17, 82, 98, 106).

ORIENTATION TO LIGHT: TROPISMS. The oriented responses to light of lower animals are of two kinds: bending reactions and oriented locomotory movements. Originally applied to all oriented responses, the term tropism is now restricted in animal physiology to the bending reactions of sessile animals. Examples are the heliotropic bending of hydroid polyps (*Eudendrium*) and sea anemones (*Cerianthus*), and the bending of sabellid tubes towards the light. Moore (1927), who made a particular study of *Cerianthus*, found that the number of degrees through which the animal turned was proportional to the logarithm of light intensity.

Oriented Locomotory Responses. In the simplest type of locomotory response to light, an animal seeks or avoids an illuminated region by a kind of trial and error activity classified as photokinesis. In a non-directional light gradient animals displaying photokinesis congregate in light or dark regions. When there is a tendency to shun the light the animals may move more rapidly or change the direction of movement more often in illuminated areas, with the result that they remain longer or come to rest in dark regions. This kind of response is shown, *inter alia*, by turbellarians.

Animals which possess suitably organized photoreceptors can make use

B.M.A.—11*

of the directional properties of light. When placed in a horizontal light beam they move directly towards or away from the light source according to whether they are photopositive or photonegative. The simplest type of reaction to directed light, known as klinotaxis, is shown by animals which make regular swaying movements, and which are able in consequence to make successive temporal comparisons of light intensity. Examples are *Euglena* and the planktonic larvae of many benthic animals. The photo-

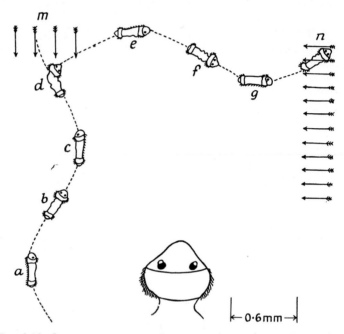

FIG. 8.13. ORIENTATION OF THE LARVA OF *Arenicola* IN A LIGHT BEAM

Arrows indicate direction of the light rays. The larva swims towards the light source in a spiral course. At *d* the light is changed from *m* to *n*, and the animal aligns itself to the new light source. (*Lower right*) enlarged view of the head, showing paired ocelli. (From Mast (1938).)

receptors in these animals are simple stigmata or ocelli partially shielded by pigment and so organized that the retina is stimulated by light coming from some particular direction with reference to the axis of the animal's body.

The larvae of *Arenicola*, like those of many other polychaetes, are strongly photopositive after hatching, and aggregate at the lighted surface of the water by means of klinotaxis. When swimming, the larva rotates on a longitudinal axis and, if it be laterally illuminated, each eye is directed alternately towards and away from the light (Fig. 8.13). When one of the eyes is directed towards the light, the body contracts and the head turns in that direction; this soon results in orientation and the animal continues to swim towards the light source.

Animals with well-developed photoreceptors orientate directly to a light source in a straight path without pendular movements. In one form of response the animal is able to orient itself through achieving balanced and equal stimulation of symmetrically disposed paired photoreceptors (tropo-taxis). Such responses are widespread in annelids, gastropods, etc. When confronted with two light sources it proceeds at some angle between them, depending on the relative intensity and stimulating power of the two lights.

More complex are those responses in which the animal moves directly towards a light source without the necessity of balanced stimulation of two receptors (telo-taxis). In this response the animal orients directly to one of two lights. When *Hemimysis*, for example, is exposed to a single light, it swims to and fro in line with the beam of light. But when an additional light is arranged with its beam at right angles to the first, some of the mysids remains in the first light beam, while others cross over and move along the second beam. The mysid is thus capable of selecting by some central process one of the two light beams for orientation, and is not dependent upon balanced stimulation of two photoreceptors. The compound eyes of *Hemimysis* are spherical and are located on movable stalks; consequently it has binocular vision over 360° and is able to orientate while proceeding towards and away from the light (50, 139).

Other forms of taxes are the dorsal-light reaction and the light-compass reaction. The dorsal-light reaction is found in many animals which normally swim horizontally with the dorsal surface uppermost, such as *Charybdea* (Scyphomedusa), *Tomopteris* (Polychaeta) and *Palaemon* (Malacostraca). In species with statocysts, both statoreception and photoreception are involved in regulating the response. The mechanism of the dorsal light reaction of *Palaemon* is depicted in Fig. 8.14. *Palaemon* is a prawn that possesses statocysts; in normal posture its dorsal surface is kept uppermost, whatever the direction of incident light. When an intact animal is held obliquely it makes pushing movements with its lower limbs that would tend to return it to the normal position. Quite otherwise is the behaviour of an animal which has been deprived of its statocysts. When turned over on its side so that its back is towards a source of lateral light, it maintains a symmetrical position without attempting to resume an upright posture. Again, if the light is coming from the side while the animal is held in its normal position, it makes pushing movements with its legs on the side opposite the light; these movements would tend to turn the animal on its side. In the absence of statocysts, therefore, *Palaemon* orientates itself solely by phototaxis. Another prawn, *Processa*, which lacks statocysts, shows photic responses resembling those of *Palaemon* when deprived of statocysts.

There are some invertebrates which show orientation to some fixed locus, and a faculty of this kind assumes importance in an animal that has some fixed home to which it returns after each excursion. Cues from several sensory fields may be used in achieving spatial orientation, including a photic response known as the light-compass reaction. In this reaction the animal need not orientate directly towards the source of light, but instead is able to maintain some definite angle between the light source and its direction of motion. Although best known in terrestrial arthropods, there is a marine nudibranch, *Elysia viridis*, which shows this response clearly. In a horizontal beam of light it responds by oriented movements and crawls in a straight line. When the position of the light is

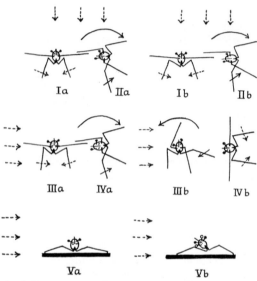

FIG. 8.14. ORIENTATION RESPONSES OF A PRAWN UNDER THE
INFLUENCE OF LIGHT AND GRAVITY

I–IV, animals suspended freely; V, resting on the bottom; *a*, intact animals; *b*, animals deprived of statocysts. Broken arrows, *left* and *above*, indicate direction of incident light. Curved arrows indicate sense of turning. Small broken arrows in figures indicate direction of thrust of leg. When the animal is suspended freely and held obliquely, the legs on the lower side make pushing movements which would return the animal to its normal position (back uppermost) if it were free to move (I*a*–IV*a*). Lateral illumination does not interfere with this statocyst reaction. When an animal with statocysts removed is held suspended, while light is coming from the side, it makes pushing movements with its legs on the side opposite the light (III*b*). When resting on the bottom and exposed to lateral light, an animal lacking statocysts compromises by inclining the body at an angle of about 45°. (After Alverdes, 1926.)

moved, the sea-slug responds by moving in a new direction, and by repeating this procedure it can be shown that the direction of locomotion pursued after each shift of the light source bears a constant relation to the direction of the light. This relationship is expressed in the angle between the longitudinal axis of the body and a line extending from the animal's eye to the light source. Each animal maintains its orientation angle constant, within certain limits which lie between 45° and 135°. The latter limitation has been explained on the basis of the structure of the eyes, which are pigmented cup-shaped ocelli provided with a lens, and so situated that only light falling within an angle of about 35° to 130° can reach the retina. Light-compass reactions are also reported in other marine animals—periwinkles, crabs and polychaetes. This type of response enables an animal to use a light source as a sensory guide for orienting itself while foraging over a wide radius, and releases it from stereotyped progression confined to the path of the light rays (50, 105).

Vertical Migration. Many planktonic animals are known to make regular vertical migrations through the water column each day. The phenomenon has been observed in many groups: tintinnids, siphonophores, polychaetes, pteropods, crustaceans, chaetognaths, appendicularians, fish, etc. Migratory planktonic species usually occur at some considerable depth below the surface during the day, and in the evening they migrate towards the surface from the day-depth (Fig. 8.15). Many oceanic species, however, do not necessarily reach the surface but merely rise to a higher level. Subsequent temporal phasing involves: a departure from the surface at or before midnight; a return to the surface just before dawn; and a sharp descent to the day-depth when the sunlight starts to penetrate the water. The subject is reviewed by Cushing (32).

The depth range is sometimes very great, for example, up to 400 m or more for species of pelagic decapod crustaceans in the North Atlantic. Different species inhabit different depths during the day, but even in one species-population the day-depth is variable, depending on age, season, weather conditions, etc.

The major determining factor in diurnal migration is light intensity. The depth to which light penetrates changes continuously during the day and from day to day, and it has proved possible to correlate changes in depth-distribution of a species with these fluctuations of light intensity. The daily ascent from the day-depth takes place during falling light intensity. At great depths, where the amount of daylight is always low, the ascent may begin early, in some cases even at midday. Descent in the morning occurs during increasing light intensity. The midnight sinking noticed in many species is seemingly due to a passive condition induced by total darkness. The short rise at dawn represents a return by the animals to the mean optimal light intensity for the population.

There is general agreement that vertical migration depends on changing light penetration during the day. Migratory planktonic animals aggregate in a band or region of optimal light intensity. At levels below the optimum, locomotory movements are initiated or increased; and at intensities above the optimum, movements slow down. Experimental evidence for several species reveals that there is a linear relationship between velocity of locomotory movements and $\log_{10}$ light intensity.

Under laboratory conditions *Daphnia*, a freshwater cladoceran, can be made to execute a complete cycle of vertical migration by varying cyclically the light-intensity. At low intensities, the movement of *Daphnia* is independent of the direction of the light and is determined solely by photokinesis; the dawn rise is a manifestation of this factor. The photokinetic response continues even in blinded animals. Superimposed on the photokinetic response at high light intensities is a phototactic response, in which the animal moves towards the light at reduced light intensities, and away from it when the light intensity is increased. In this way, *Daphnia* is able

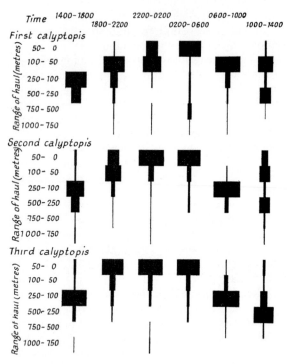

FIG. 8.15. DIAGRAM SHOWING VERTICAL MIGRATION IN CALYPTOPIS STAGES 1–3 OF *Euphausia superba* IN THE FALKLAND ISLANDS SECTOR OF THE ANTARCTIC From Fraser, 1936.)

to follow a zone of optimum light intensity. One or both of these mechanisms may be expected to operate in regulating the vertical migrations of some pelagic marine animals (61, 62).

ADAPTATIONS TO WEAK AND BRIGHT LIGHT. Adaptations of this kind are best known in arthropods and vertebrates. Attention has already been drawn to the migratory pigments found in crustacean and fish eyes, and to the occlusible tapeta of certain nocturnal fishes (p. 310). Apposition eyes of arthropods are adapted to function at high light intensities, superposition eyes at low intensities. On migration of the iris pigments the apposition eye may function as a superposition eye. Retinomotor changes in the fish eye act so as to screen the rods from strong light. An occlusible tapetum is found in some nocturnal fish. The tapetum reflects some fraction of the light, which has already passed through the retina once, back upon the sensory cells; in consequence, a greater proportion of the light falling initially upon the retinal surface is absorbed.

The two types of photosensory cells, the rods and cones, of the vertebrate eye function most effectively over different intensity ranges. The rods function at low intensities: when exposed to bright light they become insensitive; on return to darkness they regain sensitivity over a period of an hour in man. The cones are less sensitive and are able to function over a range of higher intensities.

Diurnal fish possess duplex retinae, containing both rods and cones. Nocturnal fish and those from deep waters possess pure rod retinae.

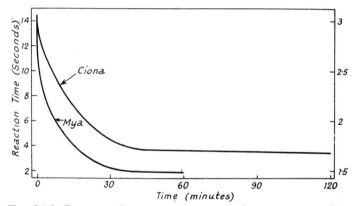

FIG. 8.16. COURSE OF DARK-ADAPTATION IN A LAMELLIBRANCH *Mya*
AND AN ASCIDIAN *Ciona*

The curves were established from reaction times to a standard flash after various periods in the dark. Ordinates, reaction times in seconds: left, *Ciona*; right, *Mya*. (Curves from Hecht (1919), redrawn and smoothed.)

Enhanced sensitivity to weak light is brought about by an increase in the length and density of rods, and in the number of rods connected to each tertiary neurone. The latter arrangement allows a greater summation of photoreceptor response, but reduces visual acuity.

DARK ADAPTATION. In general, animals become more sensitive to light after having been in the dark for some time. Curves for two invertebrates, showing recovery of sensitivity to light during the course of dark adaptation, may be seen in Fig. 8.16, derived from the work of Hecht.

In man and other animals with duplex retinae, vision, during the progress of dark adaptation, is taken over by the rods. The spectral distribution of sensitivity for the rods, based on visual purple, is different from that of the cones (*vide* p. 325). As the eye becomes dark-adapted, the spectral sensitivity curve shifts towards lower wave-lengths, the phenomenon known as the Purkinje shift. There are, consequently, two spectral curves, with maxima at 554 mμ and 507 mμ (in man). These give the distribution of spectral sensitivity in the photopic (light-adapted) and scotopic (dark-adapted) eye, respectively. Since light of longer wave-lengths is preferentially absorbed in penetrating sea water, it can be argued that the Purkinje shift has biological meaning when read in terms of the light conditions obtaining in an aquatic environment.

SPECTRAL SENSITIVITY. Animals are never equally sensitive to all regions of a spectrum having an equal energy content, and for many reasons it is important to know the spectral sensitivity of their photoreceptors. Determinations of this factor have been carried out on many species by several methods. Briefly these involve study of the behaviour of the animal in differently coloured lights, and measurement of the electrical activity of photoreceptors (either retinal action potentials or optic nerve impulses), when the retina is stimulated with light of selected wave-length and known intensity. The spectral sensitivity curves obtained by these methods are termed action spectra.

Some spectral sensitivity curves for lower animals, based on behaviour studies, are shown in Fig. 8.17. These are all marine species with the exception of the freshwater sunfish *Lepomis auritus*. The data for *Cerianthus* were obtained by measuring the reaction time for the heliotropic response to light of different wave-lengths. For *Mya*, the reaction time for withdrawal of the siphons was measured. Telotaxis in two differently coloured light beams was used to determine the action spectrum of *Palaemonetes* larvae. The behavioural response of *Myxine* which was utilized was movement preparatory to swimming when the animal was illuminated. For the sunfish, the visual rheotropic response was employed. Further action spectra, for *Limulus* and *Eledone*, based on electrical responses of retina and optic nerve, are shown in Fig. 8.18. Most of these curves have the same general shape, but there are significant differences in wave-length of maximal sensitivity, ranging from 490 to 550 mμ.

Action spectra based on electrical responses of retina and optic nerve have been determined, *inter alia*, for the octopus and crustaceans (euphausiids, lobsters) and the king crab (*Limulus*) (Fig. 8.18). The maximal spectral sensitivity of the eyes of many marine animals lies in the blue and green regions of the spectrum between 460 and 530 mμ (76, 99, 120).

COLOUR VISION. Colour is one of the attributes of an object which make it visually recognizable. The fundamental discrimination between wave-lengths takes place in the retina, specifically in the cones of the vertebrate eye, but colour vision occurs only when wave-length differences are recognized in the c.n.s. To demonstrate colour vision in animals necessitates tedious training experiments (123).

Crustaceans are the only marine invertebrates in which colour vision has been postulated. The evidence is derived from: decorating-responses of spider crabs in coloured aquaria; selection of coloured shells by hermit crabs; background responses of shrimps (*Crangon*); and optomotor responses of crabs and prawns to vertically oriented moving coloured stripes. The latter can change colour with respect to yellow and red environments independently of intensity (140).

There is a wealth of observations relating to colour vision in fishes. Experimental techniques have involved the preference method (e.g. voluntary selection of one among several colours), learning and background responses. Minnows which have been taught to associate a given colour with food subsequently distinguish blue and green from each other,

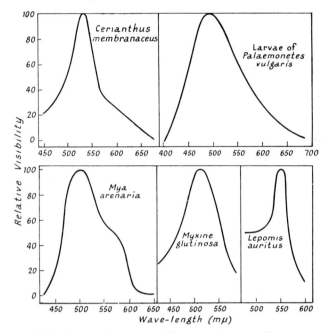

FIG. 8.17. ACTION SPECTRA OF VARIOUS ANIMALS, DETERMINED
BY BEHAVIOUR STUDIES

(Sources: *Cerianthus*, from Moore (1927); *Palaemonetes*, White (1924); *Mya*, Hecht (1921); *Myxine*, Steven (120); *Lepomis*, Grundfest (1932).)

and from yellow and red. On different backgrounds, or in lights of different colours, various teleosts show chromatic adjustments which depend on environmental colour independently of intensity. The most convincing proof of colour vision in fish has been secured by means of conditioned reflexes. Blennies (*Blennius pholis*) were given a visual stimulus associated with an electric shock. During the course of training the fish learnt to discriminate grey from other colours whenever they were contrasted, but failed to discriminate varying intensities of grey. Blennies, it was found, possess a definite and wide range of colour vision, and were able to discriminate blue, green and red from grey (66).

Photosensitive Pigments

For light to affect photosensitive tissue it must be absorbed by some pigment and produce a photochemical change leading eventually to sensory

excitation. The first of these photolabile pigments to be isolated was visual
purple or rhodopsin, associated with rod function in some vertebrate eyes.
Rhodopsin consists of a carotenoid retinene₁ (vitamin A₁ aldehyde) conjugated with a protein opsin. An allied pigment, porphyropsin, is found in
the rods of many fishes: its prosthetic carotenoid is retinene₂ (vitamin A₂
aldehyde). Marine fishes usually possess rhodopsin. Porphyropsins are
characteristic of freshwater teleosts, but also occur in some marine forms

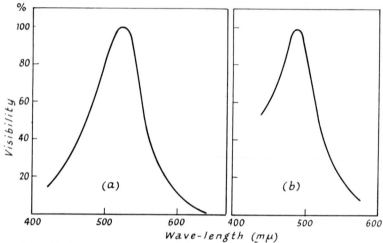

FIG. 8.18. (*a*) AVERAGE VISIBILITY CURVE FOR THE LATERAL EYE OF LIMULUS.
ACTION SPECTRUM DETERMINED FROM IMPULSE DISCHARGE IN SINGLE OPTIC
NERVE FIBRES (from Graham and Hartline, 1935). (*b*) SPECTRAL SENSITIVITY
CURVE FOR THE EYE OF *Eledone*. DATA DERIVED FROM RETINAL ELECTRICAL
RESPONSE (from Bliss (1943), after Piper.)

(Labridae, Coridae) and in species which migrate to and from the sea
(alewife, salmon, trout). The eel (*Anguilla*) and killifish (*Fundulus*) have
both pigments, but predominantly rhodopsin (Fig. 8.19) (125).

The absorption maximum of rhodopsin lies at about 500 mμ, with
variations for different species between 490 and 502 mμ. Some visual
purples from fish have peaks as follows: *Petromyzon marinus*, 497 mμ;
Squalus acanthias, *Pleuronectes platessa*, *Trigla lucerna* and *Gadus pollachius*, 500 mμ. Deep-water elasmobranchs, conger eels and deep-sea
teleosts have golden rhodopsins, called chrysopsins, with absorption maxima around 485 mμ. The absorption bands of porphyropsins are displaced
towards the red, with maxima around 522–533 mμ. (30, 31, 33, 38, 39,
40, 41, 57, 74, 125, 126).

Rhodopsins of invertebrates similarly consist of a retinine chromophore
linked with a protein moiety. These show maximal absorption in the range
460–520 mμ (*Euphausia*, 460 mμ; lobster, 515 mμ; hermit crab, 500 mμ;
king-crab, 520 mμ; squid, 493 mμ; octopus, 475 mμ) (69, 75, 80, 127).

The absorption characteristics of the visual pigments determine the spectral sensitivity of the retina. So long as there is not differential absorption elsewhere in the optical system, the absorption spectrum of visual purple should be reflected in the action spectrum of the photoreceptor or organism, and many studies offer confirmation. The scotopic visibility curve for vertebrate eyes is a close replica of the spectral distribution of visual purple sensitivity in the species concerned.

The lenses of fishes and squid that live near the surface often contain a

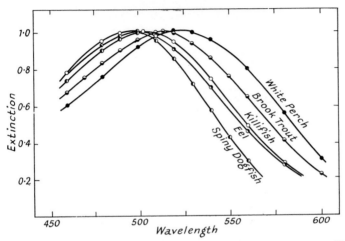

FIG. 8.19. ABSORPTION SPECTRA OF PHOTOSENSITIVE PIGMENTS FROM THE RETINAE OF FISH, ILLUSTRATING THE TRANSITION FROM AN EXCLUSIVELY RHODOPSIN TO AN EXCLUSIVELY PORPHYROPSIN SYSTEM

The dogfish possesses only rhodopsin; eel and killifish predominantly rhodopsin; brook trout predominantly porphyropsin; white perch only porphyropsin. (From Wald (125).)

yellow pigment absorbing in the blue and near ultra-violet. In deep-sea fishes and squid such pigments are generally absent and the lens transmits blue and ultra-violet light equally as well as longer wave-lengths. Ultra-violet light is rapidly absorbed by sea water and quickly disappears below the surface (24, 37).

Coastal waters vary greatly in their absorption characteristics, depending on turbidity, but transparency is frequently greatest in the green region of the spectrum. The greatest transparency of clear ocean water is at a wave-length of 480 mμ, i.e. in the blue region of the spectrum (*vide* Chapter 1). Absorption in both coastal and deep waters increases greatly above 550 mμ. It is within this general range of 480–550 mμ that the rhodopsins or visual purples of fish and invertebrates are most sensitive. It follows then that visual pigments having absorption maxima in this range will possess maximal efficiency in a marine environment. Furthermore there is now evidence accumulating that luminescent light, of animal origin,

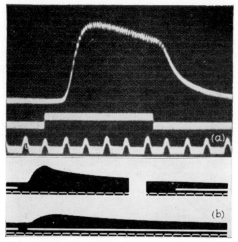

FIG. 8.20. RETINAL ACTION POTENTIALS; (*a*) OCTOPUS (*Eledone moschata*).
(*b*) EYE-SPOT OF STARFISH (*Asterias*)

Upward deflexion indicates negativity of lead towards external ends of sensory cells. Time scale, all records, $\frac{1}{5}$ sec. Duration of exposure shown below retinal potentials. Interruption of upper starfish record was 3 sec. ((*a*) from Fröhlich, 1921; (*b*) from Hartline *et al.* (64).)

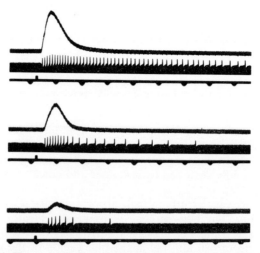

FIG. 8.21. ELECTRICAL RESPONSES OF THE LATERAL EYE OF *Limulus*

Action potentials of an isolated ommatidium and its nerve strand, in response to short flashes of light (20 msec) at three intensities (relative values, top to bottom, 1·0, 0·1, 0·01). *Upper trace*, retinal action potential; *lower trace*, spike potentials. Flash indicated by black bar above time trace near beginning of each record. Time scale, 0·2 sec. (From Hartline *et al.* (64).)

may be of considerable significance for vision in the ocean depths where there is little residual daylight, and it is of interest that the emission spectra of some species lie in this general range (about 470–510 mμ). A good functional correlation exists between the spectral sensitivities of marine crustacea and fish and the spectral composition of the light in their surroundings. Oceanic euphausiids and deep-sea fishes have visual pigments absorbing maximally in the blue (460–480 mμ), corresponding to the blue colour of attenuated daylight and of luminescence in oceanic water (p. 19). Similarly, surface animals and those over the continental shelf, where the light is generally blue-green or green, have maximal sensitivity to wave-lengths around 500–530 mμ (fish, lobsters, crabs) (24, 76).

Electrical Activity of the Eye

Two kinds of electrical activity can be recorded from the neighbourhood of the eye, namely retinal potentials and optic-nerve potentials. When electrodes are connected to front and back of the eye, a potential difference between the two regions is detected. Illumination of the eye produces a potential change known as the retinal action potential or electro-retinogram. This is in the direction of increased negativity of the free distal ends of the photoreceptor cells. In the vertebrate eye, with its inverted retina, there is an initial negative/positive response at the onset of light (*a* and *b* waves), and the potential change is completed with a positive off-effect at cessation of illumination. The components of the electro-retinogram (ERG) refer to changes taking place in the visual cells.

Electroretinograms have been obtained from the eyes of various invertebrates. The response to light is often a simple negative wave succeeded by a sustained negative potential at a lower plateau level throughout the duration of illumination (*Limulus, Loligo, Asterias,* etc.) (Figs. 8.20, 8.21). The ERG recorded from the compound eye of *Ligia* begins with a negative on-effect, quickly followed by an early positive deflexion and rapid return to base line during illumination, and ends with a positive off-effect (56, 64, 112, 140).

Photic stimulation of the eye produces a train of action potentials in the optic nerve. This is well illustrated in records from single optic nerve fibres of *Limulus* (Fig. 8.22). When stimulated with a long light exposure, the optic fibre begins to discharge after a short latent period, initially at a high frequency, soon followed by a rather steady discharge at a lower frequency; with light off, the discharge ceases. This is an on-effect, the eye responding to onset of illumination. Intracellular recording reveals that photic stimulation produces slow waves of depolarization in the retinular cells. These seem to be electronically coupled with the eccentric cell in which a slow wave is induced leading to spike potentials (8, 55, 140).

Other eyes have on/off systems, for example bivalve molluscs. The pallial nerve of *Spisula* contains a few photosensitive neurones which begin to discharge when illumination stops and continue to discharge rhythmically in darkness. This is an off-response mediating a shadow reflex by which *Spisula* withdraws its siphons (79). In the mantle eye of the scallop (*Pecten*), there are two retinal layers: one, internal, discharging to onset of light; the other, external, to cessation of illumination or reduction of intensity. The highly complex vertebrate eye contains on/off systems, some fibres responding with an on burst, continued discharge during illumination and an off burst; others respond with on/off bursts only; still others show only off effects.

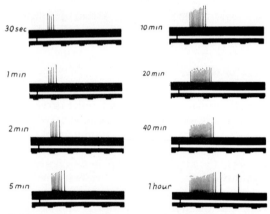

FIG. 8.22. DARK-ADAPTATION OF A SINGLE VISUAL RECEPTOR
IN THE EYE OF *Limulus*

The records show action potentials of a single optic nerve fibre in response to illuminating the eye with a test flash of light. The test flashes were applied at various times in the dark (indicated in the records) following a period of light-adaptation. Flash duration (8 msec) shown as interruption of white band. Time scale, 0·2 sec. (From Hartline and McDonald (63).)

The magnitude of the retinal action potential depends on the intensity and, for short flashes, the duration of the light stimulus. Similarly, the characteristics of nervous discharge (frequency, number of impulses) in the optic nerve depend on the conditions of illumination. These relationships between stimulus and response have been used extensively for measuring certain visual functions, namely spectral sensitivity, dark-adaptation, reciprocal relationship between intensity and duration of illumination, etc.

Over a wide range the magnitude of the retinal action potential is related linearly to the logarithm of the light intensity, but the curves tend to become sigmoid at low and high intensities.

The lateral eye of *Limulus* has been used extensively in studies of photoreception. When an ommatidium is stimulated with brief flashes of light a train of impulses appears in the optic nerve, the number of which depends on the duration and intensity of the stimulus (Fig. 8.21). By varying these two factors it has been possible to determine the flash duration which just produces a single impulse at various intensities. The data so derived show that the reciprocity law (duration × time = a constant) holds for the production of a single impulse. This reciprocal relationship, found in the responses of photoreceptors, has been attributed to photochemical processes in the eye, and may be an expression of the Bunsen-Roscoe law of photochemistry.

Recovery of sensitivity during dark-adaptation in single ommatidia of *Limulus* is illustrated in Fig. 8.22. The eye was stimulated by brief flashes of light at various intervals after placing the preparation in the dark, and spike potentials were recorded from a single optic-nerve fibre. The number of spike potentials is low at first, increases rapidly during the initial period of dark-adaptation and more slowly thereafter. The time course of recovery is followed by determining the intensity of a flash necessary to elicit a single impulse, or by measuring the number and frequency of impulses evoked by a constant flash at selected intervals. The rate of recovery depends on the previous light history of the eye, varying with the intensity and duration of previous light adaptation (63).

Spectral-sensitivity curves for *Limulus* and *Eledone* derived from measurements of retinal action potentials and optic nerve potentials are shown in Fig. 8.18. The action spectra obtained by such means generally agree with spectral-sensitivity curves obtained from behaviour studies. There is reasonably close resemblance between spectral-sensitivity curves and the absorption curves of visual pigments (rhodopsin) in those instances where data from both sources are available (64).

Many arthropods can distinguish polarized light and some species make use of this ability in orientation. Cladocerans and amphipods orientate to polarized sky light, and mysids and crabs show distinct reactions to plane-polarized light vibrating in different directions. The compound eye of arthropods acts as a polarization analyser. When a single ommatidium in the eye of *Limulus* is stimulated by short flashes of plane-polarized light and spike potentials are recorded from the optic nerve, the discharge-rate is found to vary with the plane of polarization. Stimulation is maximal near 0° and 180° with respect to some particular setting, and is minimal at 90° where only half as many impulses result from a standard flash. Squid, sepiolids and octopuses are other animals that can see polarized light because the rhabdomeres of the eye function as analysers (7, 34, 70, 101, 130, 140).

MECHANORECEPTION

Tactile stimulation produces mechanical deformation of cellular surfaces. The corresponding sensitivity may take the form of a generalized cellular irritability, as in the independent effectors of sponges, or involve the stimulation of free nerve endings or specialized tactile receptors. Hydroids (*Syncoryne*), for example, bend towards a source of weak mechanical disturbances a few millimetres away (73). More sensitive mechanoreceptors detect pressure waves created by vibration of distant sources. Sound waves or high-frequency vibrations are detected by special phonoreceptors. Many animals possess tension receptors, responsive to distortion by stretch. Finally, special mechanoreceptors, the gravity and equilibrium receptors, permit the animal to orient in space.

Sensitivity to Touch and Low-Frequency Vibrations

The importance of tactile stimuli in the behaviour of animals requires no emphasis. Benthic species are continuously being exposed to contact stimuli of various kinds, free-swimming species respond to contact with solid objects, and many animals are sensitive in various degrees to distant vibrations. Tactile receptors may act as external proprioceptors, providing information about spatial position and movement of parts of the body and in this regard they act in conjunction with internal proprioceptors and equilibrium receptors.

TACTILE SENSITIVITY. The simplest type of tactile receptors are free nerve endings lying in the skin. These endings may show generalized irritability, being sensitive to a variety of noxious stimuli, mechanical, thermal and chemical. More primitive animals, such as flatworms, anneilds, enteropneusts, etc., possess individual sensory neurones scattered through the epidermis (Fig. 8.2). These may take the form of fusiform elements bearing sensory hairs distally, and giving rise to nerve fibres which extend toward the central nervous system (c.n.s.). Crustacea have sensory hairs distributed over the surface of the body, especially at joints of the appendages. Each hair is served by a sensory neurone at its base. Free nerve endings are abundant in the skin of fish, but encapsulated endings, such as occur in higher vertebrates, are rare (136).

Local tactile stimulation produces diverse responses. A gentle stimulus evokes movement in a restricted area, e.g. in a single palp or antenna. Under strong stimulation sessile and sedentary animals display withdrawal reflexes involving strong contraction of the body musculature, e.g. sea anemones, polychaetes, holothurians, phoronids, etc. Other reflexes induced by tactile stimulation are luminescence, colour changes, display of protective armament, operation of poisonous devices, etc.

Contact stimuli produce orientation reflexes of various kinds. Benthic animals such as polychaetes, which crawl over the substratum, tend to come to rest in crevices or at angles between surfaces. In the absence of other suitable contact stimuli they may bunch together. This type of orientation reflex is termed thigmotaxis. When an animal is resting on the substratum it experiences continuous asymmetrical stimulation of its tactile receptors. In the absence of ventral surface-stimulation, righting reflexes are initiated, e.g. in gastropods, starfishes, etc. Another kind of orientation reflex is rheotaxis, or orientation to water currents. Visual cues are often predominant in orientation, as in lobster and fish, but blind fish can orient themselves in a current when they are resting on the bottom, through frictional stimulation of contact receptors.

Regional differences in tangosensitivity have been studied in various marine invertebrates. In the anemone *Calliactis parasitica*, the oral disc is at least 4,000 times as sensitive as the column to mechanical stimulation; also sensitivity decreases from the base of the column upwards. Now, tactile receptors of *Calliactis* lie in the column endoderm, the mesogloea of which increases in thickness from pedal edge towards the marginal sphincter. The decrease of sensitivity in the same direction corresponds to this increase of mesogloeal tissue which exerts a shielding effect (109). Tubicolous polychaetes are most sensitive to contact in the region of the gills. In *Hydroides dianthus* (Serpulidae) the order of decreasing sensitivity for various regions of the body is as follows: gills, head, thorax and abdomen. In *Holothuria* decreasing sensitivity is shown by: tentacles, oral rim, cloacal rim, podia, anterior body region, posterior end and mid-body surface.

Contact stimuli can often be localized with great precision. Foreign bodies are deftly removed from the external surface; urchins, when attacked, direct their spines towards the region affected, etc. In quiescent spinal dogfish and teleosts a localized tactile stimulus throws the body into an S-shape, the posture of which depends on the position of stimulation. A touch anteriorly causes the tail to move to the opposite side; a touch posteriorly, to the same side. Active spinal preparations of the dogfish show persistent locomotory rhythms as long as they are free from contact, while diffuse contact stimulation of the ventral surface produces inhibition of swimming movements. These various kinds of responses to stimulation are instances of reflexes involving peripheral nerve nets or central nervous systems (*vide* Chapter 10). The neurological basis of locomotory rhythms and reflexes in selachians is considered in detail by Lissmann (91).

By recording from the facial nerve of the catfish (*Ameiurus*) Hoagland (1933) picked up action potentials following mechanical stimulation. Receptors (presumably free nerve endings of Gasserian origin) in lips and barbels are very sensitive to touch and water movements. The spikes are large, indicative of large axons; quite distinct from these are small spikes, produced by chemical agents and transmitted in small fibres of the geniculate ganglion.

Pressure receptors in the skin of selachians are of two sorts: free nerve endings and terminal corpuscles. The latter are encapsulated skeins of nerve fibres lying in the connective tissue of the fin (Fig. 8.1). When stimulated by pressure they give rise to bursts of impulses in the sensory nerves. Adaptation is slow, and discharge continues for many seconds under maintained steady stimulation. The terminal corpuscles respond to fin movements as well as externally applied pressure, and thus probably act as proprioceptors as well as tactile receptors (93).

PROPRIOCEPTORS

Proprioceptors are mechanoreceptors that respond to stretch, bending and contraction, and provide information about the movement of body parts. Those best known are the muscle spindles of higher vertebrates, but stretch receptors are also known to occur in fish muscles and in invertebrates. Compared with tactile receptors, tension receptors are usually very slowly adapting. An instance of a slowly-adapting pressure-receptor and proprio-ceptor, responsive to fin movements and pressure deformation in selachians, has been noted in the previous section.

Stretch receptors in selachian muscle, histologically unidentified, give rise to a maintained discharge in afferent nerve fibres when a load is applied to the muscle. The frequency of discharge increases with the load, the relationship between frequency and logarithm of tension being linear. On stretching the muscle there is initially a high-frequency discharge, which declines over a period of some 20 sec, owing to adaptation, and is succeeded by a steady rhythmic discharge so long as the tension is maintained. These stretch receptors continue to function rhythmically under constant tension for over an hour. When the tension is suddenly decreased, there follows a silent period before the discharge resumes at a new frequency level corresponding to the reduced tension. In a fin at rest there is a resting discharge from the muscle receptors; bending the fin one way, and then the other, increases and decreases the discharge from a given receptor. This differential response signals the degree of muscular contraction, and the sign and magnitude of fin movements (48).

Various kinds of proprioceptors have been described in different Malacostraca. These are: *A*. organs in the extensor muscles of thorax and abdomen (Malacostraca, except Brachyura): (*a*) muscle receptor organs; (*b*) N-cells in the ordinary thoracic muscles. *B*. organs of the appendages: (*a*) elastic receptors; (*b*) muscle receptors spanning the thoracico-coxal articulation; (*c*) innervated strands associated with levator and depressor muscles of the pereiopods; (*d*) "myochordotonal organs" of Barth (20, 27).

Elastic receptors (category *B*(*a*) above) occur at the joints of the walking legs of many decapods. A receptor contains an elastic strand of connective tissue spanning the joint. A group of sensory nerve cells sends distal pro-cesses into the strand, and axons into the main nerve trunk. One of these organs—that occurring at the propodite-dactylopodite joint—has been subjected to physiological study. It consists of many nerve cells ending in an elastic strand terminating at the joint. The connective tissue strand is in a stretched condition at all positions, and the amount of stretch increases during flexion. In the afferent nerves coming from the receptor organ there is a resting discharge which depends on the length of the organ. Sudden change in length, and vibrational stimuli, evoke bursts of impulses in the sensory axons (Fig. 8.23). Four types of sensory neurones have been recognized: severally, these respond to extension, flexing, and to static states of extension and flexion (21).

Muscle receptor organs (category *A*(*a*) above) occur in the dorsal body wall of abdominal and posterior thoracic segments of malacostracans (except Brachyura) (Fig. 8.24). There are two organs on each side, lying near the dorsal extensor muscle. Typically, each organ consists of a specialized receptor muscle, a stretch receptor cell, sensory fibres to the stretch receptor cell, accessory nerve fibres, and a motor innervation (of excitatory and inhibitory fibres) of the receptor muscle. The cell body of the sensory neurone lies near the muscle, and its dendrites terminate in connective tissue intercalated in the muscle. The motor fibres innervate the muscle, and the accessory fibres form synapses with the dendrites of the receptor neurones (1, 2, 3, 4, 49).

Earlier conjectures that the muscle receptor organs are responsive to stretch have been confirmed physiologically. Stretching the isolated organ gives rise to a nervous discharge in its sensory axon (*Homarus, Panulirus,*

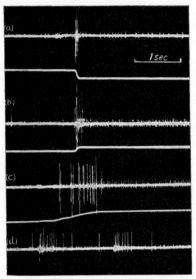

FIG. 8.23. RESPONSES OF A PROPRIOCEPTOR ORGAN IN THE LEG OF THE CRAB *Carcinus maenas* TO VIBRATION AND PASSIVE MOVEMENT OF THE PROPODITE-DACTYLUS JOINT

Recording from nerves to propodite-dactylus organ. The lower beam indicates movement of the dactylus. (*a*) Passive extension. (*b*) (*c*) Passive flexion at different rates. (*d*) Two taps on preparation box. (From Burke (21).)

Cambarus, etc.). The two organs differ considerably in their physiological characteristics (Fig. 8.25). One has high threshold and adapts quickly to strong stretching in less than a minute. The other has low threshold and maintains continuous discharge for several hours under constant stretch. Furthermore, contraction of the receptor-organ muscle itself can initiate discharge in the sensory axon. The receptor muscle linked with the quickly-adapting neurone gives twitch-like contractions and has a high fusion frequency, whereas the receptor muscle connected with the slowly adapting sensory neurone gives slow contractions and has a low fusion frequency. One of the receptor organs thus acts as a phasic receptor signalling sudden flexion of the tail; the other is a tonic receptor, transmitting information about the degree of flexion existing in each segment of the abdomen (88, 138).

By intracellular recording it has been shown that excitation of the sensory cell normally starts in the distal portion of the dendrites, which are depolarized by stretch deformation. This potential change, a generator potential, spreads electrotonically over the nearby cell soma, reducing the resting potential of the latter. When the membrane resting potential is lowered by stretch to a certain critical level, conducted impulses are initiated in the sensory axon. The accessory nerve fibres are inhibitory and form a direct

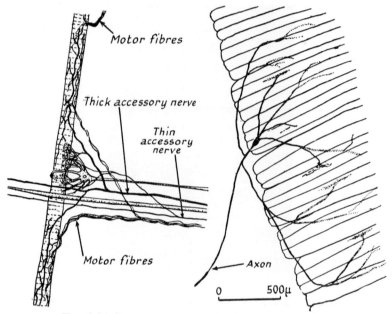

FIG. 8.24. PROPRIOCEPTORS IN DECAPOD CRUSTACEANS

(*Left*) Muscle receptor organ in thoracic muscle. (*Right*) N-cell on lateral thoracico-abdominal muscle. Both preparations from *Homarus vulgaris*. (From Alexandrowicz (1).)

peripheral inhibitory control mechanism, which can modulate the activity of the stretch receptor. Stimulation of the inhibitory fibre decreases the afferent discharge rate, or stops impulses altogether in the stretched receptor cell. The inhibitory mechanism acts by limiting depolarization of the dendrites above a certain level, thus preventing the generator potential from attaining a level sufficient to fire the cell (46, 47, 89, 97).

N-cells are simpler stretch receptors than muscle receptor organs, replacing them in the anterior thorax of decapods (Fig. 8.24). They have no specialized muscle or accessory innervation, and they are associated with the ordinary axial muscles. N-cells, functionally, are similar to slowly adapting stretch-receptor cells of other segments. In *Squilla* all the stretch-receptor organs of the dorsal axial musculature are muscle receptor organs, having slow- and fast-adapting sensory cells (110).

Muscle receptors at the coxal thoracic articulation (*B(b)*) and innervated elastic strands (*B(c)*) differ from the receptors already described in

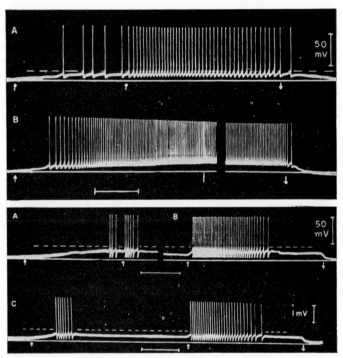

FIG. 8.25. RESPONSES OF MUSCLE RECEPTOR ORGANS OF THE
CRAYFISH (*Procambarus alleni*) TO STRETCH

Above (A,B) slow cell. A, cell impaled and stretched just above threshold, setting up five irregular discharges. At second arrow, increased stretch raised discharge rate. B, cell subjected to gradually increasing stretch between first arrow and straight line, and then held constant. The discharge is regular during maintained stretch. Gap of several seconds in record. *Below* (A,B,C) adaptation of impaled fast cell during maintained stretch. A, slow stretch for 2 sec at first arrow, additional stretch at second arrow maintained for 4–5 sec. Gap at B, when additional maintained stretch applied (third arrow). C, fast cell, extracellular recording. Steady stretch applied between arrows 1 and 2; further stretch added at arrow 2 and maintained until arrow 3. Time, 1sec. (From Eyzaguirre and Kuffler (46).)

that their cell bodies lie in the central nervous system. The former—the muscle receptor organ—consists of bundles of muscle fibres and connective tissue. Motor fibres innervate the muscle and sensory fibres end among the muscle and connective tissue fibres. The organ is so disposed that it is stretched by backward movement of the leg. The innervated elastic strands lie adjacent to the muscle receptors just described, and are associated with the depressor and levator muscles of the coxo-basipodite joint of the leg. They are connective tissue strands innervated by sensory dendrites.

In decapods, chordotonal organs occur at the distal joints of the walking legs and at the joints of antennules of decapods. They consist of elastic strands or membranes which are distorted by movement of the joint. Associated bipolar neurones send dendritic processes into the membrane to a special sensory organelle, containing sheath cells and a rod; the organelle is called a scolopale. Electrophysiological studies have shown that chordotonal organs contain both tonic position receptors and phasic movement receptors. They provide information about direction and rate of movement, and about position of the joint. The reflexes which they initiate are such that they tend to resist an imposed passive movement (22, 137, 141).

PHONORECEPTION

Sound waves travel readily through water, with higher velocity and less absorption of energy than in air. Because the air-water interface reflects most of the sound waves reaching it, very little of any sound produced above the surface succeeds in entering the water. The velocity of sound in water is given by the formula

$$V = \sqrt{\left(\frac{\gamma}{\varrho K}\right)}$$

where γ is the ratio of specific heats, ϱ is the density of the liquid, and K the compressibility. The three variables γ, ϱ and K change with temperature, salinity and pressure. When these are known the velocity can be determined from suitable tables (96). The intensity of sound in water varies inversely as the square of the distance from the source. Absorption of sound energy becomes significant only at high frequencies (122).

Invertebrates. A few invertebrates are reported to be sensitive to sounds and water-borne vibrations. Underwater sounds evoke withdrawal (startle) reflexes in sabellid worms, e.g. *Branchiomma*. Some crustaceans produce sounds, e.g. *Palinurus*, *Synalpheus*, *Uca* (p. 403), and may have limited auditory ability. It is known that *Mysis* and *Palaemonetes* can hear underwater sounds. Bethe observed that they are more responsive to deep tones and that sensitivity is reduced after extirpation of the statocysts. Simple mechanoreceptors occur on the cuticle of crustaceans. They are projecting hairs or tufts of hairs, arranged in various patterns. Hair-peg organs on lobsters are plates bearing a rod surrounded by hairs. They are deflected by water currents and respond to a flow of 0·3 cm/sec or more (determined by recording nerve action potentials during stimulation). Cuticular hair-fan organs bear terminal hairs sensitive to deflexions in one or sometimes two directions. These are possible displacement receptors for near-field effects (*cf.* lateral line of fish, *infra*) (90).

It may be that the invertebrate statocyst is primarily a rudimentary phonoreceptor like the sacculus of fishes and has secondarily acquired the rôle of statoreceptor.

Hearing in Fishes and Function of the Lateral Line System. Fishes detect sound waves and low-frequency (infrasonic) vibrations by means of the inner ear, lateral line and cutaneous receptors. The vestibule of the inner ear contains a membranous sac, the sacculus, from which arise two small evaginations, the utricle and lagena (Fig. 8.26). The latter is homologous with the cochlea of higher vertebrates. The epithelial lining of these chambers bears small patches of sense cells termed cristae or maculae. Calcareous statocysts are present in the three chambers, suspended by membranes so that they are able to vibrate freely. During vibration they stimulate the sensory epithelium. The maculus of the lagena is supplied by a separate branch of the eighth cranial nerve.

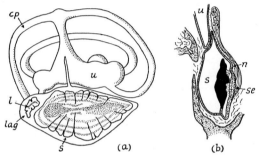

FIG. 8.26. (*a*) LABYRINTH OF *Exocoetus*. (*b*) SECTION THROUGH THE SACCULUS OF THE TROUT

cp, posterior semicircular canal; *l*, statolith of lagena; *lag*, lagena; *n*, nerve; *s*, sacculus; *se*, sensory epithelium; *u*, utriculus. ((*a*), after Plate (1924); (*b*), after von Frisch (1936).)

A connexion between the air-bladder and ear exists in some teleosts. In the simplest cases a diverticulum from the air-bladder extends to a membranous fenestra in the periotic capsule so that vibrations, picked up by the bladder, can be transmitted to the perilymph (tarpon *Megalops*, soldier-fish *Holocentrus*, etc.) In the Clupeidae the diverticulum enters the periotic capsule and becomes closely associated with the labyrinth. The most complex arrangement is found in the essentially freshwater Ostariophysi which possess a series of movable bones, the Weberian ossicles, extending from the air-bladder to the perilymph.

The lateral line system of fishes consists of free superficial neuromasts, and of concealed neuromasts lying in a series of grooves or canals in the head and along the trunk. In some elasmobranchs the lateral canal is represented by an open groove. In teleosts the canals perforate the scales along the lateral line, opening to the exterior at intervals by pores. The neuromast is a sensory structure containing a group of sensory cells bearing hair-like projections (Fig. 8.27). The system is innervated in the head by branches of the facial, glosso-pharyngeal and vagus nerves, and in the trunk by the ramus lateralis vagi (45, 77).

Behaviour experiments have shown that fish are very sensitive to under-water sounds. Killifish, for example, respond to a tuning fork (128 c/s) by movements of the pectoral fins and an increase in respiratory rate. By means of conditioned reflexes Bull (18) showed that eels are sensitive to a submerged buzzer and a tuning fork. Upper limits of sensitivity to sound frequencies in some fishes are shown in Table 8.1; the limits, however, change with intensity. The most sensitive frequency range for many fishes lies in the region of 300–800 c/s; few if any fishes without Weberian apparatus detect sounds above 3,000 c/s. To intensities normally encoun-tered, 2,000 c/s is, in practice, the upper limit of hearing for most non-cypriniform fishes. In the grunt *Haemulon* the threshold at the upper

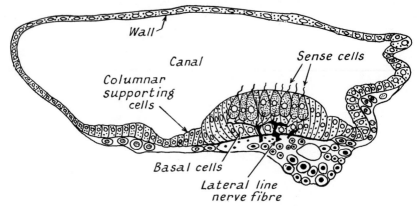

FIG. 8.27. TRANSVERSE SECTION THROUGH LATERAL SENSORY CANAL OF
Mustelus canis ($\times$ 370) (from Johnson, 1917.)

frequency of 1,100 c/s is 10^{-8} W/cm² and the lowest threshold occurs at 800 c/s, viz. 10^{-15} W/cm². Auditory thresholds are about 30 db lower in fishes having the air bladder coupled to the ear than in fishes lacking this connexion, and the lower threshold may be associated with a sensitivity to higher frequencies. In behaviour experiments minnows learnt to distinguish two tones differing by less than an octave ($\frac{1}{3}$–$\frac{1}{4}$).

By operating on the ears of minnows von Frisch showed that hear-ing is mediated by the sacculus and lagena which are sensitive to frequen-cies between 32 and 6,000 c/s; lower frequencies, below 65 c/s, are per-ceived through skin receptors (lateral line plus tactile receptors); at the lower extreme (below 32 c/s) by tactile receptors alone. Severing the audi-tory nerves or injuring the sacculus reduces sensitivity to sounds in the smooth hound *Mustelus* and squeteague (*Cynoscion*). Behaviour experi-ments have provided evidence for two distinct threshold curves for the grunt fish *Haemulon* in the low frequency range (< 800 c/s). Now, these results suggest that two different receptor systems are operating: the inner ear more sensitive to high frequency vibrations, the lateral line more sensitive to low frequency vibrations. From human experience one may also suppose that general tactile receptors respond to strong displacement of the medium occasioned by movement of nearby objects.

Further information has been revealed by electronic recording. Microphonic effects (generator potentials) have been recorded from the inner ear of various species of teleosts in response to tapping, loud speech and

TABLE 8.1

UPPER FREQUENCY LIMITS OF HEARING IN CERTAIN FISHES

Fish	Frequency (c/s)
Carcharhinus leucas	1,500
Anguilla anguilla	500–650
Phoxinus laevis	4,645–6,960
Ameiurus nebulosus	13,169
Lebistes reticulatus	1,035–2,069
Periophthalmus koelreuteri	650
Gobius niger	800
Corvina nigra	1,024[1]
Sargus annularis	1,250

[1] Maximal frequency tried.
(Sources: 44, 72, 124)

sound of a tuning-fork (60 c/s). The microphonic potential is generated in the macular region of the sacculus (57, 142).

Vibrational responses in the ear of the ray (*Raja clavata*) have been demonstrated by electrical recording from branches of the auditory nerve (94). The regions of the inner ear responsive to vibrational stimuli are the lateral part of the macula sacculi, the macula neglecta (dorso-medial aspect of the sacculus) and the lacinia utriculi (an uncovered portion of the utriculus macula). In the absence of vibrational stimuli many of the receptors display resting activity, but quiescent units, when stimulated, become recruited to take part in vibrational responses. Vestibular microphonics were observed at stimulating frequencies as high as 750 c/s, but vibrational responses were restricted to frequencies below 120 c/s.

Not much is known about the importance of sound as sensory cues for fish. The continuous production of low frequency (infrasonic) vibrations by waves and moving bodies may be utilized to a considerable extent by many species. Marshall (95) describes unusually prominent lateral line organs in some bathypelagic fishes, especially blind species (brotulids, macrourids). These may be concerned especially with detection of low-frequency pressure waves generated by moving prey. Sudden sounds frighten fish and warn them of danger, and sound production is used for warning purposes and is part of the social and breeding behaviour of some species. Parker (1910) noted three types of responses by fish to sounds. When the side of the container was struck, some species retreated from the source (*Tautoga*), others were attracted (*Prionotus*), and still others became quiescent. Male drum fishes (sciaenids) produce sounds by movements of the air-bladder, probably as a means of communication during the breeding seasons (p. 403).

The lateral line organs of fishes are sensitive to pressure waves impinging upon the animal. The delicate hairs on the neuromast sensory cells operate on the principle of microlevers, being deformed by the flow of fluid along the canals. Sand (113), who developed a technique for perfusing the hyomandibular canal, showed that flow in one direction excited some receptors, whereas flow in the opposite direction inhibited them (Fig. 8.28). The two directions of flow in the lateral line canal constitute antagonistic stimuli; and there is evidence in the neuromast organs for two kinds of receptors which react in opposite ways to flow in the two directions.

The lateral line nerve shows a constant background of spontaneous activity, on which is superimposed discharge patterns when the lateral line is stimulated by vibratory stimuli up to 350 c/s (*Fundulus, Ameiurus*). In *Fundulus* the nervous discharge synchronizes with sonic frequencies up to at least 180 c/s. An increased rate of discharge is also produced by mechanical pressure over the lateral line canal, by irregular water currents, ripples in the water and by movements of the fish's trunk. Swimming movements of other fish in the neighbourhood are also detected by the lateral line neuromasts. A microphonic potential can be recorded from the neuromast organ when the pick-up electrode is close to the cupula. In the range 14–48 c/s the electrical output is proportional to the amplitude of movement of the cupula over the hair cells (*Acerina*).

The acoustic receptors of fish are twofold, viz. the swimbladder-inner ear and the lateral line-integument. Morphologically, both the inner ear and the lateral line have a common origin in the acoustico-lateralis system and possess homologous sensory hair cells. These are displacement receptors and are sensitive to the flow of water particles past them.

The sacculus and the lagena are the regions of the inner ear concerned with hearing. In teleosts the swimbladder responds to propagated pressure waves, which become transformed into volume displacements that affect the inner ear. This sensory modality is sensitive to far-field effects: in these the energy is conveyed from a vibrating distant source as propagated longitudinal pressure waves, the amplitude of which decreases as $1/r$. The lateral line is sensitive to near-field effects: these are displacements of water particles by the source and the amplitude of the displacement decreases as $1/r^2$. A rough boundary between the regions of the two effects is the distance where the two amplitudes are equal (under some conditions, $\lambda/2\pi$).

Since the bony fish has only one receptor for propagated pressure waves (*viz.*, the swimbladder) and the ears are not acoustically isolated, it is unable to measure the time-difference between the arrival of the sound waves at two points and, therefore, it cannot localize the source of distant sound. On the other hand, the lateral line canals are paired, variously but symmetrically oriented, and acoustically isolated. Their disposition enables the fish to localize a sound source in the near field by noting differences in magnitude of displacement at two or more loci on the body surface. The near-field effect operates over quite short distances—some 10–20 cm (14, 57, 71, 121, 124).

Hearing in Cetaceans. There is considerable evidence that whales can

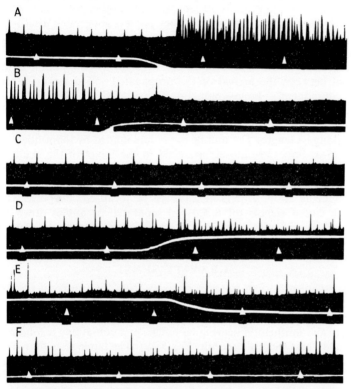

FIG. 8.28. RECORDS OF DISCHARGE IN THE HYOMANDIBULAR NERVE OF THE RAY DURING PERFUSION OF THE HYOMANDIBULAR CANAL

The white line is perfusion signal: upward displacement signals tailward perfusion; downward displacement, headward perfusion. Time signal in seconds. The records show the activity of the preparation at intervals of 1 min, when a headward perfusion of 1 min duration (AB) was followed by a tailward perfusion of 1 min duration (DE), with a rest interval of 2 min between perfusions. A strong burst of large potentials accompanies headward perfusion; the response to tailward perfusion is weak. (From Sand (1937).)

hear and that some species produce sounds underwater. During whaling operations whales are visibly affected by noises, and hearing may be responsible for the co-ordinated manner in which they surface, and for the way in which scattered schools join up with one another. Porpoises have been observed to respond to artificial noises produced in the water, and supersonic depth-finders will frighten away schools of these animals.

Toothed whales emit a variety of sounds. Dolphins give off shrill whistles (7,000–15,000 c/s) and pulse-modulated creaks with a strong ultrasonic component (up to 170 kc/s), sperm whales have been heard to make sounds, and there is some evidence from underwater recordings that whalebone whales are vocal. Dolphins hear sounds in the frequency range 0·4–153 kc/s, although the sensitivity falls off above 120 kc/s, and there is little doubt that they communicate with each other by sounds (dolphins and porpoises are social animals). They possess good pitch discrimination and make significant use of underwater noises; moreover they utilize high frequency pulses in echolocation (p. 405).

To determine the source of sound involves discrimination of a time interval between the arrival of the propagated sound waves at the two ears; consequently, bone-conduction is excluded. The external auditory meatus is patent in toothed whales, and it is occupied by a horny plate in whalebone whales; and in both types it conducts sound vibrations efficiently along its length. The middle ear is surrounded by foam-filled cavities and the ear-bones are loosely attached to the bones of the skull; consequently, both ears are acoustically isolated and perceive only the sound waves impinging upon their tympanic membranes (51, 52, 59). These arrangements allow sounds in water to be localized. Porpoises can distinguish sound signals (of 6,000 c/s) separated by angles down to 16°. Whales have many fascinating and beautiful adaptations to aquatic life, described in books by Kellogg (78) and Slijper (118).

GRAVITY SENSE

Many organisms orient towards or away from the source of the force of gravity by a form of response termed geotaxis. The specialized gravity receptor for geotaxis is the statocyst. This is a fluid-filled chamber lined by a sensory epithelium bearing hair cells, and containing a solid or semi-solid body known as a statolith (Fig. 8.29). The latter rests on part of the epithelium, or hangs from the wall, and mechanically stimulates the sense cells. Any displacement of the statocyst from its resting position, owing to movement of the animal, alters the pattern and force of stimulation and leads to appropriate adjusting reactions. These cease when the statolith has returned to its original position.

A beautiful experiment demonstrating statocyst functioning was performed by Kreidl over half a century ago. In shrimps the statoliths are lost at each moult and are replaced anew with sand grains from the environment. When iron dust was provided, it became incorporated in the statocysts in place of sand particles. These shrimps now became sensitive to the pull of a magnet: when, for example, a magnet was held above the animal, the pull on the statoliths towards the top of the statocyst caused the animal to turn over on its back.

Statocysts found in scyphomedusae and ctenophores are concerned with orientation reflexes. Medusae have eight statocysts symmetrically arranged around the margin. When the animal is tilted, stimulation of the statocysts causes the musculature of the lowered portion of the umbrella to contract more strongly than the upper portion and the animal soon rights itself. Extirpation of several neighbouring statocysts causes permanent disorientation. Ctenophores have a single apical statocyst which has nervous connexions with the comb rows. The animals are negatively or positively geotactic, swimming vertically upwards or downwards. When a geo-negative animal is tilted, some of the upper rows of cilia cease beating, and the resultant asymmetrical action of the remaining ciliary rows tends to restore the animal to its normal position. When the statocyst is removed, orientation to gravity is lost, and when the statolith is pushed to one side, some of the ciliary combs are inhibited.

Positive geotaxis is shown by many burrowing animals, turbellarians, polychaetes, holothurians, brachiopods, etc. Some of these creatures have

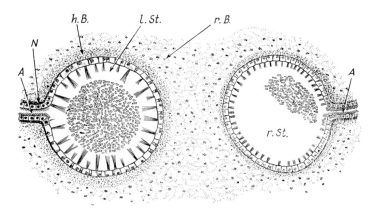

FIG. 8.29. SECTION THROUGH THE STATOCYSTS OF *Pecten inflexus*

l.St., *r.St.*, left and right statocysts; *A*, external duct; *N*, nerve; *h.B.* and *r.B.*, connective tissue. (After von Buddenbrock.)

statocysts, which are responsible for initiating and directing the response. By imposing a centrifugal force it has been possible to change the direction of the geotactic response of *Convoluta roscoffensis*. This animal has a single statocyst and is positively geotactic. When subjected to rotation, the animals deviate from the vertical axis by an angle which is the resultant of the gravitational and centrifugal forces. Two polychaetes, *Arenicola grubei* and *Branchiomma vesiculosum*, which burrow in sand, have statocysts in the head which govern their gravity reactions. *Arenicola* and *Branchiomma* always burrow vertically downward and when the aquarium in which they are placed is turned they make a compensating turn in the direction of burrowing. Removal of both statocysts abolishes the reaction.

Static reactions to turning or tilting are dependent on statocysts in some animals (mysids, decapod crustacea, the heteropod *Pterotrachea*, etc.). In the prawn *Palaemon* the reactions continue normally after extirpation of one of the two statocysts. When the animal is tilted and the statolith is shifted to one side, reflexes causing rotation in one direction begin; and movement of the statolith to the opposite side evokes reflexes in the other direction. Each statocyst possesses a two-way action and is able to control the whole system of righting reflexes.

Electrical recording from the statocyst nerves of decapods (*Homarus*, *Panulirus*, *Loxorhynchus*) reveals continuous and spontaneous discharge of nerve impulses. In the lobster (*Homarus*) four types of statocyst re-

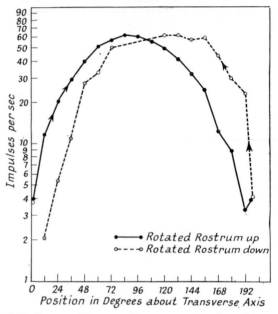

FIG. 8.30. PLOT OF NERVOUS DISCHARGE FROM THE STATOCYST
OF THE LOBSTER (*Homarus americanus*)

Response of a single type I position receptor to continuous rotation in opposite directions about the transverse axis. Read solid curve from left to right; broken curve from right to left. Each point represents average frequency over a 12° interval. (From Cohen (26).)

ceptors have been distinguished. Type I gives a characteristic response for positions maintained about the transverse axis, and serves to detect absolute position (Fig. 8.30). Type II signals static position and movement to and away from a given position. A third type is an accelerator receptor, responding to angular displacement about any axis. Accelerator receptors are spontaneously active at rest: when activated, the response consists of a burst at the onset of rostrum-down, side-down, or contralateral horizontal rotation, followed by depression at the termination of these movements. Other receptors respond to vibration conducted through a solid substrate. When iron filings are introduced into the statocyst and a magnet moved about the organ, discrete bursts of nerve impulses are recorded. The statocyst thus records static positions and is sensitive to angular movement and acceleration. It is not responsive to water-borne vibrations (25, 26, 27, 28).

Gravity responses can occur in the absence of statocysts, e.g. *Paramecium*, *Cerianthus*, blastulae of *Arbacia*, etc. Some animals react to gravity by climbing inclined or vertical surfaces. *Asterina gibbosa* climbs up the wall of an aquarium, but when a large cork float is attached so as to exert a strong upward pull, it moves down. Pull from the weight of the animal on the tube feet appears to direct the movement. Geo-negative responses on vertical surfaces are also shown by various gastropods (16, 50).

The gravity and equilibrium receptors of vertebrates are the utriculus and the semicircular canals (Fig. 8.26). The former responds to linear acceleration and tilting, the latter respond to angular acceleration. The utriculus with its contained otolith resembles a statocyst. For accounts of the functioning of these organs consult Lowenstein (92).

SENSITIVITY TO PRESSURE CHANGES

Bony fishes which possess compressible air-bladders have long been known to respond to pressure changes, but it is only recently that many invertebrates, lacking gas organs, have been found to be pressure sensitive. Some barosensitive species are listed in Table 8.2. When the water pressure is increased, these animals generally become more active and swim upward; when it is decreased, they become less active or inactive, and sink. Other pressure-sensitive animals are mussel larvae, squid and pycnogonids. Ctenophores and fishes respond actively to pressure decrease; these animals are neutrally buoyant, the fish possessing a swim-bladder, and *Pleurobrachia* having a specific gravity nearly equivalent to sea water (Table 9.3).

The animals listed in Table 8.2 include some which have high specific gravities (polychaetes, crustaceans) and which sink rapidly, and others (medusae) which, although of low density, tend to be inactive for long periods. A positive response to raised pressure has biological value to these animals in that it helps them to regulate their depth in the water, and similar behaviour causes the littoral amphipod *Synchelidium* to migrate up and down the shore as the tide floods and ebbs. A reversed (negative) pressure response occurs in *Capnella* and *Nymphon*, a pycnogonid. A reduction of hydrostatic pressure promotes swimming in *Nymphon*; it swims more actively during low water and this helps in dispersing the animal about the shore (60, 83, 102, 111).

Baroreceptors have not been identified in invertebrates. In bony fishes, changes in pressure produce locomotory responses and gaseous secretion or resorption within the air-bladder (p. 399). Suggestions have been made that the air-bladder itself has a sensory function, being sensitive to pressure changes through stimulation of receptors in its walls. Evidence for such

TABLE 8.2

BAROSENSITIVITY IN MARINE ANIMALS

Animal	Minimal change (in millibars) producing a significant response[1]
Hydromedusae	
Phialidium hemisphericum	(800)
Gossea corynetes	(800)
Eutima gracilis	(800)
Ctenophora	
Pleurobrachia pileus	50
Polychaeta	
Larvae *Poecilochaetus serpens*	(800)
Pelagic adults *Autolytus aurantiacus*	(800)
Copepoda	
Caligus rapax	(800)
Isopoda	
Eurydice pulchra	50
Decapoda	
Zoea and megalopa larvae, mostly *Carcinus*	
and *Portunus*	(500)
Megalopa larvae *Carcinus maenas*	10
Corresponding stage of *Galathea*	10
Teleostei	
Larvae of *Blennius pholis*	5
Salmo fario (freshwater)	10

[1] 1 mb = 1 cm water. A bracketed figure indicates that this was the smallest pressure change tested.
Data from Dijkgraaf (43); Hardy and Bainbridge (60); Knight-Jones and Qasim (83).)

a function is inconclusive, and proprioceptors in the body wall or extero-ceptors also may be involved (72).

TASTE AND SMELL

All organisms are sensitive in some degree to chemical changes in their environment, and the senses of smell and taste are utilized in securing food, avoiding injury and escaping from enemies. In general, chemoreception plays an important role in conjunction with other sensory modalities by enlarging the animal's sensory field and increasing its environmental experience.

On the basis of human experience the sense of taste is referred to chemical appreciation of substances in actual contact with the receptors, whereas smell refers to detection of substances at a distance. Taste or gustation, therefore, is concerned with contiguous substances proceeding into solution and thus influencing the taste receptors, whereas smell or olfaction refers to the detection of air-borne particles emanating from a distant source. In the case of aquatic organisms this distinction breaks down, since both taste and smell depend on particles in solution, whatever their source, but it is convenient to retain this distinction between contact chemore-ceptors (taste) and distance chemoreceptors (smell). A further distinction between taste and smell lies in threshold of sensitivity. Taste is concerned with substances in relatively high concentration and shows low sensitivity. The olfactory receptors, on the other hand, are much more sensitive and can detect substances in extremely low concentrations. In addition, animals possess a general chemical sense, dependent upon the general irritability of protoplasm. This general sense detects noxious chemical agents and has low sensitivity.

Chemoreception in Invertebrates. In protozoa and sponges there are no specialized chemoreceptors, and chemosensitivity is a general property of the body surface. Specialized sensory cells for chemoreception have been described in higher metazoans; these may be widely dispersed or localized in distribution. The chemical sensitivity of many marine invertebrates has been investigated, but little is known about the functioning of chemo-receptors in these animals.

Sponges, which lack a nervous system, react to chemical irritants, such as ether and chloroform, by contraction of the osculum. Consequently the flow of water and contained irritant matter through the sponge is reduced. Specialized receptors are absent and the contractile cells respond directly to the irritant substances.

Among coelenterates, sea-anemones and medusae show pronounced responses to meat juices, which represent a normal stimulus for these animals. When meat juices are placed in the vicinity of anemones, they react by expanding the body, opening the mouth and actively waving the tentacles. Discrimination is shown between food and inert substances, the latter usually being rejected. The chemical stimuli emanating from food-stuffs set up prolonged excitation, and the food objects are usually accepted. Chemoreception is localized in the tentacles and oral region, the latter being the more sensitive. Proteins, certain kinds of mucus, and soluble protein derivatives are most effective in producing a feeding-response, whereas starch and sugars are without effect. Again, the isolated oral arms of Scyphomedusae (*Aurelia, Cyanea*) give normal grasping reactions to meat juices, but not to sugars, starch and glycogen (108).

Chemoreception has been little studied in marine annelids. All parts of the body of *Nereis virens* are sensitive to dilute solutions of KOH, HCl and NH_4Cl. Sensitivity is greatest in the palps, less in tentacles and tentacular (peristomial) cirri. This animal also responds to meat juices. Various species of commensal polynoids are attracted by chemical substances given off by their hosts (starfishes, echiuroids, polychaetes) (35, 58).

The chemical senses are well developed in molluscs and are concerned with feeding responses in some species. Osphradia—sensory patches—located near the opening of the mantle cavity in most marine species, respond to tactile and chemical stimuli and test water entering the mantle cavity. Extirpation of the osphradium of carnivorous gastropods results in loss of ability to follow a scent or trail. Taste buds also occur in the buccal cavity of some species. Chemoreceptors of cephalopods occur in pitted papillae lying below the eyes.

The limpet *Patella* responds positively when splashed with sea water, and negatively to fresh water. This behaviour pattern is of value to limpets living high on the shore, where they are exposed by the tide and washed by the rain. Mantle fringes and tentacles are involved in salinity perception (6). Opisthobranchs frequently have special feeding preferences and use olfactory cues. Chemoreceptors are located on the tentacles and in the mouth. The sea hare *Aplysia juliana* feeds on green alga *Enteromorpha*; this gives off something which is highly attractive to the slug, and which initiates feeding responses when dropped into the mouth (54). Sea slugs *Chromodoris* give chemo-positive responses to secretions of other individuals, responses which lead to copulation. The scallop *Pecten* reacts strongly when exposed to juices of the starfish, its natural enemy. *Patella* likewise reacts vigorously to the odour of the carnivorous snail *Murex*. The presence in minute quantities of some factor behaving as a carbohydrate directly affects the pumping rate of oysters (19, 29). The bivalve *Scrobicularia* perceives and reacts to osmotic changes in the medium by keeping its valves closed (53). Stimulus tests reveal that the octopus is sensitive to weak acid, quinine and traces of musk. Chemical sensitivity appears to play but a small part in the life of this animal, however.

Echinoderms (starfish, urchins and cucumbers) are sensitive to food juices and various reagents, applied directly to the body or arising from a distant source. Chemoreception is important in evoking the normal food reactions of the starfish (*Asterias*). Starfish respond to juices of shellfish placed near them; indeed a hungry starfish will follow a piece of meat which is moved about the aquarium. The importance of chemical signals as an indication of prey is also shown by the behaviour of a starfish to small crabs placed on its back. So long as the crabs are uninjured they are carried without concern; but as soon as the crab is injured and its fluids escape, the tube feet reach up and pull the crab towards the starfish's mouth.

In the higher crustacea, at least, most of the body surface shows chemosensitivity. This applies especially to contact chemoreception, mediated by pore organs which consist of sensory buds lying beneath the integument and communicating with the exterior through capillary ducts. Distance chemoreception is most acute in the mouth parts and small antennae. The external ramus of the decapod antennule is provided with basiconical hair organs, variously known as aethetascs, olfactory clubs, etc., and presumably having an olfactory role. Osmoreceptors are believed to occur at the ends of the small antennae in crabs (*Jasus*). Stimulation of this region with dilute sea water (four-fifths to three-quarters full strength) initiates flight reactions. Some threshold values for chemoreception in *Crangon* are: cucumarin, 1 in 500,000; acetic acid and saccharin, 1 in 100. Glycogen is a strong attractant for *Crangon*, and for *Asterias* and *Nassarius*, all of them predators or scavengers (15, 16, 87).

The ciliated pit of ascidians appears to function as a chemoreceptor, sampling the water entering the mouth. It is believed to control feeding and release of gametes. When fed with eggs and sperm of their own species, ascidians respond by releasing gametes. Under this mode of stimulation, the neural gland, containing the ciliated pit, releases gonadotrophin which passes to the neural ganglion; the latter, being excited, then activates the gonads by nervous pathways to release gametes (23).

Fishes. In lower vertebrates the chemical senses are important receptor avenues in determining various aspects of behaviour. Well-defined chemoreceptors for smell and taste are present and, in addition, exposed mucous and external surfaces possess a diffuse chemical sense mediated by free nerve endings (Fig. 8.1).

The olfactory receptor cells of fishes are localized in an olfactory epithelium lying in nasal pits. Cyclostomes have a single olfactory aperture; fishes bear a pair of olfactory pits. In elasmobranchs the olfactory pits lie on the ventral surface of the snout, and sometimes open into the mouth. In teleosts the pits lie on the upper or lateral surface of the head and the aperture into each pit is usually divided by a skin fold into an anterior and posterior opening. Water passes through the olfactory pit from the anterior to the posterior opening (Fig. 8.31).

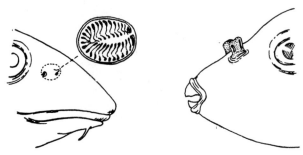

FIG. 8.31. OLFACTORY ORGANS OF TELEOSTS
(*Left*) cod *Gadus callarias*; view of the interior, showing folds. (*Right*) tentacular type of olfactory organ of *Tetraodon pardalis*. (After Bolk *et al.*, 1934.)

Peculiarities of organization are encountered in some species: in the hammerhead shark the olfactory pits are widely separated; in many teleosts each olfactory organ is prolonged posteriorly into a saccular structure; and in the Chinese sole (*Cynoglossus semilaevis*) the two sacs unite over the roof of the mouth. A naso-vomerine organ (Jacobson's organ), located in the nasal septum of some fishes, functions as an accessory olfactory structure.

The olfactory epithelium is made up of columnar supporting cells, among which occur the olfactory receptors (Fig. 8.32). These are bipolar neurones, bearing an elongated hair-like structure (the dendrite) which extends to the free surface, and giving off an axon proximally to the olfactory nerve. The distal hairs are stimulated by chemical substances, and the sensory cells originate impulses which proceed along the olfactory nerve fibres to the olfactory lobes of the brain. Free nerve endings of the trigeminal nerve are also present in the olfactory epithelium and are concerned with the general chemical sense. Allison (5) has presented an extensive review of the olfactory system of vertebrates.

Taste receptors occur in the mouth and elsewhere in fishes. In teleosts they may be widely distributed, occurring in the buccal cavity, pharynx, lips, fins, barbels or over much of the external surface. The taste organs consist of groups of sensory cells bearing terminal sensory hairs (Fig. 8.1, end knobs). Proximally they make contact with sensory fibres derived

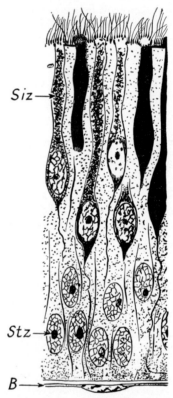

FIG. 8.32. OLFACTORY EPITHELIUM OF *Petromyzon*
(after Ballowitz and Plate.)
Siz, sense cells; *Stz*, supporting cells; *B*, boundary of subepithelial blood space.

from the VIIth, IXth and Xth cranial nerves and the ramus lateralis accessorius of the facialis.

The senses of taste and smell in fishes provide cues for recognizing and locating food, initiating avoiding reactions, for orientation, etc. Extra-oral taste buds are used for detecting food material in close proximity. Tom cod and hake have taste buds in the ventral fins, which are chemically sensitive to animal food lying on the bottom. The rockling (*Onos*) has taste buds associated with the dorsal fin as well, and when food material is applied locally to that area, it turns around preparatory to seizing it. Small action-potentials in facial fibres of the catfish have been detected after chemical stimulation of taste buds in lips and barbel with acids and meat juices. Gurnards (*Prionotus*, etc.) respond positively when meat extracts are applied locally to the free ventral fin rays. Taste buds are lacking here, and the chemical stimulus appears to be detected by nerve fibres ending in peripheral knobs. The epidermis of fish also contains elongate sensory cells, which may be concerned with the general chemical sense (116, 136).

More distant sources of food may be detected by the odours they give off. Lampreys are stimulated into locomotory activity by the body odour of trout, the stimulants in the odour being certain amines. This response of the lamprey is innate (81). Dogfish locate food largely through the sense of smell. Blennies (*Blennius*) have been conditioned to food stimuli and respond to meat extracts (nereids, limpets, mussels) in concentrations of 0·01%. The tuna (*Euthynnus*) is attracted by extracts of tuna flesh, the attractive substance residing in the protein fraction. These fish are not responsive to water which has contained food fish. Dogfish and teleosts cease to respond to hidden food when the nostrils are plugged or the olfactory nerves severed (18, 100, 132).

The role of smell in orientation is indicated by conditioned responses to naturally occurring environmental odours. Salmon can detect stream odours and discriminate between then, an ability which may be of value during migration. Pond minnows (*Hyborhynchus*) are able to discriminate between the odours of different aquatic plants (128).

In behaviour studies involving conditioning, Bull (18) has demonstrated that many species of marine teleosts are able to detect very small changes in acidity and salinity. Positive conditioned responses were obtained in many species to changes of pH 0·1 or more, and most fish could detect a change of pH 0·04–0·06. Salinity changes of the order of 0·06‰ to 0.45‰ were detected; cod, whiting, plaice and flounder distinguished a salinity difference of 0·2‰. The sensory avenues by which these changes are perceived are unknown (14).

Nervous discharges have been recorded from the olfactory stalks of various fish (catfish, tench, etc.) Many different substances produce an olfactory discharge, including meat extracts, proteins and starch. When a drop of stimulation fluid is placed in the olfactory sac there is an appreciable latency before discharge begins (0·5–5 sec), after which the response rises rapidly to a maximum and then declines more slowly (adaptation of olfactory system). Following stimulation producing much discharge there is a period of inactivity lasting 5–20 sec, during which period the olfactory organ is insensitive to a second stimulus. The olfactory organs respond to mechanical as well as chemical stimuli, and chemical stimulation is most effective when the fluid contains solid matter in suspension.

The entire integument plus mucous membranes possess chemical sen-

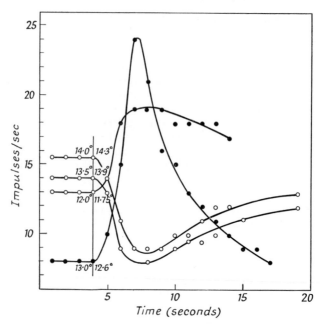

FIG. 8.33. RESPONSES OF A SINGLE LORENZINIAN AMPULLA TO
TEMPERATURE CHANGES OF $< 0.5°C$ (*Raja*)

Spike frequency recorded from branch of hyomandibular nerve, plotted against time. The vertical line, at 4 sec, marks onset of temperature change. Initial and final temperatures are marked on either side of this line; final temperature is attained at a point 3–5 sec to the right of the line. (From Sand (113).)

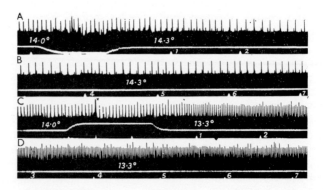

FIG. 8.34. ACTION POTENTIALS RECORDED FROM A BRANCH OF THE HYOMANDI-
BULAR NERVE OF *Raja*, SHOWING EFFECTS OF COOLING AND WARMING AN
AMPULLA OF LORENZINI

The white line below base line marks change in temperature: upward displacement, cooling; downward displacement, warming. Time signal in seconds. (From Sand (113).)

sitivity, mediated through the general chemical sense. The skin of the dogfish *Mustelus* is sensitive to acids and alkalis, less so to salts and bitter substances. Recent studies have been concerned with chemical irritants, acting through the general chemical sense, capable of repelling fish. Some threshold values (parts per million) for teleost irritants are: phenacyl bromide, 0·01; potassium cyanide, 0·1; chlorine, 1·0. Substances repellent to sharks are not necessarily effective against teleosts (67, 68).

THERMAL SENSITIVITY

Environmental temperature affects most body activities in poikilotherms. Upper and lower limiting temperatures for activity have been established for many species, and the effect determined of temperature on various processes. Extremes of temperature have a general stimulatory action on behaviour; very low temperatures produce anaesthesia, and high temperatures abnormal muscular contractions. The present problem, however, is one of thermoreception. In a temperature-gradient *Paramecia* tend to aggregate at some optimal temperature by trial and error movements (namely thermokinesis). Sudden thermal changes elicit either shock reactions or modify the rate of movement. Zoea larvae of crustaceans, for example, dart backwards when the water temperature is raised rapidly. The capacity to discriminate thermal differences is low in most marine invertebrates, and few instances of specialized thermoreceptors have been recorded.

Perception of Temperature Changes in Fishes. The ampullae of Lorenzini, found in elasmobranchs and a few teleosts, are scattered over the head of the fish. Each ampulla contains pyriform sensory cells and communicates with the exterior by an ampullary tube filled with jelly. The sense cells are innervated by the facial nerve. The ampullae exhibit a number of generalized responses to various stimuli including temperature changes (Figs. 8.33 and 8.34) and weak electrical stimuli. The latter presumably cause currents to flow along the jelly-filled tubes of the sense organs. Thermoreception is now considered unlikely, and there is as yet no evidence to show that they are actually used as electrical receptors (p. 392) (45).

Earlier behavioural studies indicated that teleosts can discriminate temperature differences of around 0·1–1°C. Employing conditioned reflexes Bull (18) determined sensitivity to thermal changes in marine teleosts. Many species were found to respond to temperature increases of 0·03–0·10°C in the surrounding water. Species responding to an increment of 0·03°C, the smallest change investigated, were *Gadus merlangus*, *Onos mustelus*, *Zoarces viviparus* and *Liparis montagui*.

REFERENCES

1. ALEXANDROWICZ, J. S., "Muscle receptor organs in the Paguridae," *J. Mar. Biol. Ass. U.K.*, **31**, 277 (1952).

2. ALEXANDROWICZ, J. S., "Notes on the nervous system in the Stomatopoda. 4. Muscle receptor organs," *Pubbl. Staz. Zool. Napoli*, **25**, 94 (1954).

3. ALEXANDROWICZ, J. S., "Receptor elements in the muscles of *Leander serratus*," *J. Mar. Biol. Ass. U.K.*, **35**, 129 (1956).

4. ALEXANDROWICZ, J. S. and WHITEAR, M., "Receptor elements in the coxal region of decapoda crustacea," ibid., **36**, 603 (1957).

5. ALLISON, A. C., "The morphology of the olfactory system in the vertebrates," *Biol. Rev.*, **28**, 195 (1953).

6. ARNOLD, D. C., "The response of the limpet, *Patella vulgata*, to waters of different salinities," *J. Mar. Biol. Ass. U.K.*, **36**, 121 (1957).

7. BAINBRIDGE, R. and WATERMAN, T. H., "Polarized light and the orientation of two marine crustacea," *J. Exp. Biol.*, **34**, 342 (1957).

8. BEHRENS, M. E. and WULFF, V. J., "Light-initiated responses of retinula and eccentric cells in the *Limulus* lateral eye," *J. Gen. Physiol.*, **48**, 1081 (1965).

9. BROWN, F. A. JR., "Hormones in crustaceans," in Vol. I, *The Hormones*, ed. Pincus, G. and Thimann, K. V. (New York, Academic Press, 1948).

10. BROWN, F. A. JR., "Endocrine mechanisms," in *Comparative Animal Physiology*, ed. Prosser, C. L. (London, Saunders, 1950).

11. BROWN, F. A. JR., FINGERMAN, M. and HINES, M.N., "Alterations in the capacity for light and dark adaptation of the distal retinal pigment of *Palaemonetes*," *Physiol. Zoöl.*, **25**, 230 (1952).

12. BROWN, F. A. JR., HINES, M. N. and FINGERMAN, M., "Hormonal regulation of the distal retinal pigment of *Palaemonetes*," *Biol. Bull.*, **102**, 212 (1952).

13. BROWN, F. A. JR., WEBB, H. M. and SANDEEN, M. I., "Differential production of two retinal pigment hormones in *Palaemonetes* by light flashes," *J. Cell. Comp. Physiol.*, **41**, 123 (1953).

14. BROWN, M. E. (Ed.), *The Physiology of Fishes*, Vol. II (New York, Academic Press, 1957).

15. BUDDENBROCK, W. VON, "Physiologie der Decapoden," in Bronn's *Klassen u. Ordn. Tierreichs*, Vol. V, 1 Abt., 7 Buch, p. 863 (Leipzig, 1945).

16. BUDDENBROCK, W. VON, *Vergleichende Physiologie*, Bd. I, *Sinnesphysiologie* (Basel, Verlag Birkhäuser, 1952).

17. BUDDENBROCK, W. VON and MOLLER-RACKE, I., "Über den Lichtsinn von Pecten," *Pubbl. Staz. Zool. Napoli*, **24**, 217 (1953).

18. BULL, H. O., "An evaluation of our knowledge of fish behaviour in relation to hydrography," *Rapp. Cons. Explor. Mer*, **131**, 8 (1952).

19. BULLOCK, T. H., "Predator recognition and escape responses of some intertidal gastropods in presence of starfish," *Behaviour*, **5**, 130 (1953).

20. BULLOCK, T. H. and HORRIDGE, G. A., *Structure and Function in the Nervous Systems of Invertebrates*, Vol. 2 (San Francisco and London, W. H. Freeman and Co., 1965).

21. BURKE, W., "An organ for proprioception and vibration sense in *Carcinus maenas*," *J. Exp. Biol.*, **31**, 127 (1954).

22. BUSH, B. M. H., "Leg reflexes from chordotonal organs in the crab," *J. Exp. Biol.*, **15**, 567 (1965).

23. CARLISLE, D. B., "On the hormonal and neural control of the release of gametes in ascidians," ibid., **28**, 463 (1951).

24. CLARKE, G. L. and DENTON, E. J., "Light and animal life," *The Sea*, Ed.

Hill, M. N., Vol. 1, p. 456 (New York, London, Interscience Publishers, 1962).

25. COHEN, M. J., "Oscillographic analysis of an invertebrate equilibrium organ," *Biol. Bull.*, **105**, 363 (Abstr.) (1953).

26. COHEN, M. J., "The function of receptors in the statocyst of the lobster *Homarus americanus*," *J. Physiol.*, **130**, 9 (1955).

27. COHEN, M. J. and DIJKGRAAF, S., "Mechanoreception," *The Physiology of Crustacea*, Ed. Waterman, T. H., Vol. 2, p. 65 (New York, London, Academic Press, 1961).

28. COHEN, M. J., KATSUKI, Y. and BULLOCK, T. H., "Oscillographic analysis of equilibrium receptors in Crustacea," *Experientia*, **9**, 434 (1953).

29. COLLIER, A., RAY, S. M., MAGNITZKY, A. W. and BELL, J. O., "Effect of dissolved organic substances on oysters," *Fish. Bull. U.S.*, **54**, 167 (1953).

30. CRESCITELLI, F., "The nature of the lamprey visual pigment," *J. Gen. Physiol.*, **39**, 423 (1956).

31. CRESCITELLI, F. and DARTNALL, H. J. A., "A photosensitive pigment of the carp retina," *J. Physiol.*, **125**, 607 (1954).

32. CUSHING, D. H., "The vertical migration of planktonic crustacea," *Biol. Rev.*, **26**, 158 (1951).

33. DARTNALL, H. J. A., "Visual pigments of the bleak (*Alburnus lucidus*)," *J. Physiol.*, **128**, 131 (1955).

34. DAUMER, K., JANDER, R. and WATERMAN, T. H., "Orientation of the ghost crab *Ocypode* in polarized light," *Z. vergl. Physiol.*, **47**, 56 (1963).

35. DAVENPORT, D., "Specificity and behavior in symbioses," *Quart. Rev. Biol.*, **30**, 29 (1955).

36. DEBAISIEUX, P., "Les yeux de Crustacés." *La Cellule*, **50**, 7 (1944).

37. DENTON, E. J., "Recherches sur l'absorption de la lumière par le cristallin des Poissons," *Bull. Inst. Océanogr. Monaco*, No. 1071 (1956).

38. DENTON, E. J. and NICOL, J. A. C., "The chorioidal tapeta of some cartilaginous fishes," *J. Mar. Biol. Ass.*, **44**, 219 (1964).

39. DENTON, E. J. and SHAW, T. I., "The visual pigments of some deep-sea elasmobranchs," *J. Mar. Biol. Ass. U.K.*, **43**, 65 (1963).

40. DENTON, E. J. and WALKER, M. A., "The visual pigment of the conger eel," *Proc. Roy. Soc. B.*, **148**, 257 (1957).

41. DENTON, E. J. and WARREN, F. J., "The photosensitive pigments in the retinae of deep-sea fish," *J. Mar. Biol. Ass. U.K.*, **36**, 651 (1957).

42. DETWILER, S. R., *Vertebrate Photoreceptors* (New York, Macmillan, 1943).

43. DIJKGRAAF, S., "Über Druckwahrnehmung bei Fischen," *Z. vergl. Physiol.*, **30**, 39 (1942).

44. DIJKGRAAF, S., "Untersuchungen über die Funktionen des Ohrlabyrinths bei Meeresfischen," *Physiol. Comp. Oecol.*, **2**, 81 (1950).

45. DIJKGRAAF, S., "The functioning and significance of the lateral-line organs," *Biol. Rev.*, **38**, 51 (1963).

46. EYZAGUIRRE, C. and KUFFLER, S. W., "Processes of excitation in the dendrites and in the soma of single isolated sensory nerve cells of the lobster and crayfish," *J. Gen. Physiol.*, **39**, 87 (1955).

47. EYZAGUIRRE, C. and KUFFLER, S. W., "Further study of soma, dendrite, and axon excitation in single neurons," ibid., **39**, 121 (1955).

48. FESSARD, A. and SAND, A., "Stretch receptors in the muscles of fishes," *J. Exp. Biol.*, **14**, 383 (1937).

49. FLOREY, E. and FLOREY, E., "Microanatomy of the abdominal stretch receptors of the crayfish," *J. Gen. Physiol.*, **39**, 69 (1955).
50. FRAENKEL, G. S. and GUNN, D. L., *The Orientation of Animals* (Oxford, Clarendon Press, 1940).
51. FRASER, F. C. and PURVES, P. E., "Hearing in cetaceans," *Bull. Brit. Mus. (Nat. Hist.) Zool.*, **2**, 103 (1954).
52. FRASER, F. C. and PURVES, P. E., "Hearing in cetaceans," *Bull. Brit. Mus. (Nat. Hist.)*, **7**, No. 1 (1960).
53. FREEMAN, R. F. H. and RIGLER, F. H., "The responses of *Scrobicularia plana* to osmotic pressure changes," *J. Mar. Biol. Ass. U.K.*, **36**, 553 (1957).
54. FRINGS, H. and Frings, C., "Chemosensory bases of food-finding and feeding in *Aplysia*," *Biol. Bull.*, **128**, 211 (1965).
55. FUORTES, M. G. F. and POGGIO, G. F., "Transient responses to sudden illumination in cells of the eye of *Limulus*," *J. Gen. Physiol.*, **46**, 435 (1963).
56. GRANIT, R., *Sensory Mechanisms of the Retina* (Oxford Univ. Press, 1947).
57. GRANIT, R., *Receptor and Sensory Perception* (Yale Univ. Press, 1955).
58. GROSS, A. O., "The feeding habits and chemical sense of *Nereis virens*," *J. Exp. Zool.*, **32**, 427 (1921).
59. GUNTHER, E. R., "The habits of fin whales," *'Discovery' Rep.*, **25**, 113 (1949).
60. HARDY, A. C. and BAINBRIDGE, R., "Effect of pressure on the behaviour of decapod larvae (Crustacea)," *Nature*, **167**, 354 (1951).
61. HARRIS, J. E. and MASON, P., "Vertical migration in eyeless *Daphnia*," *Proc. Roy. Soc. B.*, **145**, 280 (1956).
62. HARRIS, J. E. and WOLFE, U. K., "A laboratory study of vertical migration," ibid., **144**, 329 (1955).
63. HARTLINE, H. K. and McDONALD, P. R., "Light and dark adaptation of single photoreceptor elements in the eye of *Limulus*," *J. Cell. Comp. Physiol.*, **30**, 225 (1947).
64. HARTLINE, H. K., WAGNER, H. G. and MacNICHOL., E. F. JR., "The peripheral origin of nervous activity in the visual system," *Cold Spr. Harb. Symp. Quant. Biol.*, **17**, 125 (1952).
65. HENKES, H. E., "Retinomotor and diurnal rhythm in crustaceans," *J. Exp. Biol.*, **29**, 178 (1952).
66. HERTER, K., *Die Fischdressuren und ihre sinnesphysiologischen Grundlagen* (Berlin, Akad.-Verlag, 1953).
67. HIATT, R. W., NAUGHTON, J. J. and MATTHEWS, D. C., "Relation of chemical structure to irritant responses in marine fish," *Nature*, **172**, 904 (1953).
68. HIATT, R. W., NAUGHTON, J. J. and MATTHEWS, D. C., "Effects of chemicals on a schooling fish, *Kuhlia sandvicensis*," *Biol. Bull.*, **104**, 28 (1953).
69. HUBBARD, R. and ST. GEORGE, R. C. C., "The rhodopsin system of the squid," *J. Gen. Physiol.*, **41**, 501 (1958).
70. JANDER, R., DAUMER, K. and WATERMAN, T. H., "Polarized light orientation by two Hawaiian decapod cephalopods," *Z. vergl. Physiol.*, **46**, 383 (1963).
71. JIELOF, R., SPOOR, A. and VRIES, H. DE, "The microphonic activity of the lateral line," *J. Physiol.*, **116**, 137 (1952).
72. JONES, F. R. H. and MARSHALL, N. B., "The structure and functions of the teleostean swimbladder," *Biol. Rev.*, **28**, 16 (1953).
73. JOSEPHSON, R. K., "The response of a hydroid to weak water-borne disturbances," *J. Exp. Biol.*, **28**, 17 (1961).

74. KAMPA, E. M., "New forms of visual purple from the retinas of certain marine fishes: a re-examination," *J. Physiol.*, **119**, 400 (1953).
75. KAMPA, E. M., "Euphausiopsin, a new photosensitive pigment from the eyes of euphausiid crustaceans," *Nature*, **175**, 996 (1955).
76. KAMPA, E. M., ABBOTT, B. C. and BODEN, B. P., "Some aspects of vision in the lobster," *J. Mar. Biol. Ass. U.K.*, **43**, 683 (1963).
77. KATSUKI, Y., YOSHINO, S. and CHEN, J., "Neural mechanism of the lateral-line organ of fish," *Jap. J. Physiol.*, **1**, 264 (1951).
78. KELLOGG, W. N., *Porpoises and Sonar* (Univ. Chicago Press, 1961).
79. KENNEDY, D., "Neural photoreception in a lamellibranch mollusc," *J. Gen. Physiol.*, **44**, 277 (1960).
80. KENNEDY, D. and BRUNO, M. S., "The spectral sensitivity of crayfish and lobster vision," *J. Gen. Physiol.*, **44**, 1089 (1961).
81. KLEEREKOPER, H. and MOGENSEN, J., "Role of olfaction in the orientation of *Petromyzon*," *Physiol. Zool.*, **36**, 347 (1963).
82. KNIGHT-JONES, E. W., "On the nervous system of *Saccoglossus cambrensis*," *Phil. Trans. B.*, **236**, 315 (1952).
83. KNIGHT-JONES, E. W. and QASIM, S. Z., "Responses of some marine plankton animals to changes in hydrostatic pressure," *Nature*, **175**, 941 (1955).
84. KNOWLES, F. G. W., "The problems of the number [of] hormones concerned in the pigment movements of crustaceans," *Bull. Biol.* (Suppl.), **33**, 149 (1948).
85. KNOWLES, F. G. W., "The control of retinal pigment migration in *Leander serratus*," *Biol. Bull.*, **98**, 66 (1950).
86. KNOWLES, SIR FRANCIS G. W., Bt. and CARLISLE, D. B., "Endocrine control in the Crustacea," *Biol. Rev.*, **31**, 396 (1956).
87. KRIJGSMAN, B. J. and KRIJGSMAN, N. E., "Osmorezeption in *Jasus lalandii*," *Z. vergl. Physiol.*, **37**, 78 (1954).
88. KUFFLER, S. W., "Mechanisms of activation and motor control of stretch receptors in lobster and crayfish," *J. Neurophysiol.*, **17**, 558 (1954).
89. KUFFLER, S. W. and EYZAGUIRRE, C., "Synaptic inhibition in an isolated nerve cell," *J. Gen. Physiol.*, **39**, 155 (1955).
90. LAVERACK, M. S., "Responses of cuticular sensory organs of the lobster," *Comp. Biochem. Physiol.*, **5**, 319 (1962) and **10**, 261 (1963).
91. LISSMANN, H. W., "The neurological basis of the locomotory rhythm in the spinal dogfish," *J. Exp. Biol.*, **23**, 143 and 162 (1946).
92. LOWENSTEIN, O., "Labyrinth and equilibrium," *Symp. Soc. Exp. Biol.*, **4**, 60 (1950).
93. LOWENSTEIN, O., "Pressure receptors in the fins of the dogfish *Scylliorhinus canicula*," *J. Exp. Biol.*, **33**, 417 (1956).
94. LOWENSTEIN, O. and ROBERTS, T. D. M., "The localization and analysis of the responses to vibration from the isolated elasmobranch labyrinth," *J. Physiol.*, **114**, 471 (1951).
95. MARSHALL, N. B., *Aspects of Deep Sea Biology* (London, Hutchinson, 1954).
96. MATTHEWS, D. J., *Tables of the Velocity of Sound in Pure Water and Sea Water* (London, Hydrographic Dept., Admiralty, 1939).
97. MENDELSON, M. "Some factors in the activation of crab movement receptors," *J. Exp. Biol.*, **40**, 157 (1963).
98. MILLOTT, N., "Sensitivity to light, etc., of the echinoid *Diadema*," *Phil. Trans. B.*, **238**, 187 (1954).

99. MILLOTT, N. and YOSHIDA, M., "The spectral sensitivity of the echinoid *Diadema antillarum*," *J. Exp. Biol.*, **34**, 394 (1957).

100. MONCRIEFF, R. W., *The Chemical Senses* (London, Leonard Hill, 1951).

101. MOODY, M. F., "Photoreceptor organelles in animals," *Biol. Rev.*, **39**, 43 (1964).

102. MORGAN, E., NELSON-SMITH, A. and KNIGHT-JONES, E. W., "Responses of *Nymphon gracile* (Pycnogonida) to pressure cycles of tidal frequency," *J. Exp. Biol.*, **41**, 825 (1964).

103. NAGANO, T., "Physiological studies on the pigmentary system of Crustacea. 2. The pigment migration in the eyes of the shrimps," *Sci. Rept. Tôhoku Univ.*, Ser. 4, **18**, 65 (1947).

104. NAGANO, T., "Physiological studies on the pigmentary system of Crustacea. 4. Studies on the diurnal rhythm of the eye pigments of the shrimps," ibid., Ser. 4, **18**, 286 (1950).

105. NEWELL, G. E., "An experimental analysis of the behaviour of *Littorina littorea* (L.) under natural conditions and in the laboratory," *J. Mar. Biol. Ass. U.K.*, **37**, 241 (1958).

106. NEWTH, D. R. and ROSS, D. M., "On the reaction to light of *Myxine glutinosa*," *J. Exp. Biol.*, **32**, 4 (1955).

107. NICOL, J. A. C., "Migration of chorioidal tapetal pigment in the spur dog *Squalus*," *J. Mar. Biol. Ass. U.K.*, **45**, 405 (1965).

108. PANTIN, C. F. A. and PANTIN, A. M. P., "The stimulus to feeding in *Anemonia sulcata*," *J. Exp. Biol.*, **20**, 6 (1943).

109. PASSANO, L. M. and PANTIN, C. F. A., "Mechanical stimulation in the sea-anemone *Calliactis parasitica*," *Proc. Roy. Soc. B.*, **143**, 226 (1955).

110. PILGRIM, R. L. C., "Stretch receptor organs in *Squilla mantis*," *J. Exp. Biol.*, **41**, 793 (1964).

111. RICE, A. L., "Observations on the effects of changes of hydrostatic pressure on the behaviour of some marine animals," *J. Mar. Biol. Ass. U.K.*, **44**, 163 (1964).

112. RUCK, P. and JAHN, T. L., "Electrical studies on the compound eye of *Ligia occidentalis*," *J. Gen. Physiol.*, **37**, 825 (1954).

113. SAND, A., "The function of the ampullae of Lorenzini, with some observations on the effect of temperature on sensory rhythms," *Proc. Roy. Soc. B*, **125**, 524 (1938).

114. SAND, A., "The mechanism of acustico-lateral sense organs in fishes, with special reference to problems in the physiology of semicircular canals," *Proc. Roy. Soc. Med.*, **33**, 741 (Otology) (1940).

115. SANDEEN, M. I. and BROWN, F. A. JR., "Responses of the distal retinal pigment of *Palaemonetes* to illumination," *Physiol. Zoöl.*, **25**, 222 (1952).

116. SCHARRER, E., SMITH, S. W. and PALAY, S. L., "Chemical sense and taste in the fishes, *Prionotus* and *Trichogaster*," *J. Comp. Neurol.*, **86**, 183 (1947).

117. SEELIGER, H. H., "Direct action of light in naturally pigmented muscle fibers. I. Eel iris," *J. Gen. Physiol.*, **46**, 333 (1962).

118. SLIJPER, E. J., *Whales* (London, Hutchison, 1962).

119. SMITH, R. I., "The role of the sinus glands in the retinal pigment migration in grapsoid crabs," *Biol. Bull.*, **95**, 169 (1948).

120. STEVEN, D. M., "Experiments on the light sense of the hag, *Myxine glutinosa*," *J. Exp. Biol.*, **32**, 22 (1955).

121. SUCKLING, E. E. and SUCKLING, J. A., "The electrical response of the

lateral line system of fish to tone and other stimuli," *J. Gen. Physiol.*, **34**, 1 (1950).

122. SVERDRUP, H. U., JOHNSON, M. W. and FLEMING, R. H., *The Oceans: Their Physics, Chemistry, and General Biology* (New York, Prentice-Hall, 1946).

123. TANSLEY, K., "Vision," *Symp. Soc. Exp. Biol.*, **4**, 19 (1950).

124. TAVOLGA, W. N., Ed., *Marine Bio-acoustics* (Oxford, London, Pergamon Press, 1964).

125. WALD, G., "The chemical evolution of vision," Harvey Lectures 1945-6, Ser. 41, p. 117 (1946).

126. WALD, G., BROWN, P. K. and SMITH, P. H., "Iodopsin," *J. Gen. Physiol.*, **38**, 623 (1955).

127. WALD, G. and HUBBARD, G., "Visual pigment of a decapod crustacean: the lobster," *Nature*, **180**, 278 (1957).

128. WALKER, T. J. and HASLER, A. D., "Detection and discrimination of odors of aquatic plants by the bluntnose minnow (*Hyborhynchus notatus*)," *Physiol. Zool.*, **22**, 45 (1949).

129. WALLS, G. L., *The Vertebrate Eye and its Adaptive Radiation*, Bull. No. 19, Cranbrook Inst. Sci. Michigan (1942).

130. WATERMAN, T. H., "Polarized light and angle of stimulus incidence in the compound eye of *Limulus*," *Proc. Nat. Acad. Sci.*, **40**, 258 (1954).

131. WEBB, H. M. and BROWN, F. A. JR., "Diurnal rhythm in the regulation of distal retinal pigment in *Palaemonetes*," *J. Cell. Comp. Physiol.*, **41**, 103 (1953).

132. WEEL, P. B. VAN, "Observations on the chemoreception of tuna," *Spec. Sci. Rep. U.S. Fish Wildl. Serv.*, Fisheries No. 91, Part 2 (1952).

133. WELSH, J. H., "Diurnal rhythms," *Quart. Rev. Biol.*, **13**, 123 (1938).

134. WELSH, J. H. and CHACE, F. A. JR., "Eyes of deep sea crustaceans. 1. Acanthephyridae," *Biol. Bull.*, **72**, 57 (1937).

135. WELSH, J. H. and CHACE, F. A. JR., "Eyes of deep-sea crustaceans. 2. Sergestidae," ibid., **74**, 364 (1938).

136. WHITEAR, M., "The innervation of the skin of teleost fishes," *Quart. J. Micr. Sci.*, **93**, 289 (1952).

137. WHITEAR, M., "The fine structure of crustacean proprioceptors. Chordotonal organs of the shore crab," *Phil. Trans.*, B, **245**, 291 (1962).

138. WIERSMA, C. A. G., FURSHPAN, E. and FLOREY, E., "Physiological and pharmacological observations on muscle receptor organs of the crayfish," *J. Exp. Biol.*, **30**, 136 (1953).

139. WILLIAMSON, D. I., "Studies in the biology of Talitridae: visual orientation in *Talitrus saltator*," *J. Mar. Biol. Ass. U.K.*, **30**, 91 (1951).

140. WULFF, V. J., "Physiology of the compound eye," *Physiol. Rev.*, **36**, 145 (1956).

141. WYSE, G. A. and MAYNARD, D. M., "Joint receptors in the antennule of *Panulirus*," *J. Exp. Biol.*, **42**, 521 (1965).

142. ZOTTERMAN, Y., "The microphonic effect of teleost labyrinths and its biological significance," *J. Physiol.*, **102**, 313 (1943).

CHAPTER 9

EFFECTOR MECHANISMS

Protoplasm, the agent of organic creation, not only possesses the power of chemical synthesis which we have previously examined, but furthermore, exhibits for the purpose of setting such power in play, the faculty of being "irritable," and consequently through its irritability the power of motion. It can, in fact, react by contracting under the action of external excitants.

> CLAUDE BERNARD, 1878. *Leçons sur les Phénomènes de la Vie, communs aux Animaux et aux Végétaux*. Trans. C. M. STERN.

THE effector structures of the body have two general functions. The first and more obvious is that of carrying out the various actions by which the animal responds to changes in its environment. The other lies in the performance of numerous internal acts concerned with furthering the vegetative functions. The structures responsible for these activities are: contractile cells and muscles; amoeboid, ciliated and flagellated cells; trichocysts and nematocysts; electric organs; exocrine glands; sound-producing organs; chromatophores; and diverse luminescent structures.

Movements of the animal are produced by muscles, amoeboid activity or by the beating of cilia and flagella. These structures are also employed in various vegetative functions, in respiration, digestion and excretion. Some effectors are continuously active throughout the life of the animal, e.g. the cilia of many metazoans. Others show discontinuous activity, regulated and controlled by co-ordinating systems. Many effectors are simple structures, consisting of a single kind of tissue—ciliated cell, muscle fibre, etc. Others are complex structures, the functioning of which involves the interaction of several kinds of tissues, e.g. complex chromatophores and luminous organs of cephalopods. Chromatophores and luminescent organs are described in following chapters, and glands in conjunction with the organs they subserve.

CILIA AND FLAGELLA

These are small vibratile structures located at cell surfaces and performing mechanical work by rapid oscillatory movements. They occur in most groups of animals with the exception of nematodes and typical arthropods. Flagella are elongate threads found on flagellates, choanocytes of sponges, the endoderm of coelenterates and on nephridial flame cells and spermatozoa of higher forms. Flagella occur singly or sparsely on each cell. When a cell bears numerous short vibratile organelles these are referred to as cilia. Cilia cover part or all of the external surface of infusorians, coelenterates, ctenophores, turbellarians, nemertines, small annelids and urochordates. In higher groups ciliated epithelia may occur in more restricted tracts on the external surface as well as lining various internal cavities and tubes.

Cilia function only in an aqueous medium, either by beating against the surrounding medium when they are situated externally, or by propelling internal fluids. Despite their minute dimensions (rarely exceeding 15 μ in length), by their conjoint efforts they perform a remarkable variety of functions with great efficiency. In small organisms they are the sole or principal means of locomotion. Other functions which they subserve, described on other pages, include respiration, collection and transport of food particles, movement of digestive fluids, circulation of body fluids, removal of waste materials and propulsion of genital products. Among sedentary invertebrates the activity of cilia in creating feeding currents is particularly noteworthy (*vide* Chapter 5). The volumes of water pumped by such mechanisms are indicated in Tables 4.5 and 4.6 (p. 167).

Structure of Cilia

With few exceptions the structure of cilia and flagella is remarkably uniform throughout the animal kingdom. Cilia of living cells are optically homogeneous. When examined with polarized light they show positive form and intrinsic birefringence, indicating the presence of longitudinal protein fibres. The filament arises from a small basal granule, which is believed to be derived from the centrosome. In ciliated epithelial cells an intracellular system of fibrils (rootlets) extends from the basal granules into the distal cytoplasm towards the nucleus, and horizontal fibrils link the basal granules together.

Following treatment with osmic acid, the flagellum or cilium separates into a bunch of unbranched fibrils. Recent studies with the electron microscope reveal that the number of fibrils is remarkably constant, there being nine strands spaced peripherally and two single strands lying centrally in the cilium or flagellum (9 + 2 structure). The cilium is invested by a membrane continuous basally with the cell membrane. The basic apparatus common to all cilia and flagella comprises these eleven fibrillae plus their basal granules (together with matrix and envelope), and it is this system that is responsible for movement. One explanation for ciliary movement postulates the following mechanism: the nine outer fibrils are contractile, whereas the central pair is specialized for conduction. Rhythmical impulses arising at one point in the basal body circulate around it, producing propagated localized contractions in each of the peripheral fibrils (23, 41, 44, 115).

Cilia are often associated together into larger vibratile units. When conical in form these compound structures are known as cirri; when organized as plate-like structures they are termed membranellae. The cirri of *Euplotes*, for example, appear to consist of a series of cilia embedded in a viscous matrix. The latero-frontal cilia on the gills of *Mytilus* consist of a series of triangular plates in close contact with one another but lacking a common matrix. The cilia in each plate or membranella beat in unison. The lips of the ctenophore *Beroë* bear giant cilia or macrocilia, each of which, arising from one cell, consists of several thousand cilia of typical pattern enclosed within a common envelope. The basal bodies of these numerous cilia are linked by a system of tubules (54).

Ciliary Movement

When observed under the microscope cilia appear to be moving at a high velocity. Actually the linear velocity is rather low; Bidder estimated the average velocity of the tips of flagella in sponges at 4 m/hour. The velocity varies during a cycle, that of the effective stroke being about five times the recovery stroke. The angular velocity, on the other hand, is of a much higher order, since cilia can oscillate through half a circle at a rate of 10–12 strokes/sec.

Cilia and flagella have several forms of movement which, on analysis, resolve themselves into three fundamentally different types. The beat of a given cilium may conform to one of these types, or to some combination thereof. The simplest type is pendular movement, in which the cilia vibrate to and fro by flexing at the base. The forward effective stroke occurs more rapidly than the return recovery stroke, but there is no difference in the path traversed during the two phases of the cycle. This type of movement is characteristic of larger compound cilia, e.g. those of heterotrichous ciliates.

A second type of movement involves flexing of the cilium, the flexure beginning at the tip and progressing towards the base. During recovery a reverse process takes place, the cilium straightening out progressively from base to tip. This type is exemplified by latero-frontal cilia of lamellibranch gills. The third type, characteristic of flagella, involves an undulatory movement, in which a series of waves passes along the length of the flagellum from base to tip.

Combinations of these several types of movement are seen in various cilia. Frontal cilia on the gill filaments of *Mytilus*, for example, show a stiff pendular movement during the effective stroke, whereas the recovery stroke is accomplished by progressive flexing of the limp cilium. Cilia usually beat in one plane and act as paddles. Flagella, however, beat in a spiral course and impart a rotatory movement which causes them to act as screws or propellers. The flagellate *Monas* can move in several different ways—forwards, backwards and laterally (Fig. 9.1). During fast forward movement the flagellum sweeps in pendular fashion through an arc of about 90° (the effective stroke), whereas the preparatory stroke involves a bending or flexure beginning at the base of the flagellum and progressing towards the tip. When *Monas* moves backward the flagellum shows waves passing from base to tip; in lateral movement the flagellum is flexed at right angles and undulates: the waves may involve the whole length of the flagellum, or be restricted to the tip (50, 74, 76, 77).

Co-ordination and Control of Ciliary Activity

Cilia appear to be inherently automatic organelles. Small pieces of ciliated epithelium or fragments of ciliated protozoans continue to show ciliary activity for some time after removal from the parent organism. Ciliary motivity is independent of the cell as a whole; the distal end of the cell, however, appears to be essential to the mechanism, and some observations suggest that the basal granules are involved.

Examination of a ciliated surface shows that the cilia beat, not in phase but in sequence. Any selected cilium is beating slightly in advance of the one behind it, and is slightly retarded with respect to the one preceding it.

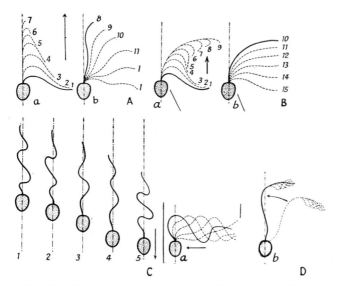

FIG. 9.1. FLAGELLAR ACTIVITY IN THE FLAGELLATE *Monas*

A, fast forward movement: *a*, recovery stroke; *b*, effective stroke. B, slow forward movement: *a*, recovery stroke; *b*, effective stroke. C, backward movement. D, lateral (*a*), and rotational (*b*) movement. (From Krijgsman, 1925.)

This sequence of phasing is termed metachronism. Since all the cilia lying in a line across the epithelium beat in phase with one another, regular waves appear to pass over the surface of the epithelium.

The direction of the metachronal waves is usually constant for each tissue. In the case of the frontal cilia on the gills of *Mytilus* the metachronal wave moves in the direction of the effective stroke of the cilia. In the lateral gill epithelium of the same animal the waves move at right angles to the effective stroke. Among ctenophores the metachronal wave of the ciliary plates usually moves in an opposite direction to the effective stroke. Metachronal waves in the direction of effective ciliary beat are probably associated with transport of large particles or mucous masses; waves at right angles or opposite to the beat are better suited for creating water currents. The relations between metachronism and direction of ciliary beat are explored in detail by Knight-Jones (67).

Because of the difficult experimental conditions which ciliated cells present, the mechanism of metachronism has not been easy to resolve. Co-ordination of ciliary beat by transmitted impulses is likely, especially when cilia are well separated and the direction of beat is different from the direction of the metachronal wave (so-called neuroid transmission). But when the cilia are closely spaced and the directions of beat and meta-chronism coincide, co-ordination may be achieved by mechanical means involving viscous drag of the medium (115).

Reversal of the direction of ciliary beat has been reported for a number of animals but, apart from the Protozoa, it is a rare phenomenon. Reversal of direction of locomotion in ciliates and small turbellarians appears to result from a change in the direction in which the cilia beat. In *Paramecium* ciliary reversal is obtained by treatment with KCl and by applying an electrical field. Parker has reported that cilia on the lips of the sea anemone *Metridium* reverse their beat in the presence of food or KCl; the metachronal wave is also reversed by the latter treatment.

Cilia may be entirely autonomous or may be subject to control by the organism. In addition to such examples of changes in direction and manner of beat already instanced, the cilia of certain animals are subject to inhibition. Gray notes that cases of ciliary control are chiefly characteristic of locomotory cilia, such as those of ciliates, ctenophores, planarians, and planktonic larvae of annelids, molluscs and polyzoans. Notable exceptions are labial cilia of *Metridium* and tentacular cilia of polyzoans.

The velar cilia of nudibranch larvae show alternations of rest and activity, and can be arrested by stimulation. When a portion of the velum is re-moved the cilia beat continuously, and nerve anaesthetics abolish the periods of ciliary arrest in the intact larva. The ciliated velar cells are innervated and it seems likely that ciliary arrest results from nervous inhibition. On the other hand lateral cilia of mussel gills are temporarily arrested when the branchial nerve is interrupted, but become active again in an excised gill after some hours (4).

Nervous control of ciliary beat is well marked in ctenophores. A form such as *Pleurobrachia* moves through the water mouth foremost by co-ordinated beating of the combs which strike in an aboral direction. At faster rates of swimming the metachronal waves of the eight rows of plates are synchronized; at slow rates co-ordination may be evident only in two rows of a quadrant, or among the combs of a single row. In certain ctenophores (especially cydippids) mechanical stimulation causes ciliary reversal, attended by a change in the direction of the metachronal wave. When a comb row is transected the combs on either side of the cut beat independently. Nervous connexions to the combs have been demonstrated and it now appears that the ciliary beat is regulated by a diffuse nerve net. The statocyst (apical sense organ), which connects with each of the paddle rows, maintains co-ordination between the rows and orientates the animal with respect to gravity.

Acetylcholine is reported to be concerned with ciliary activity; acetylcholine, cholinesterase and choline acetylase occur in ciliary tissue (gills of *Mytilus*). Ciliary movement is enhanced by acetylcholine and eserine in low concentrations, and is depressed by *d*-tubocurarine. But mussel gills are also excited by 5-hydroxytryptamine, which they contain, and the enzymes concerned with it. Both acetylcholine and 5-hydroxytryptamine are agents for the rôle of local hormones acting as pacemakers for the autonomous activity of ciliary epithelia (24, 49, 84).

Effect of External Factors

Ciliary activity is affected by various environmental factors, notably ionic concentrations, temperature variations and oxygen supply.

Cilia are very sensitive to changes in the hydrogen ion concentration of the medium, an increase in acidity bringing the cilia to rest. The effective concentration for stopping ciliary beat varies with the tissue and is related to that of the medium which normally bathes the cilia (*vide* p. 62). The ciliary arrest which occurs in lamellibranch gills when the animals are out of water for some time results from accumulation of CO_2; this has as its consequence a reduction in oxygen consumption. Marine animals are not normally subject to variations in the relative concentrations of cations other than H^+ unless they live in estuarine environments. An increase in the concentration of potassium accelerates the beat; in the absence of calcium ciliary beat declines; changes in magnesium concentrations have dissimilar effects in different tissues. A discussion of this problem is given by Gray (50).

Raising the temperature between 0–34°C increases the rate of ciliary beat. Above 37·5°C the velocity falls off and heat rigor sets in. The Q_{10} for the velocity of the frontal cilia of *Mytilus* varies from 3·1 in the temperature range 0–10°C to 1·95 in the range 20–30°C. As the temperature is altered the rate of oxygen consumption varies directly as the velocity of ciliary movement. Ciliary movement persists for about 30 min in the absence of oxygen, but oxygen is necessary for prolonged activity.

Like other contractile processes, ciliary activity is sensitive to gross changes in hydrostatic pressure (cf. p. 24). When the pressure is suddenly raised by 70 atm or more, rate of ciliary beat is immediately increased, and returns more slowly to resting level (lateral cilia of *Mytilus* gill). Subsequent decompression produces a reduction of frequency below normal, followed by slow recovery. Much greater pressures (> 300 atm) have a deleterious effect and permanent injury sets in.

Ciliary Locomotion

It is only in small aquatic animals that cilia are effective for locomotion. The amount of work done against gravity in sea water is relatively small, since the specific gravity of marine animals is generally not much higher than that of the medium (*see* Table 9.3, p. 402, for some representative values). But, on the other hand, a considerable amount of energy must be expended in overcoming the viscous resistance of the water.

When a ciliated organism is free to move it will tend to progress in a direction opposite to that of the effective beat of the cilia, whereas the water will tend to go in an opposite direction. For a given species of animal the resultant initial velocity will be directly proportional to its mass. In very small organisms having a low density, full speed will be attained as soon as the cilia begin beating; conversely, the animals will come to a dead stop as soon as the cilia become motionless. In the case of a larger animal, 1 cm in diameter and moving with a speed of 1 cm/sec, it has been calculated that the animal will glide some 20 cm before coming to rest once the cilia stop beating. And from a position of rest it will take some considerable time to attain maximal velocity (50). The absolute speed of ciliated organisms is slow. Some examples are: *Paramecium*, 1·3 mm/sec; *Monas*, 0·26 mm/sec.

Ciliary locomotion is suitable for small animals which can get along at low speeds. Small turbellarians and planktonic larvae suggest themselves as examples. Streamlining, such as many ciliates possess, reduces the water resistance which the animals encounter. For larger invertebrates, such as ctenophores, to obtain equal facility of movement in all directions a low specific gravity is necessary, and this is attained by high water content and exclusion of sulphate. Where range and power of movement are required, cilia and flagella prove inadequate, and heavy animals depend upon muscles for motive force (50, 72, 76, 101).

Trichocysts in Protozoa

Trichocysts are peculiar explosive bodies occurring in the ectoplasm of ciliates. They are fusiform or succular in shape, with the long axes more or less perpendicular to the external surface. When activated, each trichocyst discharges a long filament through a pore in the pellicle. Trichocysts are evenly distributed over the surface of the body, as in *Paramecium*; or are restricted to special areas, the proboscis of *Dileptus*, for example. Ordinary trichocysts, such as those of *Paramecium*, have a uniform appearance. In other ciliates, such as *Prorodon*, there are structures known as cnidotrichocysts, containing an elongated coiled thread which can be everted.

Effective stimuli causing discharge of the trichocysts are chemical (acid and alkali), mechanical (pressure) and electrical (discrete shocks). Explosion takes place rapidly, within a few milliseconds. Owing to the small size of these structures (each trichocyst is only a few micra in diameter) little is known about the mechanism of discharge, but it is thought that hydration of protein material or an osmotically controlled flow of water into the trichocyst may be responsible.

Several functions have been ascribed to these structures. In some species, of which *Paramecium* is an example, they probably serve as organs of attachment. But the trichocysts of predatory forms such as *Dileptus* are employed in capturing food. An encounter with prey causes the trichocysts to discharge and the prey is paralysed instantly, apparently by a toxin associated with the discharged filaments.

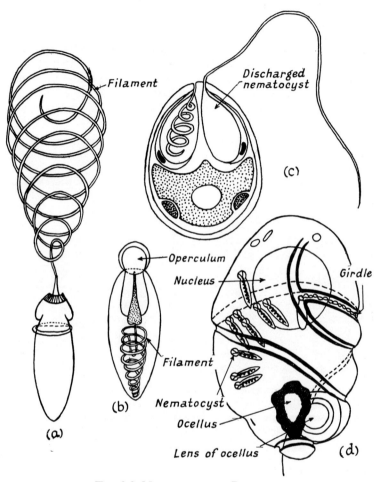

FIG. 9.2. NEMATOCYSTS OF PROTOZOA

Nematocyst of dinoflagellate *Polykrikos*, (*a*) discharged, (*b*) undischarged, (*c*) ripe spore of a myxosporidium *Myxobolus*, showing two nematocysts, *left* undischarged, *right* discharged, (*d*) *Nematodinium*, a dinoflagellate containing nematocysts. (From various sources.)

Trichocysts of typical pattern occur in many flagellates. In cryptomonads the gullet or furrow is often lined with trichocysts which discharge their threads when the organism is exposed to noxious stimuli. This is not a feeding reaction, since these flagellates are holophytic or saprophytic.
Somewhat different kinds of effector organelles are found in certain

other protozoans. In the dinoflagellates *Polykrikos* and *Nematodinium* there are trichocysts that have considerable resemblance to the nemato-cysts of coelenterates (Fig. 9.2). They are oval capsules surmounted by a cap and containing a slender spirally coiled thread. Various chemical agents cause these nematocysts to discharge, but their normal function is unknown. The polar capsules of Cnidosporidia (Sporozoa) also resemble the coelenterate nematocyst. They are oval bodies containing a long coiled filament which in some species reaches a length fifty times that of the spore (Fig. 9.2). Exposure to the digestive fluids of the host causes the contained thread to unroll and shoot out. The discharged threads serve temporarily to anchor the parasite to the gut wall of the host (47, 56, 60, 101).

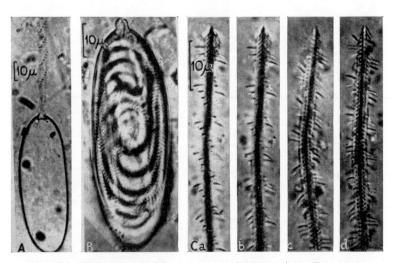

FIG. 9.3. NEMATOCYSTS (HOLOTRICHOUS ISORHIZAS) OF *Corynactis*

A, capsule and base of shaft after discharge (fresh smear in distilled water). B, nemato-cyst before discharge (dried smear in distilled water). C, shaft of an incompletely dis-charged nematocyst, showing the tip; *a–d*, focused in different planes (dried smear in distilled water). (From Robson (107).)

Nematocysts and Colloblasts

Nematocysts or stinging cells are found in coelenterates. Colloblasts or adhesive cells occur in ctenophores.

The nematocysts of coelenterates are small capsules lying in cells known as nematocytes or cnidoblasts. The capsules are minute structures, usually some 5–50 μ in length, and fusiform to spherical in shape. Within the capsule lies coiled a hollow thread which can be everted (Fig. 9.3). An operculum caps the nematocyst and there is often a bristle-like cnidocil on the outer surface of the cell. Other structures frequently present are supporting rods about the periphery of the cnidoblast, and a fibrillar network associated with the capsule.

There are two main types of nematocysts; the spirocysts of Zoantharia, and nematocysts proper found in all groups of coelenterates. The spirocysts have thin-walled capsules permeable to water, and they discharge unarmed adhesive threads. The nematocysts proper comprise a large variety of forms, distinguishable by characters of their discharged threads. All of them have thick-walled capsules impermeable to water except at discharge, and containing threads that are usually armed with spines (Fig. 9.3). In some varieties, such as the volvents, the thread is closed at the tip and forms a tightly coiled filament on discharge; this filament wraps itself around bristles and other projecting structures of the prey. In other types the threads have open tips: these are discharged into prey with sufficient force to penetrate the chitinous covering of small organisms. Often the thread is armed with spiral rows of spines over some part of its length and from the open tip a poison is discharged which paralyses the prey.

Nematocysts are most abundant on the tentacles. They are plentiful in the ectoderm of the oral region and become sparse towards the base of the polyps. They also occur in profusion on internal structures, such as gastric filaments, septal filaments and acontia.

Cnidoblasts behave as independent effectors and are not subject to nervous control. The responses both to normal stimuli and to localized electrical stimulation are closely restricted to the affected region, and repetitive stimulation is not followed by spread of excitation such as takes place in certain regions of the coelenterate nerve net (*Anemonia, Metridium*). The effective stimulus for activating the cnidoblast is primarily mechanical. Contact with solid food leads to a strong response, but mechanical stimulation with inert solids has little effect unless the stimulus is very strong (Fig. 9.4). Solutions of foodstuffs do not activate the cnidoblasts but surface active agents such as saponin bring about a vigorous discharge. Solutions of foodstuffs do permit the cnidoblasts to be readily discharged by mechanical stimulation and it is concluded that the foodstuffs sensitize the cnidoblasts chemically to mechanical stimulation. The sensitizing substance is probably lipoidal in nature and adsorbed on protein (92).

Several theories have been proposed to account for the mechanism of discharge. When the thread is everted the process begins at the base, which is continuous with the wall of the capsule, and progresses towards the tip. It has been suggested that increased pressure within the capsule forces out the filament. If the capsule is acting as an osmometer, inflowing water would build up the internal hydrostatic pressure when the nematocyst is activated. An alternative theory supposes that the inflow of water leads to swelling of colloidal material which causes eversion of the filament. In certain cnidoblasts of *Physalia* contraction of fibrils may also be involved. It has been shown that the uneverted filament in water undergoes anisometric swelling and the process of discharge appears to take the following form. On excitation water flows into the capsule, the internal pressure rises and the operculum is forced off; the base of the filament, exposed to water, begins to swell and moves outwards. As the tip advances a fresh region continues to be exposed to water and hydrates, and the process proceeds until the whole filament has everted. Meanwhile, the continued rise in intracapsular pressure favours the forward movement of the tip and, by the turgor it confers on the filament, assists it in penetrating prey (97, 107).

Nematocyst poisons have been characterized to some extent, but their exact nature has still to be determined. Some species are very virulent and are dangerous to man, notably *Physalia* and *Dactylometra*. Aqueous, alcoholic and glycerine extracts of tentacles produce different symptoms in experimental animals, effects which it is unnecessary to list in detail.

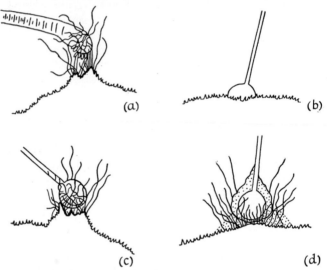

FIG. 9.4. RESPONSES TO STIMULATION OF CNIDAE ON THE
TENTACLES OF *Anemonia sulcata*

(*a*) Response of cnidae to touch by human hair; (*b*) lack of response to clean glass bead; (*c*) sensitization of cnidoblasts to a glass bead by immersion for 5 min in sea water + saliva (0·1% dry weight); (*d*) response to a glass bead smeared with alcoholic extract of *Pecten* mantle. Scale, 100 μ. (After Pantin (92).)

Tetramine (tetramethylammonium hydroxide) has been extracted from anemones in high concentration, and probably occurs in the nematocysts. It is a quaternary ammonium base with powerful paralysing action on motor-nerve endings. Some of the toxic properties of coelenterate extracts recorded for higher vertebrates, including man, may be due to anaphylactic shock from included proteins (12, 33, 96).

Certain animals which prey upon coelenterates and preserve their nematocysts make intriguing curiosities. Nematocysts are found embedded in the tentacle of the ctenophore *Euchlora* and probably are derived from small medusae on which it feeds. Certain aeolid nudibranchs, which prey upon coelenterates, conserve the nematocysts occurring in their food; these are passed into special sacs in the dorsal cerata, where they form a protective mechanism against predators (Fig. 9.5). Selection is exercised; in *Aeolis*, for example, which attacks the hydroid *Pennaria*, only one kind of particularly effective nematocyst is retained (the microbasic mastigophores), the others undergoing digestion (19, 64, 68).

Tentacles of ctenophores possess adhesive (lasso) cells, also known as colloblasts, in lieu of nematocysts. The colloblast has a hemispherical head attached to the central core of the tentacle by coiled contractile and straight filaments. Within the head are granules which discharge a sticky secretion used in capturing prey.

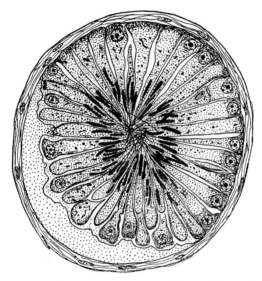

FIG. 9.5. TRANSVERSE SECTION THROUGH A YOUNG CNIDOPHORE SAC OF A NUDIBRANCH (*Aeolidiella glauca*), CONTAINING NEMATOCYSTS OF THE ANEMONE *Cereus pedunculatus* (from Naville, 1926.)

CONTRACTILE CELLS IN SPONGES

Although sponges lack a nervous system they are capable of simple contractile responses. When a sponge is exposed to air, or lies in still water, the flesh contracts and takes on a wrinkled appearance (*Stylotella*). On returning the animal to running water the surface expands once more. The most evident activity of sponges, however, is the production of a feeding current by the continuous beating of choanocytes. The feeding current is interrupted under unfavourable conditions, e.g. in still or deoxygenated water, in the presence of noxious chemicals, etc. A current can flow only when the dermal pores and the oscula are open; when these are shut the current stops. The elements responsible for contraction are the porocytes surrounding the pores, and certain epithelial myocytes lining

B.M.A—13

the pore canals and oscula. These cells behave as independent effectors, i.e. they respond directly to an external stimulus by contraction. The response is slow: following a mechanical stimulus there is a latency of 0·1–0·4 sec. The myocytes are insensitive to electrical stimuli. Temporal but not spatial summation of excitation occurs. The excited state is not transmitted; each pore and each osculum responds independently of the others, but when the stimulus is widespread the sum effect of the contractions of all the porocytes and myocytes is a general response involving the whole sponge. It is concluded that the contractile cells give graded local responses to mechanical stimuli, and a tonic response to maintained distension of the osculum. The latter response reveals itself when the pressure is released, for the osculum keeps its extended form for another minute or so (95, 105).

MUSCLE

Contractile elements occur in all phyla and include such diverse structures as the contractile fibrils or myonemes of Protozoa, independent contractile cells of sponges and muscle fibres of Metazoa. In free-swimming animals muscular contractions provide the motive power for moving about to gather food, evade enemies and engage in activities concerned with propagation of the species. Sedentary animals move parts of the body relative to one another in response to environmental stimuli and altered internal conditions. The pattern, speed and duration of such movements depend on the organization and functional characteristics of the animal's muscles. Other muscles are concerned with ingestion and digestion of foods, circulation of body fluids, respiration, excretion, secretion and colour changes.

Muscles are vesicular or skeletal, depending on the organization of the structures in which they operate; some muscles partake of both. Vesicular muscles are arranged around fluid-filled cavities against which they exert a compressive force. Such muscles occur in bands and sheets; origins and insertions are sometimes found in septa and mesenteries, but are often ill-defined, each portion of the muscle being inserted into, and pulling against, the next. Vesicular muscles contract against sacs of fluid that may be termed *fluid endoskeletons*, and the contraction of one muscle, by exerting pressure on the contained fluid, affects other parts of the cavity and other muscle systems bordering it. Examples are body-wall muscles of anemones, polychaetes; intestinal, bladder and cardiac muscles of arthropods, molluscs and vertebrates.

Skeletal muscles have their origins and insertions on the exo- and endoskeleton. They usually operate as members of lever systems and produce movement by shortening (isotonic contraction), or develop tension with little or no change in length (isometric contraction). Examples are phasic muscles of the limbs of vertebrates and arthropods, and adductor muscles of lamellibranchs. There are instances of muscles motivating hollow organs, with origins on skeletal structures and insertions on visceral organs, e.g. external muscles of the swim-bladder in gadoid fishes, and radial dilator muscles of the intestine of crustacea.

Muscles either produce movement (phasic activity) or maintain tension (tonus). Most muscles are capable of both phasic and tonic activity at different times, according to the functional conditions under which they are called to operate. Anti-gravity muscles of vertebrates, for example, maintain a basic level of tonus concerned with regulation of posture; lamellibranch adductors are holding muscles but also close the valves. Often muscles occur in pairs, producing reciprocal movements: thus the longitudinal muscle of the annelid body wall is opposed by a circular muscle layer, the former shortening, the latter lengthening a segment. Phasic skeletal muscles occur in antagonistic pairs, the two members of a pair producing movement in opposite directions. In some instances, however, the muscle works against a non-muscular mechanical antagonist, e.g. the hinge ligament of lamellibranchs and the frontal surface or compensation sac of cheilostomatous polyzoa.

Muscles are specialized for movement at various speeds, and there is all manner of gradation in contraction speeds, from slow holding muscles to phasic muscles producing rapid locomotory movements.

Most muscles are subject to nervous regulation. Some visceral muscles, notably cardiac muscle, show automatic activity which is varied under nervous influence, e.g. molluscan heart (Chapter 3). Gut muscles often contain an intrinsic nervous plexus concerned with co-ordination of activity and transmission of excitation. Locomotory muscles are excited by the nervous system (either nerve-net or central nervous system), and are the principal agents for executing spontaneous and reflex activities. Speed and strength of locomotory responses are controlled in part centrally, in part peripherally. Regulatory mechanisms involve: gradation in number of active muscle units; variation in number and frequency of nervous impulses; interaction of peripheral inhibitory and excitatory fibres; and stimulation by nerve fibres producing different degrees of excitation. Excitation mechanisms of various kinds have now been investigated in several phyletic groups (55).

Histology of Muscle

The fibres or muscle cells responsible for contraction are embedded in connective tissue, which imparts some degree of viscous resistance to contraction. The proportion of connective tissue is sometimes very high, e.g. in the longitudinal retractors of holothurians (*Thyone*). The body wall of sea anemones contains a relatively small amount of muscle associated with a thick layer of mesogloea, and it is the latter which is responsible for the viscous elastic properties of the wall (Fig. 9.6).

There is a wide range in length of fibres from different muscles. Some extremes are plain muscle fibres in vertebrate blood vessels, 15–20 μ long; and plain muscle fibres in the anterior byssus retractor of *Mytilus*, 4–6 cm long. Short plain muscle fibres are often uninucleate (coelenterates, sipunculoids, holothurians, annelids, etc.); long fibres, plain and striped, may contain many nuclei (crustacea, lamellibranchs, vertebrates, etc.). The vertebrate heart, formerly regarded as syncytial, is a multicellular structure, the intercalated discs being cell boundaries (27, 45, 89, 90, 104).

Each fibre is bounded by a membrane or sarcolemma and contains a nucleus (or nuclei), contractile myofibrils and sarcoplasm. Myofibrils can usually be distinguished with the light microscope, and under the higher magnification provided by the electron microscope they can be resolved into finer myofilaments. Some muscles have fine myofibrils distributed uniformly throughout the sarcoplasm (e.g. adductor of *Mytilus,* spine muscles of sea urchin); some have a few large fibrillae distributed around the periphery (e.g. muscles of *Beroë*, wing muscles of pteropods, etc.); while still others contain large peripheral and fine central fibrils. The relative amount of sarcoplasm shows much variation in different muscles. Particularly striking are the large skeletal fibres of crustaceans, in which

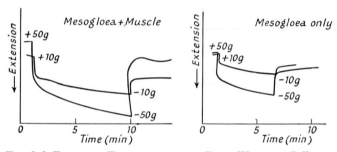

FIG. 9.6. EFFECT OF EXTENSION ON THE BODY WALL OF *Calliactis*

Curves of extension × time, under two different loads (50 and 10 g) of intact (*left*) and scraped (*right*) body wall. Note similarity of the viscous-elastic response of both mesogloea + muscle and mesogloea only. (From Chapman (27).)

the myofibrils are arranged in discrete columns, separated from one another and from the sarcolemma by thick sarcoplasmal strata.

Striped fibres, found in many phyla, contain myofibrils with cross-striations aligned across the width of the fibre (Fig. 9.7). The stripes consist of alternating anisotropic and isotropic bands, which tend to be spaced more closely in fast than in slow muscles, e.g. in crustaceans and insects. Usually the stripes lie transversely to the long axis of the fibre, but there are some muscles in which the striations are spirally arranged (e.g. adductors of some lamellibranchs).

Smooth muscles, widespread in invertebrates and vertebrates, are usually slower than striped muscles. Some invertebrate muscles contain smooth and striped components, e.g. adductors of certain lamellibranchs; the heart of *Ciona* contains fibres each of which is striped on one side but plain on the other. Bozler associates large peripheral myofibrils with fast tetanic contractions, and fine centrally dispersed myofibrils with tonus.

Muscles with fibres containing both kinds of fibrillae give both fast (phasic) and slow (tonic) contractions. These correlations are yet to be reconciled with recent physiological studies of slow and fast responses produced by one muscle, of apparently uniform structure (cf. anemones, sipunculoids, crustaceans) (20, 21, 37).

Unusual kinds of muscle fibres have been described in coelenterates, polychaetes and nematodes. Endodermal muscles of sea anemones are made up of musculo-epithelial cells, each of which consists of an epithelial cell prolonged basally into muscle fibres. A common type of polychaete muscle fibre has a U-shaped trough of myofibrillae enclosing a mass of sarcoplasm. The latter, emerging between the two limbs of the myofibrillae, contains the single nucleus. The large muscle cells of nematodes

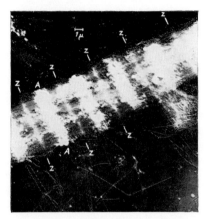

FIG. 9.7. ELECTRON PHOTOGRAPH OF A FRAGMENT OF CRAB LEG MUSCLE
(*Paragrapsus quadridentatus*)
Formalin fixed, digested briefly with trypsin and shadowed with uranium. The photograph shows myofilaments overlaid by *A* and *Z* bands. (From Farrant and Mercer (37).)

likewise consist of an outer fibrillar portion, enclosing sarcoplasm and nucleus, with long protoplasmic strands extruding to mid-dorsal and mid-ventral lines (51, 55, 100, 108).

Neuromuscular Transmission

The terminals of motor-nerve fibres form intimate associations with muscle fibres at neuromuscular junctions. These have varied forms: in skeletal muscles of vertebrates the junction is a motor end-plate, a complex structure made up of terminal branches of the axon and sarcoplasm; in vertebrate smooth muscles the motor axons branch and ramify among the muscle cells; motor fibres of crustaceans penetrate the sarcolemma and cortical sarcoplasm and terminate on end-plates close to columns of fibrils; in echinoderms large ribbon axons form extensive synaptic contacts on muscle fibres; motor axons in anemones terminate on branching end-plates, etc. (53, 93, 116).

On reaching the axon terminals, the nerve action potential excites the muscle fibre. At the vertebrate end-plate the nervous impulse produces a local depolarization which can be detected as an end-plate potential (e.p.p.). This spreads electrotonically for a short distance around the end-plate and, when of sufficient magnitude, initiates an action potential or impulse in the muscle fibre. The e.p.p. is localized and graded in size and rapidly diminishes with distance from the end-plate; when two or more impulses reach the end-plate, the graded e.p.p's can fuse with one another.

The muscle impulse is a wave of excitation which is propagated with measurable velocity over the fibre; it is all-or-nothing in character, and evokes a contractile response or twitch. The action potential is produced by transitory depolarization of the fibre membrane; following the spike potential there is a marked negative after-potential. Since the muscle membrane recovers (repolarizes) more quickly than the muscle fibre can relax, it is able to conduct impulses at high frequencies, thus maintaining a state of contraction in the muscle (clonus or tetanus).

The nerve impulse excites the neighbouring end-plate through the inter-mediation of a chemical transmitter. When the impulse arrives at the axon terminals it releases a certain amount of transmitter, which diffuses across the short distances between axon and end-plate, and excites the latter. In vertebrate skeletal muscles the transmitter is acetylcholine; this is destroyed by acetylcholinesterase, which is concentrated in the vicinity of the end-plate. The drug eserine, which inactivates acetylcholinesterase, enhances the e.p.p.; and curare, which competes preferentially with acetyl-choline for the receptors in the end-plate, reduces or abolishes the e.p.p. Nerve fibres releasing acetylcholine at their terminals are termed choliner-gic; among invertebrates, echinoderms, lamellibranchs, annelids and sipunculoids appear to possess cholinergic motor axons (p. 437). Other recognized chemical transmitters are adrenaline and 5-hydroxytryptamine. Many post-ganglionic sympathetic fibres of vertebrates are adrenergic, e.g. sympathetic fibres to the intestine and blood vessels. Adrenaline-sensitive muscles among invertebrates include: crop of *Aplysia*, proboscis of *Arenicola*, intestine of sea cucumber (*Thyone*) and crayfish. 5-hydroxy-tryptamine is released at the terminals of cardio-acceleratory fibres of molluscs (p. 112) and has an inhibitory action on lamellibranch smooth muscle (32, 34, 62, 88, 102, 104, 119).

Contraction

The characteristic response of many striped muscles to a stimulus, either nervous or electrical, is a single twitch. Following the arrival of the nervous impulse there is a brief latent period before contraction begins, a rising contractile phase or shortening, then relaxation or extension. Part of the latency is occupied by the transmission of a self-propagating action potential over the surface of the muscle fibre. In the anterior byssal retractor of *Mytilus*, for example, this occurs at a rate of 13–29 cm/sec. Lamellibranch smooth muscle is unusual in that conduction is decremental. The muscle impulse, like the nerve-action spike, is a wave of surface activity, which spreads into the interior of the fibre along a system of infolded sarcoplasmal membranes.

The contractile characteristics of muscles, like the conduction velocities of nerves, represent a balance between functional requirements and economy of effort. Some muscles develop tension rapidly, e.g. the striped mantle muscles of the squid, concerned with rapid expulsion of water from the mantle cavity, with a contraction time (to peak tension) of 60 msec, and relaxation time of some 200 msec. Others, the tonic muscles, contract

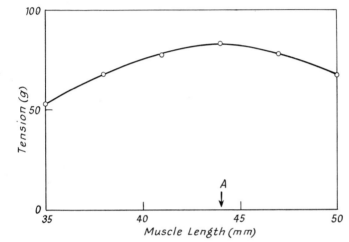

FIG. 9.8. MAXIMUM TENSION DEVELOPED AT DIFFERENT LENGTHS IN ISOMETRIC CONTRACTION OF DOGFISH JAW MUSCLE (*Scyliorhinus canicula*)

Temp. 0°C; stimulation frequency 5/sec; muscle length 37 mm, weight 600 mg. (From Abbott and Aubert (1).)

slowly but maintain strong tensions for long periods, e.g. the anterior byssal retractor of *Mytilus*, with a contraction time (to peak tension) of 5 sec and relaxation time of some 13 sec. There are many smooth muscles that are homogeneous and lack morphological differentiation, and yet give both fast and slow contractions. An instance is the mesenteric retractor of *Metridium* which gives a fast facilitated response to fast stimulation, and a smooth delayed contraction to low-frequency stimulation (contraction times of 1 sec and 15 sec respectively) (3, 16, 17, 45, 101, 108, 113).

The tension developed by a muscle during contraction is influenced by its initial length, as illustrated in Fig. 9.8. With increase in initial length there is an increase in tension until some optimal value is reached, beyond which point the tension developed begins to fall. As a rule, higher tensions are developed by the slow muscles of invertebrates. The plain adductors of lamellibranchs are notable for long-sustained contractions against strong pulling forces. The data collected in Table 9.1, although difficult to compare, give some idea of estimates of muscular tension which have been made. Estimates of tensions needed to force open the valves of lamellibranchs, by overcoming the pull of the adductor muscles, are shown in Table 9.2 (1, 2, 3, 14, 46, 65, 94).

TABLE 9.1

ESTIMATES OF TENSION DEVELOPED BY SOME INVERTEBRATE MUSCLES

Animal	Tensions
Metridium senile	Circular muscle of the column. 3·5 g/cm of body wall transverse to the muscle, corresponding to 40 kg/cm² of muscle fibre cross-section.
Asterias rubens	Tube foot. Force of a downward push, ca. 200 mg; of an upward pull, ca. 50 mg.
Holothuria grisea	Five longitudinal muscles. 13 g/cm² of body cross-section.
Pinna fragilis	Fast posterior adductor. 1·5 kg/cm² cross-section.
Venus verrucosa	Slow adductor. 35·4 kg/cm² cross-section.
Ostrea edulis	Slow adductor. 12 kg/cm² cross-section.
Pecten magellanicus	Slow adductor. 4 kg/cm² cross-section.
Mytilus edulis	Slow adductor. 11·3 kg/cm² cross-section.
	Pedal retractor. Twitch tension 2–2·5 kg/cm² cross-section. Twitch/tetanus ratio 1:3.
	Anterior byssus retractor. Twitch tension 3·5–4·5 kg/cm² cross-section. Twitch/tetanus ratio 1:8.
	Posterior adductor. Twitch tension 0·5 kg/cm² cross-section. Twitch/tetanus ratio 1:14.

TABLE 9.2

FORCES NEEDED TO OPEN LAMELLIBRANCH VALVES

Animal	Force
Ostrea circumpicta	7,880 g/cm² muscle cross-section
Mytilus crassitesta	5,386 g/cm² ditto
Cardium edule	2,856 g/cm² ditto
Chlamys senatorius	1,272 g/cm² ditto

THE MUSCLE TWITCH AND FUSED CONTRACTIONS. The response of muscles of most animals to a stimulus delivered through the motor nerves is a single contraction or twitch. There are exceptions, notably the longitudinal parietal retractors and the disc sphincter muscles of sea-anemones, where several nervous impulses are required to evoke contraction: this condition is an instance of neuromuscular facilitation (discussed on pp. 382, 419). With direct electrical stimulation even these muscles respond to a single pulse with a contraction (91).

When a muscle is excited by a train of nervous impulses it responds by a series of contractions which succeed one another at a rate depending on the frequency of excitation. When the frequency is sufficiently fast the separate contractions undergo some degree of fusion; a complete fusion of twitches, producing a steady contraction throughout the period of stimulation, is tetanus (Fig. 9.9). The ability of a muscle to be tetanized depends on its refractory period. Some muscles possessing long refractory periods cannot develop fused contractions; such a muscle remains inexcitable to a second stimulus until its contraction is spent or completed, e.g. the subumbrella circular muscles of medusae and the cardiac muscle of vertebrates. The refractory period of circular muscle of jellyfish (*Aurelia*, etc.) is 0·7 sec, whereas the twitch reaches maximal tension in 0·4–0·6 sec. Consequently, the maximal rate of effective excitation via the nerve net is about 86 per min, at which frequency partially fused contractions (clonus) are produced (Fig. 10.6, p. 423). An absolute refractory period reigns in vertebrate cardiac muscle throughout most of systole, to be succeeded by a relative refractory period during late systole and diastole; recovery is complete by the end of diastole. The heart remains inexcitable to direct electrical stimulation throughout the absolute refractory period, and gives a submaximal contraction during the relative refractory period (Fig. 3.7, p. 103) (25).

It is likely that muscular contractions in most animals are produced by trains of nervous impulses, but this is not invariably so. Each normal swimming contraction of the medusa bell (*Aurelia*) is evoked by a single impulse in the nerve net. Quick contractions concerned with escape responses sometimes depend upon a single nervous impulse. Thus it is in the sabellid *Myxicola*, where a tactile stimulus evokes a single impulse in the giant axon—the final common path to the longitudinal muscles of the body—and a quick synergic twitch (Fig. 10.11).

The tension developed during tetanus is usually greater than that produced by a single twitch, the effect increasing with frequency of stimulation, e.g. tonic muscles of lamellibranchs. Varying the frequency of excitation, therefore, is one method of regulating the strength of muscular contraction. Not all muscles react in this manner to increased frequency of stimulation, however. The mantle circular muscles of *Loligo* (cephalopod) and the body longitudinal muscles of *Myxicola* (polychaete) are motor units served by giant axons: in both instances the tension developed during tetanic contraction is no greater than that produced by a single twitch, i.e. tension remains constant with increase in frequency (Fig. 9.9). These muscles are specialized to develop maximal response to a single impulse, and mechanical summation and facilitation are non-operative (101).

REGULATION OF SPEED AND STRENGTH OF CONTRACTION: MOTOR-UNIT RESPONSE. In the two systems just described the whole muscle consists of one or a few motor units. In the polychaete *Myxicola* the whole longitudinal muscle is served by a single giant axon, and in the squid each tertiary giant axon supplies a large area of mantle muscle (p. 432). A single nerve impulse in one of these units excites all the muscle fibres and produces a maximal, all-or-nothing contraction. The triggered responses of these units are particularly well suited for an all-out effort in which there is no need for economy or accurate adjustment.

Vertebrate muscle provides the classic type of motor-unit: here a motor axon innervates a fixed group of muscle fibres and the whole muscle consists of several such groups. An impulse in one of the motor axons produces a synchronous contraction of all the muscle fibres in the motor

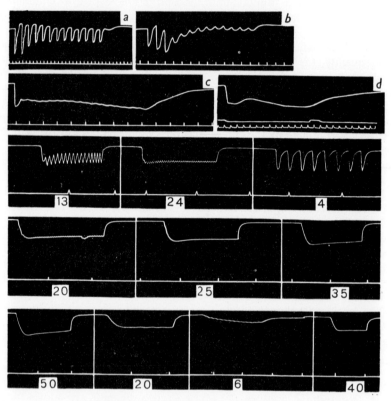

FIG. 9.9. ISOMETRIC CONTRACTIONS, A, OF *Branchiomma* MUSCLE,
B, OF SQUID (*Loligo*) MANTLE MUSCLE

A Stimulation frequencies: *a*, 34/min, *b*, 64/min, *c*, 116/min, d, 13/sec. Time trace *a–c*, 1/sec; *d*, 13/sec. (From Nicol (1951).)

B Numbers indicate frequencies/sec. of stimulation. (From Prosser and Young (1937).)

unit which it supplies. The magnitude of response of the whole muscle is determined by the number of motor units activated. Regulation of response occurs in the spinal cord and, once an impulse has left the latter, further action is a non-stop process.

PERIPHERAL FACILITATION. In the motor-unit type of response the nerve impulse is transmitted with equal facility to all muscle fibres in the unit. The muscles of many invertebrates, however, have a facilitated type of response. The contraction of muscle systems showing peripheral facilitation is brought about by a train of successive impulses, which become progressively more effective by local summation at peripheral synapses. The rate and strength of contractions are delicately regulated by varying the number and frequency of nerve impulses. Peripheral facilitation occurs in the muscle systems of certain coelenterates, and is widespread among higher crustaceans.

Coelenterates. Peripheral facilitation of muscular contractions is reported for Hydromedusae, Scyphomedusae and Actiniaria. When the column of the anemone *Calliactis* is stimulated electrically with a series of shocks (intervals of 0·5–1·5 sec), a contraction is produced in the sphincter muscle of the oral disc. There is no response to the first stimulus, whereas

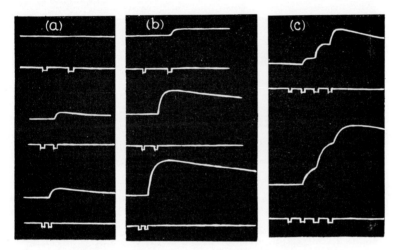

FIG. 9.10. RESPONSES OF *Calliactis* SPHINCTER TO ELECTRICAL STIMULATION

(*a*) Paired shocks at intervals of 2, 1 and 0·5 sec; (*b*) same after 60 min in sea water + 0·4 M CaCl$_2$ (95:5); (*c*) *above*, response of sphincter in sea water to stimuli at 1/sec; *below*, after 30 min in sea water + 0·4 M CaCl$_2$ (95:5) (from Ross and Pantin (110).)

responses to subsequent stimuli gradually increase, resulting in a *staircase* effect. The strength of the contraction is independent of the strength of the electrical stimulus, above threshold, and the whole system appears to work as one functional unit. For facilitation to occur the stimuli must be spaced within 3 sec of each other, and by increasing the frequency of stimulation a more rapid increase of the response is obtained (Figs. 9.10, 9.11). Since lengthening the interval results in a small increment or staircase it follows that facilitation is subject to temporal decay, and quickly falls from the initial level obtaining at the moment of stimulation. The neuromuscular junction is sensitive to changes in the ionic environment, calcium enhancing and magnesium depressing neuromuscular facilitation (110).

The coelenterate nervous system is organized as a diffuse, often non-polarized network, in which through-conduction tracts occur. Stimulation of one such tract in the mesenteries of *Calliactis* produces impulses which are propagated throughout the system to the entire sphincter muscle. Each impulse produces a transitory change at the neuromuscular junction, and facilitates the passage of subsequent impulses. The increase in magnitude of response is brought about by recruitment of muscle fibres, as facilitation progressively brings more of these into activity (91).

A comparable process of facilitation occurs in the circular muscles of jellyfish (*Aurelia, Cyanea*). These muscles, responsible for the swimming pulsations, are served by a diffuse nerve-net, and both together form a single excitable system. A single stimulus, applied anywhere to the nerve-

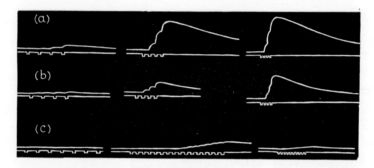

FIG. 9.11. RESPONSES OF *Calliactis* SPHINCTER TO ELECTRICAL STIMULATION
(*a*) Series of shocks at intervals of 2, 1, and 0·5 sec; (*b*) same after 28 min in 0·4 M MgCl₂ + sea water (1:1); (*c*) same after 55 min. (From Ross and Pantin (110).)

net, elicits a contraction, and the height of the response is augmented by repeated stimulation. As in the retractile response of anemones, each impulse spreads to all parts of the muscle and repeated stimulation produces stronger contractions by recruitment (25).

In addition to the quick contractions described above, muscles of sea anemones give slow smooth contractions when stimulated at frequencies lower than those which elicit fast responses. These slow contractions occur only when sufficient stimuli are delivered (six or more); the optimal frequency is rather low (interval of from 6 to 8 sec), and latency is typically prolonged (up to 2 min in *Calliactis* sphincter muscle). Now, some muscles show only slow responses (parietals of *Metridium*); others, both slow and quick contractions, according to the stimulation-frequency (mesenteric retractors of *Metridium*, sphincter of *Calliactis*). In a sense the slow responses are also facilitated in that several stimuli are required to evoke them, but once contractions are initiated, further increases occur simply by summation. In coelenterates, therefore, some muscles appear to be capable of producing two kinds of contractions, mediated perhaps by two distinct categories of nerve fibres (16, 109).

Crustacea. Skeletal muscles, at least of decapods, contain several kinds of muscle fibres which differ from each other in electrical characteristics and responses, and in mechanical responses. For example, three types of fibres have been distinguished in closure muscles of the walking legs of shore crabs, on the basis of post-synaptic potentials (10).

Peripheral facilitation is developed to a high degree in the limb muscles of higher crustaceans. These muscles are generally supplied by only a few axons, each of which subdivides and supplies all the fibres of a given muscle (Fig. 9.13). The muscle fibres thus possess multiple innervation from different axons: each axon also makes contact with a muscle fibre at many end-plates.

Of the several motor axons supplying the crustacean muscle at least one is inhibitory, whereas the others are excitatory but differ quantitatively in the speed and strength of the contractile effects which they produce. Motor and inhibitor impulses converge on the muscle fibres and a balance is struck at the myoneural junctions between antagonistic transmitter effects (52, 122).

Crustacean muscles are capable of two kinds of contraction, one a fast synchronous action, the other a slow tonic contraction which develops gradually and smoothly. In many muscles the fibres receive branches of two or more motor axons, individual stimulation of which evokes fast or slow contractions (fast and slow nerve fibres) (Fig. 9.12). A single impulse in the fast fibre sometimes causes a twitch contraction but more often several or many impulses in the fast fibre are necessary to produce a twitch. Normally many impulses are needed in the slow fibre to cause contraction—a slow smooth tetanus.

Peripheral facilitation in crustacean muscles involves summation of graded local reactions which become intensified with each additional nerve impulse. In the absence of a propagated muscle impulse there is a progressive growth of local electrical responses (e.p.p's) in the vicinity of the nerve endings. With intracellular recording, end-plate potentials are found to be distributed over the whole length of the muscle fibre. These non-propagated potentials are accompanied by local contractions, controlled continuously in rate and strength by the number and frequency of motor impulses. Normally the muscular contraction is built up by non-propagated responses. But by stimulation of the fast axons at a sufficiently high frequency, propagated action potentials are produced, associated with vigorous twitches of whole muscle fibres. These spike potentials appear to have as their consequence the elimination of inequalities in the strength of response along the length of the muscle fibre. Thus, the fast motor response in crustacean muscle may be local or propagated, depending on the rate of nervous stimulation (38, 39, 57).

Inhibitory fibres run together with the excitatory fibres to the muscles (Figs. 9.12, 9.13). The inhibitory impulse is capable of interrupting transmission of motor activity at two separate stages, i.e. between the motor impulse and production of the e.p.p. (α-action), and between the e.p.p.

and local contraction of the muscle (β-action). In both actions the inhibitory influence is restricted to the vicinity of the motor-nerve endings. The functional significance of the inhibitory fibres is not well understood. It is noteworthy that each of the inhibitory fibres usually supplies many different muscles, and hence has a widespread effect. However, there are a

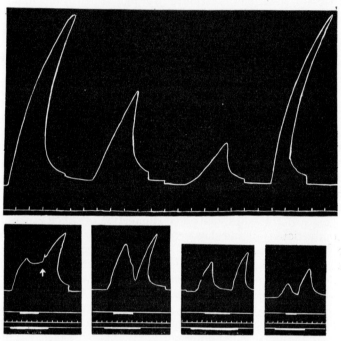

FIG. 9.12. CONTRACTIONS OF LIMB MUSCLES (FLEXOR OF CARPOPODITE)
OF ROCK LOBSTER *Panulirus*

(*Above*) the four contractions elicited by stimulation of the four motor fibres at a frequency of 30/sec. From left to right, axon of diameter 89μ, second quickest contraction; axon 91μ, third quickest contraction; axon 122μ, slowest contraction; axon 129μ, quickest contraction. (*Below*) inhibition of the four contractions. Upper signal indicates electrical stimulation of the inhibitor, lower signal stimulation of the motor fibre. Records of contractions are graded, left to right, according to their speed. Diameter of motor fibres, in same order, are, 126μ, 74μ, 81μ and 110μ. Diameter of the inhibitor fibre is 32μ. In the left hand record inhibition is only partial and shows temporary escape at the arrow. Time trace in sec. (From van Harreveld and Wiersma (52).)

few inhibitors with restricted distribution. Such may allow differentiation of function in certain muscles that have a common motor axon, e.g. opener and stretcher muscles of the decapod limb (62, 123, 125).

Considerable variation occurs in the degree of facilitation exhibited by different muscles. Many crustacean muscles receive two motor axons, one providing fast, the other slow, facilitation. In such muscles the response is regulated, not only by the number and frequency of nerve impulses, but also by switching of axons. In the Reptantia the flexor muscles of the limbs receive as many as four motor axons, whereas the claw opener has a single motor axon. The claw opener of the hermit crab *Eupagarus* receives only one motor axon, yet exhibits both slow and fast contractions. It seems that the single axon makes two kinds of synapses on the muscle, namely fast end-plates activated by high-frequency stimulation, and slow end-plates activated by low-frequency stimulation. Another functional pattern is shown by the bender muscle of crabs *Dromidiopsis* (Brachyura) and

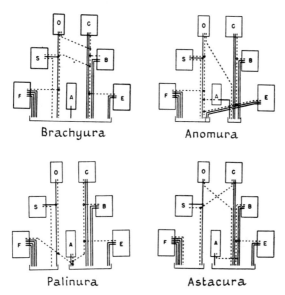

Brachyura · Anomura

Palinura · Astacura

FIG. 9.13. INNERVATION PATTERNS OF DISTAL MUSCLES IN THORACIC LIMBS OF FOUR GROUPS OF DECAPOD CRUSTACEA

O, opener; *C* closer; *S*, stretcher; *B*, bender; *F*, main flexor; *A*, accessory flexor; *E*, extensor. Solid lines represent single motor axons; broken lines, inhibitory axons; square brackets, distribution of axons between nerve bundles, the largest bundle being on the right. In the Anomura the common inhibitor is variable in position and may occur in the large nerve bundle. (From Wiersma and Ripley (1952).)

Dardanus (Anomura). This muscle is innervated by two motor axons and is responsible for both bending and rotation of the limb. Stimulation of the fast axon causes rotation in one direction; stimulation of the slow axon, rotation in the opposite direction. It is suggested that the three movements are produced by different groups of fibres in the muscle. The bender fibres possess approximately equal numbers of fast and slow endings; the headward rotator fibres have a preponderance of fast endings; and the tailward rotator fibres a preponderance of slow endings (62, 120, 121).

Despite the paucity of motor-axons, crustacean muscles exhibit a great variety of electrical and mechanical responses. This variability is explained by the variety of muscle fibres which exist, even within a given muscle, and by the interplay of effects produced by different categories of excitatory and inhibitory axons supplying the muscle fibres.

Lamellibranchs. The muscles of these animals have excited much

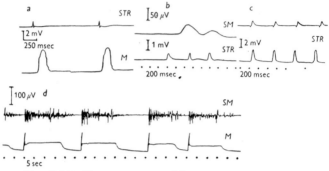

FIG. 9.14A. ELECTRICAL AND MECHANICAL ACTIVITY OF
Pecten ADDUCTOR MUSCLE

M, myograms; *SM, STR*, potentials in smooth and striated parts of muscle, respectively; *a*, striated muscle potentials recorded during swimming movements of the intact animal; *b*, smooth and striated muscle responses to tactile stimulation of the visceral ganglion; *c*, records from two experiments showing responses of the striated muscle to electrical stimulation of the visceral ganglion; *d*, electrical activity in the smooth muscle during a sequence of swimming movements.

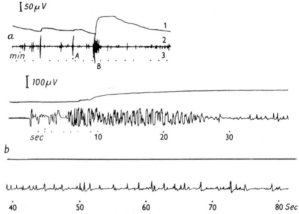

FIG. 9.14B. RECORDINGS FROM POSTERIOR ADDUCTOR MUSCLE OF *Mytilus*

Upper tracing, myogram; *below*, muscle potentials. Spontaneous activity of intact animal in water; *a*, small and large contractions; *b*, muscle potentials recorded during contraction. (From Lowy (81, 82).)

interest because of their strong maintained contractions (cf. p. 380). Those which have been singled out for study include the adductors, closing the valves, and the byssus retractor muscles. The adductor muscles exhibit fast (phasic) and slow (tonic) contractions (Fig. 9.14). Most adductor muscles contain both striated and plain fibres, mixed together (*Lima*), or segregated into separate bundles (*Pecten*). Adductor muscles sometimes show macroscopic colour differences into a grey component, striated and responsible for phasic contraction; and a white component, containing plain fibres and responsible for quick tonic contractions (*Ostrea, Pecten,* etc.).

The anterior and posterior adductor muscles are supplied by nerves from the cerebral and visceral ganglia respectively; the byssal retractor by the pedal ganglion. Anterior retractor muscles of the mantle receive their nerve supply from the cerebral ganglion. According to Pumphrey (106), the anterior adductor and mantle retractor muscles of *Mya* receive two kinds of excitatory nerve fibres. During reflex stimulation activity in one

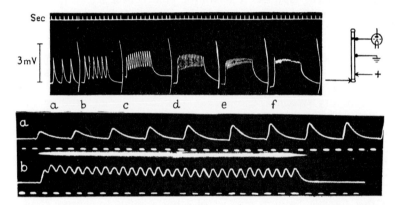

FIG. 9.15. ELECTRICAL RESPONSES OF THE BYSSUS RETRACTOR MUSCLE OF *Mytilus*
(*Above*) responses to stimulation, *a*, 0·5/sec; *b*, 1/sec; *c*, 2/sec; *d*, 3/sec; *e*, 5/sec; *f*, 7/sec. (*Below*) stimulation, *a*, 3·5/sec; *b*, 15/sec. Time trace, 0·1 sec. (From Fletcher, 1937, and Prosser *et al.* (103).)

group of motor fibres is present during fast contraction, whereas activity in the other group occurs during tonic contraction (or delay of relaxation).

A single stimulus produces but a small response; repeated stimulation elicits tetanus and increase of tension. Peripheral facilitation also occurs, as evidenced by the enhanced effect of paired shocks and staircase produced by low-frequency stimulation (cf. Fig. 9.15). Intimate details of peripheral neuromuscular organization are still unknown (17, 46, 103).

Earlier work suggested that the lamellibranch plain adductor possesses a peculiar *catch* mechanism which, when set, might maintain tension for long periods with little energy expenditure. This hypothesis postulates that the state of the contractile material alters during tonic contraction: viscosity increases, and the material "sets" in a new state. Lactic acid accumulates during prolonged contraction, revealing energy consumption. Electrical recording from muscles shows that both phasic and tonic contraction are accompanied by muscle action potentials, and during maintained tonus there is continuous electrical discharge (Figs. 9.14, 9.15).

The time course of relaxation is prolonged, and as an alternative hypothesis it has been suggested that maintenance of tonus in the smooth
muscle depends upon slow tetanic stimulation and slow decay of tension.
Following denervation the adductor muscle remains contracted and
continues to exhibit electrical discharge. This tetanically maintained contraction, of peripheral nature, may be myogenic or originate in peripheral
neural elements. The recent discovery of peripheral nerve cells in lamellibranch adductors and retractors favours the latter explanation (20, 26,
81, 82, 83).

Evidence also exists for peripheral inhibitory control in lamellibranch
plain muscle. Stimulation of the anterior byssus retractor muscle of *Mytilus*
by direct current produces a prolonged contraction, which is suppressed
by faradic stimulation of the muscle. Furthermore, d.c. contraction of this
muscle is abolished by weak a.c. stimulation of the pedal ganglion.
Relaxation of the adductor muscles of *Pecten* and *Mytilus* has been obtained by reflex sensory excitation. This could be due to central inhibition,
but the same effect is produced by electrical stimulation of the peripheral
end of a cut nerve tract supplying the slow adductor muscle of *Pecten*.
The excitatory system is cholinergic, and acetylcholine produces muscle
depolarization and tonic contraction. 5-Hydroxytryptamine causes prompt
relaxation of tonic contractions produced by acetylcholine and electrical
stimulation, without producing any changes in membrane potential; it
does not appear to rank as a natural inhibitory substance. Inhibitory fibres
probably act on local ganglion cells, reducing their activity (3, 18, 55,
56, 81, 82, 119, 124, 126).

Other Groups. Smooth muscles of other animals sometimes show two
kinds of contractions, quick and slow responses, with and without propagation of action potentials. Body-wall muscle of holothurians (*Thyone*) gives
propagated spike potentials, easily fatigued. This is a non-facilitating
muscle served by successive branches of the radial nerve in an overlapping
pattern (102). Pharyngeal retractors show two kinds of response, namely
fast and slow contractions, corresponding to which fast and slow potentials
have been recorded. The fast response is soon fatigued by repetitive
stimulation and shows no increment above fusion frequency. The slow
response, on the contrary, is facilitated to some extent under direct
stimulation (*Thyone*). With indirect stimulation via the radial nerve,
marked facilitation of the pharyngeal retractor muscle is obtained (*Cucumaria*). This facilitation is believed to take place between internuncial
neurones of the motor complex (98, 99, 103).

Golfingia retractor muscles likewise give quick phasic and slow tonic
contractions. Associated with these responses are all-or-nothing fast
spikes, fatiguing on repetitive stimulation, and graded slow potentials,
which facilitate on repetitive stimulation (Fig. 9.16). Muscle fibres are
discrete and morphologically uniform; transmission of excitation throughout the muscles is by way of parallel nerve fibres. The fast and slow muscle
potentials are preceded by nerve potentials, seemingly in large and small

nerve fibres, respectively. On present evidence, one group of nerves elicits the fast contraction, another group the slow contraction. This leaves unresolved the problem whether the two kinds of contractions in *Golfingia* muscle (as in holothurian muscle) are produced in one and the same muscle fibre. If this is the case, a situation may exist resembling crustacean neuromuscular control, whereby two kinds of excitatory fibres evoke fast propagated and slow non-propagated action potentials, respectively (103, 104, 124, 125, 126).

BIOCHEMICAL OBSERVATIONS. The shortening of muscle is dependent upon the behaviour of a particular fibrous protein, actomyosin. Composed

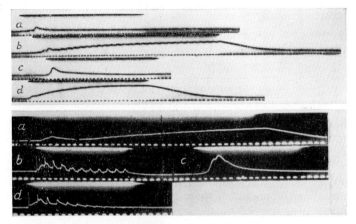

FIG. 9.16. CONTRACTIONS AND ACTION POTENTIALS FROM PROBOSCIS RETRACTOR MUSCLES OF *Golfingia gouldii*

(*Above*) contractions, *a*, *b*, at 5/sec; *c*, *d*, at 20/sec; *a*, *c* at low intensity which elicited spike only; *b*, *d* at higher intensity which elicited spike and slow wave. (*Below*) *a* contraction and *b* action potentials at 9·6/sec at intensity eliciting both spike and slow wave; *c* contraction and *d* action potential at 9·6/sec at intensity eliciting spike only. Time trace, 0·1 sec. (Prosser *et al.* (103).)

of two fractions, actin and myosin, linked together within the muscle fibre, actomyosin accounts for about half the dry weight of muscle. Myofibrils are composed largely of actomyosin, plus a small amount of tropomyosin. Myosins from widely disparate groups show much similarity in chemical properties. Another myosin, paramyosin, is a major component of smooth addector muscles of bivalve molluscs, and its presence in such large amounts has been linked with sustained contraction (the "catch" mechanism). The proteins of the sarcoplasm are globular molecules and consist largely of enzymes.

The myosin filaments are restricted to the *A* bands, whereas the actin filaments extend from the *Z* line through the *I* band into the *A* band. It is believed that the actin filaments lie between the myosin filaments, with which they form temporary cross-linkages. During contraction the actin filaments are drawn past the myosin filaments into the *A* band. The immediate energy for contraction is provided by the high-energy bonds of phosphate groups (adenosine triphosphate, ATP, and inosine triphosphate), which interact with actomyosin (20, 37, 124).

Another phosphate donor, phosphagen, is concerned with rapid regeneration of ATP during muscle activity. The distribution of phosphagens has been a matter of considerable interest, but is no longer thought to have much phylogenetic significance. Of seven known phosphagens, two—phosphocreatine and phosphoarginine—are the most commonly occurring phosphagens of muscle. Phosphocreatine is the phosphagen of vertebrates, but also occurs in protochordates, echinoderms and annelids. The other phosphagens occur in annelids and sipunculids. Some invertebrates have two phosphagens, frequently phosphocreatine and phosphoarginine, as in enteropneusts and echinoids. Indeed, in sea urchins, there are differences in phosphagens between embryo and adult (12, 13, 23, 31, 118).

ELECTRIC ORGANS

Organs which generate electrical shocks have evolved independently in several groups of fish. These include the freshwater electric eel *Electrophorus*, and marine torpedoes, rays and stargazers (*Astroscopus*). In nearly all fish the electric organ is derived from muscle. The electric organ of *Torpedo* represents modified branchial muscle; that of *Raja*, lateral caudal muscle; and the organ of *Astroscopus*, one of the eye muscles.

The two electric organs of the torpedo lie at the bases of the pectoral fins and are made up of plates arranged in vertical columns (Fig. 9.17). Each organ contains 400–500 columns and in each column there are about 400 plates (*Torpedo torpedo*). Their importance to the animal is attested by the fact that electric tissue forms about one-sixth of body volume in *Torpedo*. In the electric ray (*Raja*) the organs extend along the sides of the tail and consist of a series of prisms in parallel, each prism made up of a large number of plates. Some 13,000 discs or plates occur in each electric organ of *Raja pulchra*.

The electroplates are derived in the embryo from electroblasts. These resemble sarcoblasts, the precursors of muscle, but they have lost the ability to contract, and develop greatly expanded end-plate surfaces.

The electric organs are under nervous control and are richly innervated. In the torpedo they are supplied by branches of the vagus nerve which arise in large lobes of the medulla oblongata; in the skate the nervous supply is derived from ventral roots of spinal nerves. The terminal nervous arborization closely invests one surface of the electroplate (Fig. 9.18). Surrounding the electroplates are connective tissue, intercellular fluid and blood vessels. Present evidence indicates that each electroplate is a modified muscle fibre, with the development of an electrical potential as its chief physiological function; the innervated surface of the electric plate would thus correspond to a motor end-plate (58, 59).

During discharge each electroplate generates a small voltage (about 150 mV in *Electrophorus*) and the electrical potentials of the separate electroplates summate. The dorsal surface of the organ is positive in the torpedo, and the current travels through the organ from the ventral to the dorsal surface. Thus, the columns of electroplates discharge in parallel,

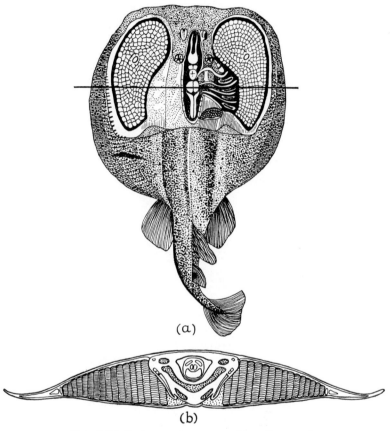

(a)

(b)

Fig. 9.17. Electric Organs of *Torpedo torpedo*

(*a*) Dissection of upper surface showing two electric organs (O). (*b*) vertical transverse section through the fish in the plane indicated by the transverse line in (*a*). (After Fritsch and Dahlgren.)

whereas the electroplates within each column act in series. Voltages developed by *Torpedo occidentalis* on open circuit, and with known external resistances, have been measured. The total peak voltage (measured without external resistance) lies between 20–30 V; that developed on open circuit reaches 220 V. Current output has been calculated for various external shunts, and has been found to increase as the voltage decreases, in a linear relationship. Calculated maximal current values are about 4 A in *Narcine brasiliensis* and 60 A in *T. nobiliana*. Maximal power developed at peak of discharge amounts to 10–35 W in *Narcine*, and 3–6 kW in *Torpedo*. Shocks of the electric skate (*Raja clavata*) are rather weak, about 4 V maximum (measured in air).

When an electric torpedo discharges, each electric organ fires off a train of some 2–7 pulses at intervals of a few msec (Fig. 9.19). Individual responses are of constant height and obey the all-or-nothing law. Each spike lasts 1·75–2·25 msec, with a rising phase of 0·5–0·7 msec; latencies vary from 1–4 msec (*Torpedo torpedo*). In skates (*Raja*) they are much

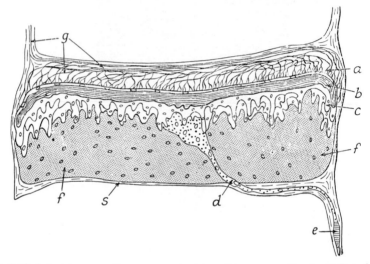

FIG. 9.18. LONGITUDINAL SECTION THROUGH AN ELECTRICAL PLATE OF *Raja batis*

g, nerve fibres passing to plate; *a–f*, parts of electric plate (*a*, outer protoplasmic and nuclear layer; *b*, striated layer; *c*, alveolar layer; *d*, stem of disc; *e*, striated zone of disc; *f*, posterior gelatinous cushion). *s*, septum. (After Ewart, 1889.)

longer, about 12 msec, with rising phase 2–2·5 msec. The spike is mono-phasic and hence non-propagated in the ray and torpedo.

The electric plates of *Electrophorus* are directly excitable, whereas those of *Torpedo* are not and can be excited only through the nerve. In the latter animal nerve section and degeneration render the organ inexcitable. Each time the electric lobe of the medulla or the nerve is stimulated a single discharge is produced in the electric organ. Reflex stimulation produces a volley of impulses in the nerve to the electric organ, accompanied by a corresponding series of electric discharges (Fig. 9.20). Functional analysis of the reflex pathway has revealed a relay centre (oval nucleus) in the medulla, where ascending fibres from the cord terminate. From this bulbar nucleus impulses are relayed to motor neurones of the electric

organ in the electric lobe. All parts of both organs discharge almost
synchronously, within a period of 1 msec, thereby providing maximal
power output. It appears that this synchrony is due to different latencies
in central neurones aided by a field effect from the electroplates initially
excited.

Membrane potentials have been measured in single electroplates of the
electric eel (*Electrophorus*). The resting potential is 84 mV across each
face, the inside of the cell being negative to the exterior. In this animal
only the posterior face of the plate is excitable; on stimulation a large spike

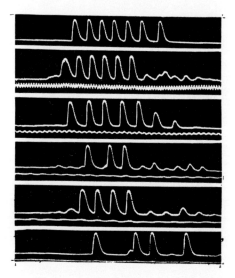

FIG. 9.19. RECORDS OF DISCHARGE OF THE ELECTRIC ORGAN OF *Torpedo torpedo*

Upper record, natural discharge; five following traces, discharge provoked by stimulation of the electric lobes with alternating current, at frequencies of 1,000, 500, 200, 150
and 100 c/s. (From Albe-Fessard (5).)

is produced, at the peak of which the membrane potential is reversed by
67 mV. During activity the voltages across the opposite faces add together,
each electroplate contributing 151 mV (on open circuit) to the total
discharge. The electrical response of the electroplate appears to be
fundamentally similar to that of a muscle fibre. An impulse is propagated
along its length at a velocity of 1·7 m/sec. It is likely that, as in muscle, the
electrical energy liberated during discharge is derived from the migration
of ions, sodium moving into the cell and potassium escaping to the exterior. Electric organs, like muscle, contain stores of phosphocreatine.
Presumably the phosphagen provides energy for restoring the resting
condition of the membrane after activity.

In *Electrophorus* (and other teleosts) the electroplate is regarded as a
transformed muscle fibre, the innervated surface of which bears a modified

muscle membrane. When excited (normally by a chemical transmitter), the surface is depolarized and develops a muscle action potential. In selachians, on the other hand, present evidence strongly suggests that the electroplate is a highly developed motor end-plate, the innervated surface of which develops an end-plate potential. This would explain why the organ of *Torpedo* is not directly excitable, and why excitability is lost after

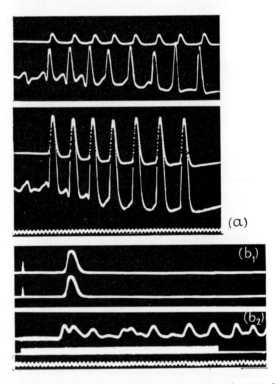

FIG. 9.20. ELECTRICAL DISCHARGES IN *Torpedo torpedo*

(*a*) Simultaneous recording of nervous discharge and corresponding reflex discharge in fragments of the electric organ connected to the c.n.s. Reflex discharge of the electric organ above; nerve impulses below, with discharge artifact. (*b₁*) Responses to stimulation of the electric lobe by a brief shock. Reception in the two symmetrical organs. (*b₂*) Stimulation of the electric lobe by prolonged current. Time trace in msec. (From Albe-Fessard (5).)

nerve degeneration or treatment with curare. The resting potential in a *Torpedo* electroplate is about 50 mV. In *Raja clavata* the peak potential developed by a discharging electroplate is about 60 mV, with little or no reversal of potential across the nervous face at the peak (22, 40).

The nerves to the electric organ are cholinergic. The organs of *Torpedo* contain appreciable quantities of acetylcholine and cholinesterase. Curare renders the organ inexcitable, and by perfusing with eserinized fluid it has been possible to demonstrate the release of acetylcholine during activity (*Torpedo, Narcine, Raja*). Injection of acetylcholine into the perfused organ produces potential changes which vary with the dose employed. These results support the theory that acetylcholine is the transmitter at the junction of nerve and electric organ.

Electric rays and torpedoes are sluggish in habits. They employ their electric organs for stunning prey, and they also discharge when irritated (p. 240). Freshwater electric fish produce small pulses which are used in direction-finding, but a comparable function has not been established for marine species. Electric rays are immune to their own shocks and to those of other electric fish in their neighbourhood, but it is not known how the animal protects itself and insulates its nervous system against its own electrical discharges (5, 6, 7, 8, 9, 42, 43, 48, 70, 71, 112).

FLOTATION AND GAS-BLADDERS

Invertebrates. Animals living in mid-water or surface regions of the ocean counteract gravity in diverse ways. When the densities of their bodies exceed that of sea water, constant locomotory activity is required to maintain height. The data assembled in Table 9.3 show the densities of some marine animals and the loads which various species would carry when maintaining themselves off the bottom. Some of the teleosts in this table have densities equal to sea water; these animals have a hydrostatic organ or swim-bladder.

Many pelagic invertebrates have densities which are not much different from those of sea water. This condition may be achieved by accumulation of ions of low specific gravity, as in *Noctiluca*, where the exact mechanism is unknown. In cranchiid squid the weight of the tissues is counterbalanced by a large volume of coelomic fluid having low density (sp. gravity 1·011). This condition is due to the high content of ammonium ions, the fluid containing 80 mM Na and 480 mM NH_4/l (29).

Many marine animals also contain highly gelatinous tissue which is very watery, and such animals have about the same specific gravity as sea water, e.g. jellyfish, ctenophores, pteropod molluscs and salps (Table 9.3). Although the body fluids are isosmotic with sea water, the specific gravities are less owing to partial exclusion of sulphate ion and its replacement by chloride. The result of this ionic regulation is to give the animal a degree of lift sufficient to offset the excess weight over sea water of the small amount of protein present (Fig. 9.21). In deep-sea sharks (squaloids), the excess weight of tissues over sea water is counterbalanced by large volumes of low density fat. The liver forms about 25% of the total volume of the fish, and contains some 70% of squalene, a hydrocarbon of low specific gravity (0·86). Deep-diving whales also contain large amounts of low-density fats (29, 30, 85). Certain animals have floats or gas-bladders in which the gas content is regulated and which act as hydrostatic organs. These can be regarded as special effector organs.

Gas-filled floats among invertebrates are found in siphonophores and cephalopods. The gas-float or pneumatophore of siphonophore coelenterates such as *Agalma* lies at the top of the colony. In the Portuguese man-of-war *Physalia* and the by-the-wind sailor *Velella* the pneumatophores are capacious and the animals float at the surface, driven by the winds that blow. In *Stephanomia*, for example, there is a gas-gland in the floor of the pneumatophore, where gas is secreted, and a pore in the roof through which gas can be released. This pore is guarded by a sphincter muscle. If

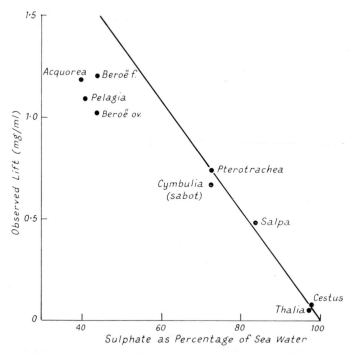

FIG. 9.21. OBSERVED LIFT OF BODY FLUID IN SEA WATER, PLOTTED AGAINST CONCENTRATION OF SULPHATE

The line shows the lift for sea waters in which the sulphate has been replaced isosmotically with chloride. The abscissa represents the sulphate concentrations of body fluids expressed as a percentage of sulphate concentration of sea water. (From Denton and Shaw (30).)

gas is removed from the pneumatophore it is refilled by secretion within 30 min. By secretion of gas into the pneumatophore or release through the pore the specific gravity of the colony can be regulated.

The pearly nautilus has an external, *Spirula* an internal shell containing gas-filled chambers (p. 641), which render them neutrally buoyant. Likewise, in *Sepia* the skeleton or cuttlebone contains gas-filled spaces that counterbalance the weight in sea water of the rest of the animal. The cuttlebone forms 9% of the total volume of *Sepia*, and has a specific gravity of 0·6. It contains a series of thin chambers laid down at frequent intervals, and these chambers contain nitrogen at a pressure of about 0·8 atm. When the chambers are formed liquid is extracted through a membrane at the posterior end, and gas slowly diffuses into the vacated space until the partial pressure equals that in the surrounding tissue (29).

The Teleostean Swim-bladder as a Hydrostatic Organ. The swim-bladder of marine teleosts has several functions: it acts as a hydrostatic organ, it is used for sound production and it aids in sound perception. As a hydrostatic organ the swim-bladder brings the density of the fish to that of sea water; consequently the fish is able to maintain position in mid-water with minimal locomotory activity and expenditure of energy. The volume of the swim-bladder of marine fish usually forms about 5% of that of the body, a value which gives a fish about the same density as sea water. Table 9.3 gives some values for the density of marine teleosts possessing swim-bladders, together with the densities of some selachians and invertebrates for comparison.

A fish living in mid-water can be presumed to have its density adjusted for life at the depth where it occurs. But when it swims up or down it is subject to changes of hydrostatic pressure; these pressure changes alter the volume of gas in the swim-bladder and change the density of the fish. Thus, when a fish ascends, the gas in the bladder will expand, the fish will become less dense and it will tend to rise to the surface. When it descends the gas in the bladder will become compressed, the density of the fish will decrease and it will tend to sink. To compensate for these changes in density the fish can adjust the volume of the swim-bladder so as to bring itself into hydrostatic equilibrium with its environment.

The swim-bladder is usually closed in marine fish and its volume is adjusted by addition or resorption of gas across its walls. When a fish swims downwards gas is added to the swim-bladder to compensate for the decrease in volume, and when it swims upwards gas is resorbed to reduce the volume of the fish. Gas is secreted into the bladder by a gas gland (Fig. 9.22) provided with retia mirabilia, and is resorbed in a special vascular area known as the oval. The gas-gland is usually situated in the anterior region of the swim-bladder. It consists of a highly glandular epithelium supplied by a rich network of large arteries and veins, which give rise to one or two sets of long capillaries. The oval, where absorption of gas takes place, is a modified region of the posterior wall of the bladder. Here the wall is thin and highly vascular in structure. The oval is surrounded by sphincter and radial muscles, which close it off from the bladder lumen or expose it, respectively. Most resorption of gas takes place across the oval. Since gases in the bladder are at a higher tension than in the blood, they tend to diffuse across the oval along the pressure gradient. By constriction of the sphincter muscles about the oval, absorption of gases from the oval can be retarded or halted.

Gas is passed into the swim-bladder against a pressure gradient by some active secretory process. In fish from shallow water the swim-bladder gas contains 12–22% O_2, but in fish from deep water there is a much greater proportion of O_2 in the bladder gas. Thus, the bladder gas of an eel *Synaphobranchus pinnatus*, taken at 1,380 m (pressure 138 atm), had the following composition (in percentages): O_2, 84·6; N_2, 11·8; CO_2, 3·6. At this depth the partial pressures in the swim-bladder would be 117 atm

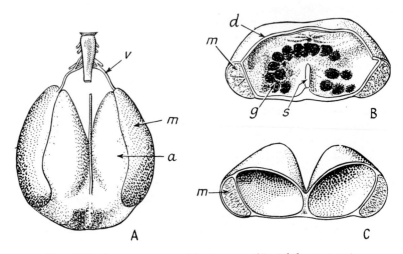

FIG. 9.22. AIR-BLADDER OF MIDSHIPMAN (*Porichthys notatus*)

A, ventral view of air-bladder. B, cross-section of bladder, showing diaphragm with its central opening, and numerous plates of the gas-gland on the ventral floor. C, cross-section of the anterior chamber showing cavities of the anterior horns and the air-bladder muscles. *a*, air-bladder; *d*, diaphragm; *g*, gas-gland; *m*, air-bladder muscle; *s*, septum; *v*, vagus nerve. (After Greene, 1924.)

for O_2 and 3 atm for CO_2. Since the partial pressures of gases in the blood would be only fractions of an atmosphere, these figures reveal the magnitude of the pressure gradient against which O_2 and CO_2 must be secreted (36, 61).

The swim-bladder gas contains different proportions of the chemically inert gases, argon, neon, etc., from those present in the mixture breathed by the fish. Relative to nitrogen the proportions of the very soluble argon are increased, and the less soluble neon and helium, decreased. It would seem that oxygen is secreted into the air-bladder as small bubbles, into which the inert gases diffuse; these bubbles carry the inert gases with them into the air-bladder (129).

A secretion of gas into the swim-bladder can be detected if a fish is subjected to an increase in hydrostatic pressure, or if gas is removed from the bladder by puncture. Conversely, over-inflation causes absorption of gases. After stimulation of the gas-bladder of *Fundulus heteroclitus* by deflation and over-inflation, the gas content of the bladder showed the following maximal ranges (the first figure refers to a fish recovering from deflation, the second to one recovering from over-inflation): O_2, 82, 0%; CO_2, 23·2, 0%; N_2, 85, 100%.

The mechanism of gas secretion has aroused much interest. It has been suggested that the secretion of oxygen depends on an increase of acidity in the blood as it passes through the gas-gland. When the blood becomes more acid the affinity of haemoglobin for oxygen is diminished (Bohr effect); moreover the oxygen capacity may be diminished in the presence of acid. It has been shown, however, that the acidified blood of certain deep-sea teleosts is saturated at oxygen tensions lower than those existing in the swim-bladder. It is unlikely, therefore, that a mechanism based on the Bohr effect exists for splitting off oxygen from the blood. The very close association of long afferent and efferent capillaries in the rete mirabile, arranged on the counter-current principle, allows maximal exchange of gases by diffusion between these two sets of vessels. The effluent blood, in consequence, may be thoroughly drained of oxygen. It is beginning to appear as if the glandular epithelium of the gas-gland is responsible for actively taking up and secreting this oxygen into the bladder.

Inflation and deflation of the swim-bladder are controlled by reflexes initiated by stimulation of exteroceptors (eyes and labyrinth). Efferent fibres to the swim-bladder pass along autonomic nerves (pneumogastric and sympathetic), but many aspects of control still have to be worked out. When the bladder is actively secreting, the gas-gland becomes dilated with blood and the secretory mucosa relaxes and the resorbent mucosa contracts; opposite changes occur in the mucosa when gas is being resorbed and the bladder is undergoing deflation. After vagotomy the secretory mucosa relaxes and the resorbent mucosa contracts, vessels of the gas-gland become constricted and gaseous secretion ceases. Stimulation of the intestinal vagus nerve causes reciprocal effects. Section of the sympathetic nerve supply causes only a slight rise in the O_2 content of the bladder. The vagus nerve is believed to contain two categories of nerve fibres: adrenergic, causing gaseous secretion and contraction of the muscularis mucosa; and cholinergic, causing contraction of the resorbent mucosa. Whether the effect of the secretory nerves is a direct one on the cells of the gas gland, or indirect on the blood supply is unknown. Changes in the tonus of the mucosa appear to be important in determining the direction and magnitude of gaseous exchange (35).

The ecology of the swim-bladder shows many interesting features. In shallow waters over the continental shelf the majority of free-swimming teleosts possess swim-bladders. Such fish are able to maintain position in mid-water with little apparent locomotory effort. In contrast a bladder is frequently absent in bottom-dwelling and littoral species of the neritic

TABLE 9.3

Densities and Sinking Factors for Various Marine Animals

$$\left(\text{Sinking factor} = 1{,}000 \times \frac{\text{density of animal}}{\text{density of sea water}}\right)$$

Animal	Density	Sinking Factor	Remarks
Coelenterata			
Aurelia aurita	1·027	1000	—
Anemonia sulcata	1·045	1018	—
Ctenophora			
Pleurobrachia pileus	1·0274	1000·2	—
Polychaeta			
Nereis diversicolor	1·074	1044	—
Crustacea			
Calanus finmarchicus	1·056	1029	—
Hemimysis lamornae	1·104	1075	—
Palaemon serratus	1·114	1086	♀ not in berry
Homarus vulgaris	1·170	1140	♂
Carcinus maenas	1·2076	1177	♂
Cancer pagurus	1·2784	1243	—
Mollusca			
Mytilus edulis	1·5793	1539	—
Chlamys opercularis	1·4895	1451	—
Littorina littoralis	1·9076	1867	—
Buccinum undatum	1·5003	1461	—
Aplysia punctata	1·0415	1014	—
Sepia officinalis	1·0351	1008	large specimen
Octopus vulgaris	1·0528	1026	large specimen
Echinodermata			
Asterias rubens	1·0713	1044	—
Echinus esculentus	1·0917	1063	—
Ophiothrix fragilis	1·3720	1338	—
Holothuria forskali	1·0401	1013	—
Antedon bifida	1·1903	1161	—
Cephalochordata			
Amphioxus lanceolatus	1·067	1040	—
Elasmobranchii			
Scyliorhinus canicula	1·076	1049	—
Raja clavata	1·074	1046	—
Squatina squatina	1·071	1044	—
Teleosts			
Mugil auratus	1·010	980	vol. of swim-bladder 5·6%
Zeus faber	1·018	992	ditto 4·3%
Conger conger	1·027	1001	ditto 4·7%
Crenilabrus melops	1·034	1008	ditto 4·9%
Gadus callarias	1·050	1023	swim-bladder present
Clupea harengus	1·061	1034	ditto
Gobius paganellus	1·110	1081	vol. of swim-bladder 0·3%
Pleuronectes platessa	1·063	1036	swim-bladder absent
Blennius pholis	1·070	1042	ditto
Scomber scombrus	1·071	1043	ditto
Callionymus lyra	1·084	1055	ditto
Solea solea	1·087	1059	ditto

(Data from Lowndes (72, 73, 75, 78, 79, 80) and Jones and Marshall (1953).)

zone. These fish usually rest on the bottom and only rarely swim upwards towards the surface, and then with effort. Examples of the last group are flat fish (Heterosomata) and gobies (Gobiidae). But young flat fish, in their larval pelagic stages, possess a swim-bladder. In the open oceans a swim-bladder is found in surface-dwelling species such as flying fishes, but is often absent in large oceanic species, e.g. tunnies. Pelagic teleosts dwelling between 100–500 m frequently possess a well-developed swim-bladder, e.g. Mycotophidae. These animals frequently undertake long vertical migrations and their swim-bladders have well-developed gas-glands and retia mirabilia. The swim-bladder is absent in many bathypelagic species and bathybenthic species (61, 85).

During conditions of asphyxia, marine fish draw upon the oxygen in the swim-bladder. This mechanism is of some value to species with air-bladders under conditions of temporary anoxia (111).

SOUND PRODUCTION

Although it has long been known that some marine animals produce sounds, it is only in recent years that detailed information has been secured by under-water recording. Sound production occurs in three groups of marine animals, namely crustaceans, fish and toothed whales. These animals make noises with snapping or stridulating devices (crustacea and fish), with swim-bladders (teleosts) or with the larynx (cetacea).

Crustacea. Many members of the higher crustacea make noises by stridulation, i.e. by rubbing parts of the exoskeleton against one another or by snapping their claws. In warm shallow waters the most consistent sound-producers are populations of snapping shrimps (spp. of *Alpheus* and *Synalpheus*). The snapping shrimp has a giant claw and produces a sharp snapping sound by suddenly moving the finger against the fixed portion of the chela. The sound spectrum ranges from 0·1 to at least 24 kc/s, with a broad peak from 2–15 kc/s. The peak sound pressure at a distance of 1 m is 200 dyn/cm². In natural populations of snapping shrimps there is a diurnal variation in level of noise, which becomes greater at night. The changes in noise levels probably represent increased activity of the shrimp at those times.

Many other crustaceans have specially differentiated stridulating organs. The spiny lobster *Palinurus*, for example, has a stridulating apparatus on the basal joints of the large antennae. Sound-producing crabs often have a ridged or striated area on one of the claws, which is rubbed against a modified area on the edge of the carapace or on one of the walking legs, e.g. *Pseudozius, Ocypode*. *Squilla* produces sounds by rubbing the uropods against the under-surface of the telson. The stridulating apparatus may be confined to the males, or occur in both sexes.

In some crustaceans the sounds appear to have a warning significance. *Palinurus* makes a creaking noise with its antennae when it is disturbed and other rock lobsters near by retire into their retreats. The snapping shrimp shoots its pistols for stunning small prey or discouraging too inquisitive visitors. *Ocypode*, a littoral crab, stridulates to warn other crabs that its burrow is occupied. And male fiddler crabs, *Uca*, living on sandy shores, drum on the ground with their large chelipeds as part of the breeding display (11, 28, 69, 114).

Fish. Some species of fish are surprisingly vocal. Noises are produced by stridulation, i.e. by moving parts of the skeleton against one another or by using the swim-bladder as a resonator. Horse-mackeral, trigger-fishes, etc., emit harsh sounds by grinding the pharyngeal teeth. In boar-fishes, file-fishes and others the spines of the fins produce harsh noises when moved against one another or against neighbouring parts of the skeleton.

The swim-bladder of teleosts is commonly involved in sound production. In this role it acts in one of two ways:

1. As a resonator, by picking up and amplifying noises made by adjacent structures. In trigger-fishes (*Balistes*) the swim-bladder functions as a resonator for sounds produced by stridulation of the post-clavicles against the cleithra, and in *Haemulon* for grinding noises produced by the pharyngeal teeth.

2. As an intrinsic sound-producer. In this role the swim-bladder is set into resonant vibration by contractions of adjacent muscles, as in gurnards (Triglidae), toad-fish (*Opsanus*), midshipman (*Porichthys*), etc. (Fig. 9.22).

The muscles which throw the swim-bladder into resonant vibration are attached to it in various ways. In some species the external muscles extend from the air-bladder to adjacent structures, to the anterior ribs in the cod *Gadus callarias* and to the lateral body wall in sciaenids (*Cynoscion*). In others the external muscles are attached solely to the air-bladder, as in the pollack (*Gadus pollachius*), gurnards, midshipman, toad-fish, etc.

By suitable electrical stimulation of nerves and muscles supplying the air-bladder, sounds have been produced which are characteristic of the fish under investigation. The air-bladder in the gurnard (*Trigla*) contains a perforated transverse partition which is set into vibration by air forced from one compartment of the bladder into the other. When the anterior spinal nerves supplying the external swim-bladder muscles are stimulated, the transverse diaphragm is set into vibration and grunting noises are produced. Kymograph recordings made from the squeteague reveal that the abdominal wall vibrates at a frequency of 24/sec. These movements are induced by the external swim-bladder muscles which contract at the same rate.

The frequency and intensity of noises made by various fish have been measured in recent years. In the majority of species tested the principal frequencies measured lie between 75 and 300 c/s. The croaker (*Micropogon undulatus*) produces a rapid burst of drumming noises, each pulse lasting 2 msec and having a frequency range of 100–10,000 c/s. The sea-robin *Prionotus carolinus* produces a modified rhythmic squawk or cackle, with a frequency range of 100–2,500 c/s and a principal frequency of 250 c/s. The toad-fish (*Opsanus tau*) gives off a series of intermittent boops, each lasting 0·5 sec and having a frequency range of 100–600 c/s; the principal frequency is 200 c/s. All these fish have drumming muscles. A sea-horse (*Hippocampus hudsonius*) that stridulates and amplifies the sound in the air-bladder emits clicking sounds at frequencies below 4,800 c/s. The maximum intensity measured was 22·6 dyn/cm^2 at a distance of 15 cm.

Although it is certain that many fishes produce noises it is by no means certain what is their significance. It has been suggested that, in some species, the noises are recognition signals, perhaps to bring about aggregation at breeding time. Sounds made by both sexes of *Hippocampus europaeus* are most frequent and intense during the breeding season and male gobies and blennies (*Bathygobius soporator* and *Chasmodes bosquianus*) use calls in courtship. In some sciaenids only the males possess a drumming apparatus. The calling of *Opsanus* appears to be associated with nest-guarding, perhaps as a means of asserting territorial rights. In other species sound production may be associated with aggressive behaviour or defensive manoeuvres, or may have social significance in gregarious fish, which can signal to each other when they discover food.

Under-water recordings made in Chesapeake Bay (Virginia) have revealed interesting changes in the sound-producing activities of croakers (*Micropogon undulatus*), a species in which both sexes drum. Croakers migrate in large numbers into Chesapeake Bay each spring. The chorus produced by these fish begins in the evening with fading light and continues until midnight, coinciding with the feeding period. The noise level was followed over a period extending from May to July and a seasonal variation was discovered, the noise reaching peak intensity during the first half of June. During this period the group voice of the croakers had fallen about an octave: in early June the main frequency was about 600 c/s, and had changed in early July to 250 c/s. Now the frequency of resonant vibration is inversely proportional to the length of the swim-bladder. It seems that the shift in average frequency reflects a change in the composition of the fish population. As older fish with larger bladders and deeper tones migrated into the Bay, they gradually become the dominant group in the croaker-population (85, 86, 117).

Toothed Whales (Odontoceti). Porpoises and dolphins are known to produce various kinds of under-water sounds. White whales (*Delphinapterus*) at sea are very vocal, producing a variety of high-pitched whistles and ticking noises under water. Recordings made from the bottle-nosed dolphin (*Tursiops truncatus*) reveal bird-like whistles, approximately 0·5 sec in duration, and under-water clicks repeated at rates of 5–100/sec. The whistles have a pitch-range beginning at 7,000 c/s and ending at about 15,000 c/s. The dominant frequencies of the clicks are in the sonic range, but there is a strong ultrasonic component, extending to 75 kc/s or higher. Dolphins lack vocal cords; their sounds are produced within the nasal passage, either by movement of valves or flaps in the nares or by the rapid passage of air past them. Dolphins have an acoustical range up to 120 kc/s, and they perceive the echoes of their clicking sounds. Moreover, they are able to analyse and interpret the echoes so as to locate and differentiate the nature of the surfaces which are reflecting the sounds: in these respects they employ a sonar system of great precision and refinement (63).

REFERENCES

1. ABBOTT, B. C. and AUBERT, X. M., "The force exerted by active striated muscle during and after change of length," *J. Physiol.*, **117**, 77 (1952).
2. ABBOTT, B. C. and LOWY, J., "Mechanical properties of *Mytilus* muscle," ibid., **120**, 50 P (1953).

3. ABBOTT, B. C. and LOWY, J., "Mechanical properties of *Pinna* adductor muscle," *J. Mar. Biol. Ass. U.K.*, **35**, 521 (1956).

4. AIELLO, E. L., "Factors affecting ciliary activity on the gill of the mussel," *Physiol. Zool.*, **33**, 121 (1960).

5. ALBE-FESSARD, D., "Données sur les caractères de la commande centrale de la décharge chez la Torpille et chez la Raie," *Arch. Sci. Physiol.*, **5**, 197 (1951).

6. ALBE-FESSARD, D., "Étude des facteurs périphériques d'organization de la décharge de la Torpille," ibid., **6**, 105 (1952).

7. ALBE-FESSARD, D. and BUSER, P., "Analyse microphysiologique de la transmission refléxe au niveau du lobe électrique de la Torpille (*Torpedo marmorata*)," *J. Physiol. Path. Gén.*, **46**, 923 (1954).

8. ALBE-FESSARD, D. and COUCEIRO, A., "Constitution élémentaire de la décharge naturelle de l'organe électrique de la Raie," *J. Physiol. Path. Gén.*, **42**, 529 (1950).

9. AMBACHE, N. and SAWAYA, P., "Use of *Holothuria* for acetylcholine assays of electric-organ extracts from *Narcine*," *Physiol. Comp. Oecol.*, **3**, 53 (1953).

10. ATWOOD, H. L., "Differences in muscle fibre properties as a factor in 'fast' and 'slow' contractions in *Carcinus*," *Comp. Biochem. Physiol.*, **10**, 17 (1963).

11. BABS, H., "Über Stridulationsorgane bei dekapoden Crustaceen," *Naturw. Wschr.*, **36**, 697 (1921).

12. BALDWIN, E., *Dynamic Aspects of Biochemistry*, 3rd. ed. (Cambridge Univ. Press, 1957).

13. BALDWIN, E. and YUDKIN., W. H., "The annelid phosphagen," *Proc. Roy. Soc. B.*, **136**, 614 (1950).

14. BATHAM, E. J. and PANTIN, C. F. A., "Muscular and hydrostatic action in the sea-anemone *Metridium senile*," *J. Exp. Biol.*, **27**, 264 (1950).

15. BATHAM, E. J. and PANTIN, C. F. A., "The organization of the muscular system of *Metridium senile*," *Quart. J. Micr. Sci.*, **92**, 27 (1951).

16. BATHAM, E. J. and PANTIN, C. F. A., "Slow contraction and its relation to spontaneous activity in the sea-anemone *Metridium senile*," *J. Exp. Biol.*, **31**, 84 (1954).

17. BAYLISS, L. E., BOYLAND, E. and RITCHIE, A. D., "The adductor mechanism of *Pecten*," *Proc. Roy. Soc. B.*, **106**, 363 (1930).

18. BENSON, A. A., HAYS, J. T. and LEWIS, R. N., "Inhibition in the slow muscle of the scallop," *Proc. Soc. Exp. Biol. N.Y.*, **49**, 289 (1942).

19. BIDOT, M., "Notes sur les Eolidiens," *Rev. Suisse Zool.*, **33**, 251 (1926).

20. BOURNE, G. H. (Ed.), *The Structure and Function of Muscle*, Vol. I and II (New York and London, Academic Press, 1960).

21. BOZLER, E., "Über die Frage des Tonus-substrates," *Z. vergl. Physiol.*, **7**, 407 (1928).

22. BROCK, L. G., ECCLES, R. M. and KEYNES, R. D., "The discharge of individual electroplates in *Raja clavata*," *J. Physiol.*, **122**, 4P (1953).

23. BROWN, R. and DANIELLI, J. F. (Ed.), "Fibrous proteins and their biological significance," *Symp. Soc. Exp. Biol.*, No. 9, pp. 183–281 (1955).

24. BÜLBRING, E., BURN, J. H. and SHELLEY, H. J., "Acetylcholine and ciliary movement in the gill plates of *Mytilus edulis*," *Proc. Roy. Soc. B.*, **141**, 445 (1953).

25. BULLOCK, T. H., "Neuromuscular facilitation in Scyphomedusae," *J. Cell. Comp. Physiol.*, **22**, 251 (1943).

26. BULLOCK, T. H. and HORRIDGE, G. A., *Structure and Function in the Nervous Systems of Invertebrates*, Vol. I and II (San Francisco and London, W. H. Freeman and Co., 1965).

27. CHAPMAN, G., "Studies on the mesogloea of coelenterates. 2. Physical properties," *J. Exp. Biol.*, **30**, 440 (1953).

28. CRANE, J., "Display, breeding and relationships of fiddler crabs (*Uca*)," *Zoologica, N.Y.*, **28**, 217 (1943).

29. DENTON, E. J., "Buoyancy mechanisms of sea creatures," *Endeavour*, **85**, 3 (1963).

30. DENTON, E. J. and SHAW, T. I., "The buoyancy of gelatinous marine animals," *Proc. Physiol. Soc., J. Physiol.*, **161**, 14P (1961).

31. DUBUISSON-BROUHA, A., "Muscle proteins of the lobster," *Bull. Acad. Belg. Cl. Sci.*, **39**, 121 (1953).

32. ECCLES, J. C., *The Neurophysiological Basis of Mind* (Oxford, Clarendon Press, 1953).

33. ESSEX, H. E., "Certain animal venoms and their physiologic action," *Physiol. Rev.*, **25**, 148 (1945).

34. EULER, U. S. VON, CHAVES, N. and TEODOSIO, N., "Effect of acetylcholine, noradrenaline, adrenaline and histamine on isolated organs of *Aplysia* and *Holothuria*," *Acta Physiol. Latinoamer.*, **2**, 101 (1952).

35. FÄNGE, R., "The mechanisms of gas transport in the euphysoclist swim-bladder," *Acta Physiol. scand.*, **30** (Suppl. 110), 133 pp. (1953).

36. FÄNGE, R., "The structure and function of the gas bladder in *Argentina silus*," *Quart. J. Micr. Sci.*, **99**, 95 (1958).

37. FARRANT, J. L. and MERCER, E. H., "Studies on the structure of muscle. 2. Arthropod muscles," *Exp. Cell. Res.*, **3**, 553 (1952).

38. FATT, P. and KATZ, B., "Distributed 'end-plate potentials' of crustacean muscle fibres," *J. Exp. Biol.*, **30**, 433 (1953).

39. FATT, P. and KATZ, B., "The electrical properties of crustacean muscle fibres," *J. Physiol.*, **120**, 171 (1953).

40. FATT, P. and WOODIN, A. M., "The release of phosphate from the electric organ of *Torpedo*," *J. Exp. Biol.*, **30**, 68 (1953).

41. FAWCETT, D. W. and PORTER, K. R., "A study of the fine structure of ciliated epithelia," *J. Morph.*, **94**, 221 (1954).

42. FESSARD, A., "Some basic aspects of the activity of electric plates," *Ann. N.Y. Acad. Sci.*, **47**, 501 (1946).

43. FESSARD, A., "Diversity of transmission processes as exemplified by specific synapses in electric organs," *Proc. Roy. Soc. B.*, **140**, 186 (1952).

44. FISCHBEIN, E. and WORLEY, L. G., "The structure of ciliated epithelial cells of lamellibranchs as revealed by the electron microscope," *Anat. Rec.*, **113**, 76 (1952).

45. FLETCHER, C. M., "Action potentials recorded from an unstriated muscle of simple structure," *J. Physiol.*, **90**, 233 (1937).

46. FLETCHER, C. M., "Excitation of the action potential of a molluscan unstriated muscle," *ibid.*, **90**, 415 (1937).

47. FRITSCH, F. E., *The Structure and Reproduction of the Algae*, Vol. I (Cambridge Univ. Press, 1935).

48. GARTEN, S., "Die Produktion von Elektrizität," *Handb. vergl. Physiol.*, **3** (2), 105 (1910–14).

49. GOSSELIN, R. E., MOORE, K. E. and MILTON, A. S., "Physiological control of molluscan gill cilia by 5-hydroxytryptamine," *J. Gen. Physiol.*, **46**, 277 (1962).

50. GRAY, J., "Ciliary movement" (Cambridge Univ. Press, 1928).

51. HANSON, J., "An unusual type of muscle-fibre," *Quart. J. Micr. Sci.*, **89**, 139 (1948).

52. HARREVELD, A. VAN and WIERSMA, C. A. G., "The function of the quintuple innervation of a crustacean muscle," *J. Exp. Biol.*, **16**, 121 (1939).

53. HINSEY, J. C., "The innervation of skeletal muscle," *Physiol. Rev.*, **14**, 515 (1934).

54. HORRIDGE, G. A., "Macrocilia with numerous shafts from the lips of the ctenophore, *Beroë*," *Proc. Roy. Soc. B*, **162**, 351 (1965).

55. HOYLE, G., *Comparative Physiology of the Nervous Control of Muscular Contraction* (Cambridge Univ. Press, 1957).

56. HOYLE, G. and LOWY, J., "The paradox of *Mytilus* muscle. A new interpretation," *J. Exp. Biol.*, **33**, 295 (1956).

57. HOYLE, G. and SMYTHE, T., JR., "Neuromuscular physiology of giant muscle fibers of a barnacle, *Balanus nubilus*," *Comp. Biochem. Physiol.*, **10**, 291 (1963).

58. ISHIYAMA, R. and KUWABARA S., "The electric fish of Japan. 1. Some observations on the structure of the electric organ of the skate," *J. Shimonoseki Coll. Fish.*, **3** (3), 75 (1954).

59. ISHIYAMA, R. and KUWABARA, S., "The electric fish of Japan. 2. The electric organ of *Breviraja*," *ibid.*, **4** (2), 203 (1955).

60. JAKUS, M. A., "The structure and properties of the trichocysts of Paramecium," *J. Exp. Zool.*, **100**, 457 (1945).

61. JONES, F. R. H., "The swimbladder," in *The Physiology of Fishes*, Vol. II, Ed. Brown, M. E. (New York, Academic Press, 1957).

62. KATZ, B., "Neuro-muscular transmission in invertebrates," *Biol. Rev.*, **24**, 1 (1949).

63. KELLOGG, W. N., *Porpoises and Sonar* (Univ. Chicago Press, 1961).

64. KEPNER, W. A., "The manipulation of the nematocysts of *Pennaria tearilla* by *Aeolis pilata*," *J. Morph.*, **73**, 297 (1943).

65. KERKUT, G. A., "The forces exerted by the tube feet of the starfish during locomotion," *J. Exp. Biol.*, **30**, 575 (1953).

66. KEYNES, R. D., "Electric organs," in *The Physiology of Fishes*, Ed. Brown, M. E. (New York, Academic Press, 1957).

67. KNIGHT-JONES, E. W., "Relations between metachronism and the direction of ciliary beat in Metazoa," *Quart. J. Micr. Sci.*, **95**, 503 (1954).

68. KOMAI, T., "The nematocysts in the ctenophore *Euchlora rubra*," *Amer. Nat.*, **85**, 73 (1951).

69. KNOWLTON, R. E. and MOULTON, J. M., "Sound production in the snapping shrimps, *Alpheus* and *Synalpheus*," *Biol. Bull.*, **125**, 311 (1963).

70. KUWABARA, S., "Some properties of acetylcholinesterase in the electric organ of the skate," *J. Shimonoseki Coll. Fish.*, **4** (2), 217 (1955).

71. LISSMANN, H. W., "On the function and evolution of electric organs in fish," *J. Exp. Biol.*, **35**, 156 (1958).

72. LOWNDES, A. G., "Ciliary movement and the density of *Pleurobrachia*," *Nature*, **150**, 579 (1942).

73. LOWNDES, A. G., "The displacement method of weighing living aquatic organisms," *J. Mar. Biol. Ass. U.K.*, **25**, 555 (1942).
74. LOWNDES, A. G., "The swimming of unicelluiar flagellate organisms," *Proc. Zool. Soc.*, **113A**, 99 (1943).
75. LOWNDES, A. G., "Some applications of the displacement method of weighing living aquatic organisms," ibid., **113A**, 28 (1943).
76. LOWNDES, A. G., "*Monas, Peranema*, and *Volvox*. Additional experiments on the working of a flagellum," ibid., **114**, 325 (1944).
77. LOWNDES, A. G., "Recent work on flagellar movement," *Sci. Progr.*, **35**, 62 (1947).
78. LOWNDES, A. G., "The densities of some common Echinodermata from Plymouth," *Ann. Mag. Nat. Hist.*, Ser. 12, **6**, 623 (1953).
79. LOWNDES, A. G., "The densities of some common aquatic mollusca from Plymouth," ibid., Ser. 12, **6**, 951 (1953).
80. LOWNDES, A. G., "Density of fishes," ibid., **8**, 241 (1955).
81. LOWY, J., "Contraction and relaxation in the adductor muscles of *Mytilus edulis*," *J. Physiol.*, **120**, 129 (1953).
82. LOWY, J., "Contraction and relaxation in the adductor muscles of *Pecten maximus*," ibid., **124**, 100 (1954).
83. LOWY, J., MILLMAN, B. M. and HANSON, J., "Structure and function in smooth tonic muscles of lamellibranch molluscs," *Proc. Roy. Soc.*, B., **160**, 525 (1964).
84. MARONEY, S. P. JR. and RONKIN, R. R., "Cholinesterase and ciliary activity in the gill of *Mytilus*," *Biol. Bull.*, **105**, 378 (1953).
85. MARSHALL, N. B., *Aspects of Deep Sea Biology* (London, Hutchinson, 1954).
86. MARSHALL, N. B., "The biology of sound-producing fishes," *Symp. Zool. Soc. Lond.*, No. 7, 45 (1962).
87. MURRAY, R. W., "The response of the ampullae of Lorenzini of elasmobranchs to electrical stimulation," *J. Exp. Biol.*, **39**, 119 (1962).
88. NICOL, J. A. C., "Muscle activity and drug action in the body-wall of the sabellid worm *Branchiomma vesiculosum*," *Physiol. Comp. Oecol.*, **2**, 339 (1952).
89. OLSON, M., "The histology of the retractor muscles of *Thyone briareus*," *Biol. Bull.*, **74**, 342 (1938).
90. OLSON, M., "Histology of the retractor muscles of *Phascolosoma gouldii*," ibid., **78**, 24 (1940).
91. PANTIN, C. F. A., "The nerve net of the Actinozoa," *J. Exp. Biol.*, **12**, 119 (1935).
92. PANTIN, C. F. A., "The excitation of nematocysts," ibid., **19**, 294 (1942).
93. PANTIN, C. F. A., "The elementary nervous system," *Proc. Roy. Soc.* B., **140**, 147 (1952).
94. PANTIN, C. F. A. and SAWAYA, P., "Muscular action in *Holothuria grisea*," *Zoologia, S. Paulo*, No. 18, p. 51 (1953).
95. PARKER, G. H., *The Elementary Nervous System* (London, Lippincott, 1919).
96. PHILLIPS, J. H. Jr. and ABBOTT, D. P., "Isolation and assay of the nematocyst toxin of Metridium senile," *Biol. Bull.*, **113**, 296 (1957).
97. PICKEN, L. E. R., "A note on the nematocysts of *Corynactis viridis*," *Quart. J. Micr. Sci.*, **94**, 203 (1953).

98. Pople, W. and Ewer, D. W., "Studies on the myoneural physiology of Echinodermata. 1. The pharyngeal retractor muscle of *Cucumaria*," *J. Exp. Biol.*, **31**, 114 (1954).

99. Pople, W. and Ewer, D. W., "Studies on the myoneural physiology of Echinodermata. 2. Circumoral conduction in *Cucumaria*," ibid., **32**, 59 (1955).

100. Prenant, A., "Recherches sur la structure des muscles des Annélides polychètes," *Arch. Zool. Exp. Gén.*, **69**, 135 pp. (1929).

101. Prosser, C. L. (Ed.), *Comparative Animal Physiology* (London, Saunders, 1950).

102. Prosser, C. L., "Activation of a non-propagating muscle in *Thyone*," *J. Cell. Comp. Physiol.*, **44**, 247 (1954).

103. Prosser, C. L., Curtis, H. J. and Travis, D. M., "Action potentials from some invertebrate non-striated muscles," *J. Cell. Comp. Physiol.*, **38**, 299 (1951).

104. Prosser, C. L. and Melton, C. E. Jr., "Nervous conduction in smooth muscle of *Phascolosoma* proboscis retractors," ibid., **44**, 255 (1954).

105. Prosser, C. L., Nagai, T. and Nystrom, R. A., "Oscular contractions in sponges," *Comp. Biochem. Physiol.*, **6**, 69 (1962).

106. Pumphrey, R. J., "The double innervation of muscles in *Mya arenaria*," *J. Exp. Biol.*, **15**, 500 (1938).

107. Robson, E. A., "Nematocysts of *Corynactis*. The activity of the filament during discharge," *Quart. J. Micr. Sci.*, **94**, 229 (1953).

108. Robson, E. A., "The structure and hydrodynamics of the musculo-epithelium in *Metridium*," ibid., **98**, 265 (1957).

109. Ross, D. M., "Quick and slow contractions in the isolated sphincter of the sea anemone, *Calliactis parasitica*," *J. Exp. Biol.*, **34**, 11 (1957).

110. Ross, D. M. and Pantin, C. F. A., "Factors affecting facilitation in Actinozoa. The action of certain ions," ibid., **17**, 61 (1940).

111. Safford, V., "Asphyxiation of marine fish with and without CO_2 and its effect on the gas content of the swimbladder," *J. Cell. Comp. Physiol.*, **16**, 165 (1940).

112. Sawaya, P. and Mendes, E. G., "Cholinesterase activity of electric organ of Narcine," *Zoologia, S. Paulo*, No. 16, p. 321 (1951).

113. Schmandt, W. and Sleator, W. Jr., "Deviation from all-or-none behavior in a molluscan unstriated muscle: decremental conduction and augmentation of action potentials," *J. Cell. Comp. Physiol.*, **46**, 439 (1955).

114. Schöne, H., "Complex behavior," in *The Physiology of Crustacea*, Ed. Waterman, T. H., Vol. 2, p. 465 (New York, London, Academic Press, 1960).

115. Sleigh, M. A., *The Biology of Cilia and Flagella* (Oxford, London, New York, Pergamon Press, 1962).

116. Smith, J. E., "The motor nervous system of the starfish, *Astropecten irregularis*," *Phil. Trans.* B., **234**, 521 (1950).

117. Tavolga, W. N. (Ed.), *Marine Bio-acoustics* (Oxford, London, Pergamon Press, 1964).

118. Thoai, N. van and Roche, J., "Les phosphagènes," *Biol. Rev.*, **39**, 214 (1964).

119. Twarog, B. M., "Responses of a molluscan smooth muscle to acetyl-choline and 5-hydroxytryptamine," *J. Cell. Comp. Physiol.*, **44**, 141 (1954).

120. WIERSMA, C. A. G., "The innervation of the legs of the coconut crab, *Birgus latro*," *Physiol. Comp. Oecol.*, **1**, 68 (1949).
121. WIERSMA, C. A. G., "A bifunctional single motor axon system of a crustacean muscle," *J. Exp. Biol.*, **28**, 13 (1951).
122. WIERSMA, C. A. G., "On the innervation of the muscles in the leg of the lobster, *Homarus vulgaris*," *Arch. Néerl. Zool.*, **8**, 384 (1951).
123. WIERSMA, C. A. G., "Neurones of arthropods," *Cold. Spr. Harb. Symp. Quant. Biol.*, **17**, 155 (1952).
124. WIERSMA, C. A. G., "Comparative physiology of invertebrate muscle," *Annu. Rev. Physiol.*, **14**, 159 (1952).
125. WIERSMA, C. A. G., "Neural transmission in invertebrates," *Physiol. Rev.*, **33**, 326 (1953).
126. WIERSMA, C. A. G., "Neuromuscular mechanisms," in *Recent Advances in Invertebrate Physiology* (Univ. Oregon Publications, 1957).
127. WIERSMA, C. A. G. and RIPLEY, S. H., "Innervation patterns of crustacean limbs," *Physiol. Comp. Oecol.*, **2**, 391 (1952).
128. WIERSMA, C. A. G. and RIPLEY, S. H., "Further functional differences between fast and slow contractions in certain crustacean muscles," ibid., **3**, 327 (1954).
129. WITTENBERG, J. B., "The secretion of inert gases into the swim-bladder of fish," *J. Gen. Physiol.*, **41**, 783 (1958).

CHAPTER 10

NERVOUS SYSTEM AND BEHAVIOUR

> In the multicellular animal, especially for those higher reactions which
> constitute its behaviour as a social unit in the natural economy, it is
> nervous reaction which *par excellence* integrates it, welds it together
> from its components and constitutes it from a mere collection of organs
> an animal individual.
>
> SIR CHARLES SHERRINGTON, 1947. *The Integrative Action of the*
> *Nervous System.*

CO-ORDINATION in metazoans is accomplished by two mechanisms,
chemical (hormonal) and nervous. In a broad sense, all chemical substances
which penetrate into the body, or are released by the cells in the normal
course of metabolism and circulate in the body fluids, bring about changes
in the organism. Many higher animals, however, have evolved endocrine
glands which discharge chemical mediators into the blood stream, and
various aspects of hormonal co-ordination are noted in other chapters.

All animals above the sponges possess a specialized conducting tissue,
the nervous system, for controlling the visceral activities of the organism,
and for mediating and co-ordinating responses to environmental events.
In simpler animals the nervous system is diffuse and has the appearance
of a network. In more complex organisms there is a tendency for the
integrative functions of the nervous system to be localized in special centres
—ganglia, brain and nerve cords—which contain most of the nerve cell
bodies, and from which nerve fibres go to and from the periphery and the
various organs. The most advanced nervous systems are found in active,
highly organized animals, arthropods, cephalopods and vertebrates. In
their highest expression, such nervous systems permit complex behaviour,
variability of response to change of environmental circumstances and
utilization of past experience in the life-span of the animal. In short,
animals endowed with complicated nervous systems are able to perceive
a greater range of environmental stimuli, and react to them in intricate
and varied ways (85).

CO-ORDINATION IN ABSENCE OF A NERVOUS SYSTEM

Excitation and conduction are regarded as generalized properties of
protoplasm, occurring in all cells. Conduction of an excitatory state
across the cell surface, or even from cell to cell, has been described in
plant cells, eggs and other non-nervous elements. Transmission across
ciliary fields by non-nervous mechanisms is well known in animals, and
special conditions are found in protozoans, which lack anything that can
be termed nervous tissue. During transmission a wave of depolarization

proceeds over the plasma membrane. In nervous tissues the universal properties of excitation and conduction are accentuated as the primary activities of the nerve cell.

Protozoa. Many ciliates possess a neuromotor system which is possibly concerned with conduction and co-ordination of contractile responses. This system consists of a regular network of fibrils, sometimes connected with a region of differentiated cytoplasm known as the motorium, and linking cirri, membranelles, etc. (Fig. 10.1). Destruction of the motorium or interruption of the fibrils results in disturbances of locomotion and

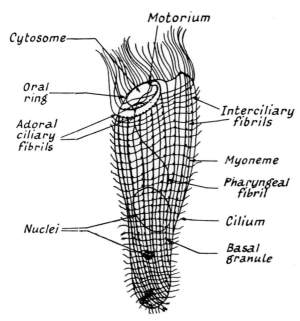

FIG. 10.1. NEUROMOTOR SYSTEM OF A CILIATE *Boveria teredinidi.* (From Pickard, 1927.)

co-ordination of movement in ciliates (*Euplotes, Chlamydodon,* etc.). Co-ordinated movements of cilia and other organelles depend upon some integrating mechanism, and this may be the neuromotor system, as the experiments just cited suggest (69, 110).

NERVOUS TRANSMISSION

Nerve cells (neurones) consist of a cell body and fibres, the latter sometimes separable as dendrites and axons (Fig. 10.2). Dendrites conduct impulses towards the cell, axons away from the cell. Some types of neurones lack dendrites, e.g. primary sensory cells in which the impulse originates in the cell body, and certain ganglion cells where axons terminate directly on the cell body. Unipolar neurones are widespread in invertebrates: each cell

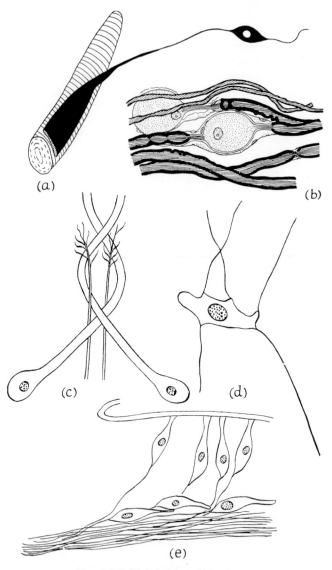

FIG. 10.2. VARIETIES OF NEURONES

(*a*) Ribbon (motor axon) on muscle fibre of *Astropecten*; (*b*) bipolar (sensory) neurones in a spinal ganglion of *Raja batis*; osmophilic sheaths are shown in black; (*c*) medial giant axons of *Nereis*; (*d*) multi-polar nerve cell in the ventral cord of a terebellid worm; (*e*) primary sensory neurones in a parapodium of *Nereis*. ((*a*) After Smith, 1950; (*b*) after Ranvier, 1875; (*c*) after Hamaker, 1898; (*d*), (*e*) after Retzius, 1891, 1892).)

gives rise to a single process which then subdivides; synapses occur between nerve fibres, and the cell body functions as a trophic centre outside the main path of transmission (Figs. 10.12, 10.14). In nervous systems neurones are arranged in complex patterns. From the receptors sensory impulses are fed into the nervous system; impulses pass from neurone to neurone across interneural boundaries (synapses), and proceed along efferent axons towards the effector organs.

When a nervous impulse proceeds along a nerve fibre it is accompanied by a wave of surface depolarization, which is revealed as a transitory rise of electrical potential known as the action potential. This takes the form of a negative spike potential which rises rapidly to a maximum and then decays at a decreasing rate. The action potential is all-or-none in nature, i.e. the height of the spike is unaffected by the intensity of the stimulus above threshold. Immediately after excitation or the passage of an impulse the fibre is inexcitable and refractory to another impulse. This phase is followed by a relative refractory period of reduced excitability, and later by a stage of heightened excitability, the supernormal phase.

A quiescent nerve fibre possesses a resting potential which depends on differences in the distribution of ions across the fibre-membranes. Analyses of axoplasm have revealed high internal concentrations of K^+, amounting to about 360 mM in cuttlefish giant axons, and low levels of Na^+ and Cl^- (Table 2.8). The low internal chloride is balanced by an accumulation of large organic ions within the fibre. The interior of the fibre is negative to the exterior, and this potential difference is due to the high concentration gradient of potassium across the membrane. By the use of micro-electrodes inserted into squid giant axons, direct measurements have been made of resting and action potentials. At rest the potential is some 60 mV negative; during activity the inside of the membrane becomes about 50 mV positive (the action potential) and consequently reverses in sign (Fig. 10.3).

When the fibre-membrane is depolarized a brief change occurs in membrane permeability. There is initially a large increase of sodium permeability, and sodium ions rapidly penetrate into the fibre. Near the peak of the action potential a change occurs from high sodium to potassium permeability. According to recent hypothesis the first stage of the action potential consists of a flow of capacity current. The rising phase of the action potential is produced by an inward surge of sodium ions, the falling phase by an accelerated outward movement of potassium ions, which restores the resting potential. The immediate source of energy for the nervous impulse, therefore, is derived from the movement of ions down the concentration gradients. The axon possesses some active secretory mechanism, which restores and maintains the ionic gradient across the membrane by pumping out sodium. The secretory mechanism for discharging sodium appears to be coupled with one that controls potassium influx. The organic anions within the fibre are non-diffusible, and the chloride distributes itself according to the Donnan equilibrium.

The changes in Na^+ and K^+ per impulse are minute relative to the total concentrations of ions within the fibre. Even in the absence of some restoring mechanism the axon is able to transmit many impulses before it is fatigued. This effect depends on the size of the axon: a large fibre has a greater potassium store, and hence fatigues less readily than one of small diameter.

Transmission of an impulse is explained on the basis of the local-circuit theory. On applying a stimulus to a nerve there is a local build-up at the cathode of electrotonic potential, which is the local response to the stimulus. If the latter is above threshold the local potential gives rise to a

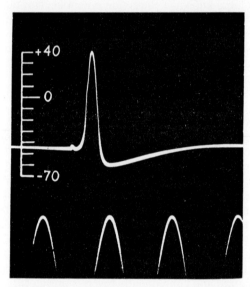

FIG. 10.3. ACTION POTENTIAL RECORDED BETWEEN THE INSIDE AND THE OUTSIDE OF THE GIANT AXON OF THE SQUID *Loligo*

Time marker, 500 c/s. The vertical scale indicates the potential of the internal electrode (in volts). (From Hodgkin and Huxley (1945).)

propagated response, the action potential. In this process the action potential continually stimulates adjoining regions of the fibre by current flow away from the active point, and a self-propagating disturbance arises, which proceeds along the fibre to its terminus (30, 31, 43, 46, 47, 48, 49, 50, 51, 60, 63, 109).

Conduction Speed

The speed of conduction in nerve tracts and in nerve fibres depends on a number of variables. There are probably intrinsic differences in axon velocities of different species, but these are not sufficient to mask the part played by other factors. In any given fibre, conduction speed varies with the temperature, the Q_{10} for molluscan nerve, for example, lying between 1·4 and 1·8 (114). Some of the older data, derived from mechanical recording, are too low when compared with more precise measurements by electronic methods, but they still indicate the relative velocities of different fibre-systems. The principal factors determining the overall speed of conduction are: continuity of fibres; axon diameter; thickness of myelin sheath.

Conduction tends to be slow in nerve-nets and in neuropile. The nervous system of coelenterates consists of a network of neurones, most of which extend only short distances before making contact with other elements. Similarly, in the nerve cords of higher animals (annelids, crustaceans), the neuropile contains many small neurones, whose processes extend through only one or two segments before establishing synaptic contact with other neurones in series. Nerve fibres in nerve-net and neuropile are generally very small, at most a few micra in diameter, and this alone keeps conduction velocity at a low level. Apart from this factor, impulses which have to pass across many synaptic junctions are subjected to synaptic delay at each junction, and the speed of transmission in such a system is reduced correspondingly. Some data for transmission speeds in individual fibres, nerve-nets and neuropiles are presented in Tables 10.1 and 10.2.

Transmission velocity is also related to axon diameter and thickness of myelin sheath. Large nerve fibres conduct faster than smaller nerve fibres in the same animal. The exact numerical relationship between speed and size is still uncertain. In giant fibres of squid and cuttlefish, which provide a wide spectrum of axon diameters, velocity has been found to increase as the diameter raised to the 0·61 power (91), or linearly with diameter (approximate increase of 6·5 m/sec for 100 μ increase in diameter (45)). In the fanworm *Myxicola infundibulum*, which possesses a tapering giant-axon, the velocity varies approximately as the square root of diameter (77).

Many worms are highly extensible (nemertines, various polychaetes), and during contraction and extension giant-axons in the nerve cord undergo twofold alteration in diameter. Stretched giant axons, however, show no change in conduction rate (*Marphysa, Lumbriconereis*, etc.), a condition suggestive of compensatory changes in submicroscopic structure and impedance in the axonic membrane (26).

The majority of invertebrate nerve fibres are non-medullated, i.e. they possess no osmophilic myelin sheath. By the use of suitable techniques, nevertheless, it can be shown that all nerve fibres are invested by a layer of oriented lipoid. This lipoidal layer is only some 1% of total fibre diameter in giant axons of squid and sabellid polychaetes. A few invertebrates and all vertebrates possess heavily myelinated fibres (Figs. 10.2, 10.12). Some examples of invertebrates having medullated nerve fibres are *Clymene* (polychaete), *Mysis* and *Palaemon* (crustaceans).

A comparison of different fibres shows that conduction velocity is influenced by sheath thickness, and is much higher in medullated than in non-medullated fibres. In the giant axons of shrimp, for example, where the myelin sheath forms some 20% of fibre diameter, a fibre of 50 μ cross-section has the same velocity as a squid giant axon of 650 μ (about 25 m/sec) (53, 98, 111).

Nerve-nets

Phyletically the nerve-net has preceded central nervous organization and appears among invertebrates in the body wall of coelenterates, echinoderms, balanoglossids, and in the alimentary tracts of many more highly

TABLE 10.1

RATE OF NERVOUS TRANSMISSION IN NERVE-NETS AND NEUROPILE

Animal	Nervous tissue	Temperature (°C)	Velocity (m/sec)
Coelenterata			
Aequorea forskalea	Marginal ring nerve	20	0·7–0·9
Geryonia proboscidalis	Nerve-net of circular muscle	—	0·50
Physalia physalis	Nerve-net of filaments	26·1	0·121
Mastigias papua	Nerve-net of bell	25·5	0·57
Cassiopeia xamachana	ditto	18	0·136, 0·234
Renilla köllikeri	Nerve net	15–17	0·065–0·102
	ditto	21	0·04–0·065
Pennatula phosphorea	ditto	15	0·05
Leioptilus gurneyi	ditto	20·5	0·26
Metridium marginatum	Nerve-net of column	21	0·12–0·15
Calliactis parasitica	ditto	18–20	0·04–0·10
	Radial net of disc	18–20	0·6
	Net of sphincter and mesenteries	18–20	1–1·2
Nemertea			
Cerebratulus sp.	Nerve cord	—	0·059–0·09
Polychaeta			
Aphrodite sp.	ditto	15	0·545
Polynoë pulchra	ditto	13	2·93
Cirratulus sp.	ditto	11–20	0·90
Xiphosura			
Limulus sp.	Cardiac nerve plexus	—	0·40
Echinodermata			
Cucumaria sykion	Radial nerve	24–27	0·17, 0·28
ditto	Circumoral nerve	20–23	0·11

(Various sources)

organized animals, e.g. polychaetes, crustaceans and vertebrates. We shall examine, first, the nervous system of coelenterates before passing on to other groups, because the former have been much studied and display the nerve-net in its simplest form.

Coelenterates. The nervous system of coelenterates consists of a diffuse network of neurones lying underneath the epithelia. Most of our information relates to medusae and actinians; variations in detail may be expected in other groups, but the broad pattern is probably similar.

In Scyphomedusae there is a plexus of bipolar and multipolar nerve cells beneath the epithelium. The bipolar neurones form a network of through-conducting tracts in the sub-umbrella surface, the fibres connecting with one another by axonic synapses. The neurones make contact on the one hand with aggregations of ganglionic cells below the marginal sense organs, and on the other with muscle cells. In actinians there is a widespread nervous plexus of bipolar and multipolar neurones between the epithelia and the muscles. This plexus is particularly well developed in the ectodermal muscle of the disc and tentacles, and connects with an endodermal plexus in the column. Primary sense cells, especially numerous in tentacles and oral disc but occurring also in columnar endoderm and pedal disc, feed into the nervous plexus, which connects on the efferent side with muscle fibres (54, 82).

The chief physiological characteristics of the nerve-net are diffuse spread of excitation, local and equipotential autonomy, so-called decremental conduction, and facilitation. Ingenious experiments devised by Parker, in which the body wall of an anemone *Metridium* was slit in various ways, showed that excitation can be conducted in any direction over the body of the anemone from a point of stimulation, i.e. nerve tracts are diffuse and non-polarized. A mechanical stimulus applied to a tag of the body wall, so long as the latter remains continuous with the column at some point, evokes retraction of the oral disc. Electrical stimulation of the intact column of *Calliactis* produces a retractile response consisting largely of contraction of the marginal sphincter (Figs. 10.4, 10.5). A single stimulus is without effect, and a contraction is evoked only by a succession of electrical stimuli. This response is frequency-dependent, owing to the operation of peripheral facilitation (p. 383). Under mechanical stimulation the strength of the response varies with the strength of stimulation. This is due to the fact that a mechanical stimulus evokes a battery of impulses from the sense organs, and these increase in frequency and number with the intensity of the mechanical stimulus, thus facilitating the response.

These retractile responses are mediated by fast through-conduction pathways. Histological evidence for one of these is provided by longitudinally directed tracts of large neurones in the mesenteries of *Metridium*, neurones which supply the longitudinal retractor muscles.

Disc and tentacles form a reaction system characterized by greater variety and asymmetrical character of responses. A single stimulus produces a small local response; stimulation at progressively increasing frequencies produces stronger and more widespread responses, beginning with local contraction of a single tentacle, extending to more distant parts of the oral disc and finally involving complete contraction of the whole anemone (*Calliactis*). Similarly, the stronger the mechanical stimulus, the more widely the reaction is propagated around the disc. The responses produced are components of the normal feeding reaction, and are called up in succession through facilitation. The graded responses which can be elicited in the disc are the result of interneural facilitation between parts of the nerve-net, each impulse paving the way for entry of its successors into other sectors of the disc. Conduction in the nerve-net of the disc, therefore, involves facilitation between parts of the nerve-net, in addition

TABLE 10.2
CONDUCTION VELOCITIES IN NERVE FIBRES OF SOME MARINE ANIMALS

Animal	Nerve	Fibre diameter (μ)	Temperature (°C)	Velocity (m/sec)
Polychaeta				
Nereis virens	giant axons	ca. 40	24	5
	large lateral	30	24	4·5
	median unpaired	10	24	2·5
	median paired			10
Diopatra cupraea	giant axon	ca. 100	—	2·4
Pista palmata	ditto	ca. 50	—	2·05
Sthenelais fusca	ditto	—	11–20	4·66
Eunice sp.	ditto	—	—	2
Arenicola cristata	ditto	ca. 20–30	—	5
Lepidametria commensalis	ditto	ca. 30	—	1–4
Clymenella torquata	ditto	ca. 40	—	5, 7
Haploscoloplos bustorus	ditto	ca. 40	—	3·5, 5
Nephthys sp.	ditto	ca. 25	—	10
Lumbriconereis hebes	ditto	ca. 125	—	3–4
Glycera dibranchiata	ditto	ca. 15–20	—	7
Eudistylia polymorpha	ditto	up to 300	14	4–6
Spirographis spallanzanii	ditto	ca. 100–200	—	4–10
Protula intestinum	ditto	250–500	—	
Myxicola infundibulum	ditto	100–1000	17·5–22	3·2–21
Crustacea				
Palaemon serratus	median giant fibre	25–50	17	18·4–23
Homarus vulgaris	limb	—	22·3	1·9, 9·2
Homarus sp.	limb	—	—	12·0

		82-163 mean 121	15·5-29·8	8-18·4 mean 11·7
H. americanus	central giant-axon	82-163 mean 121	15·5-29·8	8-18·4 mean 11·7
Munida sp.	limb	50	—	6·4
Callinectes sapidus	limb	—	22-3	1·5, 5
Maia squinado	limb	1-3, 4-8, 10-20	21	1·4, 2·1, 5·3
ditto	limb	30	23-5	0·1-0·5, 1·1-1·8, 2·5-3·7
Carcinus maenas	limb	30	21	3·1-5·5
ditto	limb		20-5	3-5
Callianassa californiensis	giant fibres	30-40	20-2	6-7·5
Xiphosura				
Limulus polyphemus	limb	—	22-3	1·3, 4·6
Limulus sp.	limb	—	—	3,25
Mollusca				
Pleurobranchaea californica	pedal	—	12-15	0·78
ditto	ditto	—		0·58
Mytilus edulis	pedal	—	24	0·93
M. californianus	pedal	—	18-22	0·64
Loligo opalescens	fin nerve giant fibres	—	—	16
	fin nerve small fibres	—		2·5
L. forbesi and Sepia officinalis	stellar nerves	30-718	20	2·2-22·8
L. pealei	ditto	260-543	21-5	18·2-24·8
ditto	ditto	480-520	20	22·6-26·8
ditto	stellar nerve giant fibres	ca. 500	20	20
ditto	stellar nerve small fibres	—	20	4
Octopus hongkongensis	pallial		14	2

(Various sources)

to neuro-muscular facilitation. Apparent decremental conduction in the disc is due to decrease in number of impulses as a volley of the latter spreads out from the point of stimulation. Besides facilitated fast retractor responses, anemones also show very slow contractions. These are called

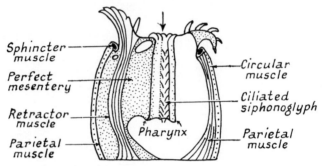

FIG. 10.4. DIAGRAMMATIC VERTICAL SECTION THROUGH THE SEA-ANEMONE *Metridium*. (From Pantin (82).)

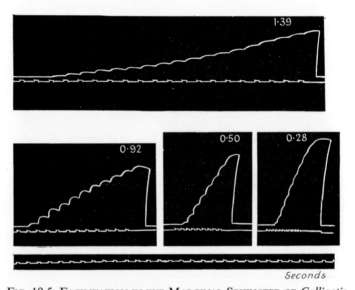

FIG. 10.5. FACILITATION IN THE MARGINAL SPHINCTER OF *Calliactis parasitica* AS THE RESULT OF REPETITIVE ELECTRICAL STIMULI

Figures refer to intervals (in seconds) between successive shocks. (From Pantin, 1935.)

forth by low-frequency stimulation and display long latency, smooth and often variable character, e.g. slow contraction of the longitudinal parietal muscles of *Metridium*. Several electrical stimuli are necessary to evoke the slow response, which tends to increase with number of stimuli. Excitation concerned with slow responses may be propagated through epithelial or muscle sheets rather than in a nerve net.

Despite the existence of diffuse conduction in the nerve-net, actinians still display much complexity in their responses. Differentiation of activity is possible because of varied sensibility, differentiation of the nerve net into functionally distinct systems, the operation of facilitation and inhibition, occurrence of several modes of muscular contraction, etc. The strength and nature of the response are governed also by the past history and physiological condition of the animal, thus bringing the response into line with its present needs (10, 80, 82, 83, 94).

The circular (swimming) muscles of jellyfish (Scyphomedusae) form another system that is regulated by peripheral facilitation (*Aurelia*, *Cyanea*). In these animals, repeated excitation of the sub-umbrella nerve-net recruits more muscle fibres by facilitation, and produces stronger contractions (Fig. 10.6). The spontaneous swimming contractions, which are normally initiated by the marginal sensory organs, also depend upon peripheral facilitation, which determines the strength of the pulsations. Single-fibre action potentials recorded from the bell of *Aurelia* show that the net is non-polarized and that interneural facilitation is absent under normal conditions. Each spontaneous beating of the bell is accompanied by an action potential which spreads diffusely over the nerve-net (17, 55, 84).

In colonial anthozoans the responses of different parts of the colony are more or less co-ordinated by a common nerve-net. Visible effector activities of sea pens (Pennatulacea) are movements of the polyps (protrusion and retraction), contraction of the whole animal, peristaltic waves of movement and luminescent waves. Luminescent waves and possibly general contractility are under control of a through conducting nerve-net; peristalsis may be an inherent property of the muscle, while the movements of polyps are largely independent of each other. Other colonial corals show various degrees of co-ordination in the responses of polyps, between those in which polyp retraction is always local to those in which there is a widespread response involving all polyps. These responses are mediated by nerve-nets in which there exist increasing degrees of facility for interneural transmission across the colony.

Balanoglossids. These are sluggish burrowing animals possessing simple and diffuse nervous systems. Underlying the epidermis is a network of nerve fibres and various diffuse nerve cords. Nerve cells are widely distributed beneath the epithelia; primary sensory cells in the epidermis connect with the sub-epidermal plexus; and efferent fibres proceed to the effectors (muscles, and probably glandular and ciliated cells) (19, 66, 100).

Conduction in the balanoglossid nerve plexus is diffuse and decremental, and pieces of the body wall show a high degree of autonomy. These features are in agreement with the structural picture of diffusely arranged sensory, intermediate and motor neurones. Decremental conduction, as in coelenterates, would appear to involve facilitation for overcoming synaptic resistance in interrupted pathways. Cords and other nerve tracts are distributive in function, rather than integrative.

Diffuse conduction is revealed by continued transmission of excitation following cuts in various directions through the trunk and proboscis (*Balanoglossus, Saccoglossus*). The three main regions of the body possess mechanisms for nervous reflexes, and show local muscular responses to tactile and photic stimuli. The sub-epithelial plexus is the site of this diffuse nervous transmission in the absence of longitudinal nerve cords. Dorsal and ventral nerve cords form through-conduction systems, and when the

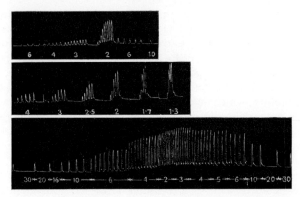

FIG. 10.6. FACILITATION IN A STRIP-PREPARATION OF THE SCYPHOMEDUSAN *Rhopilema*

Figures refer to intervals between shocks in seconds. (From Bullock (17).)

cords are cut the shortening reflex is impaired, probably owing to inter-ruption of giant-axon pathways (*vide* p. 434).

Locomotion in *Saccoglossus* and other enteropneusts is accomplished largely by ciliary activity, aided by peristaltic movements of the proboscis. The cilia on the trunk appear to be under nervous control, and peristaltic contractions are regulated by the dorsal nerve cord. Autonomous nervous activity is centred to a large extent in the proboscis, which is responsible for much of the neural drive of the animal. Such activity is not localized in any one part of the proboscis, but the dorsal nerve cord is necessary for longitudinal conduction (66).

Contractions of the body wall of solitary sea-squirts (*Phallusia*, etc.) show well-marked facilitation under repetitive stimulation (Fig. 10.7). What part the nerve-net plays in the mediation of these responses still awaits clarification (58, 59).

Echinoderms. The nervous system of echinoderms shows interesting features intermediate between the nervous network as exemplified by actinians, and the central nervous organization of annelids and higher groups. Smith (103) makes a functional resolution of the asteroid nervous system into three components: a sensori-association plexus, which is a true nerve network; a motor system; and a central system comprising the circumoral nerve ring and radial nerve cords. Much mechanical activity consists of localized responses of spines, pedicellariae, tube feet, etc., and is an expression of the functioning of a peripheral nerve-net; superimposed on this local activity, or acting conjointly with it, are co-ordinated responses of locomotory reaction-systems, controlled by the central nervous system (c.n.s.) (*Asterias, Astropecten, Marthasterias*).

In the lateral and dorsal walls of the arms there is a diffuse peripheral or dorsal sheath plexus. A median radial nerve cord runs along the ventral

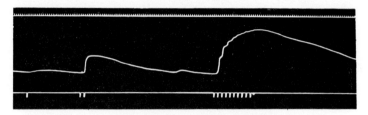

FIG. 10.7. RESPONSES OF BODY WALL OF *Ascidiella aspersa* TO
ELECTRICAL STIMULATION

Movements of branchial siphon recorded. Stimuli: single shock, pair of shocks and series of ten shocks. Time marking, above, in seconds. (From Hoyle (58).)

surface of each arm and connects at its base with the circumoral nerve ring.

The sensori-association plexus of the dorsal sheath displays typical features of the nerve-net, autonomy, diffuse and decremental conduction, and facilitation. For example, pedicellariae react equally well to stimulation whether in the intact animal or borne on isolated pieces of dorsal sheath (*Asterias*). All pedicellariae immediately about the area of mechanical disturbance respond to the stimulus, due to diffuse conduction, but the responses fall off with distance. To repetitive weak mechanical stimuli the responses become progressively greater. Pertinent observations on sea-urchins (*Strongylocentrotus, Arbacia*) show that responses of the spines are independent of strength of electrical stimulation, but become more extensive with increase in frequency and number of stimuli. As in actinians, interneural and neuromuscular processes of facilitation would appear to offer an explanation for these observations (102, 103).

Superimposed on the diffuse plexus of the dorsal sheath there is a system of through-conduction tracts. These are transversely oriented in the arms, and connect with lateral motor centres. Evidence for their functioning is provided by experiments such as the following. When a shadow is cast over part of the dorsal sheath, the papulae in the stimulated region contract. Longitudinal cuts, below the stimulated region but lateral to the motor centres, abolish the response.

Some of the motor neurones are connected directly with the peripheral plexus. These include motor neurones of the pedicellariae, spines, papulae, muscles of the body wall and podia. These neurones receive impulses from the diffuse plexus or through-conduction tracts and can be excited through local circuits without the intervention of the radial nerve cords.

The central co-ordinating action of the circumoral ring and radial nerve cords is revealed by analyses of locomotory activities. During locomotion

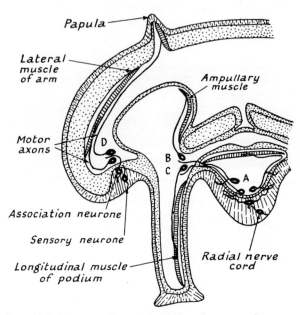

FIG. 10.8. NERVOUS ELEMENTS IN THE ARM OF A STARFISH
A, distributive neurones of medial nerve cord. B, C, motor neurones of foot complex. D, lateral motor system. (From Smith (103, 104).)

the animal progresses with one arm leading and co-ordinated stepping movements of the tube feet. Movements of the latter are brought about by contraction of longitudinal muscles in the foot which drive water into the relaxed ampulla, causing retraction; and contraction of the ampullary muscles, which drive water into the relaxed podium, causing protraction. Ampullary muscles and longitudinal muscles of the foot are thus antagonistic in action and operate reciprocally. In addition to these movements, stepping involves swinging the foot through an arc in line with the direction of progression, through the activity of special postural muscles. Motor neurones supplying the podial and ampullary muscles lie at the base of the podium in the foot complex (Fig. 10.8, B, C), and are connected with the radial nerve tracts by segmental distributive neurones (A).

Removal of the radial nerve cord abolishes longitudinal conduction and co-ordinated locomotory responses in the arm. The movements of the tube feet are regulated by five centres, each of which lies at the junction of the circumoral ring with a radial nerve (Fig. 10.9). From each centre fibres enter the contiguous radial nerve, and also proceed in both directions around the ring to the other arms. During normal locomotion of a starfish one of these centres becomes dominant, co-ordinates the direction of

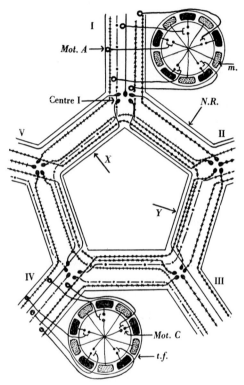

FIG. 10.9. SCHEMATIC DIAGRAM OF NERVE CENTRES AND TRACTS INVOLVED
IN THE INNERVATION OF THE TUBE FEET OF STARFISH

I–V, radial cords of arms I–V; centre I, one of the five nerve centres of the circumora ring; *Mot. A, Mot. C*, motor neurones of the first and second orders, respectively; *m*, segment of the tube foot musculature; *N.R.*, nerve ring; *t.f.*, tube foot. Motor neurones of the first order (*Mot. A*) lie in the radial perihaemal canal and their axons invade the tube foot, where they make synaptic connexion with second-order motor neurones (*Mot. C*); the latter supply the postural muscles of the foot. (From Smith (103).)

stepping movements in all arms and causes the animal to move in one particular direction.

A similar innervation pattern has been discovered in the circumoral ring and radial nerves of sea cucumbers (*Cucumaria*), where the responses of the pharyngeal retractor muscles have been analysed. Here, also, the motor fibres from one radius are distributed to each of the other radii. The synapses of this system are non-frequency sensitive, and conduction around the ring is decremental. The latter condition is apparently due to the way the fibre tracts are organized: the number of motor fibres going from any one radius to another radius decreases with distance.

The central nervous system of echinoderms lies at a low level. Noteworthy features are: presence of association and motor centres; organization of nerve tracts into restricted conducting pathways which feed distributory nerves into motor centres; and the existence of patterns of neuronal organization serving to co-ordinate activities of the whole organism. Fundamentally, these animals are provided with a nerve-net for localized responses, and a simple c.n.s. for control and co-ordination of widespread activities (64, 65, 87, 88, 103, 104, 105, 106).

Peripheral autonomy involving nerve nets and local reflex arcs is also seen in pelecypods, the isolated organs (palps, siphons, etc.) of which respond to stimuli (27).

STOMATOGASTRIC OR SYMPATHETIC NERVOUS SYSTEM. The visceral (stomatogastric) nervous systems of invertebrates are imperfectly known. The gut contains several kinds of effectors, namely glands, ciliated cells, muscles, of which the muscles certainly, and some glands probably, are under nervous control. In polychaetes and crustaceans nerves proceed from anterior ganglia and from the nerve cord to the alimentary canal. In addition, various parts of the gut are frequently provided with a nerve-net and display autonomous activity. Innervation of the hearts of invertebrates is described in Chapter 3. Accounts of the visceral nervous systems of lower chordates are available (60, 75).

Many polychaetes possess stomatogastric nerves which arise anteriorly from brain, connectives and suboesophageal ganglia, and which proceed to the anterior gut (pharynx, oesophagus, stomach). Visceral ganglia are distributed along the course of these nerves, which terminate in plexuses in the gut wall (aphroditids, eunicids, etc.). The stomatogastric system of *Arenicola* takes the form of a plexus of nerve bundles connecting the supra-oesophageal ganglia and circumoesophageal commissures with a ring ganglion at the anterior end of the oesophagus. This visceral plexus continues along the length of the oesophagus (123). *Petta* possesses sympathetic nerves which run from the abdominal nerve cord to visceral ganglia and a plexus in the intestine.

The alimentary canal of various polychaetes shows rhythmic activity, originating in an intrinsic nerve-net. In intact specimens of *Tomopteris* (a transparent animal), rhythmic pulsations can be seen which take the form of peristaltic waves along the gut. Isolated extrovert preparations (proboscis and oesophagus) of *Arenicola marina* show bursts of vigorous rhythmic contractions, alternating with periods of relative rest. The rhythmic activity, with a periodicity of 6–7 minutes, forms part of the feeding cycle (Fig. 10.10, cf. Fig. 4.6, p. 147). Excitation originates in a diffuse oesophageal nerve plexus, from which it radiates to the proboscis and anterior body wall through proboscidial nerves, and evokes rhythmic muscular contractions. This behaviour pattern is responsible for the digging activity of the proboscis. *A. marina* is a specialized burrowing species, highly adapted for life in sand and mud (117, 120).

Much variation exists in organization of the stomatogastric nervous system of Crustacea, but the following are typical features, especially of decapods. An anterior stomatogastric system, arising from tritocerebral ganglia on the circumoesophageal connectives, sends sympathetic nerves to oesophageal and gastric ganglia. These are motor centres from which motor branches proceed to the upper lip, oesophagus and stomach. Sensory cells in these organs are believed to be reflexly connected with the effectors through the c.n.s. From the caudal ganglia other sympathetic

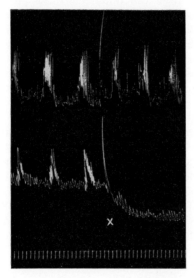

FIG. 10.10. KYMOGRAPH TRACING OF ACTIVITY OF BODY WALL AND EXTROVERT PREPARATION OF *Arenicola marina*

Extrovert *above*, body wall *below*. At *X*, the nerve cord was cut between the two strips. Time tracing, 1/min. (From Wells, 1937.)

nerves supply the intestine, the wall of which contains a nervous plexus. Peristaltic and anti-peristaltic waves churn and propel the intestinal contents. The intestine is capable of autonomous activity, and movements continue even in an isolated preparation (37, 108). The stomatogastric nervous systems of these and other groups are described by Hanström (41).

NERVE-NETS—CONCLUSIONS. In the preceding section salient features of the nerve-nets of several phyla have been reviewed. This somewhat extended phyletic treatment is warranted by their simplicity of organization and their importance in providing information about possible ways in which nervous systems have evolved. The diagnostic feature of nerve-net organization is the existence of a pervasive plexus of unpolarized neurones. Interneural transmission is by axonal contact. The nerve-net may constitute the entire nervous system, as in coelenterates, or exist conjointly with distributive pathways (balanoglossids), or co-ordinating centres (echinoderms). Typically, the nerve-net displays diffuse conduction, a necessary corollary of its organization, and is also characterized by so-called decremental conduction and facilitation. Decremental conduction is a consequence of facilitation, and refers to the need for a barrage of impulses in order to force excitation into distant parts of the nerve-net. Facilitation, however, is not an exclusive characteristic of the nerve-net: interneural facilitation is found in the polychaete nerve cord, and neuromuscular facilitation in claw-muscles of decapod crustacea.

The nerve-net by itself can initiate intrinsic phasic activity, through functional differentiation of temporary or permanent pacemakers. Through-conduction pathways exist, even in coelenterates, as special condensations of fibre-tracts. Distributive pathways are well marked in balanoglossids, and assume a co-ordinating role in asteroids. Functional polarization is manifest in some regions of the net, in the different levels of facilitation required for transmission in opposite directions. Central and reflex nervous organization has probably developed through condensation of associative, distributive and efferent neurones into centralized ganglia and cords spatially arranged in patterns conformable to overall organization of body form. This has been accompanied by progressive suppression of peripheral nets. Enteric nets, such as those of the *Arenicola* extrovert, are best regarded as outliers of the central nervous system, secondarily developed in conjunction with specialized effector structure and habits, and acting as semi-autonomous nervous centres. Nerve-nets of other phyla still await exploration, e.g. polyclads, nemertines, phoronids (*see*, however, Silén (101)), ascidians, etc.; many features of those already studied would be further clarified by electrical recording.

Through-conduction Systems

Nerve-nets and neuropile consist mostly of short nerve fibres, but many animals have, in addition, through-conduction tracts which extend long distances. Often the fibres concerned are conspicuously large and are termed giant axons. Giant-axon systems have evolved independently in many groups, in which they mediate quick responses to harmful stimuli, withdrawal reflexes and the like.

In the mesenteries of sea-anemones, such as *Metridium*, there is a well-defined through-conduction system of large fibres extending 7 or 8 mm before forming synapses. The conduction velocity in these tracts is much higher than elsewhere, and there is little synaptic delay. Functionally, the through-conduction system is concerned with transmitting impulses which call forth the protective withdrawal reflex (82).

Among animals more complex than coelenterates, the following have giant-axon systems: cestodes, nemertines, many polychaetes, decapod cephalopods, many crustaceans, especially decapods, brachiopods, phoronids, enteropneusts and lower vertebrates. Several patterns can be recognized: in some animals the giant axons are unicellular neurones (poly-chaetes *Sigalion* and *Halla*); in others they are multicellular and syncytial (sabellids, cephalopods). It is quite common to find giant axons extending long distances through the c.n.s. (polychaetes, crustaceans), or into peripheral nerves (crustaceans, cephalopods). Brief descriptions of the giant-axon systems of some representative species will illustrate various characteristics and form a basis for interpreting their functions (73, 101).

Polychaetes. Polychaete families with well-developed giant-axon systems are Nereidae, Arenicolidae and Sabellidae. In *Neanthes virens* there are two lateral giant fibres and a single median fibre which extend throughout the length of the nerve cord. Nerve cells require further study, but it appears that the median fibre is connected with nerve cells anteriorly and

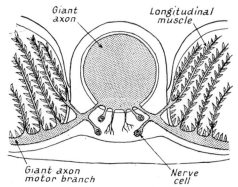

FIG. 10.11 SECTION THROUGH THE NERVE CORD OF *Myxicola infundibulum*

The giant axon is joined to many nerve cells and gives off motor branches to the longitudinal muscles and integrating branches to the neuropile.

the lateral fibres with nerve cells at all levels. The lateral fibres make contact in each segment with a pair of anastomosing neurones which extend into the peripheral nerves. There is also a peculiar system of paired small medial giants, which consist of a chain of simple units connected in series by synapses (Fig. 10.2). A giant-fibre system is highly developed in sabellids and serpulids, which possess one or two large axons extending throughout the length of the nerve cord (Fig. 10.11). The giant axons arise from nerve cells in the brain and connect with trophic nerve cells throughout their length. In each segment they give off motor branches to the longitudinal muscles.

The intersegmental giant axons of tubicolous and burrowing polychaetes are involved in the quick shortening or withdrawal reflex by which the animal jerks back into its shelter when disturbed. Conduction velocities are high when compared with neuropile transmission, up to 5 m/sec in *Neanthes* and 20 m/sec in *Myxicola* (Table 10.2). Since the axons extend through many segments and serve wide-spread muscles, an impulse arising at any level can bring about synergic contraction of the latter. In *Myxicola*

the single giant axon forms the final common motor path for all the longitudinal muscles involved in the withdrawal reflex, and can be excited at all
levels in the animal. The giant axons of *Protula* (Serpulidae) are connected
with a patch of sensory epithelium in the head, and are normally stimulated
in this region. They form a co-ordinating system lying penultimate to the
effectors. In *Neanthes* the single medial giant is fired by sensory stimuli in
anterior segments, the two small medial giants by stimuli in the posterior
three-quarters and the lateral giants by stronger stimuli at all levels of the
body. Transverse septa (synapses) occur in the lateral giant fibres of
Neanthes, but the fibres are not physiologically polarized and can transmit
in either direction (21, 24, 27, 73, 74).

Crustacea. Among Crustacea, giant-fibre systems occur in copepods,
stomatopods and decapods. Giant axons have been studied most intensively
in the freshwater crayfish, but comparable systems are found in lobsters
(*Homarus*), shrimps and prawns (*Palaemonetes, Palaemon,* etc.). Paired

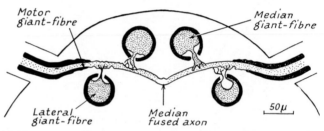

FIG. 10.12. TRANSVERSE SECTION THROUGH THE DORSAL PART OF AN ABDOMINAL
GANGLION OF THE PRAWN *Palaemon serratus,* SHOWING SYNAPSES OF THE MEDIAL
AND LATERAL GIANT-FIBRES WITH THE MOTOR FIBRES (after Holmes (52).)

median giant fibres originate in the brain and extend throughout the nerve
cord; besides these, a pair of lateral giants is found in thoracic and abdominal segments. The lateral giants are divided into segmental units by oblique
partitions or synapses, and the median giants of *Palaemon* show incomplete
septa. It appears that both lateral and medial giant fibres are syncytial
structures, connected with many nerve cells throughout their lengths. Fine
processes from lateral and medial giant axons form synapses with motor
neurones in each segment; from the motor neurones efferent axons proceed into the peripheral nerves (Fig. 10.12). The giant-axon system of
decapods is concerned with mediating an escape response: excitation of
this system causes the antennae to be drawn together and extended, and
the abdominal flexors to contract; the tail gives a sharp flip, and the animal
darts backwards through the water (20, 52, 113).

Cephalopods. Giant axons of cephalopods (squid and cuttlefish) arise
from two first-order giant cells in the brain (posterior region of the pedal
ganglion) (Figs. 10.13, 10.18). The axons of these cells cross and fuse, and
in their further course form synapses with processes of second-order giant
neurones in the pallio-visceral ganglion. Second-order giant fibres pass

out in posterior infundibular, visceral and pallial nerves, and those running in the latter make contact with a third set of giant fibres, arising in the stellate ganglion. The third-order giant fibres are multicellular in origin, each arising from some 300–1,500 cells (Fig. 10.14). The axons run

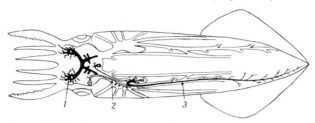

FIG. 10.13. DIAGRAM OF THE GIANT-AXON SYSTEM OF *Loligo*

Nerve centres and nerves in outline; giant axons in solid colour or stipple. 1, 2, 3 first- second- and third-order giant axons. (From Young, 1936.)

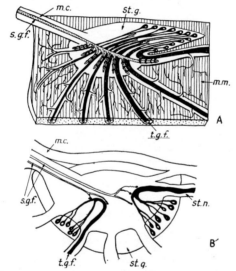

FIG. 10.14. GIANT AXONS OF CEPHALOPODS (A, *Loligo*, B, *Sepia*)

A pre-synaptic (second-order) giant fibre is shown terminating on third-order giant fibres. The latter have a multi-cellular origin and proceed to the mantle muscles. *m.c.*, mantle connective (pallial nerve); *m.m.*, mantle muscle; *s.g.f.*, second-order (preganglionic) giant fibre; *st.g.*, stellate ganglion; *st.n.*, stellar nerve; *t.g.f.*, third-order giant fibre. (From Young, 1936, 1938.)

out in the stellar nerves to the mantle, each giant axon supplying a large area of circular muscle in the mantle wall. Activation of the giant-axon system elicits nearly simultaneous contraction of the entire circular musculature of the mantle; the compressed water is forced out of the funnel and drives the animal forward or backward, according to the direction in which the funnel is pointed.

Giant axons are characteristic of decapods. In *Sepia* the cell bodies of the third-order giant neurones are scattered through the stellate ganglion; in *Loligo* they are confined to the posterior lobe (Fig. 10.14). In octopods the same posterior lobe is present and contains cells resembling neurocytes but lacking processes. This lobe, known as the epistellar body, has assumed a neurosecretory role in the octopus, and extirpation leads to loss of muscular tone in the mantle.

Balanoglossids. In most balanoglossids there are conspicuously large neurones in the collar nerve cord. From an anterior group of cell bodies giant fibres pass into the proboscis, while a more posterior group gives rise to axons which run posteriorly to reach the longitudinal musculature of the trunk (Fig. 10.15). Functionally, these giant axons form high-speed

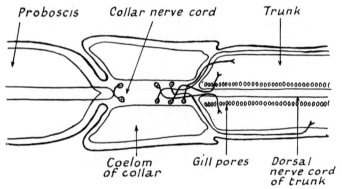

FIG. 10.15. DIAGRAMMATIC LONGITUDINAL SECTION THROUGH A
BALANOGLOSSID, SHOWING THE GIANT-FIBRE SYSTEM
Cell bodies of giant fibres shown in the collar nerve cord. (After Bullock, 1944.)

conduction systems for protective avoiding reflexes, and probably serve as final common paths to the muscles involved. Effective stimulation, through these systems, brings about contraction of the proboscis and of the longitudinal musculature of the trunk (66).

Many giant-axon systems still await functional analysis, but studies now available reveal that giant axons of invertebrates are generally involved in mediating protective avoiding reactions. They are of widespread occurrence in burrowing and tubicolous species, in which they are involved in the reflex withdrawal response, whereby the animal jerks back into its shelter when disturbed (polychaetes, brachiopods, balanoglossids). Fast through-conduction pathways in sedentary anemones are concerned with closure of the oral disc. Giant-axon systems of active cephalopods and crustaceans, as we have seen, are concerned with quick escape responses, utilizing jet propulsion and paddle-action. Giant-axon systems conduct quickly, and may produce significant saving of reaction time. It has been estimated that in *Myxicola,* the giant axon reduces response time to one-half compared with slow neuropile conduction. A second common feature of giant-axon systems is that one or a few fibres serve large muscle masses and, because of fast conduction speeds, they produce nearly synchronous muscular contractions. An interesting adaptation is described in the squid where the giant fibres to the mantle are graded in diameter. The arrangement is such that the largest fibres generally form the longest pathways, and conduction rates and transmission distances are so adjusted that contraction of the whole mantle sac takes place nearly simultaneously (80).

JUNCTIONAL TRANSMISSION

There is now convincing evidence, both histological and physiological, that the junctions between neurones, and between neurones and effectors, are regions of protoplasmic and functional discontinuity. This concept is, in fact, necessary to explain the complex and selective nature of nervous activity. The transmission of an impulse along a nerve fibre results from self-propagation of electrotonic potential and, on arriving at the terminals of the fibre, the excitatory state in some way activates the next unit in series, either another neurone or an effector cell.

Synaptic Organization

Synapses are found in all nervous systems. In the nerve-nets of coelenterates axons intertwine or run alongside each other for short distances, forming functional junctions. These synapses are structurally non-polarized since equal axonal areas are in contact with each other (Fig. 10.16). Experiments show that conduction is diffuse in these nerve-nets and that two-way transmission must take place across the synapses, i.e. they are functionally non-polarized as well.

Corresponding types of junctions are found in other groups, e.g. annelids and crustaceans. The two giant axons of sabellids and serpulids form an unpolarized synapse in the brain, where they cross over and make contact with each other. The synapse is unpolarized, allowing two-way transmission, and is of the relay type, an impulse in one fibre (pre-synaptic) evoking a corresponding impulse in the other. When electrical activity at the junctional region is recorded, pre- and post-synaptic action potentials are seen, as well as a local synaptic potential (Fig. 10.17). Synaptic delay is of the order of 0·8 msec (*Protula*). The local response is propagated as an electrotonic potential for short distances: in *Protula* it shows decrement to half amplitude in 3 mm. From the local response a propagated all-or-nothing post-synaptic potential arises. In the nereid *Neanthes virens* large overlapping septa or macrosynapses occur at regular intervals in the lateral giant fibres of the nerve cord, and these junctions allow conduction in either direction. Oblique partitions are also found in the lateral giant fibres of the prawn (*Palaemon*) and other decapod crustaceans. These synapses are non-polarized and permit two-way conduction with very slight delay (about 0·1 msec).

Two-way synapses are usually of the relay type. This appears to be the situation in through-conduction systems of sea pens, sea anemones, etc., as well as the giant-axon synapses of polychaetes just described. Certain coelenterate responses, however, depend upon interneural facilitation, whereby several impulses are necessary to overcome synaptic resistance (integrative synapses). This is the normal condition in the oral disc of anemones, and becomes operative in through-conducting systems of other coelenterates under abnormal conditions—following magnesium anaes-

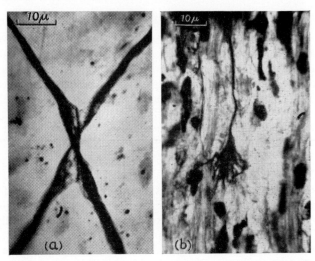

FIG. 10.16. DETAILS OF NERVE FIBRES IN THE SEA ANEMONE *Metridium senile*
(a) Crossed axons in synaptic contact; (b) end-plate of axon on retractor muscle sheet. (From Pantin (82).)

thesia or after paring down the conduction tract—when relay synapses revert to the integrative type (20, 21, 24, 52, 92, 111).

Invertebrate junctions just described are non-polarized and possess a single synaptic interface. In polarized junctions the preganglionic fibres terminate in small swellings (boutons), fine twigs or spiral windings (Figs. 10.14, 10.18). Efferent axons become attenuated near their ends and terminate on muscles and other effectors as fine fibrils, swellings, plates, ribbons, etc. (Figs. 10.2, 10.16). Processes of transmission between nerve and effector cell may be identical with interneural transmission. From a functional viewpoint, polarized synapses have been classified as: one-to-one or relay, several-to-one or integrative, and one-to-several or multiplying.

A well described relay type of synapse in invertebrates is that between second- and third-order giant axons of squid. In a fresh preparation the impulses in the postganglionic fibre faithfully follow the frequency of preganglionic firing (Fig. 10.19). A local or synaptic potential can be distinguished after fatigue and is evoked by direct stimulation of the ganglion.

It appears after a delay of 0·5 msec, and it is propagated with decrement (reduction to ½ amplitude in 0·5 mm). Also investigated have been one-to-one (relay) synapses between giant axons in the c.n.s. and peripheral motor fibres of decapod crustaceans.

The excitation of most giant-fibre systems probably depends upon some degree of sensory summation, implying the existence of integrative (several-to-one) synapses between afferent fibres and the giant axon. Complex multiple synaptic junctions have been recognized on giant nerve cells, viz. on first-order giant cells of the squid and cephalic giant-cell bodies of

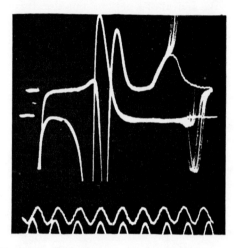

FIG. 10.17. SYNAPTIC TRANSMISSION BETWEEN THE TWO GIANT AXONS
IN THE ANTERIOR END OF *Protula*

The upper beam gives pre- and post-synaptic potentials from electrodes 3 and 6 mm back of extreme anterior end; lower beam shows ascending and descending spikes 9 and 12 mm from this end. Time in msec. (From Bullock (24).)

serpulids (Fig. 10.18). The stellate ganglion of octopods is an integrative centre containing synapses between small pre- and post-ganglionic fibres. Electrical recording from this region shows a high development of facilitation, and a burst of pulses at some optimal frequence is required to produce maximal response. In multiplying synapses the post-fibre shows repetitive discharge. Wiersma investigated an instance of the latter in the crayfish, where a single impulse in a central giant fibre gives rise to repetitive firing in efferent fibres within the roots of the abdominal ganglia (22, 23, 24, 124, 125).

CHEMICAL TRANSMISSION

Current theory postulates that when a nerve impulse reaches the end of a nerve fibre it causes a chemical transmitter to be released at the nerve ending. In the case of the vertebrate motor axon the transmitter is acetylcholine: on release it diffuses across the short distance separating nerve and muscle membranes, and depolarizes the muscle end-plate. The transient local depolarization of the latter is manifest as an end-plate potential (e.p.p.). This is not itself propagated, but it electrically discharges or stimulates a small surrounding region of muscle fibre, and so gives rise to a propagated wave of muscular excitation. Crustacean muscle fibres show a different functional pattern: here the end-plates are distributed widely over each muscle fibre, and the numerous end-plate potentials often produce local contractions, without propagated action potentials.

Acetylcholine exists in bound form at vertebrate motor nerve endings and is released on the arrival of a nervous impulse. It is rapidly destroyed (hydrolysed) by a specific enzyme, acetylcholinesterase, concentrated at

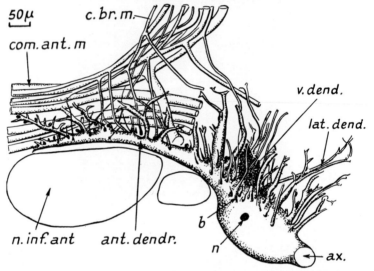

FIG. 10.18. First-Order Giant Cell in the Brain of the Squid (*Loligo pealei*)
ant. dendr., anterior dendrite of giant cell; *ax.*, axon of giant cell; *b*, interaxonic bridge; *com. ant. m.*, commissura anterior magnocellularis; *c. br. m.*, brachio-magno-cellular connective; *lat. dend.*, lateral dendrites of giant cell; *n*, nucleus; *n. inf. ant.*, nervus infundibuli anterior; *v. dend.*, ventral dendrites of giant cell. (From Young (1939).)

the end-plate, thus preparing the neuromuscular junction for the arrival of a new impulse. Nerve fibres which release acetylcholine at their terminals are designated cholinergic fibres. Apart from the end-plate of vertebrate striated muscle, transmitter action by acetylcholine occurs in the heart (vagus fibres), smooth muscle, peripheral ganglia and glands (autonomic fibres), and in central synapses (spinal cord) (31, 32, 33, 34, 36).

Adrenergic nerve fibres form another category and their chemical transmitter is adrenaline or noradrenaline. Adrenergic nerve fibres supply heart, smooth muscle, glands, chromatophores, etc. Still other transmitters are suspected in invertebrates, e.g. 5-hydroxytryptamine as a neuro-cardiac transmitter in molluscs (122).

Effects of Pharmacological Agents on Junctional Transmission

Information about transmitter action at synapses has been secured by applying pharmacological agents to nerve and muscle. Acetylcholine activates the end-plate and ganglionic synapse, brings about contraction of striated muscle, slowing of the heart, discharge from electric organs, pigment dispersion in fish chromatophores, etc. Many of the usual effects of acetylcholine can be mimicked by muscarine; acetylcholine is then said to have a muscarinic action. Nicotine in small doses has a stimulatory effect on the ganglionic synapse and on muscle, and the action of acetylcholine

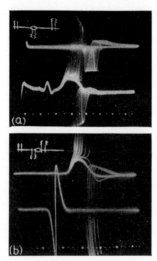

FIG. 10.19. SYNAPTIC TRANSMISSION IN THE STELLATE GANGLION OF *Loligo*

Single shock was delivered to pre-ganglionic fibres at start of each sweep recurring 33 times per sec. (*a*). Recording from ganglion and post-ganglionic fibre. With continued stimulation the post-ganglionic spike progressively fatigues, arising later out of the local potential and finally failing. Time, 0·5 msec. (*b*). Recording from pre-ganglionic fibre just in front of the ganglion, and from the post-ganglionic fibre. Time, 0·25 msec. (From Bullock, (22).)

at these loci is referred to as the nicotine action. Eserine and di-isopropyl fluorophosphate (DFP) potentiate the action of acetylcholine. Curarine, by preferentially competing with acetylcholine at the end-plate, blocks transmitter action. The effect of stimulating adrenergic nerves can be mimicked by application of adrenaline; its action is blocked by ergotoxine.

PHARMACOLOGICAL OBSERVATIONS. In previous chapters (3 and 9), dealing with circulatory systems and effectors, we have classified some cardio-regulator and motor nerves as cholinergic or adrenergic. Evidence for chemical transmitters in nervous systems of many invertebrate groups is fragmentary. To supplement the accounts given in earlier pages, a brief survey is presented of chemical transmitter activity in nervous systems of lower phyla.

EVIDENCE PERTAINING TO CHOLINERGIC SYSTEMS. As an initial approach we observe that acetylcholine is not confined uniquely to nervous systems, and occurs in bacteria, protozoa, non-innervated vertebrate tissue (placenta) and even in plants. The function of acetylcholine, therefore, may transcend that of chemical transmission, even in metazoan animals provided with nervous tissue. Acetylcholine and cholinesterase are lacking in sponges. In primitive nerve-nets of coelenterates there is no evidence for cholinergic and adrenergic systems. Acetylcholine has not been detected in coelenterates, but cholinesterase sometimes occurs in significant amounts (hydroids, anemones). Cholinesterase content is very low or absent in Scyphomedusae and ctenophores. In apparent agreement with these analyses it is known that neuromuscular systems of Scyphomedusae and actinians are insensitive to acetylcholine, eserine and curare (7, 17, 81, 90, 93).

In the lower triploblastic phyla, platyhelminthes, nemertines and annelids, there is some evidence for cholinergic systems. Cholinesterase has been found in turbellarians (*Procerodes*) and nemertines (*Cerebratulus, Lineus*). More data are available for annelids. Acetylcholine and cholinesterase occur in the body wall, especially muscles, of polychaetes (*Arenicola, Spirographis*), and *Sipunculus*. Sensitivity to acetylcholine is shown by the body wall of nemertine (*Cerebratulus*), polychaetes (*Branchiomma*), leeches (*Pontobdella*) and sipunculoids (*Sipunculus*), pharyngeal retractor of *Golfingia* and extrovert of *Arenicola*. Eserine potentiates the action of acetylcholine in some of these animals (7, 76).

The highest sensitivity to acetylcholine thus far discovered in any invertebrate is shown by the heart of a lamellibranch *Mercenaria*, which is inhibited in concentrations of 10^{-10} to 10^{-12} (Chapter 3). Acetylcholine has been detected in various molluscan tissues: foot, oesophageal ganglia of *Aplysia*; purple gland of *Murex*; mantle muscle and cerebral ganglia of *Octopus*, etc. Cholinesterase occurs in gastropods, lamellibranchs and cephalopods; the cholinesterase content of squid ganglia is relatively high. Sensitivity to acetylcholine varies greatly in different molluscs: positive responses are given by the foot of *Buccinum*, siphons of *Hiatella*, mantle muscles of *Sepia*, etc. Eserine potentiates the action of acetylcholine, and curarine inhibits acetylcholine-induced contractions in muscle of *Sepia*. The eserinized perfusate of central nervous and mantle tissues of *Eledone* shows acetylcholine activity, but this is not increased by stimulation; neither are acetylcholine and eserine stimulants for squid giant synapses (7, 15).

Relatively high levels of acetylcholine and cholinesterase have been found in ganglia and nerve cord of various crustacean species (*Homarus, Cancer, Callinectes*). Crustacean muscle is insensitive to acetylcholine, even at high levels (10^{-3}); it is without effect on intestinal muscle, but accelerates the heart. Eserine and curare have no effect on neuromuscular transmission in crustaceans. The nervous system of crustaceans is equally insensitive to acetylcholine, except in very high concentrations (10^{-3}), and there is no evidence that it is involved in synaptic transmission (7, 115).

Echinoderm tissue (muscle, gut) contains appreciable quantities of acetylcholine, and nerve and muscle are rich in cholinesterase. A high sensitivity to acetylcholine has been reported (longitudinal muscle of holothurians; retractors of Aristotle's lantern in echinoids), and eserine has an augmentative effect. Following stimulation, a substance having the biological properties of acetylcholine appears in the perfusate. Tunicates are relatively insensitive to acetylcholine and eserine: acetylcholine appears to be absent from tissues, and cholinesterase activity is weak (5, 7).

Conclusions: Cholinergic nerves are recognized in vertebrates, but the evidence for invertebrate phyla is more equivocal. The high sensitivity to acetylcholine, the presence of acetylcholine and cholinesterase and the potentiating effect of eserine point to the existence of cholinergic motor nerves in certain annelids, molluscs and echinoderms. Acetylcholine in these fibres would function as a neuromuscular chemical transmitter. Even within the same phylum, however, the range of sensitivity shows extraordinary variation, e.g. in annelids and molluscs. Cholinergic systems in coelenterates and ascidians appear to be precluded by the low sensitivity to acetylcholine shown by these animals. The presence of acetylcholine and high levels of cholinesterase in cephalopod and crustacean nervous systems stands unexplained in the face of low sensitivity to acetylcholine and cholinesterase inhibitors. It appears unlikely that acetylcholine functions as a neuromuscular transmitter in crustaceans (28).

EFFECT OF ADRENALINE. Many invertebrate animals are sensitive to adrenaline. Among those preparations which give a clear-cut positive response to adrenaline are innervated body wall of *Aphrodite, Arenicola*; *Arenicola*-extrovert joined to the oesophagus; holothurian muscle; the retractor of Aristotle's lantern in echinoids; and the proboscis of *Balanoglossus*. It has a strong stimulatory action on the heart of many invertebrates (Chapter 3). Adrenaline acts irregularly on the limb muscles of crustaceans, but only in high concentrations (10^{-4}). High levels are also required to affect ascidian body wall. It is without effect on body wall of actiniarians, *Branchiomma* (polychaete), *Pontobdella* (leech) and slow adductor muscle of *Pecten* (7, 76, 93).

In lower chordates (selachians and teleosts) adrenaline is produced in the suprarenal bodies. Its effect resembles that produced by stimulation of certain visceral nerves (75).

Chromaffin cells have been identified in nerve cords of leech and several polychaetes, and in the heart of *Limulus*. The leech ganglion is said to contain adrenaline, while the posterior salivary glands of octopods contain noradrenaline. Adrenaline acts as a neuromuscular transmitter and hormone in vertebrates, and seemingly in those invertebrates in which adrenaline and chromaffin tissue have been identified. Even in the absence of adrenergic nerves, adrenaline, as a secreted hormone, can affect the activity of an organ. The demonstration of so many adrenaline-sensitive tissues in invertebrates poses the problem whether adrenaline is a normal mediator in these animals, or whether sensitivity is a fortuitous accompaniment of other biochemical activities (6, 78).

Neurosecretion

The nervous system usually exerts regulatory control over body activities by means of efferent fibres, which carry signals to the end-organs concerned. But many instances are now accumulating to show that nervous regulation may be more indirect, involving release of hormones—neurosecretion—by specially modified neural structures. The posterior pituitary gland is an example of an endocrine body of nervous origin, and many analogous instances occur among invertebrates. Cephalopods show an interesting transition, in which the giant neurones of the stellate ganglion of decapods become transformed into the neurosecretory cells of the epistellar body of octopods. Special secretory cells have been found in the nervous systems of many groups, including nemertines, annelids, molluscs, crustaceans, fishes and other vertebrates.

Among polychaetes aggregations of neurosecretory cells have been recognized in the supra-oesophageal ganglia and nerve cord of *Nereis* and *Aphrodite*. Modified nerve cells containing secretory granules occur in cerebral and visceral ganglia of opisthobranchs (*Aplysia* and *Pleurobranchaea*).

Neurosecretory systems are better known in arthropods. In the Malacostraca there are well-defined groups of neurosecretory cells in the thoracic ganglia, brain and eyestalks (Fig. 10.20). These cells are modified neurones, and their axons run to special storage organs. One of these is a sinus gland associated with the optic lobe, another lies on the course of the post-commissure nerve. The storage organs are made up of the swollen terminals of the neurosecretory axons, which contain abundant secretory material (prawns, crabs, etc.). Large aggregations of neurosecretory cells are also found in the c.n.s. of *Limulus* (4, 12, 14, 29, 42, 68, 97).

Other peripheral elements of a neurosecretory nature have been described in crustacea (stomatopods, decapods). Such are the neuropile networks known as the pericardial organs that lie in the wall of the pericardial sinus. The pericardial organs are connected with the c.n.s. via longitudinal trunks (1, 2) (Fig. 3.20, p. 118).

The notion of a secretory function in specialized nerve cells was proposed by Gaskell for so-called chromaffin cells, which are believed to secrete adrenaline. Among lower chordates (cyclostomes, fishes) chromaffin tissue is found in the suprarenal bodies, which contain glandular cells akin to post-ganglionic neurones, and which are innervated by the sympathetic system (61a). The suprarenal bodies are endocrine glands, which discharge adrenaline into the blood stream. Chromaffin cells, which have been identified in the nerve cord of the leech, several polychaetes and in the heart of *Limulus*, are thought to have a similar function. In the annelids, at least, adrenaline is believed to originate in the cell body, from which it is transported along the axon to be released at the terminals.

The sinus gland of crustaceans resembles the posterior pituitary of vertebrates in being a storage-release centre for products produced elsewhere (in the x-organ and other central nervous secretory centres of crustaceans, in the hypothalamus of vertebrates). The cytological appearance of the secretory neurones in crustaceans suggests that secretory material is formed in the cell body, is transported along the axon, and stored in the sinus gland. Under the influence of impulses from the neuro-

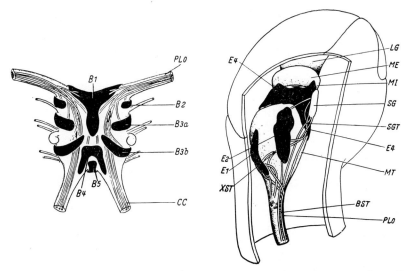

FIG. 10.20. NEUROSECRETORY SYSTEMS IN THE LAND CRAB *Gecarcinus lateralis* (*Left*) Dorsal view of the brain; (*right*) anterior view of the right eye-stalk. Black areas (*B1—B5, E1,E2,E4*) indicate locations of neurosecretory cells. Double lines indicate some fibre-tracts to neurosecretory cells. *BST*, brain/sinus gland tract; *CC*, circumoesophageal (tritocerebral) connective; *LG*, lamina ganglionaris; *ME*, medulla externa; *MI*, medulla interna; *MT*, medulla terminalis; *PLO*, optic lobe peduncle; *SG*, sinus gland; *SGT*, sinus-gland tract; *XST*, x-organ/sinus-gland tract. (From Bliss *et al.* (1954).)

secretory cell bodies, the storage products are released from the sinus gland in activated form as hormones.

Among the known regulatory functions of the sinus gland/x-organ neurosecretory system of crustacea are: acceleration and inhibition of moult; adjustment of respiratory levels; calcium deposition; control of chromatophore activity and retinal pigment migration. The triggering factor for hormonal release may be external, as in the case of chromatophore responses, in which afferent impulses from the retina enter the c.n.s. and eventually reach the neurosecretory centres. In many other instances we must postulate internal releasing agencies for functional activities such as onset of moult, metabolic rhythmicity, etc. Extracts of the pericardial organs of crustaceans have an excitatory action on the crustacean heart similar to adrenaline. These organs appear to be concerned with circulatory regulation (3, 11, 68).

INTEGRATIVE FUNCTIONS OF THE NERVOUS SYSTEM

Animals are not mere automatons, passive machines pulled this way and that by each external stimulus to which they are sensitive. Their responsiveness is variable, and changes during development, and over shorter periods according to their more immediate past history. There are recognizable behaviour patterns characteristic of each species; these patterns are modified by experience and, to the observer, appear directed towards goals, which may be attained in various ways.

Life histories of many animals show how conative behaviour alters during development. Free-swimming larvae of benthic species, for example, are frequently photopositive at first, later becoming photonegative. They then go through a searching and settling phase in which they select a suitable substratum and settle there. If a suitable bottom is not encountered the planktonic life can be prolonged, but discrimination becomes progressively less refined. Such a behaviour pattern is observed in larvae of *Spirorbis, inter alia,* and increases their chances of finding the optimal kind of substratum. After settling and metamorphosing, other behaviour patterns characteristic of the adult appear (67).

In simplest nerve-nets occur many of the essential features of central nervous activity, namely reflex functioning, co-ordination of different action-systems, and modification of spontaneous behaviour under pressure of external stimulation. Within the nerve-net of anemones there is structural and functional differentiation, recognizable in distinct neural patterns and in regional differences in transmission. This nervous network contains a fast through-conduction system, serving quick retractor reflexes and slow co-ordinated contractions. Slow responses of anemones consist of a co-ordinated sequence of contractions in several muscles and are noteworthy for their extreme variability. The responses to low-frequency electrical stimulation resemble in many respects the spontaneous contractions recorded from the whole animal. Stimulation seems to alter the state of intrinsic excitability, releasing a phase of spontaneous activity. Contraction of one set of muscles is often accompanied by reciprocal inhibition of the opposing set, and co-ordination of the separate parietal components is achieved by the through-conduction system (10, 82, 94).

Hydromedusae show several distinct kinds of responses, and have a specialized nervous system consisting of distinct but intercommunicating parts which transmit excitation to various muscle groups. Symmetrical contractions (beating) of the bell are regulated by a non-polarized through-conducting network, excitation of which produces brief contractions of the circular muscles (*Geryonia*). The feeding response involves bending the manubrium towards a stimulated tentacle, and general contraction of the stimulated and other tentacles. Movements of the manubrium are mediated by a radial conducting system, exciting the radial muscles of the manubrium, whereas tentacular contraction is co-ordinated by a through-conducting pathway in the marginal nerve. The two conducting systems serving circular and radial muscles are independent of each other in *Geryonia*, and transmission can occur simultaneously in each. In *Aequorea*, on the contrary, the feeding response stops swimming, inhibition depending on some process in the ganglionated ring nerves (56, 57).

Reflex and Integrative Activities of Invertebrate Central Nervous Systems

Nerve-nets mediate reflex activity in so far as this is regarded as a sequence of events involving receptor, connecting neurones and effector. At higher levels a central nervous system (ganglia and nerve cords) is involved in the arc, and forms a node from which impulses, originating in peripheral receptors, are *reflected* peripherally to the effector organs. In bilaterally symmetrical animals such systems typically comprise cephalic ganglia and ganglionated cords, to which afferent fibres proceed from the periphery, and from which efferent fibres proceed to effectors. A simple reflex, as a theoretical concept, would involve a temporal sequence of effective environmental stimulus, discharge of receptor, excitation of efferent neurones, and activation of effector. Probably no reflex is as simplified as this. Even in the nerve-net of lower metazoans, excitation of one set of effectors may be attended by reciprocal inhibition of antagonists. Reflexes, then, involve co-ordinative activity of systems of effectors; central neurones, by virtue of their functional organization, regulate the relative activities of the various effectors.

Animals which have become elongated and bilaterally symmetrical have the sense organs concentrated at the anterior end. This is the region chiefly exposed to environmental stimuli as the animal advances, or when it protrudes its anterior region from the shelter in which it is lodged. *Pari passu*, with elaboration of sensory fields, nerve centres have become concentrated in anterior regions and serve as relay centres for the enlarged peripheral sensory fields. Segmentation involves duplication of ganglionic regions along the length of the animal, each ganglion acting as a relay centre for local reflexes. The central nervous system may be regarded as a unit governing integrated activities of the whole organism, whereas subsidiary metameric centres control regional activity.

REFLEX ACTIVITY. Reflex functioning in invertebrates has received nothing like the same attention as the spinal reflexes of vertebrates, nor may the same integrated pattern of functional activities be expected because of the diversity of neural organization in different phyla.

All animals show reflexes, even those whose nervous systems are built entirely on the plan of the nerve-net. Interest in these activities is focused on the basal neural mechanisms responsible for each reflex act, and their integration into the total behaviour of the animal. The closure reflex of the sea-anemone has probably been the most intensively studied coelenterate reflex. This response (described on p. 383) involves endodermal stimulation, transmission along a specialized through-conduction system in the longitudinal mesenteries, facilitation at the junction between nerve-net and oral sphincter, and contraction of the latter (*Calliactis*). Besides this closure-response, anemones have other complicated activities. The series of manoeuvres by which *Calliactis* transfers itself to a whelk shell recalls a chain-reflex, initiated by specific chemical stimulation (p. 582) followed by sustained activity of basal muscles, detachment of the pedal disc, etc. An analogous sequence of activities leads to the swimming response of *Stomphia*—chemical stimulation from a predator, activation of pacemaker in the nervous system of the column, and excitation of several muscular systems in succession. The execution of distinct and varied responses by these and other coelenterates seems to be controlled by different parts of the nerve net, components which sometimes can be distinguished otherwise, either visually or by electrical characteristics (62, 86, 94, 95, 96).

The peristaltic contractions responsible for swimming movements in flatworms are reflexly controlled (*Yungia*). The brain is a sensory centre of low threshold, impulses from which bring the locomotory mechanisms into activity. After decapitation and removal of the brain the animal becomes quiescent, owing to the higher threshold of remaining receptor pathways. The neuromuscular mechanism for co-ordinated swimming movements is still present, however, and swimming can be induced by mechanical stimulation of the cut anterior end of the animal (70).

Ambulation in polychaetes is produced by peristaltic waves of the body musculature and movements of the parapodia. The transmission of excitation responsible for these waves takes place in the nerve cord. Patterns of ambulation are centrally controlled, but can be evoked by appropriate reflex stimulation. In the lugworm *Arenicola*, for example, peristaltic locomotion is controlled by segmental reflexes. Progression of waves of swelling and shrinking along the body involves reciprocal excitation and inhibition of longitudinal and circular muscles in each segment in turn.

Errant polychaetes have several forms of locomotion, crawling and swimming. Fast creeping in *Nereis* involves the successive movement of groups of from four to eight parapodia. Accompanying the wave of parapodial beat, the longitudinal muscles of one side contract, while those of the other side relax. The tips of the parapodia are applied to the ground during the backward stroke, and the motive power for traction is supplied by the longitudinal muscles. At the beginning of locomotion the ambulatory pattern spreads rapidly over the body in an antero-posterior direction; subsequently, the pattern is transmitted at a slow rate in an anterior direction, i.e. the direction of progression. It seems likely that the rhythmic contractile waves producing peristaltic locomotion in polychaetes involve neural activity of several kinds: the propagation and setting of a reflex pattern along the length of the c.n.s.; potentiation by chain reflexes involving tactile or muscular receptors; and activation of antagonistic central arcs controlling the tonus of reciprocal segmental muscles (39, 40).

The distinctive reflex responses of certain polychaetes have been analysed sufficiently to reveal some part of the neural pathways involved in their regulation. Some examples are: startle reactions of nereids and sabellids to tactile stimuli (p. 431); the response of *Protula* (a serpulid) to sudden decrease in light intensity; the burrowing of *Branchiomma*. In *Protula* a patch of primary photoreceptors in the head connects with the giant axons, which are the penultimate neural units on the efferent side of the reflex arc. *Branchiomma* is positively geotropic, and regulates the direction of burrowing by means of information received from statocysts and tactile receptors. Statocysts, located in the head, send impulses through the length of the nerve cord, and it is on the basis of this information that particular muscles are thrown into activity in posterior segments, so that the animal always burrows with its tail directed downwards, whatever the position of the statocysts (24).

Reflex responses in molluscs and arthropods are mediated almost exclusively by central ganglia. The extremely interesting condition occurring in animals of these two phyla, whereby muscular activity is graded peripherally by excitatory and inhibitory fibres, is described in Chapter 9. Locomotory movements in decapod crustacea are reflexly controlled, the legs moving in a definite pattern relative to each other. However, when one leg is removed, changes in the locomotory pattern occur at once, and the remaining limbs assume new movement-sequences. In explanation it appears that the c.n.s. must contain alternative nervous settings for different ambulatory patterns, which can be brought into operation as required by particular external conditions.

Stimulation of individual large fibres in the crustacean c.n.s. often brings about widespread contractions or reactions. A single impulse in the medial giant fibres, in particular, produces motor reactions throughout the animal. In another instance a whole reflex pattern (the defensive reflex) is obtained by stimulation of a single fibre in the circumoesophageal connective. Neurones are notably sparse in the crustacean nervous system, and complex reflexes are evoked by a narrow range of stimuli and mediated on the efferent side by greatly restricted motor pathways. The stereotypy of crustacean responses is in contrast to the greater plasticity of much vertebrate behaviour, founded on a richer and more varied basis of central neural organization (125).

SPONTANEOUS ACTIVITY. Spontaneous activity is a common feature of animal behaviour, and the question arises as to what extent this kind of activity is entirely intrinsic in origin and to what extent it is influenced by environmental agencies. Spontaneous cyclic or rhythmic functions are encountered at all levels of organization, and various instances have been noted on other pages, e.g. rhythmic beating of hearts, respiratory movements, diurnal rhythmicity of pigment responses, etc. Some of the evidence relating to the intrinsic regulation of such functions will now be examined.

Rhythmic activity occurs in many kinds of cells. Among unicellular algae and protozoa there are estuarine and littoral species which display persistent rhythms related to tidal periodicity. The estuarine flagellate *Euglena limosa*, for example, continues to perform periodic migrations under constant laboratory conditions, in rhythm with natural tidal excursions (35).

In higher animals there are tissues which show periodic or rhythmic activity, e.g. the periodic beat of the myogenic heart, although such activity is often under nervous control. Periodic or rhythmic activity is a cellular characteristic, shared by nerve cells.

Spontaneous Activity in Animals possessing Nerve-nets. Simply organized animals having nervous systems organized as nerve-nets often show complex behaviour patterns. In an apparently simple animal, such as the jellyfish *Aurelia*, the bell contracts rhythmically, executing periodic swimming movements. Bouts of activity are interrupted by periods of quiescence, and each outburst consists of a series of contractions variable in frequency. The activity is due to rhythmic discharge from a series of ganglionic pacemakers lying at the bases of the marginal tentaculocysts; these pacemakers discharge into the nerve-net. Although spontaneous, the activity of the pacemakers can be altered by external stimuli, leading to modification of the response (84).

Anemones such as *Metridium* display slow but continual muscular movements. In the column, such activity consists of a sequence of regular reciprocal contractions of parietal and circular muscles, and the behaviour may be markedly rhythmic, with a period of about 10 min. Activities of different parts of the body wall are usually co-ordinated, and contraction of one part of the parietal musculature is followed by contraction of others. It appears that co-ordination of movement takes place through one part of the body wall acting as leader, other regions following this contraction with long delays. Activity of this nature is inherent in *Metridium* and continues unaltered in the absence of external stimulation (Fig. 10.21). The pattern of activity, however, changes from time to time, and particular phases may be initiated by external stimuli such as food and light (Fig. 10.22). In complete darkness, and with other environmental conditions maintained constant, alternating phasic activity may still show a rough diurnal rhythm. It is concluded that inherent and spontaneous phasic activity is influenced by periodic stimulation, such as diurnal illumination, which determines the period of rhythmicity (8, 9, 80, 82).

Phasic Activity in Animals with Central Nervous Systems. Spontaneous phasic activity appears at all levels of central nervous organization, in manifold aspects of internal functioning and external behaviour. Periodic discharge of ganglionic pacemakers controlling circulation and respiration are cogent instances of the former. Crabs and molluscs, under laboratory conditions, show periodic fluctuations of oxygen-consumption, in sympathy with diurnal and tidal changes; such respiratory cycles are probably due to cyclic variations in levels of muscular activity (p. 153). Diurnal phasing of locomotory activity has now been recorded for many marine animals, e.g. turbellarians, gastropods and starfishes.

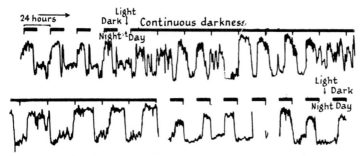

FIG. 10.21. ACTIVITY OF *Metridium senile* OVER A PERIOD OF 48 DAYS (KYMOGRAPH RECORDS)

Alternating 12-hour periods of dark and light correspond to night and day at the beginning of the record; at the end they are reversed. During these periods a light-controlled rhythm is apparent. In the intermediate period of prolonged darkness a phasic rhythm develops which is unrelated to external diurnal or tidal rhythm. (From Batham and Pantin (9).)

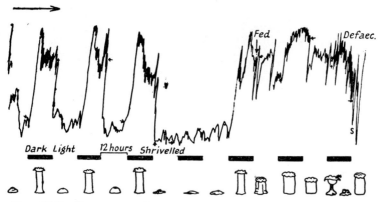

FIG. 10.22. KYMOGRAPH RECORD OF ACTIVITY IN THE SEA ANEMONE *Metridium senile*

A pronounced light-controlled rhythm in the first half of the record is abolished by feeding. The sketches below show the appearance of the anemone at successive periods. (From Batham and Pantin (9).)

Convoluta roscoffensis is a littoral species of flatworm that executes rhythmical tidal migrations. These movements bring it to the surface of the sand during tidal ebb, thereby exposing its algal symbionts to light (p. 666). Rhythmic activity with tidal phasing continues in this animal in the laboratory, in absence of tidal influences. Starfish (*Astropecten*) likewise show a rhythmic pattern of activity, moving about most actively at dawn, and lying quiescent beneath the sand at midday. The environmental factor controlling this diurnal activity is light. Animals will maintain a persistent rhythm for several days in total darkness, but the rhythm gradually disappears. Hunger modifies the vigour of this activity but does not control its periodicity. There is apparently an inherent tendency towards rhythmic behaviour, the timing of which is set by recurrence of day and night (38, 71, 79).

Simple ascidians show a constant pattern of spontaneous activity which in *Phallusia* takes the form of regular contractions of the siphons (squirting) at intervals of 6 to 9 min. The contractions of both siphons are

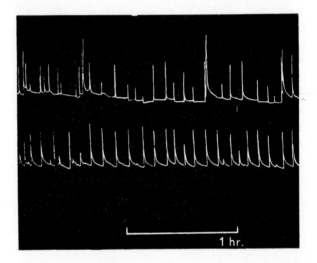

FIG. 10.23. SPONTANEOUS SQUIRTING OF *Phallusia mammillata*

Records show movements of siphons of a deganglionated animal. Upper tracing, branchial siphon; lower, atrial siphon. (From Hoyle (59).)

synchronous, and the frequency may shift fairly quickly under constant conditions to higher or lower rates usually twice or one-half the normal rate. The pacemaker for this activity is situated in the body wall, either in the musculature or in the nerve-net. The periodicity is not abolished by deganglionation, which does, however, affect co-ordination, tonus and reflex responses (Fig. 10.23). Spontaneous activity is also shown by isolated muscle strips (*Phallusia*) and isolated siphons (*Ciona*, *Styela*). This activity is intrinsic, as in sea anemones, and is sensitive to environmental changes, increasing during starvation and declining in the presence of food (58, 59).

Among animals which possess well-defined ganglia and central nervous systems it is sometimes possible to assign the regulation of spontaneous activities to particular centres. The behaviour patterns of some polychaetes are particularly interesting in this regard. *Arenicola* is a burrowing polychaete, showing rhythmic behaviour concerned with irrigating and cleaning its burrow, and with feeding. The animal feeds by protruding its proboscis at regular intervals and taking in sand (p. 227). Vigorous muscular contractions of the proboscis alternate with periods of rest, a whole cycle occupying some 7–8 min. Contractions of the proboscis of *Arenicola* are controlled by a plexus in the oesophageal wall; from the oesophagus the intermittent rhythm invades the proboscis and may also spread into the anterior three segments of the body wall (Fig. 10.10). Impulses from the oesophageal plexus reach the c.n.s. via proboscidial nerves, and excitation of the body wall will not extend past a point where the ventral nerve cord is cut.

In addition to the feeding cycle the behaviour of *Arenicola* is characterized by an irrigation cycle showing a periodicity of about 40 min. This is three-phasic, consisting of periods of headward creeping, headward irrigation and tailward irrigation. Water is pumped through the burrow by the development of peristaltic waves along the wall of the trunk. The phasing and intermittence of activity are due to a pacemaker located in the nerve cord, the activity of which is spontaneous and not dependent on external stimuli. Pacemaker activity, however, is influenced by external conditions—for example, the vigour of pumping is reduced in stagnant water.

In *Arenicola* neither pacemaker—in oesophagus or cord—directly affects the rhythm of the other. The integration of activity depends on the extent to which their influences spread through the neuromuscular system. In brief, the two pacemakers compete for activity, the oesophageal pacemaker predominantly controlling the proboscis and buccal region, whereas the irrigation pacemaker is dominant over most of the body wall (118, 120, 123).

Spontaneous activity cycles, controlled by visceral pacemakers, occur in other polychaetes, e.g. the isolated proboscides of *Nereis* and *Glycera*. *Sabella*, a tubicolous polychaete, drives water through its tube by pumping movements of the body wall. Control of periodic irrigation in this animal depends on pacemaker activity of the ventral nerve cord. In *Chaetopterus* irrigation is carried out by the regular, sequential beating of three parapodial fans. The rhythm is spontaneous and originates in ganglia of the ventral nerve cord; it is sensitive, however, to environmental influences (119, 121).

ELECTRICAL EVIDENCE OF SPONTANEOUS CENTRAL ACTIVITY. The ganglia and nerve centres of many animals are in a state of continuous electrical activity, which appears as rhythmical oscillations of potential or periodic discharges of impulses (brain waves). The brain waves seen in electro-encephalograms of vertebrates find their counterpart in recordings made from invertebrate nerve ganglia. It is rather striking that many nerve centres continue to exhibit rhythmic electrical activity even when isolated from all incoming sensory messages, e.g. in isolated abdominal ganglia from the crustacean nerve cord.

Spontaneous central activity in vertebrates shows much uniformity in all groups investigated. Characteristic of these animals are smooth slow waves (spectrum chiefly 1–30/sec), which can be recorded from deafferented and isolated fragments of brain. Slow rhythmic waves of this nature have been described in only a few invertebrates. The central nervous systems of the latter are characterized rather by fast spike-like activity, the dominant frequency range of which is some twenty times that of vertebrates.

Most invertebrate studies have involved arthropods. Central ganglia of crayfish (*Cambarus*) and horse-shoe crab (*Limulus*) reveal complex asynchronous activity taking the form of fast spikes (500–1,200/sec), and slow and intermediate waves (40/sec or less) (Fig. 10.24). Fast peaks

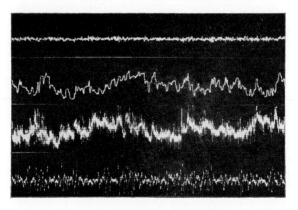

FIG. 10.24. RECORD OF RHYTHMIC ELECTRICAL ACTIVITY IN
CENTRAL GANGLIA OF *Limulus*

(*Top*) recording from connectives between deafferented cephalothoracic and first abdominal ganglia. (*Second from top*) similar but fast activity reduced by filtering. Whole records = 5 sec. Lower two records filtered to reveal slow activity. (*Third from top*) whole record = 2 sec. (*Bottom*) record = 0·5 sec. (From Bullock (18).)

dominate the records; slow waves are more conspicuous in ganglia, and spike potentials in connectives and nerve roots (*Limulus*).

Various interpretations have been placed upon the vertebrate encephalogram. According to one viewpoint, the slow waves in vertebrates and invertebrates are outward manifestations of slow oscillations of potential in groups or masses of nerve cells. We may regard rhythmic activity as an inherent property of some central neurones. Such cells have been compared to relaxation oscillators, which are continually being charged by intracellular metabolic processes, and periodically discharge whenever a critical value is reached. Nerve cells with high threshold may fire only a single pulse when stimulated, others may respond with repetitive discharge, e.g. many peripheral ganglionic neurones. Alterations in the chemical environment greatly alter excitability. Spontaneously active cells possess high levels of intrinsic excitability, resulting in instability and spontaneous discharge.

Spontaneous and rhythmic discharge of single neurones is well recognized in peripheral receptors (e.g. lateral line of fish). In *Limulus* the electrocardiogram shows slow waves accompanied by a burst of nervous impulses for each heart beat. The slow waves correspond to the activity of pacemaker cells, and these synchronize discharges from smaller neurones regulating heart beat. Slow waves in central ganglia may also represent synchronous slow beating of cells. Spontaneously active neurones in the c.n.s. of the crayfish regularly discharge impulses in series. Such cells form part of a population of endogenous pacemakers, some of which are unaffected by sensory stimulation, whereas others are influenced by sensory input (18, 20, 44, 89, 90).

Apart from rhythmic oscillations controlling periodic visceral functions, and rhythmic discharges forming background activity of peripheral receptors, we may well conjecture as to the physiological significance of constant ganglionic electrical activity. Is it a novel form of nervous activity, distinct from the transitory potentials seen in nervous transmission? Is it the physical manifestation of continuous patterns of nervous functioning, regulating inherent phasic activities and behaviour patterns characteristic of each species? Circus conduction in closed circuits, and slow fluctuations in master pacemaker centres, may maintain and regulate long-term behaviour activities which are set or modified by periodic environmental stimuli. But as yet we possess no clear concept of the underlying mechanisms determining phasic behaviour, modification of response, establishment of the memory trace and utilization of past experience, to wit, those particular ethological patterns characteristic of each species.

INSTINCTIVE AND PLASTIC BEHAVIOUR. The general pattern of behaviour possessed by an animal is predetermined by heredity and restricted by limits of specific organization. Among lower animals much instinctive behaviour is of a relatively inflexible type, in which a given stimulus evokes a predictable type of response and range of responses. Under natural conditions it is probably only on rare occasions that an animal is subjected to the simple form of stimulation employed in the laboratory for studying behaviour. In nature an animal is exposed to a complex of different sensory stimuli, the intensities and durations of which affect the pattern of response. Analysis of sensori-neuro-response mechanisms, however, is greatly facilitated by the analytical approach.

Instinctive behaviour refers to certain patterns of activity characteristic of a species at certain stages of its life-history. Such activities, to the observer, appear directed towards the survival of the individual or the reproduction of the species. They are frequently complex in nature, and appear to be evoked by specific stimuli to which the individuals of a species are inherently susceptible.

Like the majority of benthic animals, polychaete worms are usually restricted to particular kinds of substratum, characteristic of each species.

In some instances the proper substratum, inhabited by the species, is selected by the pelagic larva. An example is provided by the mitraria larva of *Owenia fusiformis*, which has a pelagic phase of some four weeks, during which time it swims with an upward tendency. When ready to metamorphose it swims towards the bottom and moves along slowly in contact with the latter. If it encounters a bottom of fine sand or grit, similar to that in which the adults live, the larva responds by settling down, metamorphosing and building a tube. Larvae of *Notomastus* and *Ophelia* likewise select a substratum corresponding to that in which the adults occur; an important factor in inducing settlement of *Ophelia* larvae is the presence of suitable micro-organisms in the substratum (126).

These polychaete larvae show inherent susceptibility to particular environmental stimuli, which call forth a specific pattern of response. Similarly, we find adult polychaetes which show preferential selection of environmental habitat on the basis of some particular stimulus. Certain commensal polynoids, for example, react positively to specific chemical influences from a particular host species, ignoring other species closely related to the host (Chapter 14). Many polychaetes are tubicolous and build tubes of characteristic form and composition. When material from the substratum is incorporated in the tube, such material is selected in accordance with specific preference, and the tube is moulded by the worm into a characteristic shape (p. 647).

Selection of food, although not as extensively studied in marine as in terrestrial species, likewise shows preferences suitable to the animal's habits and feeding apparatus. Some species, such as octopuses, hunt moving prey and depend on patterns of visual stimuli. Others are tactile feeders, e.g. the sole (*Solea solea*) which feels the substratum with cheek villi. Others, again, react to chemical clues, e.g. the whelk *Buccinum*, a carrion feeder which finds its food by smell. The feeding behaviour of these animals is innately determined, and to find its full expression it must be triggered by particular stimuli. The same specificity of response is shown sometimes in escape- or avoiding-reactions to natural enemies. Certain gastropods and scallops, for example, have a common pattern of escape behaviour to carnivorous starfish, such behaviour being quite dissimilar from that elicited by other non-predatory animals. The response is evoked by a chemical stimulus emanating from the starfish, or by contact with the tube feet; the mollusc then takes to flight, either by leaping, crawling or swimming, according to the habits of the species. More specific and complex in their manifestations are the reproductive habits of many species, e.g. of fishes which depend upon particular sequential stimuli to carry through the entire spawning process (25, 112).

The very rigidity of much instinctive behaviour, particularly complex instinctive acts, is related to the intricacy of the situations in which the participants become involved. It seems as if the animal has no comprehension of situations as a whole, no knowledge of goals, and no method of juggling and relating perceptive concepts. In the absence of such cerebral equipment the completion of a complex behavioural act—say, sexual display, spawning and nest-guarding in a teleost—depends upon an obligatory series of ordered responses to particular stimuli presented in definite temporal and spatial patterns. Of the total available field of stimulation, only some one entity may be utilized for triggering a reaction, e.g. the red belly of the male stickleback which acts as sign stimulus for fighting among males during the breeding season. Failure of one stimulus in a series may block the chain of reactions, and appearance of a signal in a novel setting may lead to a misdirected response. Innate pathways in the c.n.s. appear channelled or preset for particular actions under particular conditions. Under normal circumstances the system is such that fruition of endeavour follows.

Variability of Response. Animals generally show a certain amount of variability in behaviour and response. Even among the lowest animals the effect of a stimulus depends to some extent upon the creature's physiological condition and recent history. Under repetitive stimulation of an irritative nature, protozoans often respond by a series of negative avoiding-reactions of various kinds. The repertoire of responses, however, is limited, and the kinds of responses are simple and stereotyped in nature.

Alteration of response with repetition of stimulus has been observed in coelenterates and echinoderms, and the experiments serve to underline certain differences between sensory adaptation and true learning. Responses of actinian tentacles (*Metridium*, *Stoichactis*, etc.) change with continued feeding, and at one time this result was attributed to loss of hunger. Further analysis shows that the responses of the tentacles disappear even when the animal is not permitted to swallow the food. Muscular fatigue is not involved, since the tentacles can be caused to contract an equivalent number of times without reducing responsiveness. Furthermore, when the tentacles on one side of the animal are plied with food, which is removed before it is swallowed, those tentacles fatigue, whereas the tentacles of the opposite side remain unaffected. An analogous situation exists in the behaviour of certain ciliary fields, which reverse direction when subjected to food and mechanical stimulation. When the animal is satiated with food, ciliary reversal can still be evoked by continued application of food but not by mechanical stimulation. The alterations in responses produced by these experiments are due, not to fatigue of effectors or to changes in the nerve-net, but to the onset of sensory adaptation or accommodation (85, 116).

Plasticity of response is little more advanced in echinoderms, as the following experiments show. When obstructions of various kinds are placed on the arms of starfish, they are removed by the efforts of the animal. In the brittle-star *Ophiura* (*Ophioderma*) *brevispina*, various reactions are tried successively to get rid of the foreign body, and as each effort fails to remove the irritant it is abandoned and another commenced. Finally, as a last resort, the arm is amputated. When confronted with such situations the animal shows no improvement of performance with repeated trials. Other experiments suggest that starfish possess limited powers of learning. Starfish (*Asterias*) can right themselves with any arms, but by restraining certain of them it is possible to train animals to use preferentially one or two particular arms for turning over. Such an induced habit persists for several days. Again, by applying nocuous stimuli as reinforcement, it is possible to train animals to reduce the number of fruitless efforts made in trying to shake off an obstruction.

LEARNING AND CONDITIONING. Most animals are capable of learning or profiting by experience. In contrast to mere sensory adaptation, learning involves some lasting change in the central nervous system of the animal whereby its behaviour in a given situation becomes dependent on previous experience of the same or a similar situation. True learning has been demonstrated only in animals with central nervous organization, and appears to be an emergent condition of ganglionic arrangement or organization of grey matter.

Animals differ enormously in their capacity for learning. Differences depend not only on neural complexity, but also on the sensory avenues open to the animal and on its modes of effector responses. Simple levels of learning have been discovered in the more primitive phyla, including flatworms and annelids. Experiments have been designed so as to bring about a reversal of response to a stimulus after combining with another, more potent, stimulus. In *Leptoplana* the normal response to illumination is an increase in locomotory rate, whereas mechanical stimulation of the head causes the worm to stop. By touching the worm each time it is illuminated. it has proved possible to train it to remain motionless in the light. The new association is weakened and disappears when the mechanical stimulation is omitted, but learning takes place more rapidly on a second occasion.

Similar reversals in sign of response have been obtained with polychaetes. *Neanthes virens* normally shows a negative response to illumination and mechanical stimulation. The animal emerges from its tube when mussel juice is presented; when this stimulus is presented at the same time as a photic or tactile stimulus, the response to the latter becomes positive after some eighty trials. Again, the normal negative response of *Hydroides dianthus* to shadows is withdrawal. In some animals the response is poorly developed but can be strengthened by associating a tactile stimulus with it.

Marine animals with most highly-developed central nervous systems are decapod crustaceans, cephalopods and fishes, and it is among them that we may expect to find the most complex and varied behaviour patterns. It is in these animals, again, that modifiability of response and learning reach greatest development.

The behaviour of shore crabs, notably *Uca*, reveals various interesting social features, such as defence of territory, visual and auditory signalling. *Carcinus maenas*, when tested in a simple maze, shows some ability to improve with practice. Experiments with other crabs—hermit crabs, fiddler crabs—have involved reversal of some proclivity. Fiddler crabs, for example, learn to reverse the direction they normally take in escaping from a particular situation. Good performances have been secured after some thirty to fifty trials in some animals (99).

The octopus has proved to be a most rewarding animal for experimental studies of learning, and an attempt has been made to correlate certain aspects of its behaviour with central nervous organization. Octopuses inhabit niches from which they venture forth to attack prey of suitable character and size. In an aquarium they attack living crabs which they recognize by sight. By presenting a crab in various situations, it has been possible to analyse certain aspects of octopus behaviour. When an octopus is shown a crab together with a white signal square, and it is given an electric shock after making an attack, it soon learns not to attack when this situation appears again (Fig. 10.25). It continues, however, to attack

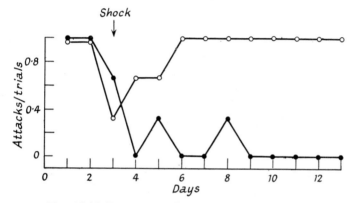

FIG. 10.25. PROGRESS OF LEARNING IN THE OCTOPUS

In the experiments the octopus was fed with crabs, and in some trials a white square was presented with the crab. Whenever the octopus attacked the crab + white square, it was given an electrical shock. After 2–5 days of training, the octopus learnt to distinguish between the two stimulus-situations (crab alone, hollow circle, and crab + square, solid circle), i.e. to leave the crab alone when the white square appeared. The graphs show the ratio of number of attacks to trials during the course of experimentation (abscissae in days). (From Boycott and Young, (13).)

crabs when these are presented alone. Memory of the former situation, whereby an octopus learns not to attack a crab shown with a white square, persists for 2–3 days in the absence of reinforcing stimuli.

The brain of the octopus consists of discrete anatomical lobes, severally possessing sensory, motor and associative functions and surgical interference has thrown some light on the part played by them. When the upper lobes of the visual system are removed, subtle changes in behaviour occur and the ability to learn is seriously impaired. The animal is uninhibited and is no longer restrained by painful stimuli; the vertical lobe seems to be concerned with permitting pain impulses to affect the memory centre. Following lesions to the lower lobes the octopus no longer attacks crabs unless they are placed close to the animal; these lobes seem to reinforce visual signals.

Two memory stores are recognized in the octopus, one for visual memory in the optic lobe, and one for tactile memory in the posterior buccal lobe; here are lodged the memory traces. Associated separately with each centre is a parallel series of upper and lower lobes. Mixing of signals from diverse receptors occurs in the upper lobes of the visual system. Transitory associations are set up in self re-exciting circuits, whereby early signals of distant events are retained long enough to be matched with later arriving contact impulses. Such transitory associations, successively reinforced, are transmitted to the memory centre. Injuries to higher and lower lobes may adversely affect learning by impeding the presentation of information to the memory centre, and the relaying of information outwards for execution (13, 14, 27, 127).

The behaviour of fish is varied and complex, involving many different kinds of activities, e.g. schooling, migration, nuptial display, nest-building, guarding of eggs, etc. Training experiments reveal that fish learn readily. Conditioning to particular stimuli and forming of associations obviously play an important part in the lives of many species, e.g. in enabling the animal to locate some particular feature in its environment and find its way about.

Many studies of conditioned reflexes in fishes have been concerned with determining powers of sensory discrimination, and have not been designed specifically to throw light on processes of learning. As an example may be cited experiments in which a wrasse (*Crenilabrus*) was conditioned to respond to sound, with food as the unconditioned stimulus. Positive responses appeared after twenty trials with food, and the association was well established in thirty-two trials. In specifically designed learning experiments, rock wrasse (*Ctenolabrus*) have learnt to swim around obstructions to reach food. Individual fish showed much diversity of behaviour in the maze, and some animals were evidently more capable of profiting by experience than others. Learning was enhanced by accentuating the sensory clues, which produced stronger imprinting on the memory trace (107). Second-order learning (i.e. second-order conditioned reflex) has proved possible in the goldfish. The fish were trained initially with an optic stimulus and food as a reward, and an olfactory stimulus was then associated with the conditioned optic stimulus (16).

No clear-cut picture emerges from correlated studies of behaviour and physiology of the teleost brain. In some teleosts decerebration and removal of the habenular ganglion failed to abolish learning or impair visual form-discrimination (*Gasterosteus, Phoxinus, Gobio*). In other species, however, forebrain injuries produced marked disturbances of behaviour, affecting mating, schooling, etc. (*Carassius, Box*, etc.). The function of the forebrain in teleost behaviour appears to be a highly variable one, closely linked with the importance of the various sensory avenues in any given species. Thus, smell is the most important sense in some species; touch or sight in others. Among the latter should be included those species with highly developed visually directed activities such as breeding behaviour and schooling. Further experiments have shown that the optic tectum contains a mechanism involved in second-order learning. The forebrain thus possesses affector and associative centres for certain aspects of behaviour, and these are linked with association centres at lower levels (72).

REFERENCES

1. ALEXANDROWICZ, J. S., "Notes on the nervous system in the Stomatopoda," *Pubbl. Staz. Zool. Napoli*, **24**, 29 (1953).
2. ALEXANDROWICZ, J. S., "Nervous organs in the pericardial cavity of the decapod crustacea," *J. Mar. Biol. Ass. U.K.*, **31**, 563 (1953).
3. ALEXANDROWICZ, J. S. and CARLISLE, D. B., "Some experiments on the function of the pericardial organs in crustacea," ibid., **32**, 175 (1953).
4. AMAR, R., "Formations endocrines cérébrales des Isopodes marins," *Thès. Fac. Sci. Univ. Paris*, Marseilles: Impr. Marseillaise (1951).
5. AMBACHE, N. and SAWAYA, P., "Use of *Holothuria grisea* for acetylcholine assays of electric-organ extracts from *Narcine brasiliensis*," *Physiol. Comp. Oecol.*, **3**, 53 (1953).
6. AUGUSTINSSON, K.-B., FÄNGE, R., JOHNELS, A. and Östlund, E., "Histological, physiological and biochemical studies on the heart of two cyclostomes, *Myxine* and *Lampetra*," *J. Physiol.*, **131**, 257 (1955).
7. BACQ, Z. M., "L'acétylcholine et l'adrénaline chez les Invertébrés," *Biol. Rev.*, **22**, 73 (1947).
8. BATHAM, E. J. and PANTIN, C. F. A., "Inherent activity in the sea-anemone *Metridium senile*," *J. Exp. Biol.*, **27**, 290 (1950).
9. BATHAM, E. J. and PANTIN, C. F. A., "Phases of activity in the sea-anemone, *Metridium senile*, and their relation to external stimuli," ibid., **27**, 377 (1950).
10. BATHAM, E. J. and PANTIN, C. F. A., "Slow contraction and its relation to spontaneous activity in the sea-anemone *Metridium senile*," ibid., **31**, 84 (1954).
11. BLISS, D. E., "Neurosecretion and the control of growth in a decapod crustacean," in *Bertil Hanström. Zoological Papers in Honour of his Sixty-fifth Birthday*, Ed. Wingstrand, K. G. (Lund, Zoological Inst., 1956).
12. BLISS, D. E. and WELSH, J. H., "The neurosecretory system of brachyuran crustacea," *Biol. Bull.*, **103**, 157 (1952).
13. BOYCOTT, B. B. and YOUNG, J. Z., "A memory system in *Octopus vulgaris*," *Proc. Roy. Soc. B.*, **143**, 449 (1955).
14. BOYCOTT, B. B. and YOUNG, J. Z., "The subpedunculate body and nerve and other organs associated with the optic tract of cephalopods," in *Bertil Hanström. Zoological Papers in Honour of his Sixty-fifth Birthday*, Ed. Wingstrand, K. G. (Lund, Zoological Inst., 1956).
15. BRYANT, S. H., "Transmission in squid giant synapses," *J. Gen. Physiol.*, **41**, 473 (1958).
16. BULL, H. O., "Behavior: conditioned responses," in *The Physiology of Fishes*, Ed. Brown, M. E. (New York, Academic Press, 1957).

17. BULLOCK, T. H., "Neuromuscular facilitation in Scyphomedusae," *J. Cell. Comp. Physiol.*, **22**, 251 (1943).
18. BULLOCK, T. H., "Problems in the comparative study of brain waves," *Yale J. Biol. Med.*, **17**, 657 (1945).
19. BULLOCK, T. H., "The anatomical organization of the nervous system of Enteropneusta," *Quart. J. Micr. Sci.*, **86**, 55 (1945).
20. BULLOCK, T. H., "Problems in invertebrate electrophysiology," *Physiol. Rev.*, **27**, 643 (1947).
21. BULLOCK, T. H., "Physiological mapping of giant nerve fiber systems in polychaete annelids," *Physiol. Comp. Oecol.*, **1**, 1 (1948).
22. BULLOCK, T. H., "Properties of a single synapse in the stellate ganglion of squid," *J. Neurophysiol.*, **11**, 343 (1948).
23. BULLOCK, T. H., "The invertebrate neuron junction," *Cold Spr. Harb. Symp. Quant. Biol.*, **17**, 267 (1952).
24. BULLOCK, T. H., "Properties of some natural and quasi-artificial synapses in polychaetes," *J. Comp. Neur.*, **98**, 37 (1953).
25. BULLOCK, T. H., "Predator recognition and escape responses of some intertidal gastropods in presence of starfish," *Behaviour*, **5**, 130 (1953).
26. BULLOCK, T. H., COHEN, M. J. and FAULSTICK, D., "Effect of stretch on conduction in single nerve fibers," *Biol. Bull.*, **99**, 320 (1950).
27. BULLOCK, T. H. and HORRIDGE, G. A., *Structure and Function in the Nervous Systems of Invertebrates*, Vols. I and II (San Francisco and London, W. H. Freeman and Co., 1965).
28. BULLOCK, T. H., NACHMANSOHN, D. and ROTHENBERG, M. A., "Effects of inhibitors of choline esterase on the nerve action potential," *J. Neurophysiol.*, **9**, 9 (1946).
29. CARLISLE, D. and FAGE, L., "Note préliminaire sur la structure du système neurosécréteur du pédoncle oculaire de *Lysmata seticaudata*," *C. R. Acad. Sci., Paris*, **236**, 2541 (1953).
30. DAVSON, H., *A Textbook of General Physiology* (London, Churchill, 1951).
31. ECCLES, J. C., *The Neurophysiological Basis of Mind* (Oxford, Clarendon Press, 1953).
32. FATT, P. and KATZ, B., "The electric activity of the motor end-plate," *Proc. Roy. Soc. B.*, **140**, 183 (1952).
33. FATT, P. and KATZ, B., "Some problems of neuro-muscular transmission," *Cold Spr. Harb. Symp. Quant. Biol.*, **17**, 275 (1952).
34. FATT, P. and KATZ, B., "Distributed 'end-plate' potentials' of crustacean muscle fibres," *J. Exp. Biol.*, **30**, 433 (1953).
35. FAURÉ-FREMIET, E., "The tidal rhythm of the diatom *Hantzschia amphioxys*," *Biol. Bull.*, **100**, 173 (1951).
36. FELDBERG, W., "Central excitation and inhibition from the view point of chemical transmission," *Proc. Roy. Soc. B.*, **140**, 199 (1952).
37. FOX, H. M., "Anal and oral intake of water by Crustacea," *J. Exp. Biol.*, **29**, 583 (1952).
38. GAMBLE, F. W. and KEEBLE, F., "The bionomics of *Convoluta roscoffensis*," *Quart. J. Micr. Sci.*, **47**, 363 (1904).
39. GRAY, J., "Croonian lecture: aspects of animal locomotion," *Proc. Roy. Soc. B.*, **128**, 28 (1939).
40. GRAY, J., "Studies in animal locomotion. 8. The kinetics of locomotion of *Nereis diversicolor*," *J. Exp. Biol.*, **16**, 9 (1939).

41. HANSTRÖM, B., *Vergleichende Anatomie des Nervensystems der wirbellosen Tiere* (Berlin, Springer, 1928).
42. HANSTRÖM, B., "The brain, the sense organs, and the incretory organs of the head in the Crustacea Malacostraca," *Bull. Biol.* (Suppl.), **33**, 98 (1948).
43. HILL, D. K., "Advances in the physiology of peripheral nerve," *J. Mar. Biol. Ass. U.K.*, **29**, 241 (1950).
44. HOAGLAND, H., *Pacemakers in Relation to Aspects of Behavior* (New York, Macmillan, 1935).
45. HODES, R., "Linear relationship between fiber diameter and velocity of conduction in giant axon of squid," *J. Neurophysiol.*, **16**, 145 (1953).
46. HODGKIN, A. L., "The ionic basis of electrical activity in nerve and muscle," *Biol. Rev.*, **26**, 339 (1951).
47. HODGKIN, A. L., "Ionic movements and electrical activity in giant nerve fibres (Croonian lecture)," *Proc. Roy. Soc. B.*, **148**, 1 (1958).
48. HODGKIN, A. L. and HUXLEY, A. F., "Propagation of electrical signals along giant nerve fibres," *Proc. Roy. Soc. B.*, **140**, 177 (1952).
49. HODGKIN, A. L. and HUXLEY, A. F., "Movement of sodium and potassium ions during nervous activity," *Cold. Spr. Harb. Symp. Quant. Biol.*, **17**, 43 (1952).
50. HODGKIN, A. L. and KEYNES, R. D., "Movements of cations during recovery in nerve," *Symp. Soc. Exp. Biol.*, **8**, 423 (1954).
51. HODGKIN, A. L. and KEYNES, R. D., "Active transport of cations in giant axons from *Sepia* and *Loligo*," *J. Physiol.*, **128**, 28 (1955).
52. HOLMES, W., "The giant myelinated nerve fibres of the prawn," *Phil. Trans. B.*, **231**, 293 (1942).
53. HOLMES, W., PUMPHREY, R. J. and YOUNG, J. Z., "The structure and conduction velocity of the medullated nerve fibres of prawns," *J. Exp. Biol.*, **18**, 50 (1941).
54. HORRIDGE, G. A., "Observations on the nerve fibres of *Aurellia aurita*," *Quart. J. Micr. Sci.*, **95**, 85 (1954).
55. HORRIDGE, G. A., "The nerves and muscles of Medusae. 1. Conduction in the nervous system of *Aurellia aurita*," *J. Exp. Biol.*, **31**, 594 (1954).
56. HORRIDGE, G. A., "The nerves and muscles of Medusae. 2. *Geryonia proboscidalis*," *ibid.*, **32**, 555 (1955).
57. HORRIDGE, G. A., "The nerves and muscles of Medusae. 4. Inhibition in *Aequorea forskalea*," *ibid.*, **32**, 642 (1955).
58. HOYLE, G., "The response mechanism in ascidians," *J. Mar. Biol. Ass. U.K.*, **31**, 287 (1952).
59. HOYLE, G., "Spontaneous squirting of an ascidian, *Phallusia mammillata*," *ibid.*, **31**, 541 (1953).
60. HUXLEY, A. F., "Electrical processes in nerve conduction," in *Ion Transport across Membranes*, Ed. Clarke, H. T. (New York, Academic Press, 1954).
61. JOHNELS, A. G., "On the peripheral autonomic nervous system of the trunk region of *Lampetra planeri*," *Acta Zool., Stockh.*, **37**, 251 (1956).
62. JOSEPHSON, R. K., "Three parallel conducting systems in the stalk of a hydroid," *J. Exp. Biol.*, **42**, 139 (1965).
63. KATZ, B., "The properties of the nerve membrane and its relation to the conduction of impulses," *Symp. Soc. Exp. Biol.*, **6**, 16 (1952).
64. KERKUT, G. A., "The mechanisms of coordination of the starfish tube feet," *Behaviour*, **6**, 206 (1954).

65. KERKUT, G. A., "The retraction and protraction of the tube feet of the starfish, *Asterias rubens*," ibid., **8**, 112 (1955).

66. KNIGHT-JONES, E. W., "On the nervous system of *Saccoglossus cambrensis* (Enteropneusta)," *Phil. Trans. B.*, **236**, 315 (1952).

67. KNIGHT-JONES, E. W., "Decreased discrimination during setting after prolonged planktonic life in larvae of *Spirorbis borealis* (Serpulidae)," *J. Mar. Biol. Ass. U.K.*, **32**, 337 (1953).

68. KNOWLES, F. G. W. and CARLISLE, D. B., "Endocrine control in the Crustacea," *Biol. Rev.*, **31**, 396 (1956).

69. MACLENNAN, R. F., "Dedifferentiation and redifferentiation in *Ichthyophthirius*," *Arch. Protistenk.*, **86**, 191 (1935).

70. MOORE, A. R., "The function of the brain in locomotion of the polyclad worm, *Yungia aurantiaca*," *J. Gen. Physiol.*, **6**, 73 (1923).

71. MORI, S. and MATUTANI, K., "Studies on the daily rhythmic activity of the starfish, *Astropecten polyacanthus*, etc," *Publ. Seto Mar. Biol. Lab.*, **2**, 213 (1952).

72. MORROW, J. E. JR., "Schooling behavior in fishes," *Quart. Rev. Biol.*, **23**, 27 (1948).

73. NICOL, J. A. C., "The giant axons of annelids," ibid., **23**, 291 (1948).

74. NICOL, J. A. C., "Giant axons and synergic contractions in *Branchiomma vesiculosum*," *J. Exp. Biol.*, **28**, 22 (1951).

75. NICOL, J. A. C., "Autonomic nervous systems in lower chordates," *Biol. Rev.*, **27**, 1 (1952).

76. NICOL, J. A. C., "Muscle activity and drug action in the body-wall of the sabellid worm *Branchiomma vesiculosum*," *Physiol. Comp. Oecol.*, **2**, 339 (1952).

77. NICOL, J. A. C. and WHITTERIDGE, D., "Conduction in the giant axon of *Myxicola infundibulum*," ibid., **4**, 101 (1955).

78. ÖSTLUND, E., "The distribution of catechol amines in lower animals and their effect on the heart," *Acta Physiol. scand.*, **31** (Suppl. 112) (1954).

79. OHBA, S., "Analysis of activity rhythm in the marine gastropod, *Nassarius festivus*," *Annot. Zool. Jap.*, **25**, 289 (1952).

80. PANTIN, C. F. A., "Behaviour patterns in lower invertebrates," *Symp. Soc. Exp. Biol.*, **4**, 175 (1950).

81. PANTIN, C. F. A., "Organic design," *Advance Sci. Lond.*, **8**, 138 (1951).

82. PANTIN, C. F. A., "The elementary nervous system," *Proc. Roy. Soc. B.*, **140**, 147 (1952).

83. PANTIN, C. F. A. and DIAS, M. V., "Excitation phenomena in an actinian (Bunodactis sp.) from Guanabara Bay," *An. Acad. Cienc. Bras.*, **24**, 335 (1952).

84. PANTIN, C. F. A. and DIAS, M. V., "Rhythm and afterdischarge in Medusae," ibid., **24**, 351 (1952).

85. PARKER, G. H., *The Elementary Nervous System* (Phil. and London, Lippincott, 1919).

86. PASSANO, L. M. and PANTIN, C. F. A., "Mechanical stimulation in the seaanemone *Calliactis parasitica*," *Proc. Roy. Soc. B.*, **143**, 226 (1955).

87. POPLE, W. and EWER, D. W., "Studies on the myoneural physiology of Echinodermata. 1. The pharyngeal retractor muscle of *Cucumaria*," *J. Exp. Biol.*, **31**, 114 (1954).

88. POPLE, W. and EWER, D. W., "Studies on the myoneural physiology of Echinodermata. 2. Circumoral conduction in *Cucumaria*," ibid., **32**, 59 (1955).
89. PRESTON, J. B. and KENNEDY, D., "Spontaneous activity in crustacean neurones," *J. Gen. Physiol.*, **45**, 821 (1962).
90. PROSSER, C. L. (Ed.), *Comparative Animal Physiology* (London, Saunders, 1950).
91. PUMPHREY, R. J. and YOUNG, J. Z., "The rates of conduction of nerve fibres of various diameters in cephalopods," *J. Exp. Biol.*, **15**, 453 (1938).
92. ROBERTSON, J. D., "Ultrastructure of two invertebrate synapses," *Proc. Soc. Exp. Biol. Med.*, **82**, 219 (1953).
93. ROSS, D. M., "Facilitation in sea anemones. 1. The action of drugs," *J. Exp. Biol.*, **22**, 21 (1945).
94. ROSS, D. M., "Some problems of neuromuscular activity and behaviour in the elementary nervous system," in *Essays on Physiological Evolution*, p. 253 (Oxford, Pergamon Press, 1964).
95. ROSS, D. M. and SUTTON, L., "The swimming response of the sea anemone *Stomphia* to electrical stimulation," *J. Exp. Biol.*, **41**, 735 (1964).
96. ROSS, D. M. and SUTTON, L., "Inhibition of the swimming response by food and of nematocyst discharge during swimming in the sea anemone *Stomphia*," *J. Exp. Biol.*, **41**, 751 (1964).
97. SCHARRER, E. and SCHARRER, B., "Neurosecretion," *Physiol. Rev.*, **25**, 171 (1945).
98. SCHMITT, F. O. and BEAR, R. S., "The ultrastructure of the nerve axon sheath," *Biol. Rev.*, **14**, 27 (1939).
99. SCHWARTZ, B. and SAFIR, S. R., "Habit formation in the fiddler crab," *J. Anim. Behav.*, **5**, 226 (1915).
100. SILÉN, L., "On the nervous system of *Glossobalanus marginatus*," *Acta Zool.*, **31**, 149 (1950).
101. SILÉN, L., "On the nervous system of *Phoronis*," *Ark. Zool.*, **6**, 1 (1954).
102. SMITH, J. E., "On the nervous system of the starfish *Marthasterias glacialis*," *Phil. Trans. B.*, **227**, 111 (1937).
103. SMITH, J. E., "The role of the nervous system in some activities of starfishes," *Biol. Rev.*, **20**, 29 (1945).
104. SMITH, J. E., "The mechanics and innervation of the star-fish tube foot-ampulla system," *Phil. Trans. B.*, **232**, 279 (1946).
105. SMITH, J. E., "The motor nervous system of the starfish, *Astropecten irregularis*," ibid., **234**, 521 (1950).
106. SMITH, J. E., "Some observations on the nervous mechanisms underlying the behaviour of starfishes," *Symp. Soc. Exp. Biol.*, **4**, 196 (1950).
107. SPOONER, G. M., "The learning of detours by wrasse (*Ctenolabrus rupestris*)," *J. Mar. Biol. Ass. U.K.*, **21**, 497 (1937).
108. SPROSTON, N. G. and HARTLEY, P. H. T., "Observations on the bionomics and physiology of *Trebius* and *Lernaeocera*," ibid., **25**, 393 (1941).
109. STEINBACH, H. B., "The sodium and potassium balance of muscle and nerve," in *Modern Trends in Physiology and Biochemistry*, Ed. Barrow, E. S. G. (New York, Academic Press, 1952).
110. TAYLOR, C. V., "Fibrillar systems in ciliates," in *Protozoa in Biological Research*, Ed. Calkins, G. N. and Summers, F. M. (New York, Columbia Univ. Press, 1941).

111. TAYLOR, G. W., "The optical properties of the shrimp nerve fiber sheath," *J. Cell. Comp. Physiol.*, **18**, 233 (1941).
112. TINBERGEN, N., *The Study of Instinct* (Oxford, Clarendon Press, 1951).
113. TURNER, R. S., "Functional anatomy of the giant fiber system of *Callianassa californiensis,*" *Physiol. Zool.*, **23**, 35 (1950).
114. TURNER, R. S., "Modification by temperature of conduction and ganglionic transmission in the gastropod nervous system," *J. Gen. Physiol.*, **36**, 463 (1953).
115. TURNER, R. S., HAGINS, W. A. and MOORE, A. R., "Influence of certain neurotropic substances on central and synaptic transmission in *Callianassa,*" *Proc. Soc. Exp. Biol. Med.*, **73**, 156 (1950).
116. WASHBURN, M. F., *The Animal Mind: A Text-book of Comparative Pyschology* (New York, Macmillan, 1936).
117. WELLS, G. P., "The behaviour of *Arenicola marina* in sand, and the role of spontaneous activity cycles," *J. Mar. Biol. Ass. U.K.*, **28**, 465 (1949).
118. WELLS, G. P., "Spontaneous activity cycles in polychaete worms," *Symp. Soc. Exp. Biol.*, **4**, 127 (1950).
119. WELLS, G. P., "On the behaviour of *Sabella,*" *Proc. Roy. Soc. B.*, **151**, 278 (1951).
120. WELLS, G. P. and ALBRECHT, E. B., "The integration of activity cycles in the behaviour of *Arenicola marina,*" *J. Exp. Biol.*, **28**, 41 (1951).
121. WELLS, G. P. and DALES, R. P., "Spontaneous activity patterns in animal behaviour: the irrigation of the burrow in the polychaetes, *Chaetopterus variopedatus* and *Nereis diversicolor,*" *J. Mar. Biol. Ass. U.K.*, **29**, 661 (1951).
122. WELSH, J. H., "Marine invertebrate preparations useful in the bioassay of acetylcholine and 5-hydroxytryptamine," *Nature*, **173**, 955 (1954).
123. WHITEAR, M., "The stomatogastric nervous system of *Arenicola,*" *Quart. J. Micr. Sci.*, **94**, 293 (1953).
124. WIERSMA, C. A. G., "Repetitive discharges of motor fibers caused by a single impulse in giant fibers of the crayfish," *J. Cell. Comp. Physiol.*, **40**, 399 (1952).
125. WIERSMA, C. A. G., "Neural transmission in invertebrates," *Physiol. Rev.*, **33**, 326 (1953).
126. WILSON, D. P., "The role of micro-organisms in the settlement of *Ophelia bicornis,*" *J. Mar. Biol. Ass. U.K.*, **34**, 531 (1955).
127. YOUNG, J. Z., "Two memory stores in one brain," *Endeavour*, **24**, 13 (1965).

CHAPTER 11

PIGMENTS AND COLOURS

Innumerable of stains and splendid dyes,
As are the tiger-moth's deep-damask'd wings.

JOHN KEATS

MARINE animals show a great range of colours, shades and patterns, some of them very striking and beautiful. The most brilliant hues are to be found in animals living in shallow waters of tropical seas among the groves of corals, gorgonians and alcyonians where multicoloured reef fishes swim or sleep. Even in cold northern seas many animals have intricate patterns of great beauty: an appreciation of these may be gained from the coloured plates in McIntosh's *Marine Annelids*, Stephenson's *Sea Anemones* and Méhuet's *Étude de la Mer*, to mention three beautifully illustrated volumes. Animal colours are due largely to reflected light of solar origin but there are fluorescent and luminescent animals that emit light of various colours; a description of luminous animals is reserved for another chapter.

ANIMAL PIGMENTS AND STRUCTURAL COLOURS

Two agencies are involved in producing the coloration of marine animals, namely, pigments that by special absorption characteristics give rise to coloured light, and structural modifications having optical effects that produce colours. Either one or other method of colour production may predominate in any species, or both may occur simultaneously and play complementary roles. Owing to the predominant influence of colour in human visual sensations we tend to emphasize and unduly magnify colour, and it is likely that many of the colours to be seen in marine animals may themselves have no biological significance. Many animals contain brightly coloured tissues and organs lying within their bodies, and concealed from view, e.g. the body wall and gonads of many gastropods and bivalve molluscs. There are other animals, brightly coloured, which are tubicolous and normally never emerge from their burrows— for example, the polychaetes *Amphitrite johnstoni* and *Myxicola infundibulum*, both bright red in colour. Many planktonic animals are translucent and colourless, or nearly so; crustacea and fishes from mesopelagic and bathypelagic waters are as a rule uniformly black, red or dark brown; and it is in the littoral and neritic zones that the greatest variety of coloured animals is to be found.

Pigments responsible for animal colours often have a superficial location, e.g. pigments located in the epidermis and dermis, or deposited in

465

the external skeleton or shell. The blue coloration of many decapod crustacea, such as the adult lobster *Homarus vulgaris*, is due to caroti-proteins deposited in the exoskeleton, whereas the epidermis is completely concealed beneath the thick calcareous cuticle and is without importance in coloration. In smaller species of crustacea—for example, the shrimps and prawns, *Crangon*, *Hippolyte* and *Processa*—the cuticle is thin and translucent, and pigments in the epidermis are responsible for surface coloration. The dark colours of some bivalve shells result from a deposition of pigment in the external cuticular layer. The colours of fishes are due particularly to dermal chromatophores, although epidermal chromato-phores also have a minor effect. The agencies responsible for structural colours are usually located in the integument; for example, the layers of guanine crystals producing the metallic sheen of many bony fish. Again, pigments may lie diffusely in tissue spaces, or be localized in cells of the skin. Sometimes the colours from deep tissues, such as muscle, blood, gonads and gut, show through the skin and colour the animal. This is particularly so in certain polychaetes, for example, *Pomatoceros triqueter*, in which the sexes are distinguishable at maturity by differences in the colour of the abdomen due to the genital products within, the male being cream in colour and the female bright pink or orange.

Extensive research is only now beginning to unravel many of the in-tricacies concerning the pigments of lower animals, but the functions, and indeed the nature, of many invertebrate pigments are still unknown. In marine animals these substances include carotenoids, porphyrins and other pyrrolic compounds, melanins and indole pigments, pteridines, ommo-chromes, purines, naphthoquinones, various protein substances, and still other materials whose identities are yet to be established. Some of these substances are endogenous in origin, being manufactured by the animal; others are exogenous, being derived from its food, although sometimes chemically altered by the animal assimilating them.

Chromoproteins are important substances in coloration and in animal physiology. They include the haemoglobins and related compounds, with a prosthetic haem group conjoined to a protein molecule; carotiproteins and melanoproteins, in which the chromatic substance is conjugated with a protein molecule; and the complex respiratory pigments haemocyanin and haemerythrin, which function in oxygen transport. Of the pigments now to be considered, some like the carotenoids, are found in many groups of animals, and are responsible for the colours of many marine forms (16, 22).

Carotenoids. Carotenoids are very widespread and occur in the majority of animals. They are divisible into two broad groups: carotenes, which are hydrocarbons; and oxygen-containing carotene derivatives, namely xanthophylls, carotenoid acids and esters. Empirical formulae are $C_{40}H_{56}$ for carotene, and $C_{40}H_{56}O_2$ for xanthophyll. Carotenoids are soluble in lipoids and in typical lipoid solvents but insoluble in water. They range in colour from yellow and orange to rich red. Carotiproteins are water-soluble compounds of considerable importance in animal coloration, and showing a wide range of colours (grey, brown, red, green, blue and dark violet) (16, 29, 37, 41, 47).

The ubiquitous occurrence of carotenoids in animals is noteworthy. Ultimately derived from plants, they are often accumulated and stored by animals. Carotenoids occur in adipose tissue, in the eyes or other photo-

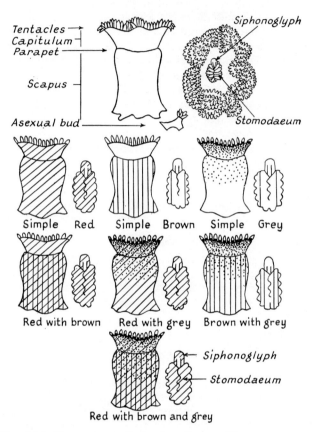

FIG. 11.1. DIAGRAMS OF DIFFERENT COLOUR VARIETIES IN THE
PLUMOSE ANEMONE *Metridium senile*

Oblique stripes, red; vertical stripes, brown; stipple, grey; unmarked, white. (From Fox and Pantin (19).)

receptors, in gonads, glands, muscle and integument. They are regular components of chromatophores in some animals, including crustaceans and fish; they occur in the eggs of many species; and they are accumulated to a notable degree in the gonads of a great many marine animals.

Carotenoids of various kinds are present in protozoans (both holophytic and holozoic forms). The transitory blooms and red tides sometimes seen at sea are caused by dense accumulations of coloured species containing carotenoids (*Noctiluca, Gonyaulax*, etc.). Carotenoids are also responsible for the bright yellow, orange, red and purple colours of many sponges (*Halichondria, Suberites, Tethya*, and many others). Echinenone and γ-carotene have been found in the red sponge *Hymeniacidon perleve*, and astacene has been extracted from *Axinella crista-galli* (60).

Carotenoids are common in coelenterates and they are often responsible for the bright red and yellow colours of these animals. They occur in the Hydrozoa (*Clava, Nemertesia*), Scyphozoa (*Lucernaria*), Alcyonaria (*Gorgonia*), Actiniaria (*Epiactis*), Madreporaria (*Caryophyllia*), and are probably present in all branches of this great phylum. Sea-anemones, which have been most intensively studied, contain both carotenes and xanthophylls. The beadlet anemone *Actinia equina* exists in several well-known colour varieties, red, brown and green. Brown and green varieties yield an orange carotenoid, and the red variety a red acidic carotenoid, actinioerythrin. The latter is conjugated with protein in the living animal. In the green variety there is also a reddish-orange xanthophyll which forms a green pigment in combination with protein (54). The plumose anemone *Metridium senile* is another species exhibiting manifold colour forms (Fig. 11.1). A variety of carotenoids occurs in this species: in general,

TABLE 11.1

Colour Varieties of *Metridium senile*

Colour variety	Melanins	Carotenoids
White	Little or none	Very little. *Astaxanthin esters* and free astaxanthin
Brown (various shades)	Varying degrees	Least: Astaxanthin esters or metridene esters, carotenes, xanthophylls, xanthophyll esters
Yellow-orange	Little or none	Considerable: *Metridene esters, xanthophyll esters*, carotenes, xanthophylls
Red with brown	Varying degrees	Much: *Metridene esters* or astaxanthin esters
Red	None	Much: *Metridene esters*, sometimes accompanied by free or esterified astaxanthin, free metridene, xanthophylls, carotenes

Note: principal carotenoids are shown in italics. Metridene is an epiphasic ester distinct from astacene. From Fox and Pantin (1944).)

the red forms contain the greatest quantities of these pigments, whereas the melanistic brown varieties yield smaller quantities but a greater range of different carotenoids (Table 11.1). *Metridium senile* stores carotenoids within its own tissues, including the gonads, but in another species, *Cribrina xanthogrammica*, the carotenoids are contained in symbiotic algae living inside the anemone (19).

A equals

$$=CH-CH=CH-\underset{\underset{CH_3}{|}}{C}=CH-CH=CH-CH=\underset{\underset{CH_3}{|}}{C}-CH=CH-CH=$$

$$\beta\text{-CAROTENE}$$

Many corals and reef anemones are bright blue in colour, possibly due to carotiproteins. The blue pigments in the umbrella of Scyphomedusae (*Cyanea, Aurelia*) known as cyaneins are carotiproteins, as is the blue pigment velellin of the siphonophores *Velella* and *Physalia*. The brown pigment responsible for the characteristic markings of *Chrysaora* appears to be a form of cyanein and sometimes, as in *Cyanea capillata*, the colour is brown or blue according to the variety. In addition, carotenoids are accumulated in the ovaries (*Aurelia*).

Carotenoids in the different groups of worms have been little studied. Nemertines, both littoral and bathypelagic, are frequently brightly coloured, due to carotenoids located in the skin and alimentary canal. Carotenoids also occur in some polyclads, serpulids and other polychaetes. The burrowing polychaete *Thoracophelia mucronata* contains considerable quantities of β-carotene (0·36 mg/g tissue) (16, 17). Brightly coloured carotenoid pigments are common in echinoderms, especially in the integument, digestive glands, gonads and eggs of asteroids, the gonads of echinoids and holothurians, and the integument of ophiuroids. Fox (1947) has observed that oxygenated carotene derivatives such as astaxanthin frequently predominate over carotenes in starfishes. These animals are often coloured in rich hues of blue, purple, violet, pink and brown, which are due to carotenoids conjugated with proteins in the integument (*Solaster, Asterias, Porania*). A sexual difference has been found in the carotenoid content of *Dendraster excentricus*, in which the males contain up to three times as much pigment as the females; in the males the pigment is concentrated in the testes (16, 29, 69).

The echinoids store large quantities of carotenoids in gonads and intestinal tissue but, in contrast to the asteroids, have little in the integument, where quinone pigments often predominate instead. In *Strongylocentrotus purpuratus*, about 75% of all carotenoids is located in the gonads, and the carotenoid content of ovaries is three times as great as that of the testes. In *Lytechinus pictus*, on the other hand, the testes contain about four times as much carotene as the ovaries, and twice as much xanthophyll. The usual carotenoids in this group are α- and β-carotenes, and the xanthophyll echinenone. The dominant carotenoid in the ophiuroid *Ophidiaster* is astaxanthin (29, 47, 53).

Representatives of the major groups of molluscs have yielded carotenoids, including many lamellibranchs, gastropods, amphineurans and cephalopods. The pigments occur variously in the skin, eyes, digestive glands, gonads and ripe eggs. In *Mytilus californianus* the females contain about two and a half times as much carotenoid (predominantly mytiloxanthin) as the males, and in both sexes the pigments tend to be concentrated in the gonads. Some nudibranchs, for example *Hopkinsia rosacea*, owe their bright colouring to xanthophylls. The cephalopods, in general, are poor in carotenoids, which have been found in the eyes, liver and ink gland but not in the skin. There is some evidence that cuttlefish and octopods excrete excess carotenoids in the ink. Starvation brings about a disappearance of carotenoids from the liver and ink of *Octopus bimaculatus* (16, 28, 29, 63).

Carotenoids are abundant and widely distributed in the Crustacea, and are responsible for most of the bright colours in this class (30). The pigments may impregnate the exoskeleton and give the animal a red coloration as in *Nephrops norvegicus*, occur diffusely in cells, or be localized in chromatophores. They also occur in the eyes, photophores, hepatopancreas, gonads, haemolymph and eggs of various species. Combined with protein, they are responsible for the sombre blue, green and brown colours of many decapods, for example *Homarus* and *Palinurus*. On boiling or treatment with protein denaturants such as formalin or alcohol, the carotenoid component is released and gives rise to the well-known red colour. The presence of carotenoids in euphausiids and copepods forms an important link between phytoplankton organisms, which synthesize these pigments, and animals higher up in the food chain. In the North Atlantic, euphausiids accumulate carotenoids more rapidly during the spring and autumn, at the times of diatom outbursts, than at other seasons. The characteristic carotenoid of crustaceans is astaxanthin, a dihydroxy-diketo-β-carotene, of which astacene is a derivative. Levels of astaxanthin in *Euphausia superba* range around 6–22 $\mu g/g$. In conjunction with protein, astaxanthin forms a water-soluble green pigment (ovoverdin) in the eggs of the lobster; similar pigments occur in *Maia squinado* and the goose barnacle *Lepas* (29, 43, 47).

In the shore crab *Carcinus maenas* carotenoids are absorbed with the food and are stored in the hepatopancreas. This store is used to supply the epidermis in males and in non-gravid females, but in reproducing females the carotenoids are transported in the blood to the ovaries and the stores in the hepatopancreas become depleted. During the development of goose barnacle nauplii (*Lepas*) there is an interesting colour change from blue to pink, which involves either a rupture of the astaxanthin-protein complex or a change in the linkage. The ovoverdin content of lobster (*Homarus*) eggs remains unaltered until just before hatching, when the protein complex is disrupted and free red astaxanthin is released (30, 41).

Tunicates frequently contain bright red, orange and yellow carotenoid pigments, including astaxanthin, various xanthophylls and carotenes. In teleosts there are many brightly coloured species having chromatophores charged with carotenoids, and in some varieties these are the dominant kind of coloured cells in the skin. The carotenoids are predominantly

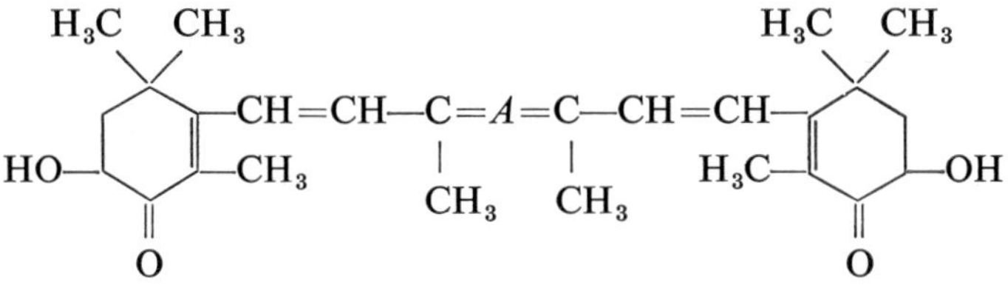

ASTAXANTHIN

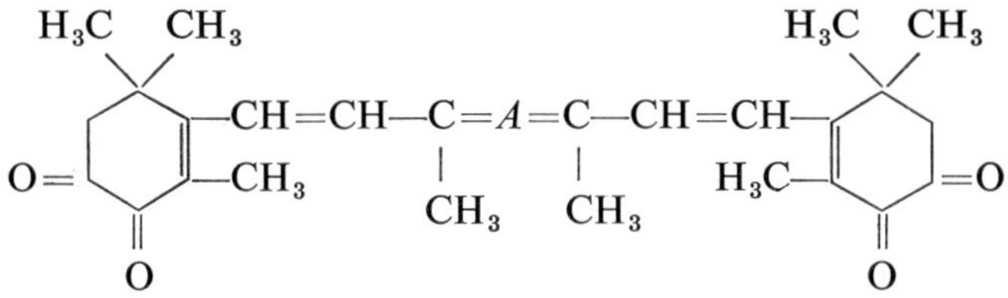

ASTACENE

xanthophylls, although some β-carotene occurs in the ovary. Carotenoids are largely desposited in the skin, although considerable amounts are sometimes present in the muscles, ovaries (especially during sexual activity) and in the liver. Some fishes store large amounts of astaxanthin derived from the consumption of invertebrate animals. *Beryx dedactylus*, for example, a brightly coloured scarlet and yellow fish, is a veritable storehouse of astaxanthin, which occurs in skin, gills, mouth, mucosa and iris. The sock-eye salmon *Oncorhynchus nerka* acquires brightly coloured flesh (due to accumulation of astaxanthin) during its sojourn in the sea. During the summer spawning period, male and female lumpsuckers *Cyclopterus lumpus* mobilize astaxanthin from the liver, and deposit it in the skin and flesh; in the killifish *Fundulus parvipinnis* the female transfers xanthophyll to the ripening eggs, and the sexually mature male increases the xanthophyll content of its skin (2, 3, 4).

A general tendency has been noted among marine animals to accumulate xanthophylls rather than carotenes. Thus in the numerically important groups of molluscs, crustaceans and teleosts, xanthophylls are the predominant or exclusive carotenoid pigments present. Certain prominent exceptions are asteroids and polychaetes among which carotene predominates. Carotenoid pigments are widely distributed in the tissues of different animals. A pronounced trend is noticeable for deposition of carotenoids in the gonads, and in many forms they are responsible for the coloration of the integument.

Pyrrols. Pyrrolic pigments are universally distributed and indeed are essential for life, since the tetrapyrrol nucleus is the basis of the chlorophyll molecule and of intracellular respiratory enzymes. The tetrapyrrol structure is found in the porphyrins, which in specific compounds bear a metallic radicle, magnesium in chlorophyll, and iron in haem and haematin. The iron porphyrins or haems, in association with proteins, form the respiratory pigments haemoglobin and chlorocruorin (32, 47, 61).

No animals above the Protozoa manufacture chlorophyll, and when this pigment is present it is exogenous in origin or is contained in symbiotic algae. Algal symbionts occur in sponges, coelenterates, turbellarians and certain other animals, and carry on photosynthesis within the tissues of their hosts (*see* Chapter 14).

Some animals contain green pigments showing affinity to chlorophyll. Phaeophorbides are found in midgut cells of certain polychaetes (*Owenia*, *Chaetopterus*), in sufficient concentration to give these organs a greenish colour (Fig. 13.2) (11, 61). The echiuroid worm *Bonellia viridis* is bright green in colour and contains a pigment known as bonellin. In the female the pigment is located in the skin, and in the degenerate male in wandering cells which partially fill the reduced body cavity. Bonellin appears to be a mesochlorin, a substance having a porphyrin skeleton and an opened isocyclic nucleus. The green pigments of other echiuroids (*Thalassema*, *Hamingia*) appear to be the same as bonellin. Other green pigments (linear-chain or closed-ring tetrapyrrols) occur in phyllodocid polychaetes.

The intestine and digestive glands of some molluscs and crustacea, and the digestive caeca of asteroids and other echinoderms, contain greenish pigments known generally as hepatochlorophyll and probably consisting of a mixture of chlorophylls and chlorophyll derivatives. Vegetal chlorophyll undergoes a certain amount of degradation in its passage through the animal. The viscera of a tectibranch mollusc *Akera* yield phaeophorbide, which is formed from chlorophyll contained in the algal food. Protoporphyrin, occurring in the integument of *Asterias rubens*, may be derived from chlorophyll pigments present in the hepatic caeca.

Some examples of colours due to haem-containing respiratory pigments have been mentioned previously. Concentrations of myohaemoglobin sometimes bring about marked differences between red and white muscles; for example, in the teleosts *Luvarus* and *Hippocampus*. In the polychaete *Myxicola infundibulum* chlorocruorin imparts a greenish tint to the inner layers of the animal's tube. Haemochromogens are widely distributed in the gut lumen of molluscs and polychaetes (20, 59).

The decomposition of haemoglobin gives rise to the bile pigment biliverdin through the rupture of the porphyrin nucleus and the release of iron, and this or related bile pigments are responsible for some animal colours. The ragworm *Nereis diversicolor* is variable in colour, different individuals being orange, brown or green. The orange and brown colours are due largely to carotenoids, but the green pigment is biliverdin formed by the breakdown of haemoglobin. The granules of biliverdin occurring in the body wall are ultimately transferred to the gut and excreted. Males, on

PROTOPORPHYRIN

CHLOROPHYLL—*a*

becoming sexually mature, and females after spawning, are bright green. It is at these times that the tissues undergo phagocytosis, and the increased breakdown of haemoglobin is accompanied by a corresponding increase of biliverdin in the body.

Biliverdin, found in leeches, results from the decomposition of ingested blood. It is also found in the roots of certain rhizocephalans (*Septosaccus, Peltogaster, Parthenopea*) where it is derived from blood haemoglobin, when present, or some other haem compound. The fate of haemoglobin in the praniza larvae of gnathiid isopods (*Paragnathia formica* and *Gnathia maxillaris*) is interesting in that it determines the colour of the animal. The parasitic stages known as pranizas feed upon the blood of fishes, and are red, green or colourless according to the condition of their gut contents. The colourless animals do not ingest the erythrocytes; in the red animals the erythrocytes remain intact for a long time; and in the green animals the erythrocytes are readily haemolysed and the contained haemoglobin decomposed into a green bile pigment. These differences between pranizas

BILIVERDIN

depend upon the fish which are parasitized, the pranizas reacting differently to the blood of different species of fish (21, 51).

Biliverdin has also been identified in anemones and occurs in the green parts of *Tealia felina*. An interesting substance having affinities with the bile pigments is calliactine, which occurs as red and violet granules in the column of the sea-anemone *Calliactis parasitica*. The skeletal pigment responsible for the colour of the blue coral *Heliopora caerulea* is a bilin related to biliverdin, and termed helioporobilin.

Various pyrrolic pigments have been described in molluscs. Pinnaglobin, found in the blood of *Pinna squamosa*, has a prosthetic porphyrin group containing manganese. The shells of many molluscs (gastropods and lamellibranchs) contain considerable amounts of pyrrol pigments, including linear chain tetrapyrroles (bile pigments) and various porphyrins. Uroporphyrin is widely distributed, and has been identified in many marine species, shells of *Calliostoma, Pteria, Pinna*, integument of *Aplysia* and *Akera*. Noteworthy is aplysiopurpurin, a deep purple pigment secreted by special glands on the underside of the mantle in the tectibranch *Aplysia*. This pigment is a mixture of unstable chromoproteins, of which the prosthetic groups behave like bile pigments (mesobiliviolin and mesobilierythrin). The secretion of aplysiopurpurin is regarded as a means of defence, the colouring material streaming through the water and forming a cloud behind which the animal makes its escape (7, 8, 42, 67).

A few fishes with green and blue skin owe these colours solely to pigments. The blue colours of wrasse (*Labrus, Crenilabrus*) are produced by carotiproteins; Fox ascribes the green colour of *Odax* to a porphyrin pigment. Finally, the peculiar green colour of the bones of certain teleosts (*Belone belone* and *Zoarces viviparus*) may be mentioned. The colour is produced by bile pigments deposited in the skeleton (2, 16, 70).

Quinones. Naphthoquinone pigments are characteristic of echinoids. The first to be discovered was echinochrome, a purple pigment occurring in elaeocytes in the perivisceral fluid of the urchins *Paracentrotus lividus*, *Echinus esculentus* and *Arbacia pustulosa*. This pigment is widespread in the body, occurring in the gut, ovaries, integument, shell and spines. In addition, the shell and spines contain a deep red pigment, spinochrome, closely allied to echinochrome. Recent work shows that these pigments exist in several forms, in different species and in different parts of the same animal.

The variation in colour found within a species of echinoid often depends upon the amounts of differently coloured spinochrome homologues present. Thus, the colour range of test and spines in *Paracentrotus lividus* is due to mixtures of spinochromes A and B in different proportions, the violet variety containing relatively more of A, the olive-green variety relatively more of B (Table 11.2). Moreover, the violet and olive-green

TABLE 11.2

AMOUNTS OF SPINOCHROMES A AND B IN SPINES AND TESTS OF
Echinus esculentus AND *Paracentrotus lividus*

Material	Amount (mg/g fresh weight)	
	Spinochrome A	Spinochrome B
E. esculentus		
spines (violet)	0·0019	Trace
shell (violet)	0·023	Trace
P. lividus		
spines (violet)	0·52	0·39
spines (olive-green)	0·17	1·07

(From Goodwin and Srisukh (31).)

colours encountered in the spines are due to the formation of salts between the pigments and calcium in the skeleton, the normal colours of the pigments being reddish. These substances differ from naphthoquinones of vegetal origin, and they are probably synthesized by the sea urchin (16, 31, 40, 47).

$$\text{ECHINOCHROME A}$$

$$\text{SPINOCHROME A}$$

ECHINOCHROME A   SPINOCHROME A

Indoles. These include indigoid pigments and melanins, basically substances containing a phenopyrrol nucleus. Indigoid pigments are produced by certain gastropods, and include indigo and the purple dye dibromindigo, secreted by *Murex*, *Mitra* and *Nucella*. This substance is the dyestuff Tyrian purple which was used so extensively by the ancients. It is produced by a special hypobranchial gland, and stored as the colourless leuco compound. When secreted and exposed to sunlight, it becomes transformed into the purple pigment dibromindigo (purpurin). No physiological role has been established for indigoid pigments in animals, and they may well be excretory products (7, 47).

In general the dark or black pigments of animals belong to the group of melanins, which have a colour range from yellow to jet black. They tend to be resistant substances, insoluble in water and the usual solvents, but dissolved by strong alkalis. Chemically they are indole derivatives of relatively high molecular weight, originating usually from tyrosine through the agency of tyrosinase. The melanins which occur in different animals in reality comprise a group of diverse substances, differing in degree of oxidation and complexity. The reactions may be summarized—

$$\text{Tyrosine} \xrightarrow[+O]{\text{Tyrosinase}} \text{DOPA} \xrightarrow[+O]{\text{Tyrosinase}} \text{Hallachrome} \xrightarrow{+O}$$

$$\text{Intermediates} \xrightarrow[+O]{} \text{Melanins}$$

The intermediate compound DOPA. is 3,4-dihydroxyphenylalanine which has been found in certain animals. Hallachrome, a red intermediate stage in the oxidation of tyrosine, occurs naturally in the polychaete *Halla parthenopeia*, where it may be involved in cellular respiration. Brown and black melanin pigments are found in sponges (*Chondrosia*), coelenterates (dark varieties of *Metridium senile*, coloured areas of the jellyfish *Pelagia noctiluca*), annelids (photoreceptors), arthropods (cuticle, chromatophores, photoreceptors), molluscs (siphons, valves of *Mytilus*), echinoderms (integument of echinoids, ophiuroids and holothurians) and in vertebrates. Characteristically, they have an intracellular location in epithelial and mesenchymal cells, or in special melanophores (the role of these cells in colour-responses is described in the next chapter). Less often they are extracellular, e.g. in the mesogloea of *Pelagia* and in the exoskeleton of crustaceans. Although usually located in the skin, they also occur in deeper tissues, as in the parietal epithelium of the plaice *Pleuronectes platessa*. In echinoderms (*Holothuria, Diadema*) the melanin pigment is elaborated by amoebocytes which deposit it in the body wall. The inky material produced within the ink sac of cephalopods is a melanin and tyrosinase is found in the epithelial tissue of that organ. When the

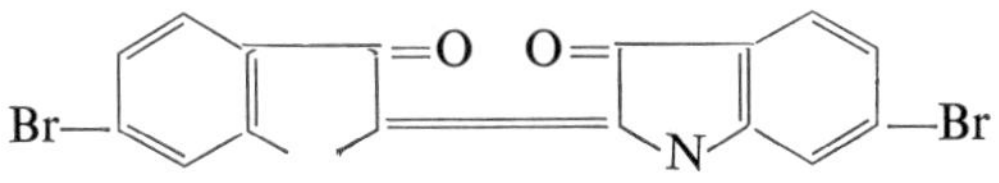

6 : 6′—DIBROMINDIGO

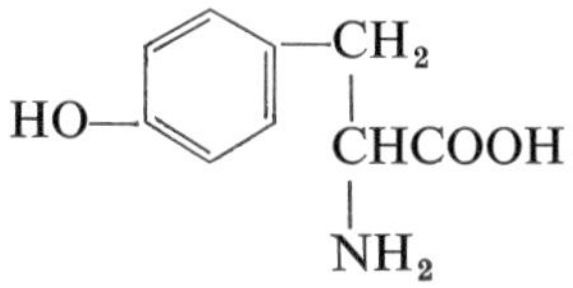

TYROSINE

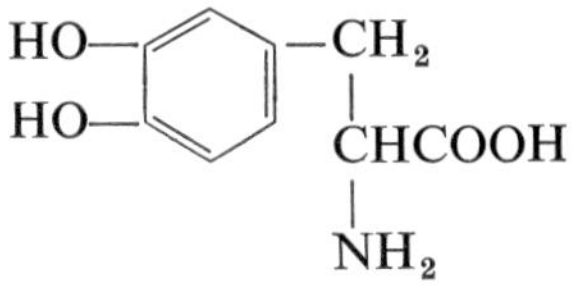

DOPA
DIHYDROXYPHENYLALANINE

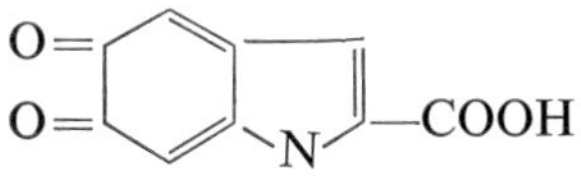

HALLACHROME

animal is disturbed it discharges an inky secretion from its mantle cavity and takes to flight behind the black screen (8, 16, 18, 19, 36, 48, 56).

Purines. Purine substances, important in the surface coloration of certain groups of animals, are derived from the metabolism of nucleoprotein (p. 290). Purines are themselves white or yellow in colour, but because of their crystalline structure they are often responsible for the structural colours encountered in so many animals (p. 479). Among coelenterates uric acid deposits occur in the anemone *Metridium senile*, where they form white bands in the endoderm of the tentacles (Fig. 11.2). In the nudibranch *Janolus cristatus* the conspicuous chalky white tips on the dorsal papillae and the white patches on the skin are due to the deposits of guanine. Structural colours produced by guanine are characteristic especially of crustacea and fishes (16, 19). The iridescent or silvery appearance of teleosts is produced by deposits of guanine. Iridophores beneath the epidermis owe their iridescence to guanine particles. Sheets of reflecting cells containing stacks of guanine crystals occur at various levels in the skin; a particularly dense and thick deposit of crystals forms the stratum argenteum in the subdermis. The effects produced by these layers are described on p. 479. The bellies of fishes are often matt white, e.g. sharks, and the guanine particles are so disposed that they diffusely reflect incident white light.

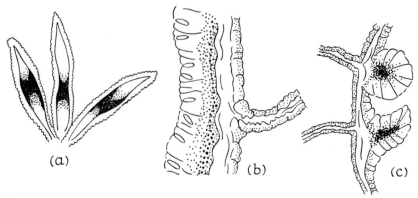

FIG. 11.2. SECTIONS THROUGH VARIOUS REGIONS OF THE BODY OF THE PLUMOSE ANEMONE *Metridium senile*, SHOWING THE LOCALIZATION OF PIGMENTS

In (*a*) transverse bands of uric acid granules are shown as solid black in three tentacles; (*b*) is a transverse section of the body wall of a red *Metridium* showing the base of a mesentery. The ectoderm (*left*) contains nematocysts and red carotenoid fat droplets at the base of the cells. In the endoderm the red fat droplets are more evenly distributed; (*c*) is a transverse section of the stomodaeal wall of a red *Metridium* showing red fat droplets in the endoderm. Red droplets are aggregated at the base of the stomodaeal ridges opposite the insertion of the mesenteries. (From Fox and Pantin (19).)

Pteridines. These are tetrazonaphthalene derivatives of widespread and possibly universal occurrence in animals.

XANTHOPTERIN

Pteridines associated with melanin are found in pigment cells of brittle stars, crustacea and fish, where they may play a role in melanogenesis (15, 30). It is suspected that red and yellow pterins localized in pigment cells (pterinophores) contribute to the coloration of crustacea, fish and other animals. Xanthopterin, a yellow pterin, is one of several components of the reflecting pigment of the compound eye of crustaceans (14, 22, 30).

Ommochromes. These are brown, yellow, red and violet pigments belonging to the class of the phenoxazons, and previously confused with melanins. Some of them show a reversible redox change of colour. Dark ommins (i.e. ommochromes of large molecular size) occur in the eyes and integument of many crustaceans. Ommochromes form the dark pigment—there are no melanins—in some prawns, e.g. *Palaemon*. Both ommochromes and melanins occur in the hypodermis of crabs (Brachyura). The pigment cells (chromatophores) of squid and cuttlefish contain ommochrome pigments exhibiting a wide range of colours—purple, red and yellow; and the bright colours of the crowns of sabellid worms are produced by ommochromes and carotenoid pigments of astaxanthin nature (12, 14, 30, 52).

Structural Colours

Among marine animals structural colours are produced by three physical processes, namely scattering, diffraction and interference. In the former the coloration is produced by preferential scattering of short wavelengths by minute particles and does not change with the angle of viewing. Diffraction and interference colours are produced by regularly organized structures and are iridescent, i.e. they change with the angle of viewing. Diffraction colours are produced by diffraction of light passing through a fine grating consisting of closely spaced parallel striae, and there is interference between the diffracted light waves of different frequencies; the grating may lie over a reflecting surface. Interference colours result from mutual interference of light waves reflected from upper and lower surfaces of thin plates of the same order of thickness as a wave-length of light (Fig. 11.3).

The beautiful sheen of the nacre of molluscan shells, of abalones, the pearl oyster and the pearly nautilus, is produced by diffraction. The nacreous layer of the shell is lamellated, and consists of more or less regularly spaced plates of calcium carbonate separated by thin layers of horny conchiolin. Where these plates (of aragonite) lie inclined to the inner surface of the shell they form a diffraction grating and give rise to diffraction colours. Pfund (58) found a periodicity in the spacing of successive laminae of 2,400 to 8,000 lines/cm in different regions of a specimen of mother-of-pearl examined, the periodicity being remarkably constant at any one locus (Fig. 11.4). In abalone shell the thickness of laminae is 0.48μ, equal to the wave-length of blue-green light (4,800Å). In shell lacking colour but displaying a pearly lustre, the laminae vary greatly in thickness. Some shells show neither colour nor pearly lustre, due to the irregular character of the chalky material in the shell, which scatters the light diffusely. Other examples of iridescent diffraction colours are seen in the chaetae of the sea mouse *Aphrodite* and the pulsating combs of ctenophores.

Invertebrates exhibiting interference colours are *Sapphirina* and cephalopods. *Sapphirina* is a pelagic copepod which gleams in the sunlight like a flashing jewel. Hypodermal cells of this animal contain thin lamellae of submicroscopic thickness, producing interference colours which change with the angle of viewing. Likewise, the iridophores of cuttlefish contain stacks of thin platelets which produce iridescent effects. Similar iridophores, containing fine particles of guanine, are found in the integument of

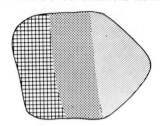

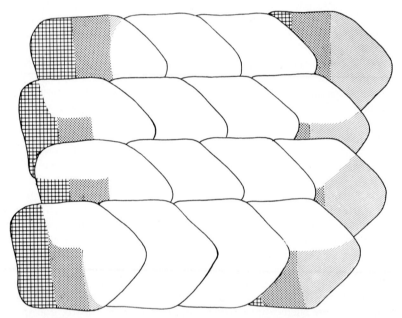

Fig. 11.3. Diagram Showing a Group of Overlapping Scales from
the Broad Silvery Flank of the Herring

Above is shown a single scale with three distinct reflecting regions distinguished diagrammatically; these correspond to three regions which, when viewed from a direction perpendicular to the surfaces of the reflecting platelets, differ from one another in colour. The reflecting plates cover almost the surfaces of the scales, and the bright silvery reflexion of the intact fish is built up by the combined reflexions of overlapping scales.

teleosts; they are iridescent. Interference effects operating to produce the silvery reflexion of fishes are considered on p. 493 (Fig. 11.3) (16, 22).

The existence of an underlying black pigmented screen may enhance the purity of the colours by absorbing the light penetrating the interference platelets. Some colours are the result of both structural and pigmentary effects. In the cuttlefish, for example, a combination of blue iridescence from underlying iridophores and yellow reflexion from expanded xanthophores gives rise to a green colour. Blue and green pigments are rare in fishes, occurring in wrasse and parrot fishes. Usually, the blue colour is due to interference by thin lamellae of guanine or to Tyndall scattering by submicroscopic particles of guanine backed by a melanin screen. The yellow of xanthophores combined with structural blue produces a mixed green colour. The beautiful metallic appearance of the iris of fishes is due to crystals of guanine. In the sapphirine gurnard *Trigla lucerna* the surface of the eye has a golden appearance, owing to the presence of guanine crystals lying subjacent to a layer of carotenoids (26).

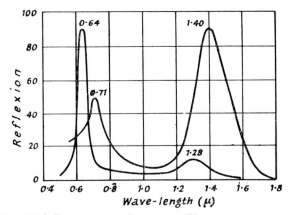

FIG. 11.4. REFLEXION OF DIFFERENT WAVE-LENGTHS FROM IRIDESCENT PIECES OF MOTHER-OF-PEARL

One piece showed reflexion maxima at $0·71\mu$ and $1·40\mu$, the other at $0·64\mu$ and $1·28\mu$. These wave-length maxima are simple multiples and demonstrate the basis of interference effects. (From Pfund (58).)

BIOLOGICAL SIGNIFICANCE OF PIGMENTS: EXOGENOUS PIGMENTS

Animals either obtain pigments from their food, or manufacture them from suitable precursors. The most widespread of exogenous pigments are carotenoids which come, ultimately, from plant sources. Animals are unable to synthesize these compounds, although they can often alter them to suit their particular needs. As an example may be cited the experiments of M. and R. Abeloos-Parize (1) who found that specimens of *Actinia equina*, reared on carotenoid-free food, were themselves deficient in carotenoids on reaching maturity. Anemones deficient in carotenoids, when fed on shrimp eggs rich in these substances, rapidly recovered their original pigmentation; moreover each animal reverted to the colour variety to which it originally belonged, namely red, brown or green. This result means that the animals either regulate the kinds of carotenoids which they absorb, or absorb all indifferently and metabolize them in different ways. In contrast to *Actinia* is the plumose anemone, *Metridium senile*, whose pigments are very stable, and which does not change in colour over long periods under diverse conditions of feeding and starvation (19).

In general, xanthophylls are assimilated and stored by most animals in preference to carotenes, but interesting exceptions are seen among the sponges where carotenes tend to predominate over xanthophylls. Also, the polychaete *Thoracophelia mucronata* contains appreciable quantities of β-carotene derived from its food, but excludes the attendant xanthophylls. Astaxanthin and related pigments, which, as we have seen, occur widely among invertebrates, are derived from the oxidation of β-carotene and certain xanthophylls in the diet (16, 19).

Other pigments of exogenous origin, previously described, are the chlorophyll derivatives and bile pigments occurring in phytophagous and parasitic species. No studies have been devoted to possible correlations between concentrations of green chlorophyll-like pigments in marine animals and the intake of algal food, but the relationship of breakdown products such as biliverdin to ingested haemoglobin is very close.

In dealing with the biological significance of pigments and colours we shall consider the following topics, namely metabolic functions, environmental influence on colour, colour patterns, inheritance of colours, sexual coloration and adaptive and cryptic coloration.

Metabolic Functions

From a review of the distribution of carotenoid pigments one striking fact that emerges is the accumulation of these pigments in reproductive organs. Carotenoids are actively mobilized into the gonads during sexual reproduction and, in some animals, they are also rendered water-soluble by conjugation with proteins. In females of the shore crab *Carcinus maenas* a yellow carotenoid increases in the blood as the ovary matures, and is laid down in that organ. Prior to spawning, carotenoids are also in active movement in fish: in the killifish *Fundulus parvipinnis* for example, the males increase the xanthophyll content of their skin, while the females transfer their stores to the ripening eggs. A careful study of *Mytilus californianus* has shown that shed ova contain qualitatively the same carotenoids as the ovaries, but the difference in amount between ripe and spent females cannot be accounted for by the carotenoid content of the eggs. Similarly, although the spermatozoa are colourless, spent males contain less carotenoid pigment than unspawned males. These facts suggest that carotenoids play some role in spawning and are used up during the process (29).

Eggs of many animals are well supplied with carotenoids, but the role they play in normal embryonic development is obscure. Some suggestions which have been made to explain the mobilization and transfer of carotenoids during reproduction are that they act as fertilization hormones, and that they form a vitelline reserve to supply the developing chromato-phores of the embryo with pigment. In eggs of the sea-urchin *Paracentrotus lividus* the total quantity of carotiprotein decreases during early develop-mental stages, i.e. it appears to be metabolized. Regeneration of pharynx and tentacles in *Actinia equina* proceeds normally even when carotenoids are deficient. Carotenoids are sometimes associated with the development of sexual coloration, especially in fishes where, as in the lumpsucker *Cyclopterus lumpus*, considerable amounts of astaxanthin appear in the skin during the summer spawning period (29, 49).

Certain other functions of carotenoids in animals are more firmly established. Vitamin A can be formed from a number of carotenoids in animals, and is involved in the visual process. Rhodopsin, the photolabile visual pigment, consists of a protein linked with vitamin A_1 as a prosthetic group, and is found in marine fishes and higher vertebrates. In euphausiids (*Meganyctiphanes norvegica*) the majority of the vitamin A (over 90%) and a high proportion of the astaxanthin are contained in the eyes.

Melanins and purines are utilized extensively for external coloration, and the former are frequently present in the photoreceptors of many invertebrates. The functional role of naphthoquinones in echinoids is still obscure. In various proportions they colour the exterior of these animals (Table 11.2), but the precise part they play in the internal economy of sea urchins still awaits elucidation. Echinochrome is released from the ripe eggs of *Arbacia*, and is considered to have a stimulatory effect upon spermatozoa.

Environmental Influence on Colour

Special diets often influence the colour of animals, and some examples have already been cited for polyclads and gnathiids. Another interesting case is the dog-whelk *Nucella lapillus*, which frequently has brown and purple pigmented shells and purple coloured eggs. These colours depend upon the food of the animal, and occur in those specimens which have been feeding upon mussels. Whelks, feeding exclusively upon *Balanus*, lack purple and brown pigments (61). An analogous case is the Japanese top-shell *Turbo cornutus* which, under experimental conditions, has a white shell when fed brown alga (*Eisenia*), and develops shell colour when cal-careous algae are added to its diet (35).

Of physical environmental influences affecting colour, light often has pronounced effects. Besides the rapid colour-responses of crustacea, cephalopods and vertebrates, slower and more durable colour alterations take place. In certain coelenterates there is some correlation between light intensity and degree of pigmentation. The anemones *Actinia equina*, *Anemonia sulcata* and *Tealia felina* augment their pigments, including carotenoids, under increased illumination. In *Anemonia sulcata* this may simply be the result of an increase in symbiotic algae, and consequently of algal carotenoids, with greater light intensity. *Actinia equina*, however, lacks algae, and light exerts a direct effect on pigmentation in this animal.

Slow transformations in the colours of animals are known as morphological colour changes, in contradistinction to rapid chromatophore responses, and have been studied especially in fishes. Early experiments by Cunningham (1893) showed that young flat fishes (*Platichthys flesus*), when kept in tanks illuminated from below, slowly became darkly pigmented on their undersurface. Similarly, the American summer flounder *Paralichthys dentatus* produces melanophores on its undersurface when it is illuminated from below in black surroundings, but this does not occur in white surroundings. But blinded fish produce melanin on the lower surface as the result of inferior illumination irrespective of whether the surroundings are black or white, a result due to direct action of light on the skin. On the other hand, the American Gulf fluke *Paralichthys albiguttus*, when kept on a white background, showed a decrease in melanophores amounting to 30% in 11 days, through the ejection of pigment cells through the skin. Other fish kept for several weeks on a black background showed an increase in epidermal melanophores (Fig. 11.5(*a*)). Killifish *Fundulus heteroclitus* similarly reveal a loss in melanin when kept for some time on white backgrounds, and an increase when a black background is substituted (55, 57, 64). Changes of a like nature occur in the melanophores and melanin of crabs (Brachyura) kept on different backgrounds. In the fiddler crab *Uca*, kept on a white background, labelled melanin is destroyed at an exponential rate, half-time of destruction is 48 h (33).

Morphological colour changes involve carotenoids as well as melanins. Thus, specimens of *Fundulus majalis* increased their yellow chromatophores after several weeks on yellow and black backgrounds, but showed a decrease on blue and white backgrounds. The green fish *Girella nigricans* showed an accelerated loss of xanthophylls when held for long periods in white containers. Some other fishes, *Fundulus parvipinnis* and *Gillichthys mirabilis*, however, maintained their level of xanthophylls on backgrounds of different colours. Among invertebrates the shrimp *Palaemonetes vulgaris* decreased its carotenoid content (astaxanthin and carotene) when maintained upon a white background, while other specimens, in dark surroundings, increased their pigment-content (Fig. 11.5(*b*)) (16, 64).

Morphological as well as physiological colour changes depend upon the albedo—that is, the ratio of reflected to incident light—and are relatively independent of total illumination over a wide range (*see* p. 504). In experiments carried out with the long-jawed goby *Gillichthys mirabilis* on white, grey and black backgrounds, it was found that the amount of melanin in the skin was greatest when the albedo was low. Fish maintained on a white background for 87 days had relatively little integumentary melanin; those on grey backgrounds had more; and those on black backgrounds had the greatest quantity. Comparable experiments concerned with guanine-deposition in *Girella nigricans* have shown that the amount of guanine in the skin varies with the albedo, being greatest in fish kept on light backgrounds (65, 66).

There is, consequently, a close relationship between physiological and morphological colour change. Background conditions which favour a dispersion of chromatophore pigment also bring about an increase in the amount of pigment and in the number of chromatophores over long periods. This is another manifestation of the effect of use and disuse seen elsewhere; for example, in the hypertrophy of muscle with exercise, and

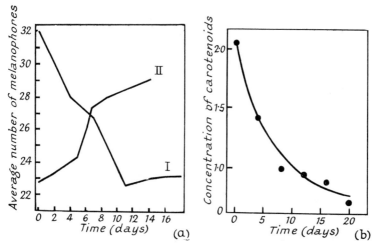

FIG. 11.5 (*a*). CHANGES IN THE NUMBERS OF MELANOPHORES IN THE SKIN OF THE FLOUNDER OR GULF FLUKE *Paralichthys albiguttus* ON DIFFERENT BACKGROUNDS

Melanophore counts were made on a unit area of skin. I: reduction in number of melanophores in a specimen kept on a white background. II: restoration of melanophores in a specimen which had been kept on a white background for four weeks, and then placed upon a black background. (Redrawn from Kuntz, 1917.)

FIG. 11.5 (*b*). DECREASE IN CONCENTRATION OF CAROTENOID PIGMENTS IN SHRIMPS *Palaemonetes vulgaris* WHEN KEPT ON A WHITE BACKGROUND

Concentration of carotenoids is expressed in terms of an artificial standard. (From Brown, 1934.)

wasting after nerve section. From an adaptive viewpoint morphological colour changes are valuable in bringing about closer resemblance to the animal's habitual environment, or protection against actinic rays.

Colour Patterns

Many marine animals are rather evenly coloured and show few or no markings. This is seen in many deep-sea fish and crustacea which are uniformly drab brown, black or red in colour. Uniform colours are also of common occurrence in numerous sedentary invertebrates from littoral and deeper waters. Sponges, particularly, are characterized by absence of markings, but many examples can readily be found in other phyla.

Colour patterns among marine animals are infinite in variety. Bold patterns in black and white, or in different colour schemes, are common in the non-segmented coelenterates and turbellarians. In coelenterates the

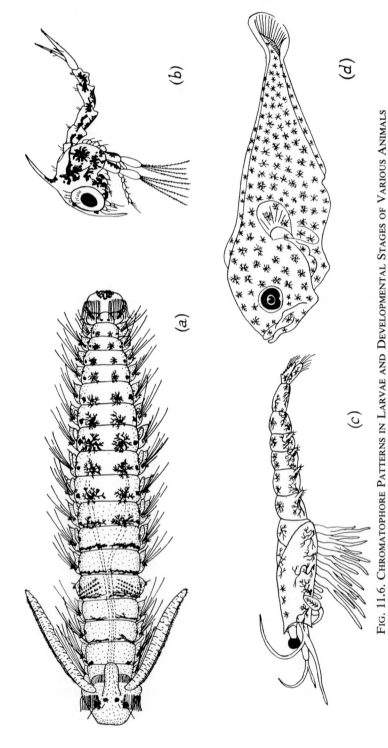

Fig. 11.6. Chromatophore Patterns in Larvae and Developmental Stages of Various Animals

(a) Larva of the rock-boring spionid Polydora hoplura; (b) first zoea of spider crab Maia squinado; (c) Praunus neglecta; (d) larval turbot Scophthalmus maximus. ((a) after Wilson, 1928; (b) after Lebour, 1928; (c) after Keeble and Gamble, 1904; (d) after Cunningham, 1896.)

colours are sometimes differentiated into radial patterns in correlation with the underlying radial symmetry of the animal; for example, in many Scyphomedusae. The close relationship between colour patterns and underlying structures is very striking throughout this phylum, and as one example we may note how endodermal melanin is accumulated along the mesenteric insertions in certain varieties of *Metridium senile*. Often skeleton and polyps are differently coloured, as in the organ-pipe coral *Tubipora* (Alcyonaria), in which the coral framework is bright red but the polyps are brownish red with green-tipped tentacles, or entirely green in colour. Beautiful and striking patterns are also seen in many polychaetes and leeches, in which colour patterns are metamerically arranged, often in association with particular underlying structures. Colour patterns in the crustacea, again, are frequently segmentally disposed, and in many echinoderms they bear a distinct relationship to both the radial arrangement and structural organization of these animals.

Colour patterns of the adult are sometimes preceded by distinct larval patterns; for example, in pelagic stages of many teleosts and crustacea (Fig. 11.6). In decapod larvae and in mysids the chromatophores are organized into definite neural, visceral and caudal groups, with accessory groups on the appendages. The first three groups constitute a primary system, which is retained throughout life in the mysids. In adult decapods, however, they are gradually masked by the development of a secondary system, homologous with the accessory group of mysids and responsible for the coloration of the adult (34). Colour changes during growth have been the subject of a special enquiry in the garibaldi fish *Hypsypops rubicunda*. The young are brilliantly coloured in blue due to a layer of guanine crystals overlying a melanin layer which absorbs longer wavelengths. Half-grown fish are dusky in colour and secretive, whereas the adults are bright orange and use their colours as advertisements of territorial occupation. In this species the relative quantities of carotenoid pigments (xanthophyll esters) increase with age, and they produce the brilliant integumentary colour of the adult (39).

Inheritance of Colours

Closely related species are often slightly dissimilar in colour and markings due to relative differences in the amounts of various pigments present. Examples are the piper and grey gurnard *Trigla lyra* and *T. gurnardus* which differ in the relative development of red and black pigments. In fishes, cephalopods and certain crustacea, integumentary pigments are located in chromatophores, and the pattern and coloration in a particular species depend upon the absolute abundance of different kinds of chromatophores and their macroscopic aggregations at particular loci. Goodrich (25) has presented illustrations to show the character of such chromatophore differences in teleosts, and Table 11.3 shows the result of a quantitative analysis of chromatophores in certain coral reef labrids (27).

Definite specific differences of this kind are, of course, genetically deter-

TABLE 11.3

Numbers of Chromatophores per Square Millimetre
in Stripes of Two Species of Labrids

	Stripes		
	Black	Blue	Green
	Thalassoma bifasciatum (from Tortugas)		
Melanophores	718	346	462
Erythrophores and xanthophores	0–550	566	0–190
Iridocytes	3,000	3,000	3,000
		Yellow	Green
	Thalassoma duperrey (from Hawaii)		
Melanophores		271	596
Xanthophores		1,057	527
Iridocytes		3,000	3,300

(From Goodrich (25).)

mined, and are transmitted from one generation to the next. In an interesting interspecific cross between the mackerel *Scomber scombrus* and the killifish *Fundulus heteroclitus*, some embryos showed, unchanged, the distinctive green chromatophores of the mackerel; others, the red chromatophores of the killifish; and still others bore chromatophore types of both parents. Here it appears that the chromatophores are determined by the variable genetic constitution inherited from the two specifically different parents. Marine species are also rich in colour varieties, and by the study of such cross-fertile animals information about the inheritance of colour patterns can be obtained.

Colour varieties are common in coelenterates, occurring in the Scyphomedusae (*Cyanea capillata*), Alcyonaria (*Eunicella verrucosa*), Actiniaria (*Epiactis prolifera*) and Madreporaria (*Madrepora prostata*). As previously indicated, some colour variation is of environmental origin, depending on food and light. In other species the colour varieties are remarkably stable and are genetically determined, as in *Metridium senile* in which four principal phases are found in nature living side by side under identical conditions (Fig. 11.1). Some species showing pronounced colour phases in other phyla are the bread-crumb sponge *Halichondria panicea*, the nemertine *Lineus ruber*, many molluscs such as the flat periwinkle *Littorina littoralis*, and the colonial ascidian *Botryllus schlosseri*. In *Metridium*, as in so many other coelenterates, asexual buds are produced and a given variety is propagated asexually for many generations, thus forming an asexually produced clone.

Genetic studies of the polychaete *Pomatoceros triqueter* and the isopod *Sphaeroma serratum* reveal something about the inheritance and significance of polymorphism in marine invertebrates. The first species occurs in nature in three distinct forms having blue, brown and orange tentacles. In Oslo Fjord, where the animals were collected, the brown varieties were found most abundantly, blue next and orange rather infrequently. The colours are produced by blue, red and yellow substances, together with minute granules of a white material, all of which are present in each animal variety although in different proportions. Some breeding experiments have indicated that blue and brown are due to simple dominant-recessive allelomorphic factors. Crosses between blue and brown types give worms with blue and brown crowns in the ratio 3:1. Blue is thus dominant, brown recessive; the inheritance of orange colour has not been determined (23, 24).

The situation in the littoral isopod *Sphaeroma serratum* is more complex, for there are five principal types of colour patterns, determined by the interaction of five pairs of multiple alleles and, in addition, an independent gene pair, rubrum. Summarized results for the complex colour phases are—

albicans: quadruple recessive, *dállooss*
discretum: triple recessive, *Dd* or *DD, llooss*
lunulatum: double recessive, *Ll* or *LL, ooss*
ornatum: single recessive, *Oo* or *OO, ss*
rubrum: dominant, *R*
normal colour: homozygote, *rr*.

It was determined that the several colour phases remain stable from one year to another at any one station, but that there is considerable variation between stations. Discretum and albicans were in the majority at all stations on the French coast, while the other mutants were rarer or sometimes lacking. Polychromatism in the harpaticid copepod *Tisbe reticulata* has also been analysed genetically. Five major phenotypic colour phases occur among females of this species, and are due to variations in carotiproteins. The different phases are determined by several series of allelomorphic factors (5, 6).

The polymorphic phases of these various animals, *Metridium, Pomatoceros, Botryllus, Sphaeroma,* etc., appear to be non-adaptive and are not themselves subject to environmental selection. By analogy with other animals studied in much greater detail, it is unlikely that random drifting of mutations through such large and widespread populations would suffice to maintain such colour phases. Rather the factors responsible for the production and organization of pigments are linked with other genes having greater or less survival value, and it is selection of the latter that causes the apparent balance of colour phases in different areas (19).

Sexual Coloration

Sexual differences in coloration appear to be adventitious in most marine invertebrates in which they occur, and result frequently from differences in the reproductive elements tinting the body, or from structural alterations associated with spawning. A striking difference in coloration between the sexes occurs in certain species of sapphirine copepods in which the males are beautifully iridescent. This is attributed to a deposition of thin lamellae in special excretory cells beneath the cuticule, as the result of tissue changes and metabolic activity associated with spermatogenesis (62). Sexual dimorphism in coloration is associated with characteristic differences in the behaviour of the two sexes during breeding. Relatively few marine invertebrates have reached the mental level consonant with such complex activities as courtship display. Sexual coloration has been reported in various Malacostraca. In fiddler crabs of the genus *Uca*, for example, the males develop gaudily coloured chelipeds and ambulatories, and a light carapace, whereas the females remain rather dark (10).

Nuptial colours are especially characteristic of teleosts where the males of many species become brightly coloured during the breeding season. Wrasse (Labridae), in particular, show pronounced sexual dimorphism in colour. The male cuckoo wrasse *Labrus ossifagus* is yellow or orange tinged with red, and marked with blue bands and patches on body and fins. The female is reddish in colour, without blue bands, but bearing two or three large black spots on the back. In *Halichoeres poecilopterus*, a common Japanese fish, both males and females are brightly coloured, but the colour patterns of the two sexes are quite dissimilar (Fig. 11.7). The adult female is bright reddish in colour, with dark longitudinal stripes, whereas the adult male becomes bright brownish green at maturity (38). Sexual colours of these kinds are utilized in nuptial displays leading to spawning.

Adaptive and Cryptic Coloration

The adaptive significance of much animal coloration is now securely established. It is apparent that many marine animals resemble in a general way the colour of their environment and are suitably concealed. In the open sea the transparent condition of the hosts of pelagic organisms— coelenterates, polychaetes, gastropods, crustaceans, tunicates, larval fishes—renders them difficult to detect. Cryptic coloration is common among animals living in inshore waters, coral reefs and floating weed, where every conceivable manner of concealing device and deceptive coloration can be found. The drab greens, browns and greys of many shore animals resemble the weeds and stones among which they shelter; for example, *Carcinus* and *Ligia*. Very effective are the dull mottled tones of many animals living on sandy and gravelly bottoms; for example, the skates, rays and flatfishes (Fig. 11.8). In contrast with these sombre liveries are the reef fishes which are notable for the brilliance and variety of their colouring. But even the bold hues and colours of these animals can be considered as cryptic against the brightly coloured background of coral reefs (46, 68).

Adjustments of colours and tones to conform to different backgrounds are quite remarkable in various higher animals. The physiological bases of these changes are treated in the following chapter. Cott (9) describes the case of the demon stinger fish of Japan *Inimicus japonicus*, which is blackish in colour when living among lava rocks, and bright red when occurring among red algae. The Nassau grouper *Epinephelus striatus*, studied by Longley (44), can assume up to eight different colour schemes which appear and disappear in a few moments (Fig. 11.9).

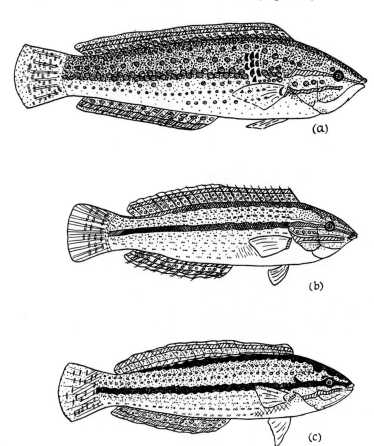

FIG. 11.7. COLOUR PATTERNS IN THE TELEOST *Halichoeres poecilopterus*
(*a*) Fully mature male; (*b*) castrated male; (*c*) fully mature female. (After Kinoshita, 1934, 1935.)

The different colours and patterns assumed during successive stages of the life cycle often bear a definite relation to the various environmental situations in which the animal occurs. Good examples are encountered in all those transparent pelagic larvae whose littoral adults have colours resembling their environment. In pelagic larvae of flat fishes and the leptocephali of eels even the blood is colourless. An interesting case is the opisthobranch *Aplysia punctata* which changes in colour with age from rose red to olive green, in correlation with changes in its algal background during migration from deeper to shallower water.

The principle of obliterative shading, first clarified by Thayer, is utilized by surface fish and other animals. In this kind of shading the darker pigments occur on the back, and grade into lighter pigments on the belly, thus counteracting the effects of superior lighting. Pelagic cetaceans and sharks make use of countershading to render themselves less conspicuous.

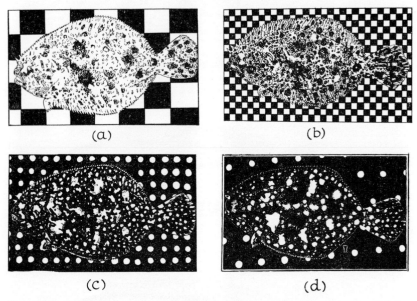

FIG. 11.8. PATTERNS ASSUMED BY FLOUNDERS (THE GULF FLUKE *Paralichthys albiguttus*) ON ARTIFICIAL BACKGROUNDS OF DIFFERENT PATTERNS AFTER ONE TO THREE DAYS

(*a*) Individual on a black and white background consisting of 2 cm squares, after having been adapted to white; (*b*) individual on black and white background, 5 mm squares, after having been adapted to a white background; (*c*) individual on a black and white background consisting of circles 5 mm in diameter. The concealing pattern in this fish was most remarkable, and the animal appeared to contain numerous holes. (*d*) Individual on a black and white background, consisting of 5 mm circles. (From photographs of Mast, 1914.)

Of equal interest are examples of inverted countershading, as in the pelagic snail *Glaucus atlanticum* which hangs belly uppermost from the surface film, and of lack of countershading, as in the shark sucker or remora (*Echeneis naucrates*) which attaches itself to larger fish with any side uppermost. Superimposed frequently upon countershading is a pattern of disruptive coloration in which the body form is broken up by irregular patches of contrasting colours. This is well seen in the disruptive phases of many reef fishes (Fig. 11.9) and in the common cuttlefish *Sepia officinalis* (Fig. 11.10).

Many pelagic fishes have silvery sides—herring, mackerel and scad are good examples—and make use of additional aids to obliterate their form in the water mass. Owing to refraction at the surface and internal scattering, most of the light entering the water becomes directed downwards, and the greater the distance from the surface the greater becomes the vertical

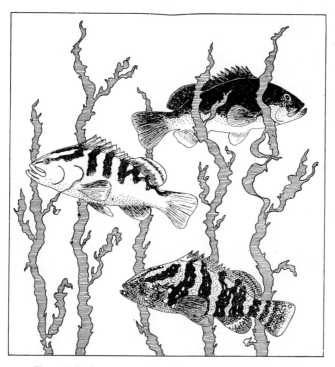

FIG. 11.9. ALTERATIONS IN COLOUR PATTERN OF THE
NASSAU GROUPER *Epinephelus striatus*

(*Upper right*) a phase in which the fish is dark above with light underparts. (*Lower right*) a phase in which the whole body becomes darkly banded. (*Middle left*) another phase in which the upper parts are sharply banded, with white underparts. (After Townsend (68).)

component of the downwardly directed light. The difference between downwardly and upwardly directed light in the open sea is very high. Pelagic fish have dark backs which absorb and scatter light; reflecting little of the incident light coming from above and scattering much of the light which they reflect from their backs, they appear dark as seen from above and merge into the dark background of the depths. The sides and flanks of many silvery pelagic fishes contain layers of oriented reflecting platelets,

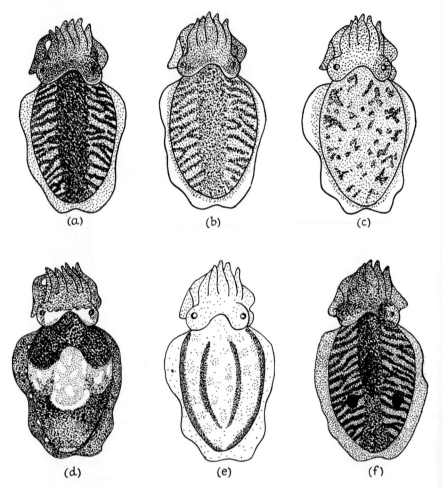

FIG. 11.10. PATTERNS ASSUMED BY THE CUTTLEFISH
Sepia officinalis UNDER DIFFERENT CONDITIONS

(*a*) The dark zebra pattern of an actively swimming animal; (*b*) the light zebra pattern of an animal swimming over a light sandy bottom; (*c*) light mottled pattern of a specimen at rest on a sandy bottom; (*d*) white stripe pattern shown in a black and white environment; (*e*), (*f*), longitudinal stripe and black spot patterns displayed on disturbance. (After Holmes, 1940.)

lying in special reflecting cells: these occur either on the outside (cod) or
the inside of the scales (herring), or deeper, in the subdermis (mackerel).
In the centre of the flanks where the surface of the body approaches the
vertical, the platelets are parallel to the surface, and in the upper and lower
flanks they are tilted towards the vertical and lie at considerable angles to
the surface of the body (Fig. 11.11). Since the distribution of light is
largely symmetrical about the fish in open water, an observer viewing

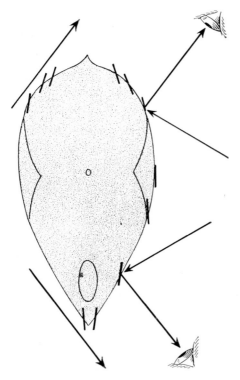

Fig. 11.11. Transverse Section Through Posterior Abdomen of a Herring
Showing the Orientations of Reflecting Platelets under the Scales

The firm black lines on the surface of the fish show how the platelets lie; arrows indicate directions of incident and reflected light rays ($\times 2$).

such a fish from one side and below, sees light coming from above reflected
from its silvery surface, and he compares it with light of nearly the same
intensity coming from above the other side of the fish (*vide* Fig. 11.11).
Similarly, an observer looking at the fish from one side and above, sees
light from below reflected from the side of the fish, and compares this
with light coming from the same direction on the other side of the fish.
The reflecting platelets are good mirrors, reflecting about 85% of the

incident light; this arrangement causes the fish to appear about as equally bright as the background over most angles of viewing, and it merges into the illuminated background of the water mass. The platelets in the skin are stacks of guanine crystals, and the high degree of reflexion is achieved by constructive interference and additive reflexions at the successive reflecting surfaces in the pile.

In the herring, which in general view appears very silvery, the individual scales of the flanks show several bands of colours ranging from blue to red. At any one place the reflecting areas of three scales overlap and regions that reflect different colours lie over one another. Since reflexion is an inter-

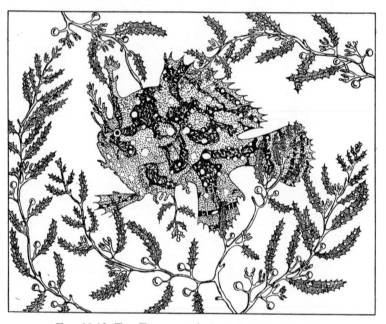

FIG. 11.12. THE FROGFISH *Antennarius marmoratus* IN
SARGASSUM WEED

ference effect, the light not reflected by one scale penetrates it and is reflected back by a deeper layer. The resultant reflexion of several different colours by overlapping scales produces a glittering silvery appearance (Fig. 11.3).

Warning coloration is a device which is widely utilized in association with noxious or poisonous properties. Brightly coloured sponges, chromodorids, some polychaetes and stinging actinians are repellent to fishes, and an association is quickly formed in possible predatory fish between the characteristic colour and form of these animals and their noxious properties. Some animals have special warning markings in association with poisonous properties. Conspicuous nudibranchs, such as *Eubranchus tricolor*, have brightly coloured defensive papillae armed with batteries of nematocysts. Many of the puffer fishes (Tetraodontidae) possess poisonous flesh and are brightly coloured. The notorious weever-fish *Trachinus vipera* has poisonous glands associated with specially modified fin rays, and is capable of inflicting a very painful wound. This animal bears a conspicuous black warning badge on its dorsal fin, which is the only part visible when the fish rests buried in the sand. The common sole *Solea solea*, itself a harmless species, mimics the weaver-fish and bears a large black patch on its upper pectoral fin, which it erects vertically. Both species inhabit the same geographical range and have similar habits.

Some examples of special resemblances to seaweeds and various animals may now be mentioned. In the littoral zone and on coral reefs there are many animals which have adopted special protective resemblances to sponges, anemones, corals, alcyonarians, etc. Especially noteworthy are the remarkable resemblances borne by many members of the floating animal communities of the Sargasso Sea to the Gulf weed among which they dwell, for example, the frog fish *Antennarius marmoratus* (Fig. 11.12) (9, 45).

The immediate surface layers of the sea possess a permanent surface fauna (apart from vertebrates and animals associated with the flotsam). Some, living partly in air and partly in water, are termed pleuston; others, living directly beneath the surface, hyponeuston. Some of the small animals in this region are transparent, e.g. fish larvae; others blue in colour. The blue coloration is produced by pigments (*Velella*, copepods, shrimp, etc.) or by interference effects (squid, *Sapphirina*) (13).

REFERENCES

1. ABELOOS-PARIZE, M. and R., "Sur l'origine alimentaire du pigment caroténoïde d'*Actinia equina* L.," *C. R. Soc. Biol., Paris*, **94**, 560 (1926).
2. ABOLINS, L., "Sexual differences of carotenoid content in the skin of *Labrus mixtus*," *Acta Zool., Stockh.*, **38**, 223 (1957).
3. ABOLINS, L. and ABOLINS-KROGIS, A., "Studies on skin carotenoids of *Crenilabrus pavo*," *Pubbl. Staz. Zool. Napoli*, **29**, 389 (1957).
4. BAILEY, B. E., "The pigments of salmon," *J. Fish. Res. Bd Can.*, **3**, 469 (1937).
5. BOCQUET, C., "Recherches sur *Tisbe reticulata*," *Arch. Zool. Exp. Gén.*, **87**, 335 (1951).
6. BOCQUET, C., LÉVI, C. and TEISSIER, G., "Recherches sur le polychromatisme de *Sphaeroma serratum* (F.)," ibid., **87**, 245 (1951).
7. COMFORT, A., "Biochemistry of molluscan shell pigments," *Proc. Malac. Soc. Lond.*, **28**, 79 (1950).
8. COMFORT, A., "The pigmentation of molluscan shells," *Biol. Rev.*, **26**, 285 (1951).
9. COTT, H. B., *Adaptive Coloration in Animals* (London, Methuen, 1940).
10. CRANE, J., "On the color changes of fiddler crabs (genus *Uca*) in the field," *Zoologica, N.Y.*, **29**, 161 (1944).
11. DALES, R. P., "The feeding mechanism and structure of the gut of *Owenia*," *J. Mar. Biol. Ass. U.K.*, **36**, 81 (1957).

12. DALES, R. P., "The nature of the pigments in the crowns of sabellid and serpulid polychaetes," *J. Mar. Biol. Ass. U.K.*, **42**, 259 (1962).

13. DAVID, P. M., "The surface fauna of the ocean," *Endeavour*, **24**, 95 (1965).

14. FINGERMAN, M., "Chromatophores," *Physiol. Rev.*, **45**, 296 (1965).

15. FONTAINE, A. R., "The colours of *Ophiocomina nigra*," *J. Mar. Biol. Ass. U.K.*, **42**, 9 (1962).

16. FOX, D. L., *Animal Biochromes and Structural Colours* (Cambridge Univ. Press, 1953).

17. FOX, D. L., "An acidogenic carotenoid in a bathypelagic nemertian worm," *Nature*, **173**, 583 (1954).

18. FOX, D. L. and MILLOTT, N., "The pigmentation of the jellyfish, *Pelagia noctiluca*," *Proc. Roy. Soc. B.*, **142**, 392 (1954).

19. FOX, D. L. and PANTIN, C. F. A., "The colours of the plumose anemone *Metridium senile* (L.)," *Phil. Trans. B.*, **230**, 415 (1941).

20. FOX, H. M., "On chlorocruorin and haemoglobin," *Proc. Roy. Soc. B.*, **136,** 378 (1949).

21. FOX, H. M., "Haemoglobin and biliverdin in parasitic cirripede crustacea," *Nature*, **171**, 162 (1953).

22. FOX, H. M. and VEVERS, G., *The Nature of Animal Colours* (London, Sidgwick and Jackson, 1960).

23. FÖYN, B. and GJÖEN, I., "Sex and inheritance in the serpulid *Pomatoceros triqueter* L.," *Nature*, **165**, 652 (1950).

24. FØYN, B. and GJØEN, I., "Studies on the serpulid *Pomatoceros triqueter*. 2. The colour patterns of the branchial crown and its inheritance," *Nytt Mag. Zool.*, **2**, 85 (1954).

25. GOODRICH, H. B., "Chromatophores in relation to genetic specific distinctions," *Amer. Nat.*, **73**, 198 (1939).

26. GOODRICH, H. B. and BIESINGER, D. I., "The histological basis of color patterns in three tropical marine fish," *J. Morph.*, **93**, 465 (1953).

27. GOODRICH, H. B., HINE, R. L. and REYNOLDS, J., "Studies on the terminal phases of color pattern formation in certain coral reef fish," *J. Exp. Zool.*, **114**, 603 (1950).

28. GOODWIN, T. W., "Carotenoid distribution in the gonads of the limpets *Patella vulgata* and *Patella depressa*," *Biochem. J.*, **47**, 249, (1950).

29. GOODWIN, T. W., *The Comparative Biochemistry of the Carotenoids* (London, Chapman and Hall, 1952).

30. GOODWIN, T. W., "Biochemistry of pigments," in *The Physiology of Crustacea*, Ed. Waterman, T. H., Vol. 1, p. 101 (New York and London, Academic Press, 1960).

31. GOODWIN, T. W. and SRISUKH, S., "A study of the pigments of the sea-urchins, *Echinus esculentus* L. and *Paracentrotus lividus* Lamarck," *Biochem. J.*, **47**, 69 (1950).

32. GRANICK, S. and GILDER, H., "Distribution, structure and properties of the tetrapyrroles," *Advanc. Enzymol.*, **7**, 305 (1947).

33. GREEN, J. P., "Morphological color change in the fiddler crab," *Biol. Bull.*, **127**, 239 (1964).

34. GURNEY, R., *Larvae of Decapod Crustacea* (London, Ray Soc., 1942).

35. INO, T., "The effect of food on growth and coloration of the topshell (*Turbo cornutus* Solander)," *J. Mar. Res.*, **8**, 1 (1949).

36. JACOBSON, F. W. and MILLOTT, N., "Phenolases and melanogenesis in the

coelomic fluid of the echinoid *Diadema antillarum*," *Proc. Roy. Soc. B.*, **141**, 231 (1953).

37. KARRER, P. and JUCKER, E., *Carotenoids*, trans. Branch, E. A. (London, Elsevier, 1950).

38. KINOSHITA, Y., "On the differentiation of the male colour-patterns, and the sex ratio in *Halichoeres poecilopterus*," *J. Sci. Hiroshima Univ.*, Ser. B, **3**, 65 (1934).

39. KRITZLER, H., FOX, D. L., HUBBS, C. L. and CRANE, S. C., "Carotenoid pigmentation of the pomacentrid fish *Hypsypops rubicunda*," *Copeia*, **1950**, 125 (1950).

40. KURODA, C. and OKAJIMA, M., "Studies on naphthoquinone derivatives, 8," *Proc. Imp. Acad. Japan*, **26**, 33 (1950).

41. LEDERER, E., *Les Caroténoïdes des Animaux* (Paris, Hermann, 1935).

42. LEDERER, E., "Biochemistry of the natural pigments," *Annu. Rev. Biochem.*, **17**, 495 (1948).

43. LENEL, R., "Localisation et métabolisme des pigments caroténoïdes chez *Carsinus maenas*," *C. R. Acad. Sci.*, **236**, 1448 (1953).

44. LONGLEY, W. H., "Studies upon the biological significance of animal coloration," *J. Exp. Zool.*, **23**, 533 (1917).

45. LONGLEY, W. H. and HILDEBRAND, S. F., "Systematic catalogue of the fishes of Tortugas, Florida," *Publ. Carneg. Instn*, No. 535 (1941).

46. MAST, S. O., "Changes in shade, color, and pattern in fishes," *Bull. U.S. Bur. Fish*, **34**, 173 (1916).

47. MAYER, F., *The Chemistry of Natural Coloring Matters*, trans. Cook, A. H. (New York, Reinhold, 1943).

48. MILLOTT, N., "Observations on the skin pigment and amoebocytes, and the occurrence of phenolases in the coelomic fluid of *Holothuria forskali*," *J. Mar. Biol. Ass. U.K.*, **31**, 529 (1953).

49. MONROY, A., ODDO, A. M. and NICOLA, M. DE, "The carotenoid pigments during early development of the egg of the sea urchin *Paracentrotus lividus*," *Exp. Cell. Res.*, **2**, 700 (1951).

50. MOORE, H. B., "The biology of *Purpura lapillus*. 1. Shell variation in relation to environment," *J. Mar. Biol. Ass. U.K.*, **21**, 61 (1936).

51. MOUCHET, S., "Contribution à l'étude de la digestion chez les Gnathiidae," *Bull. Soc. Zool. Fr.*, **53**, 442 (1928).

52. NICOL, J. A. C., "Special effectors," in *Physiology of Mollusca*, Ed. Wilbur, K. M. and Yonge, C. M., Vol. 1, p. 353 (New York and London, Academic Press, 1964).

53. NICOLA, M. DE, "The carotenoids of the carapace of the echinoderm *Ophidiaster ophidianus*," *Biochem. J.*, **56**, 555 (1954).

54. NICOLA, M. DE, and GOODWIN, T. W., "The distribution of carotenoids in some marine invertebrates," *Pubbl. Staz. Zool. Napoli*, **25**, 145 (1954).

55. OSBORN, C. M., "Studies on the growth of integumentary pigment in the lower vertebrates. 1. The origin of artificially developed melanophores on the normally unpigmented ventral surface of the summer flounder (*Paralichthys dentatus*)," *Biol. Bull.*, **81**, 341 (1941).

56. PANIZZI, L. and NICOLAUS, R., "Ricerche sulle melanine. 1. Sulla melanina di seppia," *Gazz. Chim. Ital.*, **82**, 435 (1952).

57. PARKER, G. H., *Animal Colour Changes and their Neurohumours* (Cambridge Univ. Press, 1948).

58. PFUND, A. H., "The colors of mother-of-pearl," *J. Franklin Inst.*, **183**, 453 (1917).
59. PHEAR, E. A., "Gut haems in the invertebrates," *Proc. Zool. Soc.*, **125**, 383 (1955).
60. PINCKARD, J. H., KITTRIDGE, J. S., FOX, D. L. and HAXO, F. T., "Pigments from a marine 'red water' population of the dinoflagellate *Prorocentrum micans*," *Arch. Biochim. Biophys.*, **44**, 189 (1953).
61. RIMINGTON, C. and KENNEDY, G. Y., "Porphyrins," in *Comparative Biochemistry*, Ed. Florkin, M. and Mason, H. S., Vol. 4, p. 557 (New York and London, Academie Press, 1962).
62. ROSE, M. and VAISSIÈRE, R., "Le système excréto-glandulaire des Sapphirines," *Arch. Zool. Exp. Gén.*, **87**, 134 (1951).
63. STRAIN, H. H., "Hopkinsiaxanthin, a xanthophyll of the sea slug *Hopkinsia rosacea*," *Biol. Bull.*, **97**, 206 (1949).
64. SUMNER, F. B., "Quantitative changes in pigmentation, resulting from visual stimulation in fishes and amphibia," *Biol. Rev.*, **15**, 351 (1940).
65. SUMNER, F. B., "Vision and guanine production in fishes," *Proc. Nat. Acad. Sci.*, **30**, 285 (1944).
66. SUMNER, F. B. and DOUDOROFF, P., "Some quantitative relations between visual stimuli and the production or destruction of melanin in fishes," ibid., **23**, 211 (1937).
67. TIXIER, R., "Sur quelques pigments tétrapyrroliques provenants d'animaux marins," *Mém. Mus. Hist. Nat., Paris*, N.S. A, Zool., **5**, 41 (1953).
68. TOWNSEND, C. H., "Records of changes in color among fishes," *Zoologica, N.Y.*, **9**, 321 (1934).
69. VEVERS, H. G., "The biology of *Asterias rubens*. 3. The carotenoid pigments in the integument," *J. Mar. Biol. Ass. U.K.*, **30**, 569 (1952).
70. WILLSTAEDT, H., "Zur Kenntnis der grünen Farbstoffe von See-fischen," *Enzymologica*, **9**, 260 (1941).

CHAPTER 12

COLOUR CHANGES

I took several specimens of an octopus which possessed a most mar-
vellous power of changing its colours, equalling any chameleon, and
evidently accommodating the changes to the colour of the background
which it passed over. Yellowish green, dark brown, and red, were the
prevailing colours. . . .

CHARLES DARWIN, 1832

CERTAIN animals have acquired the power of altering their shade or colour
in relation to the character of the background and incident illumination.
These animals have special pigment cells or chromatophores in their skin,
and it is by means of concentration or dispersion of pigments in the chromatophores that the colour changes are brought about. Chromatophores
are found in several phyla of marine animals—coelenterates, echinoderms,
annelids, molluscs, crustacea and vertebrates—and they probably have
evolved independently on several different occasions. Colour changes in
range and complexity of control are most highly developed in cephalopods,
decapod crustaceans and gnathostome cold-blooded vertebrates. The
subject of colour responses has been extensively reviewed, among others
by Abramowitz (3) and Parker (56).

CHROMATOPHORES

Chromatophores are classified according to the kind of pigment or reflecting material which they contain. Melanophores are dark chromatophores
containing brown or black melanin pigments. Lipophores are cells bearing
red or yellow carotenoid pigments, and are termed erythrophores or
xanthophores according to their colour. Allophores is a term sometimes
used for red chromatophores bearing reddish non-carotenoid pigments.
Guanophores, also called leucophores and iridophores, contain particles
of guanine in the form of small granules or plate-like crystals. By movements of these several kinds of pigments in various ways or combinations,
the animal is able to bring about changes in its colour pattern, and the
alterations in coloration may reach a high degree of complexity in those
animals with well-differentiated chromatophoral systems (27, 56).

Chromatophore Movements

There are two different ways in which chromatophoral movements are
effected, exemplified in cephalopods, crustacea and fishes. In cephalopods
the colour cell itself is controlled by attached muscle fibres, which are

capable of dilating it (Fig. 12.1). In crustacea and fishes, on the other hand, pigment movement is an inherent activity of a branched colour cell (Figs. 12.2, 12.3) and the pigment flows to and fro within the process of the cell. In the prawns *Palaemonetes* and *Hippolyte* the movement of pigment is due to the ebb and flow of cytoplasm through fixed tubular spaces, which collapse when the cell is contracted and fill out when the cell is expanded. Similar movements are also seen in the chromatophores of teleosts (*Gadus, Mullus, Fundulus*). During expansion and concentration of the melano-phores in these fish the pigment granules flow along stable cellular processes that maintain a fixed position. It is thought that pigment is carried along by endoplasmic streaming and that changes occur in the sol–gel condition of the cell. Fibrils arranged parallel to the cell membrane have been ob-served in the outer cytoplasmic region. Various theories to explain move-ment of pigments are now competing with one another; one of these in-vokes fibrillar contraction and squeezing of the cell contents (27, 56).

Direct and Indirect Responses

From the physiological point of view chromatophores may be said to respond to two modes of excitation; direct and indirect. In direct excitation the chromatophore itself is responding to external stimuli impinging directly upon it from the environment, and is acting as an independent effector. In indirect excitation, on the other hand, the stimuli activate receptor organs, usually but not always the eyes, and set in train a series of events which finally influence the chromatophores. The terms primary and secondary responses also have been employed frequently in referring to stimulation through extra-ocular regions and to stimulation through the eyes, respectively.

It is usual for changes in the environment to be registered in the animal's nervous system, which controls chromatophore activity through efferent nervous impulses or endocrine secretions. It is known, however, that blinded animals often continue to show chromatophore movements in response to illumination, although true background responses are usually lost. Studies on blinded *Ligia, Palaemon* and *Hippolyte* have shown that these animals blanch (due to chromatophore contraction) in darkness, and darken (due to chromatophore expansion) in light. The results of some experiments on normal and blinded sea-slaters *Ligia oceanica* are shown in Table 12.1. Blinded animals failed to show any difference in their chromatic behaviour on white and black backgrounds, but displayed graded chromatophore responses according to the intensity of overhead illumination. In experiments of this kind it is undecided whether the light is acting upon the chromatophores directly, or exerts its effect through photoreceptors other than the eyes. Tait (68) observed no direct effect of light on the chromatophores of *Ligia*, which suggests that extra-ocular photoreceptors are involved in this animal.

The prawn *Palaemon* contains white reflecting chromatophores which exhibit a direct primary response to change of illumination. In blinded

TABLE 12.1

CHROMATOPHORAL RESPONSES OF NORMAL AND BLINDED SPECIMENS OF
Ligia oceanica UNDER VARIOUS CONDITIONS OF ILLUMINATION

The results are expressed in terms of the chromatophore index in which 1 represents full
contraction, and 5 full expansion (from H. G. Smith (66).)

Condition of the animal	Background	Bright light	Dim light	Darkness
Normal	Black	5·0	4·6	2·7
Normal	White	1·7	1·4	2·7
Blinded	Black	4·2	3·9	2·7
Blinded	White	4·2	3·9	2·7

individuals of *Palaemon serratus*, *P. adspersus* and *P. elegans*, the white chromatophores continue to expand when illuminated, and to contract in darkness. The degree of dispersion of the black chromatophores of the fiddler crab *Uca* is affected by the total illumination, and in blinded animals these cells behave as independent effectors, dispersing in bright light and concentrating in darkness (18, 41).

Some fishes also continue to show chromatophore activity when blinded. These include species of *Fundulus*, *Gobius*, *Ctenolabrus* and *Lepadogaster*, which become pale in the dark, and darken when subsequently illuminated. But the chromatophore response to illumination is absent in blinded plaice *Pleuronectes platessa*. Von Frisch found that when a spot of light was focused on the skin of the wrasse *Crenilabrus*, a local dark area appeared. No such effect was observed in the gurnard *Trigla*, however. In isolated scales of the tautog *Tautoga*, the melanophores respond by dispersion to a sudden increase in light intensity. It appears then that the chromatophores of different animals show much variation in their susceptibility to direct photic stimulation.

In indirect photic stimulation of fish, at least three possible receptor surfaces are involved besides the eyes, namely, dermal photoreceptors, the pineal complex and the photo-sensitive surface of the third ventricle. No doubt their effective contributions vary greatly in different species of fish, but insufficient data are available to distinguish between them. In one study of pineal functioning in a large series of teleosts it was found that the animals could be divided into three groups: those in which the tissues overlying the pineal are sufficiently thin to allow the entry of light; those in which the tissues are opaque; and those in which the behaviour of appropriately placed chromatophores regulates the entrance of light to the pineal organ. When the pineal was covered, fishes in the first group reacted by expanding their melanophores, while fishes in the second and third groups showed slighter effects. The pineal organ of the young salmon has a functional role as a light receptor in chromatic activity (smolts of *Oncorhynchus nerka*). When the pineal is destroyed and the fish illuminated, they become intermediate in shade between normal and blinded specimens.

The melanophore response thus depends on sensory information from the eyes and pineal organ (9, 34, 56, 58, 62, 65, 78).

In colour responses mediated by the eyes it has been found that the determining factor is the ratio of reflected to incident light—that is, light reflected from the background and that reaching the eye from above. When this ratio is small, as on a black background, the animal darkens, and when this ratio is large, as on a white background, the animal blanches. These responses take place within a wide range of intensity of total illumination. To explain these results it has been assumed that the eye or retina is structurally and functionally polarized. Thus in *Fundulus heteroclitus*, various regions of the retina have been tested by rotating the eyes, and by the use of screens shielding half the eye. When light was admitted to the ventral region of the retina, but was excluded from the dorsal region, the animal darkened; and when light was admitted to the dorsal region, but excluded from the ventral region, the fish blanched. The dorsal region of the eye, consequently, is stimulated by light proceeding from below, as on a white background, and causes the fish to blanch. Light coming predominantly from above stimulates the ventral region of the eye, and results in darkening (56).

Colour Responses in Coelenterates, Echinoids and Annelids. A siphonophore *Nanomia cara* has scarlet chromatophores directly responsive to illumination. The echinoids *Centrostephanus longispinus* and *Arbacia lixula* (=*pustulosa*) darken in the light, and blanch in darkness, changes which are due to movements of chromatophores. When illuminated, *Arbacia* becomes black whether the background is light or dark, and turns brown after being in the dark for a few hours. *Centrostephanus* is dark purple in the light, and changes to grey in the dark. The chromatophores respond directly to illumination, and have maximal spectral sensitivity at about 470 mμ (*Diadema setosum*) (79, 80). Another species, *Arbacia punctulata*, does not show alterations in colour (40).

Among polychaetes there are conspicuous melanophores in the larvae of *Polydora* and *Poecilochaetus*, which expand in light and become punctate in darkness (Fig. 11.6) (49, 76). The polychaete *Platynereis dumerili* contains conspicuous yellow and violet chromatophores, which by dispersion and contraction alter the colour of the worm. The chromatophores become punctate in darkness, or in the absence of the eyes, and expanded when the intact animal is illuminated. By their expansion they serve as a shield to protect the animal against excessive illumination, rather than to adapt it to a particular background (56). It is in cephalopods, crustacea and fishes, however, that colour changes are most marked, and these three groups will be treated separately.

Colour Responses of Cephalopods. The chromatophores of cephalopods are localized in the dermis, and are more abundant on the upper surface than below. Their structure is remarkably complex, for each one consists of a central spherical sac surrounded by a system of radially arranged muscle fibres (Fig. 12.1). The sac is a pigment cell with an elastic wall, and it enlarges by contraction of the adherent muscle fibres, and shrinks to a minute sphere due to the elasticity of its wall when the muscle fibres relax and elongate. Within the fibre the fibrils run at acute angles to the cell membrane.

Chromatophore pigments are black or brown, red, orange and yellow in colour. They belong to the recently characterized group of ommo-chromes, which are phenoxazone pigments found previously in insects and crustacea. In *Sepia* the chromatophores lie in three layers, which can be distinguished by the colour of their pigments. In the outer layer the chromatophores contain a bright yellow pigment, in the middle layer an orange-red pigment and in the inner layer a brown or blackish pigment. In addition, there are immobile iridophores which contain iridescent

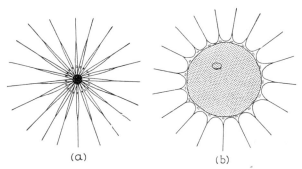

(a)   (b)

FIG. 12.1. CHROMATOPHORES WITH ATTACHED MUSCLE FIBRES
IN THE SKIN OF *Loligo*

In (a) the muscle fibres are relaxed and the pigment cell contracted and punctate; in (b) the muscle fibres are contracted, and the pigment cell expanded. (From Bozler, 1928.)

lamellae, and which form sheets in the skin beneath the other chromato-phores and on many internal organs (36, 51).

The radial muscle fibres are supplied by nerves which control their con-tractions. Stimulation of chromatophoral nerves causes the chromato-phores to expand, and severing the nerves causes the denervated area to become pale. It has been maintained that the muscle fibres can show slow tonic contractions, as well as quick single contractions and tetanus. The initial blanching which follows section of a mantle nerve in cephalopods is succeeded by a gradual darkening of the affected area, and it is the opinion of some workers that this darkening phase is due to peripheral autotonus of the radial muscle fibres. Similarly, when a piece of skin is removed, the chromatophores at first contract but afterwards pass into a state of partial expansion. Electrical stimulation of this isolated piece of skin causes con-traction of the partially expanded chromatophores. Moreover, microscopic examination shows that individual chromatophores in the preparation often exhibit rhythmical pulsations. From one viewpoint the dark phase of the animal results from peripheral autonomous tonicity of the radial muscle fibres, and blanching is due to inhibition of peripheral tonus by inhibitory nerve fibres which originate in the stellate ganglion. Such a scheme involves double innervation of the muscle fibres, motor and inhibitory. Superimposed upon peripheral tonus, however, are twitch contractions and tetanic contractions which can be produced by electrical stimulation of mantle nerves, and which normally are under central con-

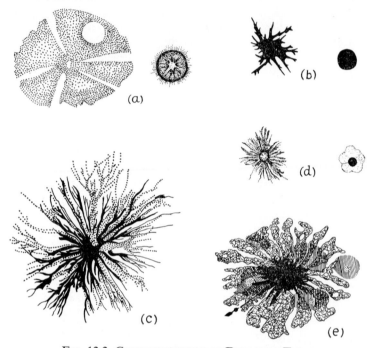

FIG. 12.2. CHROMATOPHORES OF DIFFERENT FISHES

(a) Erythrophores from the red mullet *Mullus barbatus* and *M. surmuletus*, expanded and contracted; (b) melanophores of the rough hound *Mustelus canis*, expanded and contracted; (c) combination of a red (stippled) and a black (solid colour) chromatophore from *Gobius minutus*; (d) melanophores of the weever-fish *Trachinus vipera*—(*left*) expanded, (*right*) contracted and associated with an iridosome; (e) combination of an iridophore (circles), melanophore (solid black), and xanthophores (cross-hatched) in the common goby, *Gobius minutus*. (After Ballowitz, 1913, and Parker, 1937.)

trol. It is these quick contractions that are responsible for rapid colour changes and for the waves of colour which sweep over the animal (56).

Although vision to a large extent controls chromatic changes in cephalopods, enucleated animals still show colour responses, which are no longer adaptive, however. The agencies then involved are the suckers, general tactile receptors and postural influences. When all the suckers are removed, there is considerable loss of tone in the chromatophores and the skin blanches. The chromatophores in the lower surface of the animal are always more contracted than on the upper surface, and experimental analysis has revealed that this is a postural response involving tactile stimulation of the lower surface, and reflex action through the central nervous system.

Sensory impulses from these peripheral fields impinge upon the brain where there is a hierarchy of three chromatic centres, inhibitory and general colour centres in the supra-oesophageal ganglia, and chromatophore motor centres in the suboesophageal ganglia. The supra-oesophageal chromatophore centres are symmetrically disposed, and each may act on either side of the body. These higher centres receive information from optic, tactile and static sense organs. The suboesophageal chromatophore centres—located in four lobes—contain the cell bodies of the chromatophore efferent nerves, which form the final common pathway to these structures. One

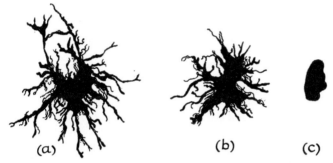

FIG. 12.3. BEHAVIOUR OF A DARK CHROMATOPHORE IN THE SHRIMP
Palaemonetes vulgaris ON DIFFERENT BACKGROUNDS

(*a*) Completely expanded chromatophore on a black background; (*b*) same chromatophore on a white background for 30 min; (*c*) completely contracted chromatophore after shrimp has been on a white background for 2 hours. (Drawn from photographs of Perkins, 1928.)

pair of lobes supplies the chromatophores of the visceral mass; the other, those of the head and arms. Each suboesophageal chromatophore centre innervates only the chromatophores of its own side of the body, and the different centres cannot substitute for one another.

From the motor centres fibres proceed in the several nerve trunks to the periphery of the body. The control of the complex colour changes of these animals through differential activities of several kinds of chromatophores —red, yellow, brown and black—must depend upon several categories of nerve fibres supplying the various kinds of peripheral colour cells, as well as considerable refinement of central control. By means of these discrete nerve fibres, temporal and spatial regulation of colour alterations and neutral shading is accomplished (8, 56).

Colour changes in cephalopods are very rapid, and often take the form of waves passing over the body. Measurements by a photo-electric method have shown that the change from complete contraction to expansion of a chromatophore in *Sepia* occurs in two-thirds of a second (Fig. 12.4) (32). Such sweeping alterations in tones and colours have cryptic value in breaking up the animal's outline, and assist it when darting upon its prey or evading a predator. Holmes (36), who has made a study of colour changes in the cuttlefish *Sepia officinalis*, finds that this animal has a definite series of patterns which are exactly repeated under suitable conditions (Fig. 11.10). These involve a zebra pattern in actively swimming animals over light sandy bottoms; a light mottled pattern when the animal

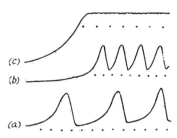

FIG. 12.4. CHROMATOPHORE RESPONSES IN AN ISOLATED PIECE OF SKIN FROM *Sepia*, RECORDED BY PHOTOCELL AND RAPID GALVANOMETER

(*a*) Single twitches, resulting from electrical stimuli at 45/min; (*b*) single twitches, partial summation at about 90/min; (*c*) nearly complete summation at 9·3 shocks/sec. Time marks ⅓ sec. (From Hill and Solandt (32).)

is at rest on sandy bottoms; very dark and extremely pale appearances on black or white backgrounds; and highly contrasted black and white patterns on a black and white background.

When hunting or when disturbed, the cuttlefish shows a whole series of remarkable colour transformations which follow one another in regular succession. Holmes writes (p. 27)—

> If further irritated the animal may respond by a total paling of the whole of its body, and upon this background may appear longitudinal black stripes, at the base of the fins and along the middle of the back. These lines flicker vividly over the pallid back, and then suddenly disappear, to be followed perhaps by a reappearance of the black spots, another total darkening, or a brief reappearance of the zebra pattern. All this time the animal darts about rapidly, as if to avoid the irritation, and its final action when it cannot do so is to eject a cloud of ink. Then at once it becomes motionless, and hides behind the black cloud which it has produced, and its colour can be observed no more.

Some cephalopods can also adapt themselves very well to the colour of their background when at rest. On a green background *Sepia* assumes a greenish tint: the orange chromatophores are contracted, and the black and yellow chromatophores, interacting with some green reflexion from the underlying iridophores, produce a greenish tint. On a yellow or red background the expanded yellow and red chromatophores exclude the iridophore layer. Different shades of grey are due to altered states of the black chromatophores, which expand or contract according to the neutral

tint of the background. Octopuses also display complex colour transformations, whereas squid (*Loligo*) and the paper nautilus (*Argonauta*)
have relatively simple chromatic responses (8, 36, 56).

In the pelagic pteropods such as *Cymbulia* and *Tiedemannia*, there are
chromatophores which are very similar to those of cephalopods. As in the
latter animals they consist of a central pigmented sac surrounded by a
series of radial muscle fibres (56).

Colour Responses of Crustacea. Among the crustacea, chromatophores
occur in copepods, isopods, many amphipods, mysids, euphausiids, and
are particularly characteristic of decapods (Figs. 12.3 and 12.5). An amphipod *Hyperia galba*, which is commensal on medusae, changes colour
according to the incident illumination, and is deep reddish-brown in light

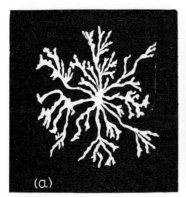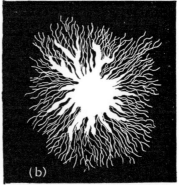

FIG. 12.5. EXPANDED WHITE CHROMATOPHORES IN THE PRAWN *Palaemon*

(*a*) From *Palaemon adspersus*, and (*b*) from *P. serratus*. (Drawn from photographs
of Knowles (41), and Stephenson, 1946.)

and colourless in darkness. Dark animals also become colourless when
attached to medusae or an inanimate object, regardless of the colour of
the background. Schlieper concluded that colour changes are regulated in
Hyperia both by light acting through the eyes, and by tactile stimuli acting
on receptors in the legs. The pale phase is of value to the animal when it is
attached to its host, a transparent medusa (56).

Littoral isopods are provided with chromatophores and demonstrate some
ability to alter their shade and colour. Species of *Ligia* and *Idotea*, which
have been used for experimental studies, have melanophores, xanthophores, guanophores and a non-cellular white pigment as well. *Ligia
oceanica*, *Idotea tricuspidata* and *I. baltica* show well-marked background
responses, darkening on black backgrounds and blanching on white backgrounds. Apart from changes in shade from light to dark, these animals
show no true colour responses to match the tint of the background, and
this is referable to the limited variety of chromatophore pigments present,
Besides these pigments the colour of cuticle and of underlying tissues

contributes to the total coloration of the animal. Only certain colour varieties are capable of background responses. In *I. baltica*, for example, background responses are restricted to animals with light-coloured cuticle (6, 39, 56, 59, 66).

Adaptive colour responses are a notable feature of the behaviour of many decapods. The chromatophores concerned in these changes are multinucleate or syncytial structures lying in the skin, and sometimes at deeper levels. Each chromatophore-group contains one or several kinds of pigments; white, red, yellow and often black, brown and blue. Even in the polychromatic groups the pigments behave independently without inter-mixture. White pigments are guanine, red and yellow pigments, carote-noids, black and brown pigments, melanins. The blue pigment, which

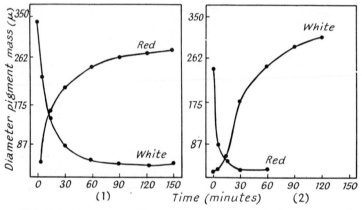

FIG. 12.6. CHROMATOPHORE CHANGES IN THE SHRIMP *Palaemonetes vulgaris* ON BLACK AND WHITE BACKGROUNDS

1. Change in diameter of a red and white pigment mass in an animal taken from a white background and placed upon a black one. 2. Change in diameter of a red and white pigment mass in an animal taken from a black background and placed upon a white one. (From Brown, 1935.)

often appears outside the colour cells in a diffuse condition under certain circumstances, is a carotiprotein. Species differ considerably in the number and relative amounts of chromatophore pigments which they possess, and this conditions the range of their background responses.

Some marine decapods adapt themselves to a wide range of background colours. Thus, *Crangon* can change to conform with white, black, grey, yellow, red and orange backgrounds, and *Palaemonetes* can match back-grounds of black, dark grey, white, blue, green, yellow and red (Fig. 12.6). The crabs *Portunus anceps* and *P. ordwayi* also show a considerable degree of colour adaptation to their backgrounds (Table 12.2), whereas the fiddler crab *Uca pugilator* shows only weak albedo responses. It has been found, however, that *Uca* has a well-marked diurnal rhythm, in which it darkens during the day and blanches at night. Such an inherent rhythm is absent in

TABLE 12.2

State of Chromatophores in the Bermudan Red Crab *Portunus ordwayi* on Backgrounds of Different Colours

C, concentrated; D, dispersed; I, intermediate condition of pigments (from Abramowitz)

Background	Chromatophores			
	White	Black	Yellow	Red
White	D	C	C	C
Black	C	D	D	D
Blue	C	D	C	D
Red	C	D	D	D
Yellow	I	C	D	C
Green	D	D	C	I

Palaemonetes, but *Hippolyte* displays both a daily rhythm and a response to environmental conditions (*see* p. 524). Not all decapods show such colour responses, however. They are absent in *Homarus, Libinia* and *Pagurus*, for example, and old individuals of *Carcinus* lose much of their early ability to change their colour, and chromatophores usually become fully expanded (11, 13).

The blue pigment mentioned above is ephemeral in nature, and in *Hippolyte* is associated with the pale nocturnal phase. Similarly, in *Palaemonetes*, the appearance of the blue pigment is associated with blanching. Thus, when a dark animal is placed on a white background, its red-yellow chromatophores contract, and after a few minutes they become invested by a cloud of bluish pigment which invades the surrounding tissue spaces. The blue coloration lasts about an hour, and then gradually vanishes.

Special alterations in chromatophore patterns occur during the breeding season in certain decapods. In various species of *Palaemon* and *Palaemonetes* the mature females develop special patches of leucophores on the egg-bearing segments during the breeding season. These white pigment cells are located directly over the gonads, and serve to mask the eggs and reduce the shadow which they create (46). In the genus *Uca* there is a general trend towards the development of a dazzling white carapace during the display season. Field studies have shown that bright sun is necessary for the maximal daily development of display-colour, and bright species reach their peak in the tropical eastern Pacific where strong sunlight and high tidal ranges prevail (24).

It is now a well-established fact that the chromatophores of crustacea are under endocrine control and are not directly innervated. In the prawn *Palaemonetes* interruption of the dorsal blood vessel abolishes colour responses in the region behind the cut, and removal of the eye-stalks causes the animal to darken. Injection of extracts of the eye-stalks brings about contraction of the red chromatophores and dispersion of the white chromatophores in a dark animal. These experiments revealed that the eye-stalks contained hormones concerned with regulating the chromatophores.

Within the eyestalk of decapod crustacea there is a neurohaemal organ known as the sinus gland (Fig. 12.7(a)), which is a centre where neurosecretory material, produced elsewhere, is stored and released into the blood stream. In some groups the sinus gland lies elsewhere, in isopods near the optic lobes of the brain. Secretory cells in various parts of the central nervous system (x-organ of the eye-stalk, brain, thoracic ganglia) send axons to the sinus gland, where their swollen terminals form the

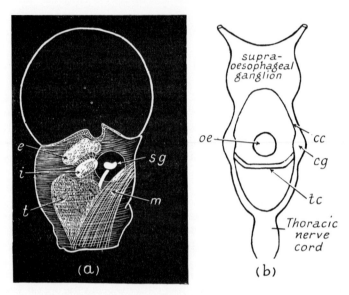

FIG. 12.7. (a). Location of the Sinus Gland in the Eyestalk of the Prawn *Palaemon serratus*. The Right Eye is Viewed from Above, and a Small Aperture has been Cut in the Cuticle above the Sinus Gland (from Knowles, 1950)

(b) Diagrammatic Representation of the Anterior Region of the Nervous System of the Sand Shrimp (*Crangon vulgaris* (from Brown and Ederstrom (15), and Turner (1948).)

cc, circumoesophageal connective; cg, connective ganglion; e, medulla externa; i. medulla interna; m, muscle; oe, oesophagus; sg, sinus gland; t, medulla terminalis; tc, tritocerebral commissure.

secretory mass of the organ. From the manufacturing cells the secretory material (the hormonal precursors) passes down the axons and is stored in the sinus gland, whence it is released into the blood stream when occasion demands. Another important neurosecretory organ of malacostracans occurs in the post-commissure (tritocerebrum) (Fig. 12.7(b)).

Release of hormonal material from the neurosecretory organs is regulated by the nervous system, presumably by the discharge of impulses down the same axons that conduct the secretory material to the storage depots (5, 10, 45).

Various lines of evidence have shown that a multiplicity of chromato-phorotropic principles is involved in the pigment-cell responses of crustacea. The operation of two hormonal principles in *Ligia oceanica* was indicated by different time relations of the background responses. One factor causes blanching of the body (W-factor); the other, darkening (B-factor). Experimental work on decapods has involved studying the effects of extirpation of eye-stalks, injection of extracts, comparison of extracts on different species, and attempts to separate and purify the various chromatophorotropins.

Three physiological groups have been distinguished among higher crustacea on the basis of chromatic changes brought about by removal of eye-stalks and injection of eye-stalk extracts. The first group includes many isopods, mysids and reptant decapods (*Palaemon, Palaemonetes*, etc.). In this group removal of the sinus glands causes the dark chromatophores to disperse and the body to darken. On administration of sinus-gland extract the body blanches as the result of concentration of the dark pigments.

The second group is represented by the sand shrimp *Crangon*. Removal of the eye-stalks in *Crangon* is followed by temporary darkening of the tail and blanching of the remainder of the body. Injection of extracts of the sinus glands into an animal shortly after removal of the eye-stalks brings about concentration of the black pigment in the tail, and the whole body is consequently blanched. The main action of the sinus glands, therefore, is to concentrate the dark pigments and effect blanching of the animal.

The third group includes brachyurans and some isopods. In the fiddler crab *Uca pugilator*, removal of the eye-stalks brings about rapid blanching through concentration of red and black pigments and dispersion of the white pigment. Injection of sinus-gland extract into crabs from which the eye-stalks have been removed causes darkening although the white pigment remains dispersed.

Brown distinguished three different chromatophorotropins in the sinus gland, varying in relative concentrations or effectiveness in different groups. One of these principles has a marked effect in expanding the dark chromatophores, and is referred to as the *Uca*-darkening hormone. A second factor shows a pronounced effect in concentrating the red chromatophores of *Palaemonetes*, and is known as the *Palaemonetes*-lightening hormone. These two factors were partially isolated by treating extracts of sinus glands with ethanol. By this procedure were obtained two factors: one, alcohol-soluble, causing concentration of the red pigment in *Palaemonetes*, and another, alcohol-insoluble, having a pronounced effect in causing dispersion of the black pigment in *Uca*. These two principles, *Uca*-darkening and *Palemonetes*-lightening, have been recognized in the sinus glands of all three physiological groups distinguished above (shrimps *Palaemonetes* and *Crangon*; hermit crab *Pagurus*; blue crab *Callinectes*; shore crab *Carcinus*).

The sinus glands of *Crangon* also yield yet another factor, relatively insoluble in alcohol. When injected into eye-stalkless animals, it results in concentration of red and black pigments in the telson and uropods and, consequently, lightening of the tail. This principle is known as the *Crangon* tail-lightening hormone. It occurs in the sinus glands of the first two groups, but is absent from the third group (brachyurans) (11, 13).

Subsequent evidence has shown that chromatophorotropins are also secreted in other parts of the nervous system. When the central stubs of eye-stalkless animals are stimulated electrically, changes in coloration result, indicating the release of chromatophorotropins from sources other than the sinus glands. Extracts of the tritocerebral commissure of *Crangon* contain two principles, a body-lightening hormone and a body-and-tail-darkening hormone. These same factors have been identified in the central nervous system of many other malacostraca. The *Uca*-darkening hormone, previously recorded in the sinus gland, occurs in optic and supra-oesophageal ganglia, whereas a white-pigment-concentrating principle is most concentrated in the circumoesophageal connectives (7, 14, 63).

The complex picture of chromatophore control which is now emerging may be underlined by reference to the prawn *Palaemon serratus* which contains many types of chromatophores, differing in position, shape and colour. These are differently affected by extracts of sinus glands and post-commissures, and at least five, and possibly more, factors appear to be involved in their concentration and dispersion (43, 44, 64).

Partial separation of the chromatophorotropins of *P. serratus* by electrophoresis has yielded two substances, one of which concentrates all the red pigments of the body, and another which concentrates the large red chromatophores and disperses the small red chromatophores of the body and tail. They are possibly hormonal precursors giving rise to more mobile agents that produce specific responses of each kind of chromatophore (48).

The control of crustacean chromatophores, although solely hormonal, is nevertheless extremely complicated. Five or more chromatophorotropins are involved, some of which have antagonistic effects. They occur both in the sinus glands and in other regions of the central nervous system. Some are found in all crustacea examined; others are more restricted in distribution. Although the total effect of these various chromatophorotropins has not been determined for all the pigment cells of each group, it would seem that the multiplicity of factors involved should eventually provide an explanation for the intricate combination of chromatophore movements that go to make up the complex colour responses of these animals (22, 27, 47).

Colour Responses of Fishes. The lower marine vertebrates characteristically possess chromatophores, and respond by colour changes to alterations in their environment (Fig. 12.2). The hagfish *Myxine glutinosa* becomes dark on a black background in two or three days, and blanches on a white ground. Colour changes in elasmobranchs are also rather slow, for example, the European dogfish *Scyliorhinus canicula* requires three to four days to change from pale to dark, or to make the reverse change. Certain dark species of selachians—*Torpedo torpedo, Raja clavata,* and *R. batis*—show little or no capacity for colour changes when placed on white backgrounds. The responses of the smooth hound *Mustelus canis,* on the other hand, are fairly rapid, for the animals change from pale to dark in two hours, and from dark to pale in two days. The chromatophores involved in these activities are epidermal and dermal melanophores, dermal xanthophores, guanophores and a third class of light-brown chromato-

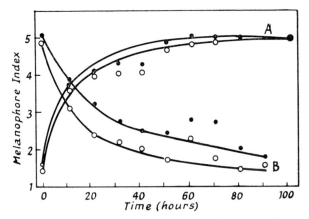

FIG. 12.8. BACKGROUND RESPONSES IN THE EUROPEAN DOGFISH
Scyliorhinus canicula

Hollow circles, dermal melanophores; solid circles, epidermal melanophores. The upper curve *A* shows the degree of dispersion undergone by melanophores on transferring a fish from a white to a black background. The lower curve, *B,* shows the melanin concentration which occurs on changing from a black to a white background. (Redrawn from Waring (70).)

phores. Of these the dermal melanophores are chiefly responsible for colour changes (Fig. 12.8). In some species, such as the nurse-hound *Scyliorhinus stellaris,* the chromatophores are spatially organized to form specific colour patterns (56).

In general the chromatophores of selachian fish are under pituitary control, as was first demonstrated by Lundstrom and Bard. Removal of the pituitary gland in *Mustelus canis* and *Squalus acanthias* is followed by permanent blanching of the fish, and melanophore expansion is brought about by subsequent injection of pituitary extract. The hormone responsible for expansion of the melanophores and darkening of the skin in *Mustelus* and other selachians is known as B-substance or intermedine. Its production has been traced to the neuro-intermediate lobe of the pituitary gland (2, 35, 54, 55, 71, 72).

Although the pituitary gland, responding to stimulation through the eyes, brings about darkening of the fish, it is still uncertain what mechanism is responsible for blanching. One important, perhaps sole, factor is a decrease in the concentration of intermedine in the circulation. Parker has shown that when part of a dark young *Mustelus* is perfused with Ringer's solution, the perfused area becomes lighter, due to loss of chromatophore-expanding substance, intermedine, from the tissues. A further mechanism has been proposed by Hogben and Waring, namely that the anterior lobe of the pituitary produces a chromatophore-concentrating or W-substance, which brings about blanching of the fish. When the anterior lobe of the pituitary is removed from a dark specimen of *Raja* or *Scyliorhinus*, no change in colour results, but when the same operation is carried out on a pale fish, the animal darkens even when kept on a white background (2, 56, 70, 71).

In addition to pituitary control of chromatophore responses, Parker considers that in one species at least, *Mustelus canis*, the chromatophores are also regulated by concentrating nerve fibres. When a transverse cut is made in the pectoral fin of this fish a pale band appears distal to the incision, and a similar pale band can be produced by cutting or by electrical stimulation of peripheral nerves. These effects are ascribed to excitation of nerve fibres which elicit contraction of the chromatophores. Similar results have not been obtained with species of *Squalus*, *Raja* or *Scyliorhinus*. Now, the innervation of chromatophores in vertebrates is by way of the sympathetic nervous system. In elasmobranchs, however, grey rami that would normally carry such fibres to the spinal nerves, and thence to the skin, are absent; such sympathetic fibres as do run to the periphery accompany blood vessels, with which they are concerned (52, 54, 55, 77, 81).

In summary, physiological colour changes in selachians are restricted and limited in extent and only certain species show background responses. Colour changes in general are rather slow, and may require several days to reach completion. The chromatophores are controlled by the level of pituitary hormones in the blood. Intermedine, from the intermediate lobe, brings about chromatophore expansion and darkening of the fish. Even in dark species like *Torpedo torpedo*, which show no responses to changes in background, the pituitary is responsible for maintaining the expanded condition of the chromatophores.

Teleosts. The colour responses of many teleosts form very characteristic features of their behaviour. The chromatophores responsible include melanophores containing brown or black melanin pigments, xanthophores and erythrophores containing yellow and red carotenoids, reddish allophores, and guanophores containing guanine. The pigment cells are located in the epidermis and dermis and, in particular, form two well-defined layers at the upper and lower boundaries of the dermis (Fig. 12.9). Their distribution and relative numbers vary from species to species; frequently they are organized in grouped associations of melanophores with iridosomes, xanthophores or erythrophores. In their fully contracted condition the melanophores appear as dark spots, but when expanded they assume a variety of radiate and stellate shapes which are characteristic of each species. Other kinds of chromatophores show similar peculiarities of form (Fig. 12.2) (29, 56).

Perhaps some of the most striking colour changes among teleosts are to be seen in certain tropical reef fishes such as the sea-perches (*Epinephelus*), which have a whole series of colour phases, and can switch from one to another in the course of a few minutes. The Nassau grouper *E. striatus* has eight different colour liveries which vary from one very dark phase to one creamy white, and intermediate phases dark above, light below, with variegated markings and bands in shifting patterns (Fig. 11.9). These several colour phases have considerable cryptic value against the

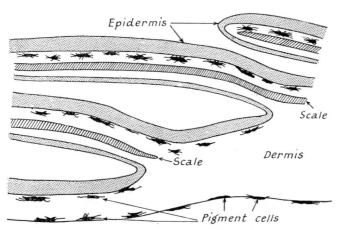

Fig. 12.9. Section through the Skin of a Teleost, Based on the Pollack *Gadus pollachius*, to Show the Arrangement of Pigment Cells. (After Schnakenbeck, 1926.)

multicoloured backgrounds of the coral reefs. Indeed Longley, in his submarine researches, records how he was able to evoke different colour phases in reef fishes by leading individuals, with offers of food, from one kind of environment to another (23, 50, 69).

Flat fishes (pleuronectids) are noteworthy for the complexity of their colour responses, adapting the fish in colour, shade and pattern to its background. As a result of these changes the animals are rendered well-nigh invisible on the muddy, sandy or gravelly bottoms which they frequent, and the resemblance is heightened by the tendency of the animals to bury themselves partially in the substratum. In experiments carried out with the Mediterranean flounder *Bothus podas* on backgrounds with various checkerboard patterns, the fish were found to harmonize very closely with the patterns used; colour changes, however, were restricted to the black, brown, grey and white tints of its normal environment. More remarkable is the American flounder *Paralichthys albiguttus* which simulates very closely artificial backgrounds made up of regular black and white areas.

On the skin of the fish, areas appear similar in size and shape to the background, without, however, any actual reproduction of the figures (Fig. 11.9). Moreover, on blue, green, yellow, orange, pink and brown backgrounds the flounders become coloured in tones very similar to those of the bottom. Red tints, however, are not accurately copied (Fig. 12.10) (56).

Other species with striking colour changes are the wrasse *Crenilabrus roissali*, which appears in hues of blue, green, yellow and red; and the killifish *Fundulus heteroclitus*, which changes in shade from light grey to

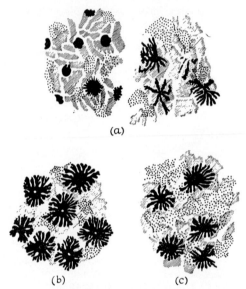

(a)

(b)   (c)

FIG. 12.10. CHANGES IN THE CHROMATOPHORES (MELANOPHORES AND XANTHO-PHORES) OF THE AMERICAN FLOUNDER OR GULF FLUKE *Paralichthys albiguttus*, ON DIFFERENT BACKGROUNDS

Guanophores, cross-hatched; xanthophores, stippled; melanophores, solid black. (*a*) Two regions from a specimen on a white background; (*b*) specimen on a black background; (*c*) specimen on a yellow background. (Redrawn from Kuntz, 1917.)

dark, and assumes tints of pink, yellow, green or blue on appropriate backgrounds. Light and dark neutral tints result from contraction and expansion of melanophores; whereas matching of coloured backgrounds involves appropriate movements of erythrophores and xanthophores, and the interplay of light effects from the guanophores as well. In *Fundulus heteroclitus*, for example, the yellow chromatophores partly expanded over the blue guanophores of the stratum argenteum give the green colour seen in fish which have been retained on a green background. In fish kept on blue backgrounds the xanthophores are maximally contracted, revealing the blue stratum argenteum beneath. Similar histological transformations have been described in the flounder (Fig. 12.10).

Though usually regarded as static, the guanophores of some fishes may show movements similar to other chromatophores. Guanine crystals in the iridocytes or guanophores of *Gobius minutus*, *Callionymus lyra* and *Fundulus heteroclitus* are able to concentrate and disperse within the cells. The guanophores also appear to expand on white backgrounds, and contract on black ones, responses the reverse of those occurring in melanophores. However, the behaviour of guanophores is poorly understood (56).

The rapidity with which colour changes are accomplished in different species shows much variation and is some index of the effectiveness of nervous control over this response. In the American summer and winter flounders *Paralichthys dentatus* and *Pseudopleuronectes americanus*, the animals change from pale to dark in 1–5 days, and make the reverse change

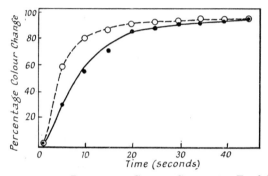

FIG. 12.11. PHOTOELECTRIC RECORDS OF COLOUR CHANGES IN *Fundulus heteroclitus* ON SUDDENLY CHANGING THE COLOUR OF THE BACKGROUND

Hollow circles, light background, fish turning yellow. Solid circles, dark background, fish turning brown. (Redrawn from Hill, Parkinson and Solandt (31).)

in 2–7 days. It is noteworthy, however, that these times are shortened by repetition, and in a specimen of the gulf fluke *Paralichthys albiguttus*, which was repeatedly transferred from black to white, and vice versa, the time in which a background response occurred was reduced from 5 days to less than 2 min. In the cunner *Tautogolabrus adspersus* blanching and darkening are carried out in 50 min, and in the common killifish *Fundulus heteroclitus* in 40–60 sec (Fig. 12.11). Some times recorded for expansion and contraction of erythrophores are still more rapid, being accomplished in 15 sec in the sea robin *Prionotus strigatus* and 22 sec in the squirrel fish *Holocentrus ascensionis* (31, 53).

The chromatophores of teleosts have long been known to be under some degree of nervous control. In a pioneer study on the turbot *Scophthalmus maximus* Pouchet showed that by interrupting the sympathetic chain or specific nerves the peripheral field distal to the injury darkened through melanophore expansion, thus indicating that nervous impulses normally cause the chromatophores to contract (Fig. 12.12). Subsequently, Ballowitz demonstrated the rich innervation of these structures.

The nervous supply of the chromatophores is derived from the sympathetic system. There are chromatic centres in the c.n.s. and from these
centres nerve tracts run through the cord. The efferent fibres have the usual
arrangement characteristic of the sympathetic system, and arise from pre-
ganglionic neurones in the lateral cord. They enter the vertebral ganglia via
white rami communicantes, and form synapses there with post-ganglionic
neurones (Fig. 3.1). The fibres continue their course through sympathetic
trunks, and finally enter grey rami to reach the spinal nerves, in which they

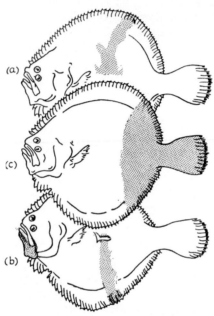

Fig. 12.12. The Effects of Interrupting Peripheral and Sympathetic
Nerves on Coloration of the Turbot Scophthalmus (Rhombus) maximus

(a) Darkening of an area of the skin as the result of cutting spinal nerve branches;
(b) darkening of an area of the body and chin, as the result of cutting spinal nerve
branches and the inferior maxillary branch of the trigeminus; (c) darkening of the
posterior region as the result of destruction of the sympathetic chain in the posterior
haemal canal. (From Pouchet, 1876.)

extend to their terminations about the chromatophores in the skin. It has
been found that the pre-ganglionic chromatic fibres emerge from the cord
at a restricted level, in Crenilabrus pavo, for example, at the eighth vertebra.
On reaching the sympathetic chain they take ascending and descending
paths, and form synapses with many post-ganglionic neurones along their
course. Descending fibres enter the tail and ascending fibres finally enter
the head, whence they reach the periphery through cranial nerves.

The mechanism of nervous control of chromatophores in teleosts has
been investigated by nerve section, stimulation and the effect of "autono-

mic" drugs. When peripheral nerves are cut (*Pleuronectes, Pseudopleuro-nectes, Fundulus*), dark dermal bands appear in a few minutes due to expansion of the paralysed melanophores. The extent of the region affected corresponds to the area innervated by the interrupted sympathetic nerve fibres. Electrical stimulation of the nerves proximal to the injury is without effect, but stimulation distally causes the denervated region to blanch. Moreover, when such an experimental animal is transferred to white sur-roundings, the denervated region no longer participates in the general blanching which ensues in the remainder of the body. The affected area remains dark for several days (two to three days in *Fundulus heteroclitus*) and then gradually fades. It is concluded that in a normal animal the sympathetic nerve fibres exert a tonic contracting effect on the melano-phores. When the peripheral tonus is diminished or removed, as the result

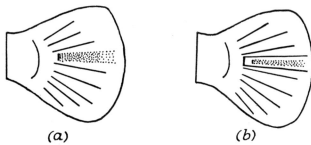

(a) (b)

Fig. 12.13 (a). Caudal Fin of a Killifish *Fundulus*, Showing a Dark band Produced by a Transverse Cut near the Base of the Tail. (b). A Faded Band in the Tail of a Killifish within which a New Short Cut has been Made. This Cut has Induced the Formation of a New Dark Band Distal to the Injury. (From Parker, 1934.)

of stimulation of the eye by a dark background, or artificially by nerve section, the chromatophores expand. On a light background, however, the resultant retinal stimulation leads to an inhibition of the original inhibition, the tonic state reasserts itself and the melanophores become concentrated (62, 71).

An alternative theory has been advanced by Parker who believes that the chromatophores of teleosts are subject to dual nervous control by antagonistic fibres, one category causing contraction of the colour cells, the other expansion. If a small transverse cut is made near the base of the caudal fin of the killifish *Fundulus* so as to sever the caudal nerves but still avoid the major blood vessels, a dark band appears in the fin distal to the incision (Fig. 12.13). When this fish is kept on a light background for several days the band gradually fades away, but a new cut peripheral to the former injury brings about a revival of the original dark band. Interruption of the chromatic fibres at the spinal level in a light-adapted fish with a faded tail band results in dispersion of the normal melanophores; this is followed by dispersion of the melanophores in the tail band, beginning at the margin (minnow *Phoxinus*). An explanation advanced to account for these facts is that dispersing nerve fibres are present as well as concentrating nerve fibres, and that the injury initiates a stream of impulses in the dispersing fibres. Fading is due to diminution of impulses in these nerve fibres, which are stimulated anew by a fresh cut. Alternatively, the injury may release the melanophores from the control of concentrating fibres and allow an inherent dispersing tendency in the melanophores to operate (30, 57).

Other observations based on fin cutting and electrical stimulation have been explained on the basis of concentrating and dispersing nerve fibres. During the regeneration period which follows tail injury in *Fundulus*, the melanophores show differential behaviour. On black or white backgrounds some of the chromatic cells are capable of complete concentration but not full expansion; some respond by full pigment dispersion but incomplete concentration; some react normally by complete dispersion and concentration; others fail to show any response. These results are explained on the basis of differences in the regeneration of individual nerve fibres: some melanophores have received one or other kind of nerve fibre but not both; others have regained both dispersing and concentrating fibres; while other cells still lack innervation (1, 71).

Additional evidence for the innervation of melanophores has been sought in the effects of drugs which simulate the action of autonomic fibres. Adrenaline and ephedrine cause the melanophores to contract; after treatment with ergotoxine (which blocks the action of adrenaline), the melanophores expand to adrenaline. Acetylcholine, pilocarpine and eserine induce melanophore expansion. Certain differences exist in the behaviour of the species tested with these drugs (*Fundulus*, *Salmo*, *Pleuronectes*, etc.). The action of acetylcholine is linked with the activity of dispersing nerve fibres, and that of adrenaline with concentrating nerve fibres, which are regarded as adrenergic. Teleosts, it may be noted, also possess suprarenal glands located in the anterior kidney region, and adrenaline secretion from these structures possibly contributes to the temporary pallor accompanying handling or excitement (65).

Apart from adrenaline the chromatophores of teleosts are subject to some degree of hormonal control from the pituitary gland. The intermediate lobe produces intermedine or B-substance which affects the degree of dispersion of the melanophores. In more primitive teleosts such as *Anguilla*, posterior pituitary extracts bring about dispersion of melanin and darkening, whereas in other fishes such as *Fundulus* and *Pseudopleuronectes* it is without effect. On the other hand, if a *Fundulus* having a pale denervated area of skin is tested, that region darkens. Thus, there is some evidence that the melanophores are sensitive to intermedine in this species. Intermedine is concerned with maintenance of a dark condition on a dark background—the dark background response—in certain teleosts, and there is accumulating evidence for a melanophore-concentrating hormone in the pituitary of teleosts, as well. This occurs in a region known as the mesoadenohypophysis, and it brings about concentration of melanin in some species. It, in turn, may be concerned with maintenance of the light-background response (27, 56, 61, 71, 72).

In *Fundulus* and in many other teleosts the dominant mechanism of chromatophore control is nervous, and this has to a large degree supplanted the more primitive method of hypophysial regulation. Loss of the hypophysis is without effect on the colour response of *Fundulus*, which is still able to change from pale to dark on a black background and to make the reverse change on a white background, as well as a normal fish. The times of these colour changes are very rapid, occurring in one or two minutes, in contrast to the lengthy periods of several hours required for colour changes in elasmobranchs, where the chromatophores are regulated by pituitary secretions (71).

The xanthophores and erythrophores of teleosts respond to background changes independently of the melanophores. In *Fundulus* and in *Holocentrus* it has been found that colour bands involving lipophores can be produced by incisions in the fins, and the presence of antagonistic nerve fibres bringing about concentration or dispersion of lipophores has been assumed on the basis of the same kind of evidence as that obtained in the study of melanophore innervation. In the case of the erythrophores of *Holocentrus,* electrical stimulation of the medulla causes contraction, and section of peripheral nerves brings about expansion of the colour cells. The last result appears to be due to cessation of tonic concentrating impulses. Pituitary extracts made from *Holocentrus* are without effect on the erythrophores. The xanthophores of *Fundulus*, however, are dispersed by intermedine (28, 53).

Apart from background responses chromatophores are also involved in the nuptial coloration of teleosts. These breeding liveries, in the male or female, result from localized accumulations of melanophores or lipophores in definite patterns, or from regulation of the degree of chromatophore expansion. For example, in males of *Fundulus* a dark ocellus appearing on the dorsal fin during the breeding period represents a massing of melanophores. In the Adriatic perch *Serranus scriba*, the nuptial dress can be produced by pituitary extracts, which bring about peripheral expansion of lipophores (56, 60).

The Japanese labrid *Halichoeres poecilopterus* shows pronounced sexual dimorphism, and the mature males acquire a permanent colour pattern which is markedly dissimilar from that of the female (p. 490; Fig. 11.7). These colour patterns are brought about by differences in the arrangement and relative numbers of various chromatophores in the skin. In the normal male, melanophores and guanophores are scattered over the whole scale, and the former are greatly expanded. Together with the xanthophores they are responsible for the bottle-green colour of the body. The tail is bluish in colour due to guanophores, and bears reddish spots resulting from concentrations of erythrophores. The appearance of sexual coloration in the male parallels the hypertrophy of interstitial tissue in the testis, and castration causes a reversion of coloration in the male to the immature and female condition. In consequence the melanophores on the body contract and degenerate along with guanophores. Xanthophores gradually disappear over the body and are replaced by erythrophores, and a reverse change takes place in the tail. As a result the fish becomes reddish in colour, with a yellow tail. Kinoshita (37) concludes that testicular hormones are responsible for maintaining the sexual coloration of the male fish.

In the gobiid *Chloea sarchynnis* of Japan, it is the female which develops sexual coloration during the spring breeding period. In this condition the lower jaw, throat, ventral fin and anal fin become jet black. The alteration in colour is due to a localized increase in the number of melanophores, increased melanin content and melanophore expansion. Assumption of breeding dress is paralleled by an increase in ovarian interstitial tissue, and the changes in melanophores characteristic of the breeding dress can be induced by injection of oestrogenic preparations (38).

In summary it may be said that the primary receptor for chromatophore responses in teleosts is the eye, and photic stimulation of this organ gives rise to impulses which are registered in the brain and which lead to colour responses through the autonomic nervous system. Efferent impulses from the c.n.s. may follow either one of two pathways, through the hypophysial stalk to the pituitary body, or through rami communicantes to the sympathetic trunks and peripheral nerves. The intermediate lobe of the pituitary secretes a chromatophorotropic hormone, intermedine, which causes melanophore expansion, but in many fishes this mechanism is overridden by nervous control. Concentrating nerve fibres cause melanophore contraction, and when these are cut the pigment cells are paralysed and expand. Dispersing nerve fibres have also been postulated, but the evidence is indirect and unsatisfactory. Xanthophores and erythrophores are also subject to nervous and hormonal control, and respond independently of the melanophores.

RHYTHMIC COLOUR CHANGES

Many animals show a persistent daily rhythm in chromatic activity, even under conditions of constant illumination or constant darkness. Such rhythms may last for long periods, at least four to eight weeks in test animals (isopods, crabs) held in the dark. In *Uca pugilator* (the fiddler crab) there is an endogenous diurnal rhythm in which the animals darken by day and blanch by night: the changes in hue are produced by dispersion of the black and white pigments in the day phase of the cycle, and concentration of the same pigments in the night phase of the cycle. So strong is the diurnal rhythm in this species that it largely masks the background response. These daily changes in the chromatic behaviour of crustacea depend upon an endogenous rhythm in the secretion of chromatophorotropins. Diurnal rhythms of crustacea have attracted most attention, but chromatic rhythms also have been discovered in various lower vertebrates.

A diurnal rhythm, partially concealed by responses to background and incident illumination, may reveal itself in various ways. Animals in day and night phases may show differences in degree of response to injected chromatophorotropins, or there may be a strengthening of those background responses which correspond with the phase of the rhythm then operating, and a weakening of those which are antagonistic. Thus, crabs having diurnal chromatic rhythms adapt more readily to an illuminated

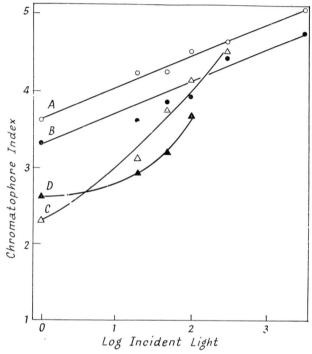

FIG. 12.14. DIURNAL RHYTHMICITY IN CHROMATOPHORE MOVEMENTS
OF THE FIDDLER CRAB *Uca pugilator*

The curves show the relations between chromatophore indices of melanophores and log of light intensities ("foot-candles") for animals as follows: *A*, day phase on a white background; *B*, day phase on a black background; *C*, night phase on a white background; *D*, night phase on a black background. The influence of an endogenous diurnal rhythm is indicated by the vertical distances between the curves *A* and *C*, and *B* and *D*, at any one level of illumination. In the day rhythm of the diurnal cycle the dark pigment is dispersed more than in the night phase. (From Brown and Sandeen (1948).)

black background during the day phase, and to an illuminated white background during the night phase, corresponding to an endogenous rhythm of darkening by day and blanching by night (Fig. 12.14).

The centre responsible for the periodicity of chromatic changes maintains its rhythm for long periods in the absence of light, but its activity can be altered by certain changes in illumination. The chromatophore rhythm of the fiddler crab *Uca pugnax* persists in constant darkness, but it is gradually inhibited by constant illumination. Under the latter condition the amplitude of the melanophore fluctuations declines to a degree which varies inversely with the intensity of illumination. A shift of six hours forwards or backwards in the timing of the rhythm can be produced in the fiddler crab by altering the timing of illumination (e.g. advancing the time of illumination six hours). Such a rhythm, six hours out of phase, may persist for several days in constant darkness. But repeated exposures to illumination by night and darkness by day are necessary to obtain reversal of the chromatophore rhythm.

The basic centre responsible for the chromatophore rhythm of crustacea retains its inherent periodicity even in the absence of rhythmic chromatophore movements. This factor becomes apparent when fiddler crabs, in which periodic chromatic movements have become weakened by prolonged illumination, are returned to darkness. The single change, from constant light to darkness in such animals, causes the reappearance of regular chromatophore fluctuations, and the time of change determines the time of occurrence of a given phase in the re-established rhythm.

Supplementary to the diurnal chromatic rhythm there is a persistent tidal rhythm with a periodicity of 12·4 hours in crabs (*Callinectes*, *Uca*). The simultaneous occurrence of these two rhythms, diurnal and tidal, results in semilunar cycles having a frequency of 14·8 days, at which intervals the diurnal and tidal rhythms are in the same phase relative to one another. Under constant laboratory conditions the tidal rhythm maintains phasing which bears a definite relationship to times of high and low tides in the normal habitat (16, 17, 19, 21, 26, 33, 73, 74).

FUNCTION OF COLOUR CHANGES

The biological significance of colour changes in adapting the animal to its background has already been discussed in this and the preceding chapter. The response may take the form of alterations in tone or shade, colour and pattern, as in many decapod crustacea and fish. In cephalopods and teleosts there are many species in which colour changes have a disruptive effect in breaking up the body outline and are suited to particular environments. Disturbance and excitement also evoke a range of colour patterns in these animals, and it is suggested that the colour changes serve to distract or confuse predators or prey (Figs. 11.9 and 11.10). Moreover, it appears that in some species, individual animals in particular colour phases are able to choose backgrounds to which they bear colour resemblance. The chameleon-prawn *Hippolyte varians* exhibits manifold alterable colour phases, green, brown, reddish and other tints, and can also assume patterns suitable for different backgrounds. Under experimental conditions it was found that certain colour varieties selected particular coloured plants, thus green prawns favoured green *Zostera*, brown ones brown *Halidrys* and *Dictyota*, and reddish specimens red *Gigartina* and *Griffithsia*.

Experimental verification of the effectiveness of colour changes in concealing fish from predators is available in the work of Sumner (67). This investigator employed mosquito fishes *Gambusia patruelis*, a fresh- and brackish-water species. Specimens were placed on white or black backgrounds for seven weeks to bring about morphological colour changes and to accentuate light and dark phases. They were then placed in white or black tanks where they were exposed to attacks by the Galapagos penguin *Spheniscus mendiculus*. Pale and dark fish were placed in each tank, where they were attacked by penguins, and the number of survivors recorded. Of a total of 1,726 fish it was found that 43% were eaten by the penguins. In the white tank 61% of the fish captured were in the dark phase and 39% were pale. In the black tank 26% of the fishes captured were dark and 74% were pale. The results show that pale fishes had an advantage in escaping predation on a white background and dark fishes had an advantage on a black background.

Other functions of chromatophores may now be considered. The primary response, in which chromatophores expand when the animal is illuminated, independently of background conditions, is found in the larvae of some fish, for example pleuronectids, in which it is succeeded in the adult by secondary background responses, and also occurs in some lower forms. A primary response in the polychaete *Platynereis dumerili*, and the echinoids *Centrostephanus longispinus* and *Arbacia pustulosa*, has been described above. The black and white chromatophores of the fiddler crab *Uca pugilator* are normally dispersed in the daytime, and concentrated at night. These conditions are determined by several factors, an endogenous diurnal rhythm, and a response to total illumination which results in increased dispersion of both black and white pigments as the intensity of illumination increases. Certain crustacea living in brightly illuminated surface waters among Sargassum weed, such as *Latreutes fucorum*, *Palaemon tenuicornis* and *Hippolyte acuminata*, are richly provided with leucophores, which form a very effective reflecting screen. Expansion of chromatophores in these animals would seem to have the function of protecting their living tissues against the harmful effects of actinic rays (40).

Another environmental response attributed to chromatophores is that of temperature regulation. In a submerged animal this would be of little consequence because of the great heat-absorbing capacity of water, but it may be a physiological factor in littoral forms periodically exposed to the air. In *Uca* the black pigments tend to concentrate as the temperature is raised, and the white pigments to disperse: these chromatophore movements lead to a condition in which there is reduced light absorption and increased reflexion, particularly at longer wave-lengths. Indeed, dark fiddler crabs, in air and exposed to sunlight, develop a body temperature 2°C higher than that of pale crabs (75).

REFERENCES

1. ABRAMOWITZ, A. A., "The double innervation of caudal melanophores in *Fundulus*," *Proc. Nat. Acad. Sci.*, **22**, 233 (1936).
2. ABRAMOWITZ, A. A., "The pituitary control of chromatophores in the dogfish," *Amer. Nat.*, **73**, 208 (1939).
3. ABRAMOWITZ, A. A., "Color changes in animals," *Tabul. Biol.*, **17**, 267 (1939).
4. BARRINGTON, E. J. W., *An Introduction to General and Comparative Endocrinology* (Oxford, Clarendon Press, 1963).
5. BLISS, D. E., DURAND, J. B. and WELSH, J. H., "Neurosecretory systems in decapod crustacea," *Z. Zellforsch.*, **39**, 520 (1954).
6. BOCQUET, C., LÉVI, C. and TEISSIER, G., "Recherches sur le polychromatisme de *Sphaeroma serratum* (F.)," *Arch. Zool. Exp. Gén.*, **87**, 245 (1951).
7. BOWMAN, T. E., "Chromatophorotropins in the central nervous organs of the crab, *Hemigrapsus oregonensis*," *Biol. Bull.*, **96**, 238 (1949).
8. BOYCOTT, B. B., "The chromatophore system of cephalopods," *Proc. Linn. Soc. Lond.*, **164** (2), 235 (1953).
9. BREDER, C. M. and RASQUIN, P., "A preliminary report on the role of the pineal organ in the control of pigment cells and light reactions in recent teleost fishes," *Science*, **111**, 10 (1950).
10. BROWN, F. A. JR., "Humoral control of crustacean chromatophores," *Amer. Nat.*, **73**, 247 (1939).
11. BROWN, F. A. JR., "Hormones in the crustacea: their sources and activities," *Quart. Rev. Biol.*, **19**, 32, 118 (1944).
12. BROWN, F. A. JR., "The source and activity of *Crago*-darkening hormone (CDH)," *Physiol. Zool.*, **19**, 215 (1946).
13. BROWN, F. A. JR., "Hormones in crustaceans," in Vol. I, *The Hormones*, Ed. Pincus, G. and Thimann, K. V. (N.Y., Academic Press, 1948).
14. BROWN, F. A. JR., "Studies on the physiology of *Uca* red chromatophores," *Biol. Bull.*, **98**, 218 (1950).
15. BROWN, F. A. JR and EDERSTROM, H. E., "Dual control of certain black chromatophores of *Crago*," *J. Exp. Zool.*, **85**, 53 (1940).
16. BROWN, F. A. JR., FINGERMAN, M. and HINES, M. N., "A study of the mechanism involved in shifting the phases of the endogenous daily rhythm by light stimuli," *Biol. Bull.*, **106**, 308 (1954).
17. BROWN, F. A. JR., FINGERMAN, M., SANDEEN, M. I. and WEBB, H. M., "Persistent diurnal and tidal rhythms of color change in the fiddler crab, *Uca pugnax*," *J. Exp. Zool.*, **123**, 29 (1953).
18. BROWN, F. A. JR., GUYSELMAN, J. B. and SANDEEN, M. I., "Black chromatophores of *Uca* as independent effectors," *Anat. Rec.*, **105**, 616 (1949).
19. BROWN, F. A. JR. and HINES, M. N., "Modifications in the diurnal pigmentary rhythm of *Uca* effected by continuous illumination," *Physiol. Zool.*, **25**, 56 (1952).
20. BROWN, F. A. JR. and SAIGH, L. M., "The comparative distribution of two chromatophorotropic hormones (CDH and CBLH) in crustacean nervous systems," *Biol. Bull.*, **91**, 170 (1946).
21. BROWN, F. A. JR., WEBB, H. M., BENNETT, M. F. and SANDEEN, M. I., "Temperature-independence of the frequency of the endogenous tidal rhythm of *Uca*," *Physiol. Zool.*, **27**, 345 (1954).

22. CARLISLE, D. B. and KNOWLES, F. G. W., *Crustacean Endocrine Control* (Cambridge Univ. Press, 1959).
23. COTT, H. B., *Adaptive Coloration in Animals* (London, Methuen, 1940).
24. CRANE, J., "On the color changes of fiddler crabs (genus *Uca*) in the field," *Zoologica, N.Y.*, **29**, 161 (1944).
25. ENAMI, M., "The sources and activities of two chromatophorotropic hormones in crabs of the genus *Sesarma*. 1. Experimental analyses," *Biol. Bull.*, **100**, 28 (1951).
26. FINGERMAN, M., "Persistent daily and tidal rhythms of color change in *Callinectes sapidus*," ibid., **109**, 255 (1955).
27. FINGERMAN, M., "Chromatophores," Physiol. Rev., **45**, 296 (1965).
28. FRIES, E. F. B., "Pituitary and nervous control of pigmentary effectors, especially in xanthophores, in killifish (*Fundulus*)," *Physiol. Zool.*, **16**, 199 (1943).
29. GOODRICH, H. B., "Chromatophores in relation to genetic and specific distinctions," *Amer. Nat.*, **73**, 198 (1939).
30. GRAY, E. G., "Control of the melanophores of the minnow (*Phoxinus phoxinus*)," *J. Exp. Biol.*, **33**, 448 (1956).
31. HILL, A. V., PARKINSON, J. L. and SOLANDT, D. Y., "Photoelectric records of the colour change in *Fundulus heteroclitus*,' ibid., **12**, 397 (1935).
32. HILL, A. V. and SOLANDT, D. Y., "Myograms from the chromatophores of *Sepia*," *J. Physiol.*, **83**, 13P (1934).
33. HINES, M. N., "A tidal rhythm in behavior of melanophores in autotomized legs of *Uca pugnax*," *Biol. Bull.*, **107**, 386 (1954).
34. HOAR, W. S., "Phototactic and pigmentary responses of sockeye salmon smolts following injury to the pineal organ," *J. Fish. Res. Bd Can.*, **12**, 178 (1955).
35. HOGBEN, L. T., "The chromatic function in the lower vertebrates: a study in the analysis of behaviour," *Adv. Mod. Biol.*, Moscow, **5**, 261 (1936).
36. HOLMES, W., "The colour changes and colour patterns of *Sepia officinalis* L.," *Proc. Zool. Soc.*, **110**, 17 (1940).
37. KINOSHITA, Y., "Effects of gonadectomies on the secondary sexual characters in *Halichoeres poecilopterus* (Temminck and Schlegel)," *J. Sci. Hiroshima Univ.*, Ser. B, 1, **4**, 1 (1935).
38. KINOSHITA, Y., "On the secondary sexual characters, with special remarks on the influence of hormone preparations upon the nuptial coloration in *Chloea sarchynnis* (Jordan and Snyder)," ibid., Ser. B, 1, **6**, 5 (1938).
39. KJENNERUND, J., "Ecological observations on *Idothea neglecta*," *Univ. Bergen Årb. naturv. R.*, **1950**, No. 7 (1950).
40. KLEINHOLZ, L. H., "Color changes in echinoderms," *Pubbl. Staz. Zool. Napoli*, **17**, 53 (1938).
41. KNOWLES, F. G. W., "The control of the white reflecting chromatophores in crustacea," ibid., **17**, 174 (1939).
42. KNOWLES, F. G. W., "Hormone production within the nervous system of a crustacean," *Nature*, **167**, 564 (1951).
43. KNOWLES, F. G. W., "Pigment movements after sinus-gland removal in *Leander adspersus*," *Physiol. Comp. Oecol.*, **2**, 289 (1952).
44. KNOWLES, F. G. W., "Endocrine activity in the crustacean nervous system," *Proc. Roy. Soc B.*, **141**, 248 (1953).

45. KNOWLES, F. G. W., "Neurosecretion in the tritocerebral complex of crustaceans," *Pubbl. Staz. Zool. Napoli*, **24** (Suppl.), 74 (1954).
46. KNOWLES, F. G. W. and CALLAN, H. G., "A change in the chromatophore pattern of crustacea at sexual maturity," *J. Exp. Biol.*, **17**, 262 (1940).
47. KNOWLES, F. G. W. and CARLISLE, D. B., "Endocrine control in the Crustacea," *Biol. Rev.*, **31**, 396 (1956).
48. KNOWLES, F. G. W., CARLISLE, D. B. and DUPONT-RAALE, M., "Studies on pigment-activating substances in animals. 1. The separation by paper electrophoresis of chromactivating substances in arthropods," *J. Mar. Biol. Ass. U.K.*, **34**, 611 (1955).
49. LEBOUR, M. V., "Stellate chromatophore in the polychaeta," *Nature*, **150**, 209 (1942).
50. LONGLEY, W. H. and HILDEBRAND, S. F., "Systematic catalogue of the fishes of Tortugas, Florida," *Publ. Carneg. Instn.*, 535 (1941).
51. NICOL, J. A. C., "Special effectors," in *Physiology of Mollusca*, Ed. Wilbur, K. M. and Yonge, C. M., Vol. 1, p. 353 (New York and London, Academic Press, 1964).
52. PARKER, G. H., "Color changes in elasmobranchs," *Proc. Nat. Acad. Sci.*, **22**, 55 (1936).
53. PARKER, G. H., "Color changes due to erythrophores in the squirrel fish *Holocentrus*," ibid., **23**, 206 (1937).
54. PARKER, G. H., "Melanophore responses in the young of *Mustelus canis*," *Proc. Amer. Acad. Arts Sci.*, **72**, 269 (1937).
55. PARKER, G. H., "Color changes in *Mustelus* and other elasmobranch fishes," *J. Exp. Zool.*, **89**, 451 (1942).
56. PARKER, G. H., *Animal Colour Changes and their Neurohumours* (Cambridge Univ. Press, 1948).
57. PARKER, G. H., "Chemical control of nervous activity. C. Neurohormones in lower vertebrates," in Vol. II, *The Hormones*, Ed. Pincus, G. and Thimann, K. V. (New York, Academic Press, 1950).
58. PARKER, G. H., BROWN, F. A. and ODIORNE, J. M., "The relation of the eyes to chromatophoral activities," *Proc. Amer. Acad. Arts Sci.*, **69**, 439 (1935).
59. PEABODY, E. B., "Pigmentary responses in the isopod, *Idothea*," *J. Exp. Zool.*, **82**, 47 (1939).
60. PECZENICK, O. and ZEI, M., "Influence of hypophyseal hormone and of nervous impulses on the colour-dress of hermaphrodite teleostean fish," *Nature*, **160**, 788 (1947).
61. PICKFORD, G. E. and ATZ, J. W., *The Physiology of the Pituitary Gland of Fishes* (New York Zoological Society, 1957).
62. SAND, A., "The comparative physiology of colour response in reptiles and fishes," *Biol. Rev.*, **10**, 361 (1935).
63. SANDEEN, M. I., "Chromatophorotropins in the central nervous system of *Uca pugilator*, with special reference to their origins and actions," *Physiol. Zool.*, **23**, 337 (1950).
64. SCHEER, B. T. and SCHEER, M. A. R., "Moulting and colour change in the prawn *Leander serratus*," *Pubbl. Staz. Zool. Napoli*, **25**, 397 (1954).
65. SMITH, D. C., "The responses of melanophores in isolated fish scales," *Amer. Nat.*, **73**, 235 (1939).

66. SMITH, H. G., "The receptive mechanism of the background response in chromatic behaviour of crustacea," *Proc. Roy. Soc. B.*, **125**, 250 (1938).

67. SUMNER, F. B., "Evidence for the protective value of changeable coloration in fishes," *Amer. Nat.* **69**, 245 (1935).

68. TAIT, J., "Colour change in the isopod, *Ligia oceanica*," *Proc. Physiol. Soc.* in *J. Physiol.*, **40**, 40 (1910).

69. TOWNSEND, C. H., "Records of changes in color among fishes," *Zoologica, N.Y.*, **9**, 321 (1929).

70. WARING, H., "Chromatic behaviour of elasmobranchs," *Proc. Roy. Soc. B.*, **125**, 264 (1938).

71. WARING, H., "The co-ordination of vertebrate melanophore responses," *Biol. Rev.*, **17**, 120 (1942).

72. WARING, H. and LANDGREBE, F. W., "Hormones of the posterior pituitary," in Vol. II, *The Hormones*, Ed. Pincus, G. and Thimann, K. V. (New York, Academic Press, 1950).

73. WEBB, H., "Diurnal variations of response to light in the fiddler crab, *Uca*," *Physiol. Zool.*, **23**, 316 (1950).

74. WEBB, H. M., BENNETT, M. F. and BROWN, F. A. JR., "A persistent diurnal rhythm of chromatophoric response in eyestalkless *Uca pugilator*," *Biol. Bull.*, **106**, 371 (1954).

75. WILKENS, J. L. and FINGERMAN, M., "Heat tolerance and temperature relationships of fiddler crab," *Biol. Bull.*, **128**, 133 (1965).

76. WILSON, D. P., "The larvae of *Polydora ciliata* Johnston and *Polydora hoplura* Claparède," *J. Mar. Biol. Ass. U.K.*, **15**, 567 (1928).

77. WYKES, U., "Observations on pigmentary co-ordination in elasmobranchs," *J. Exp. Biol.*, **13**, 460 (1936).

78. WYKES, U., "The photic control of pigmentary responses in teleost fishes," ibid., **14**, 79 (1937).

79. YOSHIDA, M., "On the light response of the chromatophore of the sea-urchin, *Diadema setosum.*, ibid., **33**, 119 (1956).

80. YOSHIDA, M., "Spectral sensitivity of chromatophores in *Diadema setosum*," ibid., **34**, 222 (1957).

81. YOUNG, J. Z., "The autonomic nervous system of selachians," *Quart. J. Micr. Sci.*, **75**, 571 (1933).

CHAPTER 13

LUMINESCENCE

As we lift our net from the water, heavy rills of molten metal seem to flow down its sides, and collect in a glowing mass at the bottom. The jelly-fishes, sparkling and brilliant in the sunshine, have a still lovelier light of their own at night. They send out a greenish golden light, as lustrous as that of the brightest glow-worm, and on a calm summer night the water, if you but dip your hand into it, breaks into shining drops beneath your touch. . . . The larger acolephs bring with them a dim spreading halo of light, and look like pale phantoms wandering about far below the surface; the smaller ctenophores become little shining spheres, while a thousand lesser creatures add their tiny lamps to the illumination of the ocean.

A. AGASSIZ, 1888

PHYSICAL CHARACTERISTICS OF ANIMAL LUMINESCENCE

THE production and display of luminescence are outstanding characteristics of many marine animals. Curiously, light-production is almost unknown among freshwater animals, except for a freshwater limpet and some species of aquatic glow-worms (10). The light emitted is a cold light in which the radiant energy is confined to the visible spectrum (400–700 mμ for man).

These blazes . . . giving more light than heat . . . you must not take for fire.

The luminescence of marine animals is often blue in colour, with maximal energy in the region λ 460–490 mμ (dinoflagellates, jellyfish, siphonophores, euphausiids lantern-fish, etc.) (Fig. 13.1). The luminescence has been found to present a continuous spectrum in the visible range. Approximate limits of the emission spectra for several forms are *Aequorea forskalea* and *Mitrocoma cellularia* (Hydromedusae), 460–600 mμ; *Chaetopterus variopedatus* (Polychaeta), 405–605 mμ (λ_{max} 465 mμ); *Cypridina hilgendorfii* (Ostracoda), 415–620 mμ; *Anomalops* and *Photoblepharon* (teleosts harbouring luminescent bacteria), 450–640 mμ. The light of these various animals appears bluish. The light of polynoid worms and ctenophores is blue-green (λ_{max} around 510–515 mμ) (Fig. 13.1) (15, 52, 54).

Lights of other colours are produced by marine animals: for example, in the deep-sea fish *Echiostoma ctenobarba*, a large luminescent cheek organ flashes with a blue or pink light, while other minute photophores, scattered all over the body, shine with a yellowish glow. The deep-sea squid *Lycoteuthis diadema* is noteworthy in that it produces light of three different colours. Chun, on the *Valdivia* expedition, was able to observe live specimens brought up from 3,000 metres in the Indian Ocean. He found that most of the light-organs in that animal shone with a white radiance, but the two anal lights were ruby red, the middle visceral light ultramarine and the two middle ocular lights clear sky blue. Beebe and his colleagues have recorded much interesting information about the light of bathypelagic fish (5, 51, 52, 54).

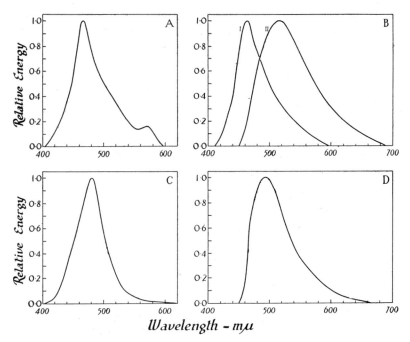

FIG. 13.1. SPECTRAL COMPOSITION OF THE LIGHT OF SEVERAL MARINE ANIMALS. A, *Atolla wyvillei*. B, I, *Chaetopterus variopedatus*, II, *Polynoids*. C, *Cypridina hilgendorfii* (FROM COBLENTZ AND HUGHES (1926). D, *Pholas dactylus*.

The intensity or energy flux of luminous flashes has been measured, and some data are shown in Table 13.4 (p.565). Single protozoa emit flashes of intensities around $1 \times 10^{-9} \mu W$/square cm of receiving surface at a distance of 1 m. The flashes of pelagic jellyfish, siphonophores and ctenophores are among the brightest recorded, having intensities up to $1 \times 10^{-5} \mu W/cm^2$ at 1 m. The light of a lantern-fish, emitting maximally under strong tactile stimulation, is $1 \times 10^{-8} \mu W/cm^2$ at 1 m. *Pyrosoma* is also very bright. Larger animals may emit more light, but this relationship has not been explored quantitatively (54).

The biological efficiency of the light emitted by any animal needs to be related to the sensitivity of particular photoreceptors. The light may have intraspecific or interspecific significance, and each animal would have to be considered separately in terms of the spectral composition of the light emitted and the sensitivity curve of the photoreceptors involved. Comparisons of the relative spectral composition of the light emitted by an animal, and of its spectral sensitivity, have been made for *Euphausia* and a lantern-fish *Myctophum*. The luminescence of both these animals is blue, with emission peaks at 475 and 465 mμ, respectively. In both the visual pigments or rhodopsins absorb in the blue region of the spectrum, with absorption maxima at λ 460 and 485 mμ, respectively. It has been estimated that the efficiency of the light of these animals, calculated in terms of visual perception by animals of the same species, is in the neighbourhood of 75%. Active swimmers in the upper regions of the sea, such as squid, prawns and fish, possess good eyes most sensitive to blue or blue-green light. Undoubtedly, these pelagic animals are the chief percipients influenced by the blue and blue-green sparks of these and other planktonic animals (5, 54).

DISTRIBUTION OF LUMINESCENCE IN MARINE ANIMALS

Light-production is known to occur with some degree of certainty in ten phyla and about thirty-five orders of marine animals. These are surveyed in Table 13.1, but this list is not exhaustive. An extensive bibliography

TABLE 13.1

SOME LIGHT-PRODUCING MARINE ANIMALS

Protozoa
Mastigophora: Dinoflagellata: *Noctiluca, Ceratium, Peridinium, Prorocentrum, Pyrodinium, Gonyaulax, Blepharocysta, Pyrocystis, Gymnodinium*
Rhizopoda: Radiolaria: *Thalassicolla, Myxosphaera, Collosphaera, Sphaerozoum, Collozoum*

Porifera *Grantia*[1]

Coelenterata
Hydrozoa: Hydromedusae: *Stomatoca, Rathkea, Laodicea, Phialidium, Liriope, Solmissus*
Siphonophora: *Praya, Hippopodius, Diphyes, Abylopsis, Agalma*
Scyphomedusae: *Pelagia, Atolla, Periphylla*
Anthozoa: Gorgonacea: *Ceratoisis, Isis, Mopsea*
  Pennatulacea: *Pennatula, Veretillum, Cavernularia, Funiculina, Umbellula, Leioptilus, Pteroeides, Renilla*

Ctenophora: *Pleurobrachia, Mnemiopsis, Beroë, Bolinopsis, Cestus, Eucharis*

Nemertea: *Emplectonema kandai*

[1] See Harvey (34) for an evaluation of luminescence in these genera.

TABLE 13.1—Some Light-Producing Animals—*continued.*

Annelida: Polychaeta:
Aphroditidae: *Acholoë, Polynoë, Harmothoë, Gattyana, Lagisca*
Alciopidae: *Corynocephalus*
Tomopteridae: *Tomopteris*
Syllidae: *Eusyllis, Pionosyllis, Odontosyllis*
Chaetopteridae: *Chaetopterus, Mesochaetopterus*
Cirratulidae: *Cirratulus, Heterocirrus, Macrochaeta*
Terebellidae: *Polycirrus, Thelepus*

Arthropoda: Crustacea:
Ostracoda: *Cypridina, Pyrocypris, Conchoecia*
Copepoda: *Metridia, Pleuromamma, Lucicutia, Heterorhabdus, Oncaea, Pontella, Chiridius, Euchaeta, Corycaeus*
Euphausiacea: *Thysanopoda, Euphausia, Nyctiphanes, Meganyctiphanes, Nematoscelis, Thysanoessa, Stylocheiron*
Mysidacea: *Gastrosaccus, Gnathophausia*
Decapoda: *Plesiopenaeus, Gennadas, Amalopenaeus, Sergestes, Systellaspis, Hoplophorus, Heterocarpus, Polycheles, Thalassocaris*
Arachnida: Pycnogonida: *Colossendeis gigas*
Mollusca: Lamellibranchia: *Pholas, Rocellaria*
Gastropoda: *Phyllirrhoe bucephala, Triopa fulgurans, Plocamophorus ocellatus, Kaloplocamus ramosum*
Cephalopoda: Decapoda: *Rondeletia, Heteroteuthis, Euprymna, Nematolampas, Lycoteuthis, Watasenia, Histioteuthis, Spirula*
Vampyromorpha: *Vampyroteuthis infernalis*
Octopoda: *Eledonella alberti*[1]

Echinodermata: Ophiuroidea: *Amphiura, Ophioscolex, Ophiopsila, Ophionereis, Ophiothrix, Ophiacantha*

Chordata: Enteropneusta: *Balanoglossus, Glossobalanus, Ptychodera*
Tunicata: *Pyrosoma, Salpa, Doliolum, Oikopleura*
Elasmobranchii: *Isistius, Somniosus, Centroscyllium, Spinax, Benthobatis*
Teleostei: *Photoblepharon, Anomalops, Monocentris, Cyclothone, Argyropelecus, Porichthys, Myctophum, Ceratias, Echiostoma,* and many others

[1] See Harvey (34) for an evaluation of luminescence in these genera.

---

dealing with the subject of animal luminescence may be found in Harvey's book *Bioluminescence* (34).

Many dinoflagellates and some radiolarians are luminescent (59). The production of light is a common occurrence in coelenterates and ctenophores, and occurs in many species. Relatively few of the many marine annelids are luminescent, and of these species the light produced by chaetopterids and certain syllids is very striking. There are few luminescent lamellibranchs and gastropods, but many deep-water cephalopods are particularly noteworthy in the brilliance of their displays and the complexity of their light-organs or photophores. The specialization and widespread distribution of light organs in this group are equalled only by teleost fishes, in which a great many different species, especially those from mesopelagic waters, bear numerous photophores. Only the ophiuroids among the echinoderms are luminescent. Light-production has appeared sporadically in several crustacean groups, and complex light organs and glandular structures occur in ostracods, copepods, euphausiids, mysids and deep-sea decapods. There are many difficulties in the way of discerning light-production in marine animals, and many more luminous animals are still to be reported. An adventitious mode of luminescence may here be mentioned. This concerns certain transparent pelagic animals, such as small crustacea, that appear luminous as the result of ingesting phosphorescent food, which then shines through their body wall.

Luminous species occur sporadically in the littoral and sublittoral fauna, under stones, on weeds and hidden in burrows and crevices.

> The fiery sparks those tangled fronds infold,
> Myriads of living points; th'unaided eye
> Can but the fire, and not the form, descry.
> CRABBE

They are particularly abundant in the surface plankton, and in the bathypelagic fauna. The remarkable phosphorescence of the surface of the sea is frequently due to dinoflagellates such as *Noctiluca*, *Peridinium* and *Gonyaulax*, while medusae, ctenophores, euphausiids and copepods and *Pyrosomae* also produce bright displays.

F. T. Bullen, in *The Cruise of the Cachelot*, has given a vivid description of one such occurrence—

> On the way, we one night encountered that strange phenomenon, a "milk sea." It was a lovely night, with scarcely any wind, the stars trying to make up for the absence of the moon by shining with intense brightness. The water had been more phosphorescent than usual, so that every little fish left a track of light behind him, greatly disproportionate to his size. As the night wore on, the sea grew brighter and brighter, until by midnight we appeared to be sailing on an ocean of lambent flames. Every little wave that broke against the ship's side sent up a shower of diamond-like spray, wonderfully beautiful to see, while a passing school of porpoises fairly set the sea blazing, as they leaped up and gambolled in its glowing waters. . . . In that shining flood the blackness of the ship stood out in startling contrast, and when we looked over the side our faces were strangely lit up by the brilliant glow.

The eggs, early developmental stages and larvae of some light-producing organisms are also luminescent. For example, segmentation stages of ctenophore eggs produce light on stimulation, and ophiuroid plutei, *Chaetopterus* trochospheres, euphausiid larvae and copepod nauplii are luminescent (25).

LUMINESCENT GLANDS AND ORGANS

The production of light is due to a chemiluminescent reaction in which a suitable substrate is oxidized and the accompanying energy transformations appear as visible light. The luminescent material is usually fabricated by the animal itself, but there are some instances in which the animal normally harbours luminescent bacteria responsible for the light emitted. True animal luminescence may be entirely an intracellular process, or it may arise in photogenic material which is secreted by the animal and discharged to the exterior to appear as extracellular luminescence. There are also some forms that possess more than one kind of light-organ and that luminesce in different ways. For example, the pelagic shrimp *Systellaspis debilis* has typical photophores as well as luminescent glands that release an extracellular secretion.

Extracellular Luminescence

In animals showing extracellular luminescence the light-producing glands are unicellular or multicellular structures which are usually restricted to definite circumscribed regions of the body. These gland cells are sometimes of two types, producing recognizably different secretory granules, both of which are concerned in the production of light.

In the nemertine *Emplectonema kandai* the photogenic cells that produce the luminescent secretion are distributed over the whole surface of the animal. The tubicolous polychaete *Chaetopterus variopedatus* is a well-known luminescent form which gives off a luminous secretion from certain glandular areas, especially the aliform notopodia (Fig. 13.2). The glandular cells responsible for the secretion contain closely packed eosinophilic granules, and are scattered singly in the epidermis or massed into distinct glands (Fig. 13.3). In other regions of the body, however, the luminescence is more transitory and is probably intracellular (7, 43).

In cirratulid and terebellid worms a luminescent "slime" is secreted by the body and tentacles. The tentacles of *Polycirrus* bear patches of luminescent cells, loaded with eosinophilic granules, which are discharged to the exterior. In *Odontosyllis* the production of light occurs during spawning. A luminous secretion is discharged into the water and this appears to arise in photogenic glands lying at the base of the parapodia and provided with ducts to the exterior (8, 9).

Among crustacea luminescence in the ostracod *Cypridina* has been more extensively studied than in any other form. The secretory cells in this animal are localized in a luminous gland which lies on the upper lip near the mouth. The gland cells are arranged in groups and discharge by pores situated on five protuberances. There is a valvular structure at the discharge pore of each of the secretory cells, and muscle fibres, which extend between the gland cells from the dorsal body wall to the oesophagus, can compress the gland and discharge its contents. Two kinds of inclusions in these cells are yellow granules of luciferin and small colourless granules of luciferase, both of which dissolve when extruded into sea water. In addition, mucus cells are present, which may discharge a mucous carrier for the luminescent secretion (55).

Luminescent copepods such as *Metridia*, *Oncaea* and *Corycaeus* pour forth a luminescent secretion from photogenic cells grouped on the head, back and tail, and occasionally the legs. Extracellular luminescence is also encountered in the mysid *Gnathophausia*. This animal discharges a luminous secretion from glands lying at the base of the mouth parts. The glands consist of a reservoir, into which the cells discharge their contents, and a duct opening to the exterior through a papilla (61). Deep-sea acanthe-

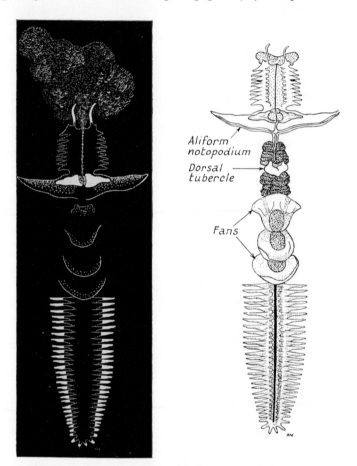

Aliform notopodium

Dorsal tubercle

Fans

FIG. 13.2. *Chaetopterus variopedatus*, A POLYCHAETE
THAT DISCHARGES A LUMINOUS SECRETION
(*Left*) animal luminescing; (*right*) dorsal view of the animal.

phyrid shrimps discharge a luminous cloud in the water emerging from the branchial chamber (14).

Panceri (56), in a pioneer study, found that the piddock *Pholas dactylus* releases a luminescent secretion into the inhalant siphon from three restricted regions of the body, namely a narrow band on the anterior edge of the mantle, a pair of bands in the inhalant siphon and two triangular spots near the retractor muscles (Fig. 13.4). The glandular cells involved are elongated, with long ducts, and contain distinct secretory granules. Förster (26) has described nerve fibres which enter and ramify among the light-cells. The pelagic gastropod *Phyllirrhoe bucephala* is a beautiful luminescent form in which light appears from scintillating points scattered over the body (Fig. 13.5). Each point corresponds to a single glandular

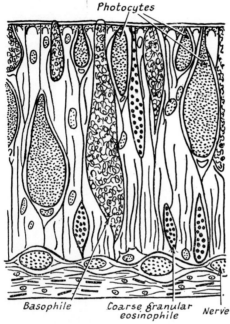

FIG. 13.3. LIGHT-PRODUCING CELLS OR PHOTOCYTES OF
Chaetopterus variopedatus
Section through the epidermis of the aliform notopodium.

cell or group of cells lodged in the epidermis. The cells are rather large and contain masses of granular material which can be secreted to the exterior. A nerve fibre proceeds to each of the glandular light-cells and forms a terminal swelling on the side of the cell body. This swelling appears like a specialized form of neuro-effector junction and displays a series of equally spaced rodlets at the boundary with the cytoplasm proper of the light-cell. *Triopa fulgurans*, *Kaloplocamus ramosum* and *Plocamophorus ocellatus* are other luminescent nudibranchs.

A myopsid squid *Heteroteuthis dispar* from deep water in the Mediterranean emits a luminous cloud when disturbed, comparable to the discharge of ink by shallow-water species. Although this has been considered another instance of symbiotic bacteria, it is probable that the luminescent secretion is produced by the animal. The luminous organ is a rather large gland partially surrounded by the ink sac. It possesses a reservoir and opens into the mantle cavity by two apertures. The gland is lined with low epithelial cells, and is provided with muscles for squeezing out the secretion. A similar light gland is present in the Japanese squid *Sepiolina nipponensis* (31).

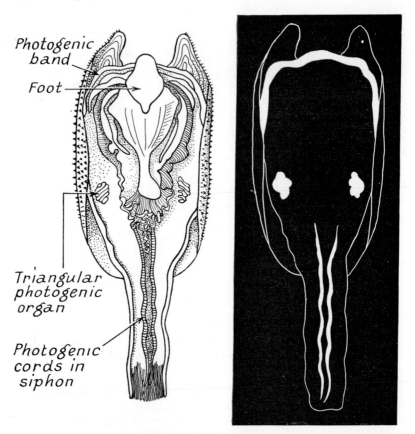

FIG. 13.4. THE PIDDOCK *Pholas dactylus*, A LUMINESCENT
LAMELLIBRANCH THAT BORES IN STONE

(*Left*) Ventral view of an animal; (*right*) appearance of a luminous animal in the dark. (After Panceri.)

Among the lower chordates various balanoglossids produce a luminous slime but the main luminescence is intracellular. Extracellular luminescence has also been described in fish, but some of the species which discharge a luminous secretion appear to harbour symbiotic bacteria, e.g. *Malacocephalus*. Beebe and Crane (3) noticed a mucous luminescent coating adhering to the teeth of the bathypelagic angler-fish *Linophryne arcturi*, and the deep-water eel *Saccopharynx harrisoni* has a pair of troughs along its back which are filled with a bluish-white luminous substance. Many of the deep-water anglers (Pediculati) are provided with a luminescent lure (illicium) representing a modified first dorsal fin ray (Fig. 13.6). The escal light-organ at the tip of the illicium has a transparent window through which the light can shine and contains a glandular chamber lined with

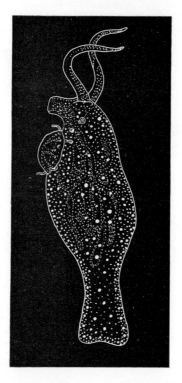

Fig. 13.5. A Luminous Nudibranch *Phyllirrhoe bucephala*, with *Mnestra parasites* Attached. (After Panceri, 1873, and Ankel, 1952.)

luminescent cells. The mechanism of light-production in these fishes awaits clarification (4, 34).

Intracellular Luminescence

Intracellular luminescence is also widespread and is usually associated with the development of special photophores. These may attain great complexity and possess reflectors, lenses and screens, as well as photogenic cells. The simplest form of intracellular luminescence is found in Protozoa. In *Noctiluca* the light appears from small granules scattered about the

B.M.A.—18*

periphery of the cell and along protoplasmic strands in the cell interior. Quatrefages observed that lighting often begins in two spots near the oral groove and then spreads as a wave over the surface of the animal. The

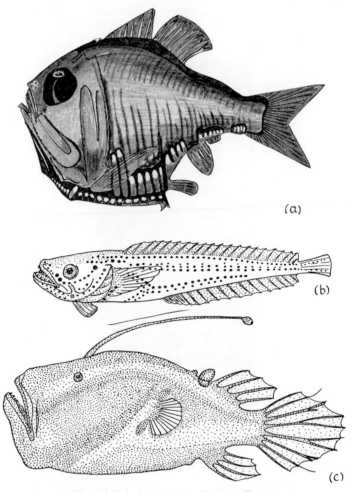

FIG. 13.6. LUMINESCENT TELEOST FISHES

(*a*) Silvery hatchet-fish, *Argyropelecus olfersii* (× 1·4) (after Clemens and Wilby, 1946); (*b*) midshipman *Porichthys notatus* (× ⅕) (after Greene, 1899); (*c*) Angler-fish *Ceratias couesi* (× ½).

actual spots of luminescence are stationary, and they flash on and off in succession as the wave of illumination passes over the cell. Luminescence is also intracellular in radiolarians, where it appears as a weak and diffuse bluish light following stimulation.

In hydromedusae the luminous cells are grouped in swellings beneath the endoderm of the marginal canal (53), and in sea pens the luminous cells occur in the endoderm of the tentacles (63).

In ctenophores light is produced by glandular structures lying within the eight radial canals. These appear as brilliant greenish streaks when the animal is stimulated (Fig. 13.7). The photogenic cells are granular elements

FIG. 13.7. A CTENOPHORE *Pleurobrachia pileus*, SHOWING THE APPEARANCE OF A LIGHTED ANIMAL (from Dahlgren, 1916.)

lying in the outer walls of the gastro-vascular canals. There is some doubt whether luminescence is intracellular in this group, or whether a luminous secretion is released into the vascular canals. It has been noted that if specimens are squeezed through cheese cloth they yield a crude luminous extract similar to that of medusae. Dahlgren, however, could detect no secretory discharge in the canals and concluded that the light was produced within the cell.

Polynoid worms such as *Polynoë* and *Acholoë* show transitory flashes of light in their elytra when stimulated. The light arises in a single layer of photogenic cells lying on the lower surface of the scale and passes through the latter before reaching the exterior. The photogenic cells are provided with a rich innervation which originates in a central elytral ganglion (Fig. 13.8) (6).

Intracellular luminescence is widespread among euphausiids and shrimps, and in some species the photophores are highly differentiated organs, possessing reflecting layer, screen and lens, associated with a group of photogenic cells. Among the euphausiids there are three to ten photophores arranged on the eye-stalks, thorax and abdomen. In their simpler form they

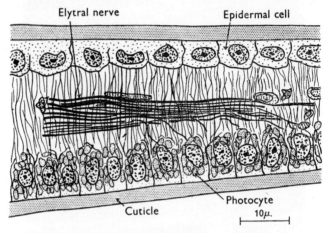

FIG. 13.8. SECTION THROUGH ELYTRUM OF *Acholoë astericola*, SHOWING PHOTOCYTES AND NERVE SUPPLY

are cup-shaped and the photogenic cells are continued distally into a rod-shaped mass. Bounding the cup externally is a refractive lamellar body. A stout nerve penetrates each photophore, and subdivides and ramifies among the photogenic cells. More complex photophores, such as those of *Meganyctiphanes norvegica*, contain lenses and a thickened corneal layer in addition (Fig. 13.9). Trojan, who has studied the optical properties of the photophores in *Nyctiphanes couchi*, has shown that the light-rays are brought into focus in front of the light-organ by a refractor and biconvex lens.

The photophores of pelagic shrimps (Caridea and Penaeidea) are distributed over the appendages and the thoracic and abdominal sterna in such a way that the light they emit is directed downwards. Their organization is rather simple in *Systellaspis* (=*Acanthephyra*) *debilis*, in which some of the photophores are narrow elongated structures having a cylindrical lens formed by a thickening of the cuticle, and an underlying layer of photogenic cells. Other organs are spherical and are bounded externally by an arched cuticular layer forming a concavo-convex lens. This overlies a layer of tall columnar photogenic cells contained in a fibrous and cellular sheath. In *Sergestes prehensilis* the cuticular lens is biconvex and is made up of two distinct layers. Underneath the lens lies the photogenic tissue, which is bounded by a reflector and a pigmented screen. A nerve penetrates the back of the photophores in some of these forms and innervates the light-cells (22). In addition to superficial photophores, some luminescent shrimps (*Sergestes*) are provided with specially modified and luminous liver tubules, known as the organs of Pesta. The light from these structures shines through the body wall. Dennell (1955) has observed the lumines-

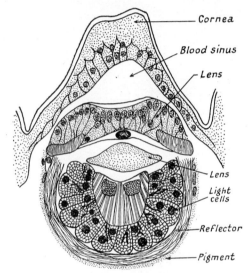

FIG. 13.9. PHOTOPHORE OF A EUPHAUSIID *Meganyctiphanes norvegica*
(After Dahlgren, 1916.)

cence of many species of deep-sea shrimps, which were kept alive in the laboratory in chilled sea water for some time.

The photophores of many deep-sea squids are striking objects (Fig. 13.10). Dahlgren traces all gradations from simple light-organs consisting of a cup-shaped invagination of the epidermis, to highly differentiated structures cut off from the overlying skin. In the cranchiid squids the photophores consist of a mass of photogenic cells backed by a reflector and lying in, or just beneath, the skin (Fig. 13.11(*a*)). In *Leachia cyclura*, for example, the ocular photophores are spherical structures consisting of a central cellular glandular mass lying within a reflector of connective tissue. Where the integument extends across the organ it is provided with chromatophores. In other oegopsid squids, such as *Watasenia* and *Abraliopsis*, the photophores are grouped underneath the eye, at the tips of the tentacles and as numerous small organs scattered over the surface of the body (Fig.

13.10). The brachial light-organs consist of a central mass of large photogenic cells surrounded by a sheath of connective tissue and a chromatophore screen (Fig. 13.12(*b*)). The ocular organs are simple flattened
structures provided with a lens-like body of connective tissue and bounded
externally by a layer of radiating rods. More remarkable are the small

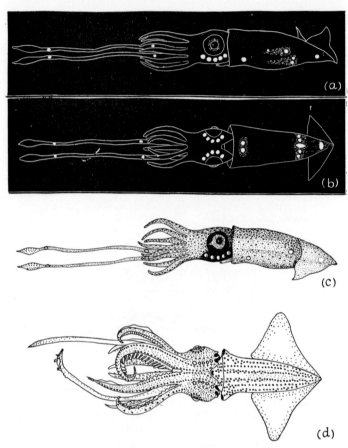

FIG. 13.10. LUMINOUS DEEP-SEA SQUID

(*a*), (*b*) and (*c*) lateral and ventral views of *Lycoteuthis* (*Thaumatolampas*) *diadema*;
(*d*) ventral view of *Abraliopsis morisii*. (After Chun, 1910.)

bead-like organs dispersed over the body and illustrated in Fig. 13.12(*a*).
These have a complicated reflector consisting of two lamellated masses and
an external lens suspended in a fibrous support. Corresponding photophores found in *Lycoteuthis* and *Calliteuthis* are provided with external
coloured layers or chromatophore screens on the light-emitting surface
(Fig. 13.11(*b*)). In some of these organs a nerve supply has been described

consisting of fibres which penetrate the pigmented wall of the photophore and ramify among the photogenic cells.

In the luminescent ophiuroids, such as *Amphiura*, *Ophiopsila* and *Ophiothrix*, light appears on the arms, less often on the body, and is localized in spines, plates or tube feet, according to the species. The structures responsible are unicellular photogenic glands, possessing long ducts which open to the exterior. No extracellular luminous secretion has been

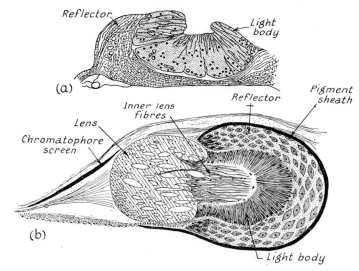

FIG. 13.11 (*a*). A SIMPLE LIGHT ORGAN OF A CRANCHIID SQUID *Liocranchia valdiviae*

The photophore consists of slightly invaginated surface epithelium, backed by a connective tissue reflector layer. (After Chun, 1910, and Dahlgren, 1916.)

(*b*) INTEGUMENTARY PHOTOPHORE OF *Calliteuthis reversa*, A BATHYPELAGIC SQUID. (After Chun, 1910.)

detected in these animals, however, and it seems that the light is intracellular in origin.

The luminescence of *Pyrosoma* and *Salpa* has been ascribed to symbiotic bacteria (12), but according to Harvey (34) the evidence favours inherent luminous ability on the part of the animal. In *Pyrosoma* each individual of the colony lightens, and the light appears in two groups of test cells lying at the entrance to the branchial cavity in the peripharyngeal blood spaces (Fig. 13.13). These cells contain curved cytoplasmic rods which may be responsible for producing the light.

Segmentation and young embryonic stages of *Pyrosoma* are also luminescent due to the participation of test cells in the developmental cycle. These test cells migrate into the developing embryo and arrange themselves about the germinal disc. When the four primary ascidiozooids arise

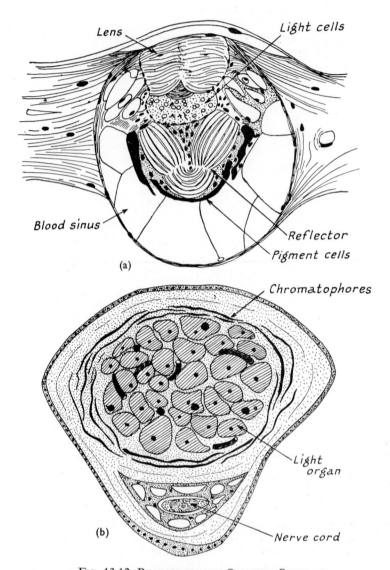

FIG. 13.12. PHOTOPHORES OF OEGOPSID SQUID

(a) Mantle light organ of *Abraliopsis morisii* (from Chun, 1910); (b) brachial light organ of *Watasenia* (after Dahlgren, 1916).

from the cyathozooid, the test cells pass into the circulation and give rise to the light-organs of the primary ascidiozooids.

Analogous conditions obtain in the Salpidae. In the solitary form of *Cyclosalpa pinnata*, for example, there are five pairs of luminous glands lying laterally between the body muscles, whereas in the aggregated form there is a single organ on each side of the body.

Only a few examples can be considered of the many diverse kinds of photophores occurring in fishes. Among selachians the small shark *Spinax*

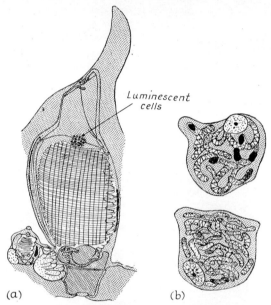

Luminescent cells

(a)   (b)

FIG. 13.13 (*a*). ASCIDIOZOOID OF *Pyrosoma*

The luminous test cells are located at the entrance to the branchial chamber. (After Buchner (12).)

Fig. 13.13 (*b*). LUMINOUS TEST CELLS OF *Pyrosoma* CONTAINING INTRACELLULAR INCLUSIONS, SOMETIMES REGARDED AS BACTERIA. (After Buchner (12).)

niger may be mentioned (Fig. 13.14). This animal, found at depths of 300–3,000 metres, gives off a bright glow from certain regions of the body. The luminous organs responsible lie in thickenings of the epidermis (Fig. 13.15). Each organ contains a group of from six to eight photogenic cells, the distal ends of which converge into a central mass containing secretory luminous material. Distally there are a few large cells which represent a lens, and lying about the organ there is a layer of chromatophores which also show a tendency to extend in front of the luminescent cells like an iris diaphragm (41, 42).

In many deep-sea teleosts, represented by forms such as the lantern fish *Myctophum*, the hatchet fish *Argyropelecus*, *Stomias*, *Photostomias* and *Astronesthes*, the photophores are numerous and are arranged in rows or groups along the body (Figs. 13.6, 13.16). Sometimes there is a large cheek organ and tentacular light organ as well (*Photonectes*, *Grammatostomias*). These structures consist of a mass of photogenic gland cells, often backed by a reflector, and sheathed in a pigmented screen. Towards

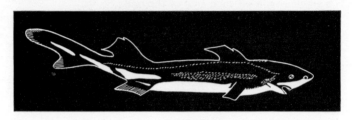

FIG. 13.14. A LUMINESCENT SHARK *Spinax niger*, WITH THE LUMINOUS AREAS LIGHTED UP. (From a drawing by Horsfall in Dahlgren, 1917.)

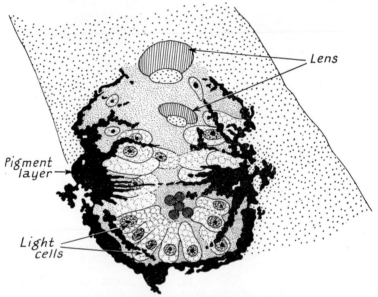

FIG. 13.15. LIGHT GLAND OF THE SHARK *Spinax niger*.
(After Johann (42), and Dahlgren, 1917.)

the free surface there is a lens for concentrating the light produced (Fig. 13.17). In certain other forms, such as *Cyclothone and Gonostoma*, the photophores are similar in structure but are provided with a long duct leading to the exterior (Fig. 13.18). Morphologically the various structures are derived from the epidermis. In the midshipman *Porichthys notatus*, a shallow-water fish of the west coast of North America, Greene has traced the development of the photophores from free epithelial buds which are

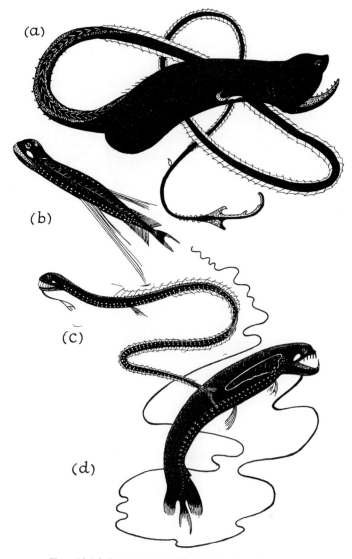

FIG. 13.16. LUMINESCENT BATHYPELAGIC TELEOSTS

(a) *Saccopharynx harrisoni*; (b) *Photostomias guernei*; (c) *Idiacanthus fasciola*; (d) *Grammatostomias flagellibarba*. (After Beebe, 1931–3, 1933–4, 1934, and Beebe and Crane (2).)

invaginated from the epidermis into the underlying connective tissue during embryogenesis. The bud enlarges, separates from the epithelium

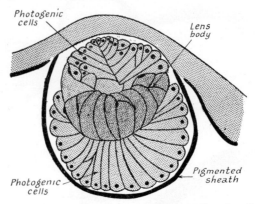

FIG. 13.17. PHOTOPHORE OF THE DEEP-SEA TELEOST *Stomias*, ILLUSTRATING A CLOSED TYPE. (After Brauer, 1904.)

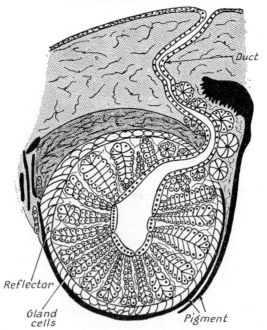

FIG. 13.18. PHOTOPHORE OF THE PELAGIC TELEOST *Gonostoma elongatum*, ILLUSTRATING AN OPEN TYPE. (After Brauer, 1904.)

and differentiates into a proximal photogenic layer and a distal lens. A dense layer of connective tissue invests the outside of the structure to form a reflector, and to this is added a pigmented screen (2, 29, 34).

Luminescence due to Symbiotic Bacteria

It is a peculiar fact that luminescence in certain cephalopods and teleosts is due to symbiotic bacteria which these animals harbour. The bacteria are housed in special sacs or organs, and emit a continuous light. We shall consider the cephalopods first. In certain myopsid decapods, including *Loligo, Sepiola, Rondeletia* and *Euprymna*, light has been observed in special glands which lie in the mantle cavity near the ink sac. It appears, however, that not all individuals, even of one sex, produce light, and in *Sepiola rondeletii*, for example, only some half the animals examined proved to be luminous.

The organs responsible for luminescence in these squid are special accessory glands associated with the accessory nidamental gland (Fig. 13.19). According to the species the luminescent accessory glands are

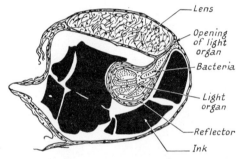

FIG. 13.19. TRANSVERSE SECTION THROUGH THE LIGHT-GLAND AND ASSOCIATED STRUCTURES OF THE MYOPSID SQUID *Sepiola ligulata*. VENTRAL SURFACE ABOVE. (After Herfurth (38).)

present in both sexes, or in the females only, and are paired or fused together to form a median organ. The light organs of *Sepiola* consist of saccular invaginations of the mantle epithelium and open into the mantle cavity through two papillae. Each organ is provided with a reflector and lens-body, and the internal spaces are occupied by photogenic bacteria.

Several workers have succeeded in isolating and culturing luminescent bacteria from the light organs of these squid, and some have concluded that they are true symbionts. The secretion of the accessory glands covers the eggs with luminescent bacteria, but Herfurth (38) found no evidence that these symbiotic bacteria actually penetrate into the egg. The accessory glands of the embryo are bacteria-free, and it is only after hatching that the glands become infected with bacteria from outside. Infection, consequently, is not transmitted through the egg and must be resumed in each generation.

Another interesting form, *Spirula*, possesses a luminous organ in the posterior dorsal region of the mantle, between the fins. This organ emits a continuous yellow-green glow, suggesting bacterial light. The cells of the organ contain small, presumably photogenic granules, which do not appear to be bacteria, and the origin of the light is still in some doubt (11, 34).

Among teleosts many examples of symbiotic relationships with luminescent bacteria are known. In *Malacocephalus laevis* luminescent granules resembling bacteria are located in large glandular sacs lying in the ventral surface of the body, and this luminescent material can be expelled by the fish (Fig. 13.20). Similar conditions occur in *Coelorhynchus japonicus*, *Physiculus japonicus* and *Hymenocephalus striatissimus*, where the luminous bacteria are housed in a gland beneath the skin and the light shines through the body wall. In the Japanese kingfish *Monocentris japonicus* the organ harbouring the luminescent bacteria is located in the lower jaw, and in *Gazza* and *Leiognathus* (=*Equula*) a ring-shaped gland envelops the oesophagus into which it opens. The luminescent organ of *Acropoma*

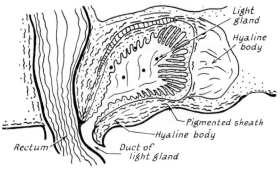

FIG. 13.20. LUMINOUS ORGAN OF THE TELEOST *Malacocephalus*. THE LIGHT-GLAND OPENS ON THE VENTRAL SURFACE CLOSE TO THE RECTUM.
(From Hickling (39).)

japonicum is embedded in the muscles of the ventral body wall and is provided with a long duct leading to the exterior. In some of these animals the tissues bordering the light-organ are organized into reflectors and lenses so as to direct the emission of light. An open gland containing what may prove to be luminescent bacteria is also found in the bathypelagic teleost *Ceratias* and other angler-fishes in the esca at the tip of the anterior dorsal fin-ray (Fig. 13.6(c)). Finally, we may mention two interesting East Indian fish *Photoblepharon palpebratus* and *Anomalops katoptron* which have a conspicuous white light-organ located immediately underneath each eye (Fig. 13.21). The interior of these organs is occupied by epithelial tissue containing rod-like bacteria (12, 27, 28, 32).

BIOCHEMISTRY OF LIGHT-PRODUCTION

The chemical substances responsible for bioluminescence have been subjected to intensive study, and the chemical reactions have been followed and measured by the light that is emitted. Animals produce light by means of biochemical reactions which come within the category of chemiluminescence, and are usually catalysed by highly specific enzymes. Luminous animals yield extracts which, when dried or treated in more sophisticated ways, are still capable of emitting light when moistened. Two requirements for the luminescent reaction to proceed are water and oxygen. The reaction is an oxidation, although the amount of oxygen necessary is sometimes very small. No light is produced by *Noctiluca* nor by photogenic extracts of *Pholas*, ostracods and pennatulids in the absence of oxygen. There are a few forms, however, in which luminescence can occur in the absence of free oxygen, namely certain radiolarians, the medusae *Pelagia* and *Aequorea*,

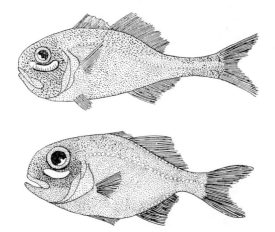

FIG. 13.21. LUMINOUS EAST INDIAN FISH HARBOURING SYMBIOTIC BACTERIA

(*Above*) *Anomalops katoptron*. (*Below*) *Photoblepharon palpebratus*. In both animals the light-gland lies below the eye. (After Buchner (12), and Harvey, 1940.)

and certain ctenophores. It would appear that this is due to an alternative source of oxygen in the preparations that were used (36).

Dubois demonstrated in 1887 that the photogenic reaction in the piddock *Pholas dactylus* involves the interaction of two substances, which he called luciferin and luciferase. Luciferin is relatively heat-stable, whereas luciferase is heat-labile and is destroyed on boiling. A separate preparation of luciferin can be obtained by heating a luminous extract so as to destroy the luciferase; and a preparation containing luciferase alone results from allowing the luminescent reaction in an extract to proceed to completion, thus exhausting the luciferin initially present. On subsequently mixing these two preparations luminescence results. Luciferin is the light-emitter and luciferase the heat-labile enzyme catalysing the luminescent reaction.

An extended search of the animal kingdom has shown that only a few animals have this response. Marine animals in which it has been demonstrated are the polychaete *Odontosyllis*, an ostracod *Cypridina*, a deep-sea prawn (probably *Acanthephyra*), a pelecypod *Pholas*, and a teleost *Malaco-*

cephalus (in which symbiotic bacteria are implicated). More refined methods of extraction and treatment have revealed the existence of luciferin-luciferase systems in other groups. The luminescent reactions distinguished so far are classified in four types (Table 13.2, from Cormier and Totter (19)).

TABLE 13.2

TYPES OF LUMINESCENT REACTIONS OCCURRING IN MARINE ANIMALS

Types	Examples
A. Pyridine—nucleotide linked: DPNH + H$^+$ + FMN—(DPNH-oxidase)→FMNH$_2$ + DPN FMNH$_2$ + RCHO + O$_2$—(Luciferase)→Light	Bacteria
B. Adenine—nucleotide linked: (1) LH$_2$ + ATP + O$_2$—(Luciferase, Mg^{2+})→Light (2) LH$_2$ + DPA + O$_2$—(Luciferase, Ca^{2+})→Light	Firefly Sea pansy, Renilla
C. Simple enzyme—substrate system: LH$_2$ + O$_2$—(Luciferase)→Light	*Gonyaulax, Odontosyllis, Cypridina, Apogon*
D. Peroxidation systems: 2LH$_2$ + H$_2$O$_2$—(Luciferase)→Light	*Balanoglossus*

Explanation: DPN, diphosphopyridine nucleotide; DPNH, reduced diphosphopyridine nucleotide; FMN, flavin mononucleotide; FMNH$_2$, reduced flavin mononucleotide; RCHO, long-chain aldehyde; ATP, adenosine triphosphate; LH$_2$, reduced luciferin or dihydroluciferin; DPA, 3^1, 5^1-diphosphoadenosine.

During the course of a bioluminescent reaction the light-emitter, luci-ferin, is raised to an excited state by the liberation of chemical energy; subsequently decaying to ground state it emits a photon. In the bacterial reaction, Type A of Table 13.2, reduced flavin mononucleotide, FMNH$_2$, reacts with oxygen and a long-chain aldehyde RCHO in the presence of luciferase to produce light. This is blue in colour, with peak emission around 490 mμ. In this system the actual luciferin may be an excited intermediate formed by the interaction of FMNH$_2$, O$_2$ and luciferase. Luciferase extract from the piddock (*Pholas*) catalyses light-emission from a mixture of FMN and DPNH, and it is possible that the luminescent system of *Pholas* is akin to that of bacteria (57).

Luminescence of Type B, found in *Renilla*, involves an interaction between *Renilla* luciferin and an adenine-nucleotide to form an inter-mediate, activated luciferin, which is then oxidized by luciferase, with light-emission.

Among simple enzyme-substrate systems (Type C), that of *Cypridina* has been studied most intensively (64). Requirements are a substrate, reduced luciferin, oxygen and luciferase. The luciferin has been crystal-lized and a formula proposed that includes an indole nucleus. When reduced luciferin, either in crude extracts or in purified form, is catalytic-ally oxidized by luciferase, it becomes excited and light is produced. Several fish, e.g. *Apogon* and *Parapriacanthus*, have luciferins and luciferases which are very similar to or identical with those of *Cypridina* and which interact with them (33). The luciferin and luciferase of the dinoflagellate *Gonyaulax polyedra* are distinct from those of *Cypridina*. The concentration of luciferin in *Gonyaulax* changes diurnally in concert with a diurnal rhythm in the intensity of luminescence, being greater at night and reduced by day. In addition, birefringent particles have been isolated from *Gonyaulax polyedra*, and identified within the cell. These particles, called "scintillons", are excited to luminesce by adding dilute acetic acid, lowering the pH to 5·7; they do not react with luciferin and luciferase (58).

An example of a peroxidation system (Type D) is the extracellular luminescent reaction of *Balanoglossus*. Requirements for luminescence are extracts containing luciferin, luciferase (both seemingly proteins) and peroxide; oxygen is not essential, the reaction is a peroxidation catalysed by peroxidase (the luciferase) (23). But oxygen is necessary for luminescence of another enteropneust, *Ptychodera* (34).

A very simple luminescent system exists in Hydromedusae. *Aequorea* is a luminous jellyfish from which a luminous proteinaceous substance called "aequorin" has been isolated. Aequorin luminesces upon addition of calcium ions, producing a flash of blue light (λ_{max} 465 mμ). Aequorin may be an oxidized intermediate, analogous to that of the bacterial system, and calcium ions may be the trigger, setting off the luminescent reaction.

The active research now being pursued into the biochemistry of bioluminescent systems is starting to unravel their complexities, and patterns are only starting to emerge. One hypothesis suggests that the indole nucleus may be involved in the light-emitter, producing blue light, and that the spectral composition of the light may be influenced by the sequence of adjoining amino acids (19).

PHYSIOLOGY OF LUMINESCENCE

Most luminescent animals seem to have some method of controlling the appearance of their light (53, 54). When this is continuous it usually indicates bacterial origin, but even bacterial light is subject to some degree of control in various animals. The methods utilized by animals for regulating the appearance of light can be classified into categories as follows. In one type the photogenic cells or a reservoir can be squeezed by neighbouring muscle fibres and the secretion poured forth to the exterior. Control in this case is indirect and is a typical neuromuscular phenomenon. Again, the gland cells themselves may be directly innervated and discharge their contents on excitation. The control of luminescence in this case becomes one of nervous regulation of glandular secretion. When luminescence is intracellular, excitation evokes cellular changes leading to the activation of photogenic material. Finally, the emission of light may be controlled by rotating the light-organ, or by the use of screens or shutters (50).

Among protozoa the dinoflagellates and radiolarians display intra-cellular luminescence and flash only on stimulation. *Noctiluca* emits a brief luminous flash lasting 50–100 msec (Fig. 13.22). When *Noctiluca* is adequately stimulated, an action potential is propagated over the cell, accompanied by a wave of luminescence. Light is emitted by small parti-cles in the cytoplasm, which are brought into action successively by the advancing potential (Fig. 13.23). With repetitive electrical stimulation, facilitation and summation of flashes occur. Mechanical stimulation gives rise to a slow generator-type potential which, when of sufficient magnitude, develops into an all-or-none propagated potential triggering off the flash (Fig. 13.22) (24).

In higher metazoa control of light-production is exercised by the nervous system.

Stimulation

A wealth of older accounts refers to various kinds of stimuli—mechan-ical, electrical and chemical—that evoke a response. Most of these have been used haphazardly, without adequate control, and the observations yield few quantitative data that afford any insight into the mechanics of the processes involved in excitation.

A hydromedusan such as *Aequorea* has light-organs distributed around the periphery of the umbrella. Localized stimulation evokes light in the immediate vicinity, without affecting distant regions. Excitation of the photocytes in these jellyfish is either direct or involves local reflexes. In the scyphomedusan *Pelagia* gentle stimulation evokes a local spot of light, which spreads under stronger stimulation until the whole bell and tentacles respond with a glow. In the sea-pen *Pennatula* Panceri showed that mechanical stimulation at any point causes a wave of luminosity to spread over the colony (Fig. 13.25). Similarly, in the sea-pansy *Renilla* tactile stimulation evokes luminous waves which pass out concentrically over the colony (20).

In ctenophores the tactile receptors involved in luminescence are situated along the rows of ciliary plates or combs. In dark-adapted *Mnemiopsis* weak stimulation causes local luminescence on a comb-row, whereas strong stimulation calls forth general luminescence from the meridians of the entire animal.

The nemertine *Emplectonema kandai* luminesces over much of the body when strongly stimulated. Local tactile stimulation produces a rather restricted light, but on stretching the worm, luminescence spreads all over the body. In the polychaete *Chaetopterus* the response to tactile stimulation is very localized, and when a particular segment is irritated, light appears only in that region. For example, when a fan or posterior segment is touched, light appears in the notopodia of the segment con-cerned, and on mechanically stimulating the twelfth segment a bright cloud of luminescent secretion is discharged from a pair of large photo-genic glands in that region (Fig. 13.2). In polynoid worms luminescence

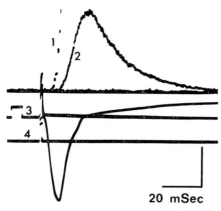

FIG. 13.22. ACTION POTENTIAL AND LUMINESCENT FLASH
RECORDED FROM *Noctiluca*

2, luminous flash (ascending curve). 3, action potential recorded intracellularly (descending curve). 4, deflexion due to electrical stimulus (24).

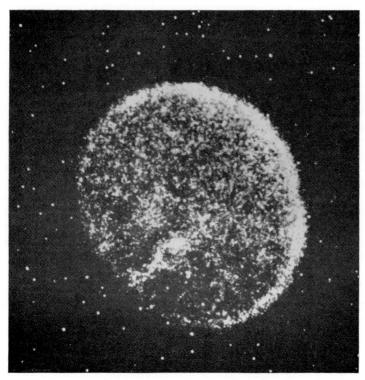

FIG. 13.23. LUMINESCENT FLASH OF *Noctiluca*

Magnification of image x270; intensity of the image was highly amplified (24).

is confined to the scales, which flash when the animal is mechanically stimulated or injured.

The luminescent system of euphausiids (*Meganyctiphanes*) is photo-sensitive. The flashes of these animals are rather protracted affairs, lasting many seconds. When stimulated by a brief flash of light *Meganyctiphanes* responds with a glow lasting a few minutes. A second flash, applied during the course of the luminescent response, briefly quenches it, after which it returns to full intensity. A weak sustained light of similar colour and intensity to the luminescence depresses the glow-response (44).

In *Pyrosoma* mechanical stimulation—touch, agitation, water currents—causes the appearance of light, and when the stimulus is localized the light appears first in a restricted area and then spreads over the whole colony. Light from another colony, or from some other source, will also evoke luminescence in a distant colony. Normal excitation, consequently, is both photic and mechanical in this form. Certain fish bearing photophores also luminesce when disturbed. Following tactile stimulation luminescence has been observed in the photophores of lantern-fish (*Myctophum*), in *Maurolicus* and in the illicium of the angler-fish *Cryptosparas*. *Myctophum* was also observed to respond to weak external illumination (a luminescent watch-dial) by flashing. In other species, well endowed with photophores, luminescence may be very difficult to elicit by mechanical stimulation (e.g. *Spinax*, *Porichthys*).

The effect of temperature on luminescence has been investigated in some forms. These studies have involved the lethal effects of high temperatures and the influence of temperature alterations on the mechanism of stimulation. *Noctiluca* gives a normal response as the temperature is raised to 42–43°C. A further increase to 48–49°C causes a steady glow, and then the light is extinguished, without the possibility of recovery on cooling. On lowering the temperature to 5–0°C the animal gives a constant glow, and will recover if warmed immediately. The ctenophore *Mnemiopsis* shows some adaptation to lowered temperature. When cooled from 20°C to 9°C no luminescent response is elicitable, but if the temperature is lowered further to 3°C and then raised to 7°C luminescence reappears on stimulation. Furthermore, animals kept for some time at 3°C luminesce regularly at that temperature. Raising the temperature above 36°C evokes luminescence in many metazoans (34).

Effect of Illumination

In most animals luminescence is not affected by previous exposure to light, but there are a few interesting exceptions. Such include the sea-pansy *Renilla* and various ctenophores, in which luminescence is inhibited by light and regained after a period in the dark. Again there are some animals, including various dinoflagellates, *Pelagia*, and *Ptychodera*, which are said to display a true diurnal rhythm of luminescent ability and will only shine at night, whether they have been kept previously in the dark or not.

A luminescent dinoflagellate *Gonyaulax polyedra* has been cultured successfully and studied in the laboratory. This species shows a true diurnal rhythmicity of luminescence, the light being dim during the day and bright at night. When a culture is transferred from light to darkness, the rhythm of luminescence continues in phase with other cells left in daylight. Continuous exposure to light inhibits the rhythm, which may be initiated once more by placing the cells in the dark. The rhythm persists for about four days in darkness. It has been observed that the amount of luminescence which develops at night depends on the amount of light received during the day, apparently through energy stores derived from photosynthesis (37, 60).

When the pennatulid *Renilla* is brought from daylight into darkness it fails to luminesce at first, but after the first half-hour the ability to luminesce gradually returns. Moreover luminescence in the dark-adapted animal can be reduced by exposure to a weak light. When small areas of a dark-adapted animal are illuminated it is found that luminescence is inhibited only in those exposed areas. The ability to transmit an excitatory wave remains unaffected under these conditions, and the light has no direct affect on the photogenic material. It seems, therefore, that illumination in some way blocks excitability in the region of the photocytes (21).

The inhibition of luminescence in ctenophores by light has long been known. Specimens of *Bolina* and *Beroë* exposed to daylight fail to luminesce, but regain the ability to lighten after 15–30 min in the dark. The inhibitory effect of light in these animals acts through two mechanisms, namely, directly on the photogenic substance and also through the sensori-nervous system. An extract obtained from animals exposed to daylight does not luminesce; moreover luminescence in an active extract can be reduced by exposing it to light, a process depending on the duration and intensity of exposure. Illumination, therefore, causes a disappearance of intracellular luminescent material. Although extracts of *Mnemiopsis* lose their power to luminesce when exposed to strong light, the exposure time required to abolish luminescence in this material is much greater than that necessary to cause an intact *Mnemiopsis* to lose its luminescent ability.

Photic inhibition in *Mnemiopsis* has been studied quantitatively by Moore who found that inhibition of luminescence by illumination obeys the Bunsen-Roscoe law, in which the time of exposure $\times$ the intensity of illumination equals a constant K. Values of K for several ctenophores (with tungsten-lamp light source) are: *Beroë ovata*, 57,285; *Mnemiopsis*, 4,776; *Cestum veneris*, 1,167 metre-candle min. (Fig. 13.24). The total amount of light impinging on the animal, therefore, is the operating factor, and the effect is photochemical. When half the surface of *Mnemiopsis* is illuminated, luminescence is suppressed in that region alone. Special nerves from photoreceptors are implicated, which establish purely local connexions with the photogenic cells, and excitation of these pathways effects destruction of the photogenic material. Mechanical stimulation of an animal previously illuminated hastens the recovery of luminescence, and this is interpreted as favouring the reconversion of a decomposition product into the photogenic material (48).

The scyphomedusan *Pelagia noctiluca* is one of the few animals which show a diurnal rhythm of luminescence. Tactile stimulation during the day is without effect, but early in the evening the ability to luminesce returns. Exposure of a responsive specimen to strong illumination (62·5–1,000 m-c) acts on the nervous mechanism, and the effect follows the Bunsen-Roscoe law. There is some doubt about the stability of these rhythms (49).

In general it appears that when luminescence is affected by exposure to light, alterations in response are achieved in two ways, either by a direct

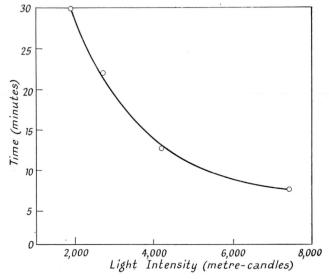

FIG. 13.24. PHOTIC INHIBITION OF LUMINESCENCE IN THE CTENOPHORE *Beroë ovata*

The curve relates intensity of illumination to mean exposure times necessary to inhibit the production of light under mechanical stimulation. (From Heymans and Moore, 1925.)

photochemical effect on the photogenic cells and their contained luminescent material; or indirectly, by acting on sensori-neural pathways. Both agencies can operate in the same animal and their relative importance varies with the species.

Direct Nervous Control

Certain forms have already been mentioned in which a luminescent slime is discharged into the water as the result of glandular secretion. On reaching the exterior, or perhaps even within the gland itself as soon as the secretory process is initiated, the photogenic material undergoes oxidation and luminesces. The term "slime" refers to the superficial appearance of the luminescent material only, and microscopic examination shows that the light originates in a multitude of scintillating spots corresponding to granules of photogenic material. In these forms it is observed that the glandular light-cells contain similar granules, which slowly break down when discharged into the sea water. Often, but not always, the luminescent material is suspended in mucus, for example in *Pelagia* and *Chaetopterus*. In the latter animal the bountiful luminous secretion from the aliform notopodia is accompanied by mucus and is dispersed in the surrounding sea water by ciliary action. The problem of how the photogenic cell, when excited, discharges its contents, is one common to all glandular cells and involves a consideration of intracellular dynamics.

In luminescent coelenterates excitation usually is transmitted as a wave over the surface of the animal. The nervous system in this group is organized on the basis of a nerve-net, and transmission associated with luminescence shows some features common to those involved in muscular movement. In *Pelagia noctiluca* luminescence appears on the bell and tentacles in response to tactile stimulation. A slight touch on the outer surface of the umbrella results in a flash of light at the point of contact, and the light then spreads but may not cover the whole surface of the bell. Under strong tactile stimulation the light is brighter and spreads over the entire umbrella surface.

In various hydroids such as *Campanularia* and in sea-pens (Pennatulacea), a local stimulus gives rise to a wave of luminescence. Special attention has been paid to the luminous responses of sea-pens (*Renilla, Cavernularia, Pennatula*, etc.). In these animals the whole colony may be luminescent (*Cavernularia*), or only the polyps (*Pennatula, Renilla*). Luminescence is intracellular, and appears as a wave of light which proceeds from the point of stimulation over the surface of the colony. The wave results from the lighting-up of zooids in regular succession. Characteristics of the luminous flashes of sea-pens and some other luminous marine animals are given in Table 13.3.

Transmission of the luminescent response in sea-pens takes place in a non-polarized nerve-net, and the excitation can proceed in any direction. Thus, stimulation at the base of a specimen gives rise to luminescent waves which ascend to the tip, and stimulation of the tip results in waves which run to the base (Fig. 13.25). When the centre of the stalk or a side branch is touched, luminescent waves proceed in both directions, up and down the stalk. Simultaneous stimulation of the base and tip of the colony gives rise to waves which meet at the centre and extinguish each other. It is furthermore observed that the luminous waves are not stopped by cutting the sea-pen in various ways, as long as a connecting bridge is left between the pieces to form a nervous pathway.

With electrical stimulation usually several shocks are necessary to evoke a response, and with continued stimulation successive flashes increase

TABLE 13.3
TEMPORAL CHARACTERISTICS OF LUMINESCENT RESPONSES

Animal	Kind of response	Latent period	Time to half maximum	Time to maximum	Decay time	Total duration	Temperature (°C)
Noctiluca scintillans	intracellular	9 msec	8 msec	17 msec	128 msec	145 msec	17–19
Aequorea forskalea	ditto	0·2–0·4 sec	0·05 sec	0·11 sec	0·45–1·35 sec	0·6–1·5 sec	14–16
Renilla köllikeri	ditto	0·12 sec	—	0·22 sec	0·77 sec	1 sec	17–19
Leioptilus gurneyi	ditto	0·18 sec	0·1 sec	0·2 sec	0·8–1 sec	1–1·2 sec	14–16
Pennatula phosphorea	ditto	0·25–0·29 sec	0·11 sec	0·22 sec	1·26 sec	1·48 sec	17–19
Mnemiopsis leidyi	ditto	4·5–10 msec	34·6 msec	59·9 msec	230 msec	290 msec	21–23·5
Acholoë astericola	ditto	18–20 msec	—	18–23 msec	45–80 msec	83 msec	16–18
Polynoë scolopendrina	ditto	13–21 msec	—	26–30 msec	108 msec	137 msec	16–18
Chaetopterus variopedatus	extracellular	4·2 sec	4 sec	10–14 sec	30 sec	5–10 min	16–18
Watasenia scintillans brachial organ	intracellular	—	—	—	—	up to 30 sec	—
mantle organ	ditto	—	—	—	—	20 min or more	—
Pyrosoma atlanticum	ditto	0·08–0·41 sec	0·15 sec	0·3 sec	6·9 sec	7·2 sec	25
Porichthys myriaster	ditto	7–10 sec	—	1 min	1·5 min	2·5 min	21–24

Fig. 13.25. Diagrammatic Representation of the Directions taken by Luminous Waves in *Pennatula*, following Tactile Stimulation

S indicates the point of stimulation; and the arrows, the course of the luminous waves which travel over the animal. (From Panceri (56).)

TABLE 13.4

Intensity of Light Emitted by Some Marine Animals

Animal	Radiant flux per cm² receptor surface at 1 cm
Protozoa	
Cytocladus major and *Aulosphaera triodon*	$5\cdot3 \times 10^{-5} \mu W$
Noctiluca miliaris	$1\cdot6 \times 10^{-7} \mu J$
Coelenterates	
Atolla wyvillei	$2 \times 10^{-3} \mu W$
Vogtia spinosa	$3 \times 10^{-3} \mu W$
Pennatula phosphorea	$7 \times 10^{-6} \mu J$
Ctenophores	
Mnemiopsis leidyi	$1\cdot2 \times 10^{-1} \mu W$
Annelids	
Acholoë astericola (single elytrum)	$1\cdot1 \times 10^{-4} \mu J$
Crustacea	
Euphausia pacifica	$2 \times 10^{-3} \mu W$
Tunicates	
Pyrosoma atlanticum	$4 \times 10^{-2} \mu W$
Teleosts	
Myctophum punctatum	$5 \times 10^{-4} \mu W$
Searsia koefoedi	$2\cdot8 \times 10^{-2} \mu W$

(Various sources)

progressively in intensity up to some plateau level (Fig. 13.26(*a*), (*b*)). In part, this increase in intensity of consecutive flashes results from facilitation at the neurophotocyte-junctions, each impulse in a series recruiting additional photocytes (cf. p. 382). Following prolonged stimulation the animal passes into a hyper-excitatory state, in which it may continue flashing repetitively long after stimulation has ceased (Fig. 13.26 (c)). Presumably the neurones of the nerve-net, when a sea-pen is in this condition, are capable of maintained repetitive discharge (21).

In ctenophores strong tactile stimulation excites a luminous response in all the ciliary rows. If one pole is stimulated a luminous wave travels towards the opposite pole, and if the middle of a row is stimulated luminous waves proceed along the meridian towards both poles. The luminescent response is readily fatigued but recovers after a period of rest. Transmission of excitation takes place in a non-polarized nerve-net accompanying each meridional canal. Transection of the canal blocks the passage of the luminescent wave. Tactile receptors for the luminescent response are limited to the eight radial canals. In addition, photoreceptors are believed to establish connexions locally with the photocytes and to be responsible for inhibiting luminescence when the ctenophore is illuminated.

Electrical stimulation of a whole meridian evokes repetitive brief flashes at frequencies ranging from 5–12/sec, the whole series ending within a few seconds (Fig. 13.26(d)). When small pieces of a meridional canal are stimulated with brief shocks, a single flash follows each electrical pulse (Fig. 13.26(e)). Data for flash duration are summarized in Table 13.3. Some characteristics of the local responses are as follows: the light intensity varies directly with the voltage and duration of stimulation (above threshold); latent period is reduced by increase in strength of stimulation; several sub-threshold stimuli summate to produce a flash; rapid repetitive stimulation, above 10/sec, produces summation of responses. It is also observed, at slow rates of stimulation (<5/sec), that consecutive discrete responses increase progressively in intensity, indicating the operation of some facilitatory phenomenon (Fig. 13.26(f)). It has not yet been established whether these local responses, recorded from small pieces of a meridian, are produced by stimulation of nerve fibres, or by direct excitation of the photocytes (16).

The luminescent response of euphausiids is excited by 5-hydroxy-tryptamine at physiological concentrations. The photophores are innervated, but it is as yet unknown whether initiation of luminescence depends on nervous or hormonal mediation (44).

Among polychaetes the polynoids have been studied rather extensively. When a worm is stimulated mechanically the area touched begins to flash, and the luminescence then spreads rapidly anteriorly and posteriorly from this point. Electrical stimulation causes the whole worm to lighten, and with alternating current separate responses corresponding to the electrical pulses can be observed. Prolonged stimulation causes the light to fade, but recovery occurs after several hours. When an animal is transected only the posterior fragment lightens, while the anterior portion remains dark. Each scale receives a nerve which enters a ganglion and gives off fibres which radiate outwards to the light cells. According to Bonhomme (6), luminescence in *Harmothoë* is evoked through reflex pathways involving peripheral tactile receptors and the ventral nerve cord. An elytrum

removed from the body gives a bright flash due to mechanical stimulation
of the severed nerve fibres but is no longer responsive to reflex tactile
stimulation.

The luminescent responses of polynoids have been investigated in detail
by means of photo-electric recording. An isolated scale subjected to a
single electrical shock usually responds by a series of repetitive flashes

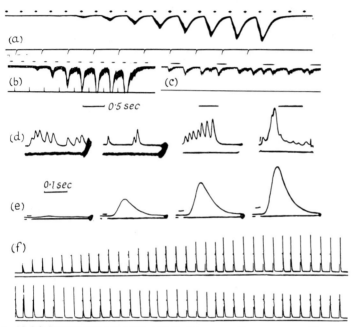

FIG. 13.26. PHOTO-ELECTRIC RECORDINGS OF THE LUMINESCENT RESPONSES
OF COELENTERATES AND CTENOPHORES

(a) Flashing of the sea pansy *Renilla*, induced by electric shocks; (b) flashing of the
sea pen *Leioptilus*, evoked by a series of electric shocks; (c) *Leioptilus:* persistent rhythmic flashing following a period of stimulation. Time scale in records a–c, 72/min,
shown above; stimuli on lower line. Flashes appear as downward deflexions of the
middle trace. (d) Multiple responses from a meridional canal of *Mnemiopsis*, each series
induced by a single shock; (e) *Mnemiopsis:* responses from a small section of a meridional
canal, showing increase in intensity of flash when the voltage is raised; (f) *Mnemiopsis:*
facilitation of luminescent responses under repetitive stimulation(1/sec). (Records d–f
from Chang (16).)

which continue for a second or more (Fig. 13.27(a)). Flashing begins at
a frequency of five or more per second, then falls off to a steady level
which is maintained for some time. The initial flashes also increase rapidly
in intensity, owing to a rise in the level of excitation whereby the second
and third responses far exceed the first. Continued flashing, either from
mechanical or electrical stimulation (a single shock), is due to repetitive
discharge from the elytral ganglion, and the progressive increment in flash

intensity depends upon some facilitatory process in the neuro-effector complex as well as summation of light intensity.

Both the tentacles and the body of *Polycirrus caliendrum* luminesce under stimulation. The response appears to be very localized, each tentacle lighting independently of the others. Luminescence proceeds over the surface of *Chaetopterus* following stimulation.

Light-production is under nervous control, and a single nervous impulse

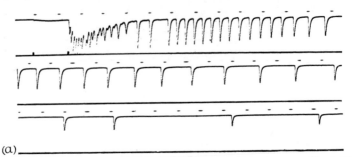

(a)

FIG. 13.27 (*a*). PHOTO-ELECTRIC RECORDING OF LUMINESCENT FLASHES OF
Acholoë astericola

Flashing induced by a pair of electrical shocks (pips on lower line). Flashes shown as downward deflexions of middle trace. Time scale above, 1/sec.

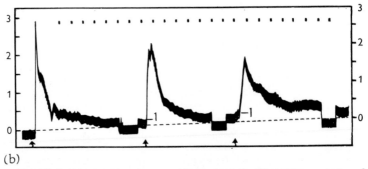

(b)

FIG. 13.27 (*b*). RECORD OF LUMINESCENT RESPONSES OF *Chaetopterus variopedatus*,
RECORDED BY MULTIPLIER PHOTOCELL AND GALVANOMETER

Stimuli (condenser shocks) indicated by arrows. Upward inflexion indicates luminous response. Time scale above, 1/min. 1, base line.

excites the glandular cells, leading to expulsion of a luminous secretion. Following stimulation the light intensity rises to a maximum in about 10 sec and luminescence persists for 5–10 min (Table 13.3, Fig. 13.27(*b*)). Repetitive stimulation leads to augmentation of the response, due to summation of the contractile processes in the luminescent glands and the secretion of more material. At low frequencies of stimulation the response is quite local, whereas rapid and prolonged stimulation leads to transmission of excitation through the nerve cord and a more widespread response from all luminescent regions of the body. Moreover, transmission takes place with greater facility posteriorly than anteriorly through the nerve cord (53). Likewise, in hemichordates, the luminescent response is mediated by the nervous system, organized as a nerve net (p. 423). Repetitive discharge in the nerve net leads to spreading of the luminous response; neuro-effector facilitation occurs, grading the intensity of the response by recruitment of photocytes (1).

Still uncertain is the method of regulation obtaining in *Pyrosoma*. The fact that light appears only on stimulation and then spreads over the colony is additional evidence that the animal produces its own photogenic material. Panceri implicated muscular tissue and presumably an associated nerve supply, extending from one individual to another, in the transmission of excitation, but there is still no clear idea how such transmission occurs and how lighting is regulated.

Some fragmentary observations on luminescence in fishes are available. In the shark *Etmopterus* luminescence follows tactile stimulation after a rather lengthy latent period. The numerous photophores of the teleost *Porichthys* lighten under electrical stimulation (Fig. 13.6(*b*)). With bursts of induction shocks luminescence appears after a latency of 8–10 sec, increases to a maximum in about 15 sec, and then slowly fades. Light can also be evoked in this species and in the bathypelagic *Echiostoma ctenobarba* by the injection of adrenaline. Anatomical studies of *Lampanyctus*, *Cyclothone* and *Argyropelecus* have shown that the photophores are innervated by branches of the trigeminal, facial and spinal nerves. The action of adrenaline suggests that adrenergic fibres are responsible for mediating the luminescent response, and these presumably are sympathetic fibres running to the photophores in the nerves just mentioned. Suprarenal tissue is also present in the anterior kidney region of teleosts, and the secretion of adrenaline into the blood stream may also be concerned with the luminescent response.

Indirect Nervous Control

Most of our information about indirect control of luminescence in marine animals is based on inferences from morphology, and physiological studies are rare. Several types of control can be recognized, but there is much specific variation in the way in which it is achieved. Examples of neuromuscular regulation of secretion may be considered first. One of the best-known is *Cypridina*, in which contraction of muscles squeezes granules of luciferin and luciferase out of separate glandular cells. On meeting in the sea water the luciferase catalyses the oxidation of luciferin, and luminescence results. In the teleost *Malacocephalus* there are ventral light-glands which are provided with smooth muscle and nerves (Fig. 13.20). The discharge of luminous slime in this fish results, in all probability, from the action of muscles which squeeze the gland (39, 40). Probably belonging to the same category are certain myopsid squid such as *Heteroteuthis*, which discharge a luminous cloud in a manner analogous to the discharge of ink in other forms. It is possible that muscular control may also be involved in certain Crustacea such as *Gnathophausia*, which pour forth a luminous material.

Of a somewhat different nature are those animals in which muscular action regulates the emission of light from photophores. In the bathy-pelagic cephalopod *Vampyroteuthis infernalis* there is near the apex of the body a pair of photophores which can be occluded by folds of skin. The teleosts *Anomalops* and *Photoblepharon*, which utilize symbiotic bacteria, have achieved regulation of luminescence in two different ways. In *Photoblepharon* a screen of black tissue is present, which can be raised over the light-organ like a lower eye-lid. In *Anamolops* the light-organ itself can rotate, thus exposing or concealing the light-source, and the fish flashes its lights on and off as it swims through the water. Pelagic stomiatoid teleosts are also able to regulate the emission of light by rotating the post-orbital light-organ (2, 30).

Another type of muscular regulation is presented by those luminescent squid whose light-organs are overlaid by chromatophores, as *Leachia*, *Watasenia* and *Abraliopsis*. The firefly squid *Watasenia scintillans* occurs in large numbers off the Japanese coast in spring and early summer, and has been available for examination alive. The large brachial light-organs of this species emit short flashes, lasting some 30 sec, with varying periodicity. Luminescence of other photophores (ocular, mantle series) varies in intensity from time to time, but may persist for 20 min or more. Mechanical and electrical stimulation causes these organs to luminesce strongly. Chromatophoral movements are probably involved in control of light-emission from photophores of *Watasenia*. The pigment cells of cephalopods, it will be recalled, are activated by muscle fibres (p. 504), and contraction and expansion of the pigment cells can control emission of light from underlying photophores. Whether light-production is controlled directly by the nervous system, as well, has not been clearly established.

Indirect control of lighting by chromatophores also occurs in certain teleosts, for example *Coelorhynchus* and *Hymenocephalus*, in which light shines through the skin from light-organs situated at deeper levels. The amount of light emitted can be increased or decreased by concentration or dispersion of chromatophores. These structures are effectors *per se*, and are subject to various degrees of nervous control in teleosts (28).

Some of the photophores which have been described above reveal a pattern of optical structure remarkably similar to that of an eye, and this has given rise to the suggestion that a device for regulating the focus may be present in some photophores. The photophores of both *Nyctiphanes* and *Abraliopsis* are complex structures in which the lenses are invested by a circular ring of tissue that could have a focusing function, but the idea is wholly conjectural, and it is uncertain whether muscle is even present in those regions.

Effect of Ionic Environment on Luminescence

Anisosmotic solutions and unbalanced salt solutions have been tested on many luminescent species. Dilute sea water or fresh water usually evokes luminescence, and fresh water was a favoured means of causing animals to luminesce (coelenterates, polychaetes and many others). Hyperosmotic sea water is without effect on *Chaetopterus*. Isosmotic solutions of single salts have effects as follows. K^+ excites luminescence in *Pelagia*, *Cavernularia*, ctenophores, *Chaetopterus* and polynoids (prolonged glow). Na^+ causes luminescence in *Chaetopterus*, polynoids (quick flashes) and *Ophiopsila* (Na^+ in excess). Ca^{++} produces a state of hyperirritability in *Pelagia*, ctenophores and polychaetes. Mg^{++} has a narcotizing effect. Ca^{++} and Mg^{++} counteract the excitatory effect of Na^+ but not K^+ in excess (polynoids). By using the inert substance choline chloride it can be shown that K^+ excites only in excess (>0.05 M KCl). The excitatory effect of Ca^{++} may be due to absence of Mg^{++}. In experiments of this kind the several ions may be acting at several loci, namely peripheral receptors, nerves and photogenic cells. In polynoid scales it seems clear that Na^+ at first stimulates the nervous system, then the photocytes; K^+ may act similarly, but always produces a protracted response indicating maximal direct excitation of the photogenic cells. Any gross alteration of the external medium is liable to produce depolarization of the nerve membrane, causing excitation (e.g. fresh water, sugar solutions, K^+, Na^+, NH_4^+, etc.). And the photocytes of different species will themselves be excited directly by these abnormal media (34).

BIOLOGICAL SIGNIFICANCE OF LUMINESCENCE

There is still much uncertainty about the possible function and significance of luminescence in marine animals, although several explanations and theories have been advanced. This is due in large part to the difficulty of observing luminescent organisms under natural conditions and of noting the possible effects of such displays on other animals. Neither is it easy to devise experiments to put to test the various theories dealing with the function of luminescence, as has been done by Sumner, for example, in his investigations of the survival value of colour responses. There are definite indications, however, that not one but several explanations are involved, and that luminescence will prove to have different functions in various species.

The luminescent bacteria and fungi usually shine continuously, but in nearly all luminous animals light emission is under the control of the animal. Harvey has suggested that the mechanism for producing light has arisen in the course of evolution from some chemical process already present in the cell, possibly one involved in cellular respiration. The widespread and irregular occurrence of vital luminescence indicates that it has appeared and evolved on many occasions. At first a fortuitous accompaniment of some intracellular reaction, without intrinsic significance, as in bacteria, it has been elaborated for special purposes in higher organisms. There is, of course, no reason why such transformations should not be occurring today, and animals may indeed be encountered showing various steps in the evolution of luminescence. In the protozoa, luminescence, it has been suggested, may be a by-product of some reaction evoked directly or indirectly by external stimulation and have no special biological role. In crustacea, molluscs and teleosts, however, the light-producing structures are frequently so complex and highly organized that it is reasonable to conclude they subserve special functions, and have considerable adaptive and ethological significance.

The main theories dealing with the function of luminescence may be summarized under the headings of protection (specific and individual), luring of food, illumination of surroundings for visual purposes and recognition signals. These will be considered as far as the available evidence permits.

A general hypothesis dealing with the luminescence of planktonic and other organisms has been outlined by Burkenroad (13). He suggests that luminescence may act in the manner of a burglar-alarm in that the light produced by an animal when disturbed by a predator may in turn attract an enemy of the predator. In this way luminescent planktonic animals may expose predator to predator along the length of the food chain. Somewhat similar is the suggestion that when one individual in a group of actively swimming animals is stimulated into luminescence, it might serve as a warning to the others and cause their flight.

The inference seems fairly strong that in certain bottom forms the display of luminescence may have the role of a sacrifice lure, e.g. polynoid worms which throw off flashing scales when irritated.

There are certain animals which discharge a luminous cloud into the surrounding sea water when irritated, such as the deep-sea shrimp *Systellaspis*, the squid *Heteroteuthis*, the mysid *Gnathophausia* and the teleost *Malacocephalus*. The light produced by these animals may have protective value by confusing or bewildering the attacker. Remarkably enough, there are some blind luminescent animals. The majority of luminescent copepods are blind, and the deep-sea ray *Benthobatis moresbyi*, which possesses a series of light-producing spots on the margin of the head, has rudimentary eyes. In these animals a visual function is definitely excluded (39).

It is uncertain whether luminescence in any animal is concerned with securing food. The light-organs on the tips of barbels and anterior dorsal fin rays in stomiatoid fishes such as *Eustomias* and *Chirostomias* and in *Ceratias* and other ceratioid angler-fishes, are suggestive of fishing lures (Figs. 13.6(c) and 13.16). The peculiar arrangement by which photophores illuminate the interior of the oro-pharyngeal cavity of certain teleosts (e.g. *Chauliodus*) may serve to attract prey into the mouth of the fish. Those mesopelagic animals with well-developed eyes and photophores may be able to detect weak light reflected from the surfaces of other organisms. Telltale gleams of this kind would provide valuable clues of the presence nearby of possible prey in bathypelagic waters where the population density is relatively low. The dark brown and black coloration of deep-sea fish, and the reds of bathypelagic crustacea, may be an adaptation to reduce such reflexion to a minimum (2, 41, 62).

Finally, there is the significance of luminescence as a means of recognition between members of a species. The best-authenticated case among marine animals is that of the polychaete *Odontosyllis*, in which both sexes luminesce during spawning. Members of this species exhibit well-marked lunar periodicity, and swarm in surface waters about an hour after sunset on the second, third and fourth days after full moon. The female displays a bright continuous glow lasting 10–20 sec while the male flashes intermittently. During the spawning process the female swims about rapidly in small circles near the surface and becomes brightly luminous. The males approach obliquely upwards from deeper water and make for the centre of the luminous ring. Both sexes then shed their gametes into the water. If the male worm fails to reach the female before her light fades, he hesitates until she becomes luminescent again, and then re-approaches her to complete the spawning act.

Certain oegopsid squid and teleosts have well-defined photophore-patterns which could serve as intraspecific recognition signals. The many species of myctophid fish differ in the number and arrangement of light-organs. Squids differ not only in the quantitative arrangement of their photophores, but in the colour of the light emitted as well. In *Watasenia* there are also differences in the photophores of the two sexes. Harvey suggests that luminescence in this last species may be a means of attraction between the sexes during the spring migration to the surface. Since both squid and fish school, the photophores may aid in holding the shoal together and the photophores of deep-sea crustaceans may have a similar function. Certain bathypelagic teleosts of the family Melanostomiatidae also show sexual differences in the structure and colours of their luminescent barbels, and these differences may have behavioural significance (2, 46).

Estimates have been made of the distances at which luminous flashes can be detected. For an eye as least as sensitive as the human eye, the distances are unlikely to exceed 10–20 m for the lights of many pelagic animals (18).

With the development of highly sensitive light-detectors capable of withstanding great pressures—bathyphotometers—much information has accumulated about the occurrence of luminescence in deep regions of the oceans. These devices yield data for intensity, spectral composition and temporal characteristics of separable flashes, but do not reveal directly the kinds of organisms producing the light. Flashes have been detected down to depths of 3,750 m; they sometimes occur in distinct horizontal layers. Frequency and intensity of flashing fall off rapidly below 1,000 m, and this is about the greatest depth at which light from the surface is still strong enough for vision. Some luminescent layers, distinguishable by their patterns of flashing and corresponding to strata of particular kinds of luminescent animals, perform vertical migrations (see p. 321). The animals tend to follow optimal light intensities but deviations have been noted which have been attributed to light adaptation, or to responses affected by the rate of change of illumination (17, 18).

Layers of bright luminescence have been found associated with shallow and deep scattering layers (which can be detected with echo-sounding gear), and present studies are directed to discovering the animals responsible for these instrumental manifestations, their densities, migrations, and the regulation of their migrations by external and internal factors including light. Likely candidates are euphausiids, shrimp and fish (5).

REFERENCES

1. BAXTER, C. H. and PICKENS, P. E., "Control of luminescence in hemichordates," *J. Exp. Biol.*, **41**, 1 (1964).

2. BEEBE, W. and CRANE, J., "Deep-sea fishes of the Bermuda oceanographic expeditions. Family Melanostomiatidae," *Zoologica, N.Y.*, **24**, 65 (1939).

3. BEEBE, W. and CRANE, J., "Eastern Pacific expeditions of the N.Y. Zoological Society. 37. Deep-sea ceratioid fishes," ibid., **31**, 151 (1947).

4. BERTELSEN, E., "The ceratioid fishes," Dana-Rept. No. 39, 276 pp. (1951).

5. BODEN, B. P. and KAMPA, E. M., "Planktonic bioluminescence," *Oceanogr Mar. Biol. Ann.-Rev.*, **2**, 341 (1964).

6. BONHOMME, C., "Recherches sur l'histologie de l'appareil lumineux des Polynoïnés," *Bull. Inst. Océanogr. Monaco*, No. 803, 8 pp. (1942).

7. BONHOMME, C., "L'appareil lumineux de *Chaetopterus variopedatus* Clap. Recherches histologiques," ibid., No. 843, 7 pp. (1943).

8. BONHOMME, C., "La luminescence de *Heterocirrus bioculatus* Keferstein," ibid., No. 871, 7 pp. (1944).

9. BONHOMME, C., "Sur un mode particular d'élimination des produits photogenès chez *Polycirrus caliendrum* Clap. et *Polycirrus aurantiacus* Grube," *Bull. Soc. Zool. Fr.*, **77**, 341 (1953).

10. BOWDEN, B. J., "Some observations on a luminescent fresh-water limpet from New Zealand," *Biol. Bull.*, **99**, 373 (1950).

11. BRUNN, A. F., "The biology of *Spirula spirula* (L.)," Dana-Rept. No. 24, 46 pp. (1943).

12. BUCHNER, P., *Endosymbiose der Tiere mit pflanlichen Mikroorganismen* (Basel/Stuttgart, Verlag Birkhäuser, 1953).

13. BURKENROAD, M. D., "A possible function of bioluminescence," *J. Mar. Res.*, **5**, 161 (1943).

14. BURKENROAD, M. D., "The Aristaeinae, Solenocerinae and pelagic Penaeinae of the Bingham Oceanographic Collection," *Bull. Bingham Oceanogr. Coll.*, **5**, Art. 2 (1936).

15. CHASE, A. M., "The chemistry of *Cypridina* luciferin," *Ann. N.Y. Acad. Sci.*, **49**, 353 (1948).

16. CHANG, J. J., "Analysis of the luminescent response of the ctenophore, *Mnemiopsis leidyi*, to stimulation," *J. Cell. Comp. Physiol.*, **44**, 365 (1954).

17. CLARKE, G. L. and BACKUS, R. H., "Interrelations between the vertical migration of deep scattering layers, bioluminescence and changes in daylight in the sea," *Bull. Inst. Océanogr. Monaco*, **64**, No. 1318 (1964).

18. CLARKE, G. L. and DENTON, E. J., "Light and animal life," in *The Sea*, Ed. Hill, M. N., Vol. 1, p. 456 (New York, London, Interscience Publishers, 1962).

19. CORMIER, M. J. and TOTTER, J. R., "Bioluminescence," *Ann. Rev. Biochem.*, **33**, 43 (1964).

20. DAVENPORT, D. and NICOL, J. A. C., "Luminescence in Hydromedusae," *Proc. Roy. Soc. B.*, **144**, 399 (1955).

21. DAVENPORT, D. and NICOL, J. A. C., "Observations on luminescence in sea pens," ibid., **144**, 480 (1955).

22. DENNELL, R., "On the structure of the photophores of some decapod crustacea," *'Discovery' Rep.*, **20**, 307 (1940).

23. DURE, L. S. and CORMIER, M. J., "Requirements of luminescence in extracts of a Balanoglossid," *J. Biol. Chem.*, **236**, PC 48 (1961).

24. ECKERT, R., "Bio-electric control of bioluminescence in *Noctiluca*," *Science*, **147**, 1140 (1965).

25. ENDERS, H. E., "A study of the life-history and habits of *Chaetopterus variopedatus*, Renier et Claparède," *J. Morph.*, **20**, 479 (1909).

26. FÖRSTER, J., "Über die Leuchtorgane und das Nervensystem von *Pholas dactylus*," *Z. wiss Zool.*, **109**, 349 (1914).

27. HANEDA, Y., "On the luminescence of the fishes belonging to the family Leiognathidae of the tropical Pacific," *Stud. Palao Trop. Biol. Sta.*, **2**, 29 (1940).

28. HANEDA, Y., "The luminescence of some deep-sea fishes of the families Gadidae and Macrouridae," *Pacif. Sci.*, **5**, 372 (1951).

29. HANEDA, Y., "Some luminous fishes of the genera *Yarrella* and *Polyipnus*," ibid., **6**, 13 (1952).

30. HANEDA, Y., "Observation on some marine luminous organisms of Hachijo Island, Japan," *Rec. Oceanogr. Wks. Jap.*, **1** (N.S.), 103 (1953).

31. HANEDA, Y., "Squid producing an abundant luminous secretion found in Suruga Bay, Japan," *Sci. Rept. Yokosuka City Mus.*, No. 1 (1956).

32. HANEDA, Y., "Observations on luminescence in the deep sea fish, *Paratrachichthys prosthemius*," ibid., No. 2 (1957).

33. HANEDA, Y. and JOHNSON, F. H., "The photogenic organs of *Parapriacanthus* and other fish," *J. Morph.*, **110**, 187 (1962).

34. HARVEY, E. N., *Bioluminescence* (New York, Academic Press, 1952).

35. HARVEY, E. N. and TSUJI, F. J., "Luminescence of Cypridina luciferin without luciferase together with an appraisal of the term luciferin," *J. Cell, Comp. Physiol.*, **44**, 63 (1954).

36. HASTINGS, J. W., "Oxygen concentration and bioluminescence intensity. 2. *Cypridina hilgendorfii*," *J. Cell. Comp. Physiol.*, **40**, 1 (1952).

37. HASTINGS, J. W. and SWEENEY, B. M., "On the mechanisms of temperature independence in a biological clock," *Proc. Nat. Acad. Sci., Wash.*, **43**, 804 (1957).

38. HERFURTH, A. H., "Beiträge zur Kenntnis der Bakteriensymbiose der Cephalopoden," *Z. Morph. Ökol. Tiere*, **31**, 561 (1936).

39. HICKLING, C. F., "A new type of luminescence in fishes. 1.," *J. Mar. Biol. Ass. U.K.*, **13**, 914 (1925).

40. HICKLING, C. F., "A new type of luminescence in fishes. 2," ibid. **14**, 495 (1926).
41. HICKLING, C. F., "The luminescence of the dogfish *Spinax niger* Cloquet," *Nature*, **121**, 280 (1928).
42. JOHANN, L., "Über eigenthümliche epitheliale Gebilde (Leuchtorgane) bei *Spinax niger*," *Z. wiss. Zool.*, **66**, 136 (1899).
43. JOYEUX-LAFFUIE, J., "Étude monographique du Chétoptère (*Chaetopterus variopedatus*, Rénier), suivie d'une revision des espèces du genre *Chaetopterus*," *Arch. Zool. Exp. Gén.*, **8**, 245 (1890).
44. KAY, R. H., "Light-stimulated and light-inhibited luminescence of the euphausiid *Meganyctiphanes norvegica*," *Proc. Roy. Soc.*, B, **162**, 365 (1965).
45. McELROY, W. O. and CHASE, A. M., "Purification of *Cypridina* luciferase," *J. Cell. Comp. Physiol.*, **38**, 401 (1951).
46. MARSHALL, N. B., *Aspects of Deep Sea Biology* (London, Hutchinson, 1954).
47. MASON, H. S. and DAVIS, E. F., "Cypridina luciferin. Partition chromatography," *J. Biol. Chem.*, **197**, 41 (1952).
48. MOORE, A. R., "Inhibizione della luminescenza nei ctenofori," *Arch. Sci. Biol., Napoli*, **8**, 112 (1926).
49. MOORE, A. R., "Galvanic stimulation of luminescence in *Pelagia noctiluca*," *J. Gen. Physiol.*, **9**, 375 (1926).
50. NICOL, J. A. C., "Physiological control of luminescence in animals," in *The Luminescence of Biological Systems*, Ed. Johnson, F. H. (Wash. D.C., Amer. Ass. Adv. Sci., 1955).
51. NICOL, J. A. C., "Spectral composition of the light of polynoid worms," *J. Mar. Biol. Ass. U.K.*, **36**, 529 (1957).
52. NICOL, J. A. C., "Spectral composition of the light of *Pholas dactylus*," ibid., **37**, 43 (1958).
53. NICOL, J. A. C., "The regulation of light emission in animals," *Biol. Rev.*, **35**, 1 (1960).
54. NICOL, J. A. C., "Animal luminescence," *Adv. Comp. Physiol. Biochem.*, **1**, 217 (1962).
55. OKADA, Y. K., "Luminescence et organe photogène des Ostracodes," *Bull. Soc. Zool. Fr.*, **51**, 478 (1926).
56. PANCERI, P., "The luminous organs and the light of the Pholades," *Quart. J. Micr. Sci.*, **12**, 254 (1872).
57. PLESNER, P. E., "Light emission mechanism of *Pholas*," *Publ. Staz. Zool. Napoli*, **31**, XLIV (1959).
58. SA, R. DE, HASTINGS, J. W. and VATTER, A. E., "Luminescent 'crystalline' particles," *Science*, **141**, 1269 (1963).
59. SWEENEY, B. M., "Bioluminescent dinoflagellates," *Biol. Bull.*, **125**, 177 (1963).
60. SWEENEY, B. M. and HASTINGS, J. W., "Characteristics of the diurnal rhythm of luminescence in *Gonyaulax polyedra*," *J. Cell. Comp. Physiol.*, **49**, 115 (1957).
61. TATTERSALL, W. M. and TATTERSALL, O. S., *The British Mysidacea* (London, Ray Soc., 1951).
62. TCHERNAVIN, V. V., *The Feeding Mechanisms of a Deep Sea Fish* Chauliodus sloani *Schneider* (London, Brit. Mus. (Nat. Hist.) 1953).

63. TITSCHAK, H. VON, "Untersuchungen über das Leuchten der Seefeder," *Vie et Milieu*, **15**, 547 (1964).

64. TSUJI, F. I., CHASE, A. M. and HARVEY, E. N., "Recent studies on the chemistry of *Cypridina* luciferin," in *The Luminescence of Biological Systems*, Ed. Johnson, F. H. (Wash., D.C., Amer. Ass. Adv. Sci., 1955).

CHAPTER 14

ASSOCIATIONS

The shell-fish called Nacre (the Pinna) lives in . . . fellowship with the pinna-guardian, a little creature of the crab family that acts as porter and doorkeeper, sitting at the mouth of the shell, which it continually keeps half open.

MONTAIGNE (*trans*. Trechmann)

COMMENSALISM, PARASITISM AND SYMBIOSIS

ASSOCIATIONS between different species of marine organisms are infinite in variety and degree of complexity, and are testimony of the pressure which has driven animals into mutual or unilateral dependence. It is customary to divide animal associations into the three broad categories of commensalism, symbiosis and parasitism. Commensalism, broadly speaking, is an external relationship between two species which live together in some degree of harmony. The salient feature of this relationship is that neither partner preys or adversely lives upon the other. Moreover, the associates are not greatly modified structurally and the association is frequently facultative. In symbiosis there is a close physiological association between two species, often for mutual benefit. Parasitism, of course, is a unilateral association, in which one member preys insidiously or lives upon the substance and digested aliments of the other, without immediately destroying it. Usually the parasite is profoundly modified for its specialized existence in a direction which can be recognized as morphological degeneration.

Although many varieties of animal associations can be fitted into these categories, there are innumerable transitional cases, associations in which the balance is weighted more on one side than the other, and commensal and symbiotic relationships that verge more towards parasitism than mutual benefit. Where there is such an infinite variety of material to study and unravel, it is perhaps only natural to encounter seriated examples which display all degrees of evolution in the field under consideration. Indeed, Caullery has emphasized that these various categories are merely useful labels for modes of relationships, centres of scatter arbitrarily chosen for our convenience. Associations among the marine organisms have been reviewed by Buchner (9), Yonge (90, 91) and Dales (16).

Plant-Animal Associations

There are many examples of relationships between plants and animals which range from mere fortuitous coexistence to deliberately selected associations involving some degree of mutual benefit. In shallow coastal

578

waters algal spores settle everywhere and attempt to colonize all available surfaces. Consequently, it is not surprising to find plants growing on the backs of many sluggish littoral and sublittoral animals such as limpets, periwinkles and crabs. Such chance associations are seasonal or are terminated when the animal moults. The algae may occasionally have concealing value to their possessor, and certain spider crabs such as *Inachus* and *Hyas* have adopted the habit of masking themselves by cementing pieces of seaweed, hydroids and sponges to the spines distributed over their bodies. The decorator crab *Podochela hemphilli* not only covers itself with bits of weed, but also performs bowing movements to simulate the waving motion of seaweed in moving water. Other forms of plant-animal associations are encountered in gall-formation among fucoids. The nematode *Halenchus fucicola* invades the tissues of the seaweed *Ascophyllum nodosum*, and gives rise to warty patches or galls (13, 32).

COMMENSALISM

Commensalism between animals involves extremely diverse relationships which are very difficult to classify in any logical system. A large part of this difficulty is simply due to our ignorance of the exact relations existing between the associated animals. There are many instances of animals, termed epizoites, living attached to other species. This kind of association may be rather fortuitous, or may assume a stable character which passes into true commensalism. The commensal relationship may be entirely an external one. In addition, many examples are known of another fairly well demarcated category in which one animal, the commensal proper, has taken up its abode in the tube or dwelling of another species, the host. This relationship is termed endoecism. There is a third category, designated inquilinism, which includes those commensals accustomed to living in the body cavities or internal chambers of their hosts. In some of these associations one partner benefits by obtaining access to new food supplies, by sharing its host's refuge, by taking advantage of repellent properties of the host, etc. Reciprocal benefit, termed mutualism, is realized in certain of these partnerships; frequently, however, they are one-sided, with benefit to only one participant. From unilateral relationships and inquilinism there are various transitions to parasitism.

Epizoites

Fortuitous associations between animals are often encountered in the littoral zone, where so many sedentary species settle on all free surfaces. For example, whelks, lobsters and crabs are often seen bearing epizoitic populations of serpulids, barnacles and other sedentary species. Epizoites sometimes display definite preference for particular species, e.g. the bryozoan *Loxosomella phascolosomata* which forms small colonies on *Golfingia vulgaris*. Many instances have been recorded of hydroids living attached to the skin of fish. Simple commensal species merely use the fish as a substratum, but at least one species is parasitic and sends feeding stolons into the host's tissues (35).

Commensalism Proper

Loose associations verging on commensalism are seen in the behaviour of certain fish. The sea bass *Serranus* is described as keeping watch outside the retreats occupied by devil fish (*Octopus*), in order to seize the remnants of crustaceans captured by the latter. Grooming is a conspicuous form of social behaviour among reef fishes of tropical waters. It is a mutually beneficial activity in which brightly coloured shrimps and small fish regularly cleanse larger fish of parasites and adhering debris (57, 58, 89). Fixed and constant associations between fishes are shown by the pilot fish *Naucrates ductor* and the shark-sucker *Echeneis naucrates*, which accompany pelagic sharks and other large fish. In the remora or shark-sucker the dorsal fin is transformed into a large sucking disc which is provided with transverse pleats and occupies the dorsal surface of the head (Figs. 14.1 and 14.2). It uses this structure to attach itself to the body of the shark, and occasionally releases its hold to snatch some of the shark's food.

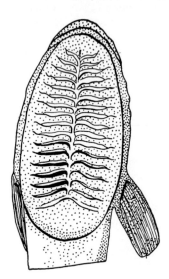

FIG. 14.1. SUCKER ON THE TOP OF THE HEAD OF THE REMORA OR SHARK SUCKER

Commensalism permits the different adaptations and structural specializations of two species to be shared, and this increases the total response range and environmental experience of the group. For the benefits accruing, however, there are frequently restrictions in other directions, resulting from a lower level or range of activity in one partner, which acts as a brake on the total activity of the ensemble. Many examples of this are seen in associations with anemones, in which more active animals are restricted to the environs of their host actinian, etc. Some degree of morphological differentiation is often evident in commensal associations, and one example involving the sucking disc of the remora has already been cited above, while others will be noted in subsequent pages. Physiological adaptations are more subtle and still await exploration. One interesting case involving the chromatophore responses of the amphipod *Hyperia galba*, which is commensal with such medusae as *Rhizostoma* and *Chrysaora*, has been treated in Chapter 12. It is obvious that such fixed associations must also involve considerable specialization of sensori-neural processes and behavioural activities, either of an inherent or of an acquired character, and recent studies, such as those by Davenport (18), draw attention to the wealth of fertile problems in this particular field.

There are numerous instances of commensalism involving a coelenterate and some other animal, and it is probably such associations that are best known. Permanent associations occur between certain spider-crabs and sea-anemones, in which the anemone is used for protection. The spider-crab *Macropodia rostrata* is always found in the neighbourhood of the anemone *Anemonia sulcata*; the crab usually stations itself close to the anemone, and when disturbed it works its way back upon the crown of the anemone, which makes no attempt to seize its guest. Both members derive benefit from this relationship, the spider-crab obtaining protection

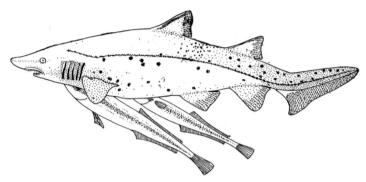

Fig. 14.2. Sand Shark (*Carcharias taurus*) with two Remoras (*Echeneis naucrates*) Attached. (Drawn from a photograph in Nat. Hist. N.Y., 1950.)

from the batteries of nematocysts and the anemone seizing food from the claws of the crab.

Much more intimate associations are established by other brachyurans. A species of Chilean crab *Hepatus chilensis* nearly always carries an actiniarian *Actinoloba reticulata* upon its back. It is the anemone, apparently, which takes the initiative in this association. When separated from a crab, it first of all rests attached to the substratum. When it makes contact with a crab it attaches itself to the latter's foot, and then works its way up to the back of the crab. Somewhat similar is the behaviour of the crab *Dromia* which carries a piece of living sponge on its back, held in position by means of its last two pairs of legs. There are two other crabs, *Melia tessellata* and *Polydectus cupulifera*, which carry anemones in their pincers (Fig. 14.3). The chelae of the crab are slender and mobile, and bear a row of sharp teeth for holding the anemone. The anemone is held with the mouth upwards and the tentacles projecting away from the crab, and when the latter is disturbed, it waves its anemone-armament from side to side. The crab also utilizes its commensal associate in feeding, and removes particles of food from the tentacles of the anemone with the aid of its second pair of limbs. When the anemones are taken away from the crab, it executes a series of manoeuvres to recover its associate, first detaching the anemone from the bottom and then placing it within its pincers. The crab seems to derive most of the benefit from this relationship.

In the hermit crabs (Pauridea) the instinct to form associations with certain other organisms is particularly well displayed. The co-partners are sometimes placed by the hermit crabs upon the gastropod shells which they inhabit, and include sponges, hydroids, zoanthids, actiniarians and bryozoans. Frequently the association is very regular in that a given species of hermit crab has a particular affinity for some species of sponge or coelenterate. The European hermit crab *Eupagurus bernhardus* is usually found with an anemone *Calliactis parasitica* on its shell, and sometimes several may be present. The association in this case is not obligatory for the anemone, which often occurs free-living as well. The anemone estab-

FIG. 14.3. *Melia tessellata* FROM THE HAWAIIAN IS., BEARING ACTINIANS IN ITS PINCERS. (After Duerden, 1905.)

lishes the association without assistance from the crab by a series of manoeuvres which have the character of chain-reflexes. An unattached anemone adheres to a *Buccinum* shell by its tentacles, which discharge nematocysts; some specific attractant is involved, the anemone responding to organic material in the *Buccinum* shell. The discharge of nematocysts also is controlled, and does not occur if the anemone is already attached to a whelk shell. After the tentacles have stuck to the shell the pedal disc detaches itself, moves to the shell, attaches itself thereto, and the tentacles are then released. Other kinds of crabs play an active role and assist the anemone to attach itself on the shell (19, 79, 80). In these associations the coelenterates with their batteries of nematocysts confer some protection on the crab, and themselves benefit by being carried about to new situations and by sharing the food caught by the crab (51, 67).

More intimate is the relationship between the small hermit crab *Eupagurus prideauxi* and the cloak anemone *Adamsia palliata* (Fig. 14.4). The latter wraps itself around the shell inhabited by the crab, and as the anemone increases in size it adds to the effective capacity of the shell so that the hermit crab finds increased accommodation for its own growth. The shell in this instance is merely a base upon which the cloak anemone can establish itself, and contributes little towards sheltering the crab. The two animals are only found in association, and their intimate relationship partakes of the nature of mutualism. Another pagurid, *Paguropsis typica*, carries an anemone *Anemonia mammilifera* directly on its back without making use of a shell (14).

The necessity of some manner of protection or immunity towards the nematocytes of the coelenterate is evident in commensal relationships of the kind just described. In the cloak-anemone–hermit-crab association, it appears that the blood of *Eupagurus* contains an antibody effective against the toxins of *Adamsia*, which are fatal to other species of hermit crabs (3).

Commensalism with coelenterates involves a wide variety of marine animals besides Crustacea. In coral reefs of the Indo-Pacific region perma-

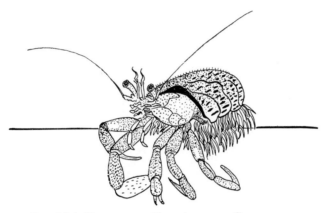

FIG. 14.4. *Eupagurus prideauxi* AND ITS COMMENSAL,
THE CLOAK ANEMONE *Adamsia palliata*

The basal disc of the anemone is wrapped around the shell inhabited by the crab, and as the latter grows, the anemone provides increased accommodation for it.

nent associations are found between damsel-fishes (Pomacentridae) and certain large actinians. Species of *Amphiprion*, for example, find shelter among the stinging tentacles of sea-anemones (*Stoichactis*, *Actinia*). The damsel-fish never ventures far from the host-anemone, and when disturbed it may even retreat into the digestive cavity of the latter. A very close association is involved in these cases, for the damsel-fish is never found apart from the anemone, is dependent on it for protection and cares for the anemone in various ways. There are indications that the damsel-fish is not insensitive to the cnidoblasts of the anemone, but the latter, in some way, becomes conditioned to the presence of the fish (31, 88).

Various pelagic coelenterates harbour or shelter a variety of commensals. Some Scyphomedusae are often accompanied by young fish: *Cyanea capillata* by young whiting (*Gadus merlangus*), and *Rhizostoma cuvieri* by Jack-fish (*Trachurus trachurus*) and hyperiid amphipods. These animals swim underneath the jellyfish, where they are sheltered and protected by its tentacles, and they may even seek protection in the subgenital cavities. The Portuguese man-of-war *Physalia* is similarly attended by young harvest fish (*Peprilus*) and man-of-war fishes (*Nomeus*) (Fig. 14.5).

Echinoderms are another group affording protection and shelter for commensals, and there are many instances of fish, shrimps, crabs, etc.,

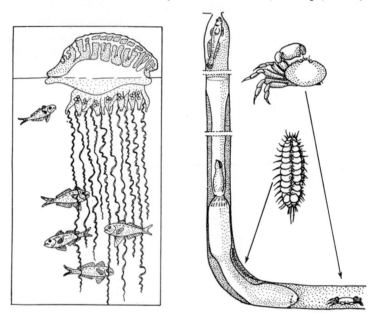

FIG. 14.5. MAN-OF-WAR FISHES SHELTERING AMONG THE
TRAILING TENTACLES OF *Physalia*

FIG. 14.6. PORTION OF THE TUNNEL OF THE ECHIUROID WORM *Urechis caupo*,
WHICH BURROWS IN SANDY MUD ON THE CALIFORNIAN COAST

The sketch shows the worm pumping water through its mucus net, and the position of its commensals. These are a goby *Clevelandia ios*, a polynoid *Harmothoë adventor*, and a pinnotherid crab *Scleroplax granulata*. (From Fisher and MacGinitie (24).)

occurring in association with sea urchins, starfish and holothurians. In these cases the commensal secures some degree of safety in the shelter of its host.

Endoecism

There are a vast number of commensals which lurk in the burrows, tubes or other dwellings of various animals, especially in the littoral and sublittoral zones where pressure of space rather than shortage of food is acute. Burrowing and tubicolous annelids, echiuroids, echinoderms, crustacea, etc., are hosts for a great variety of commensals; an illustration of a burrowing echiuroid with its several commensals is illustrated in Fig. 14.6. One of these, the polynoid worm *Harmothoë adventor*, derives not only protection from the relationship but food as well, since it seizes some of the mucus-bag by which its host carries out filter feeding (Fig. 14.6). Somewhat similar is the relation between a peculiar hydroid *Proboscidactyla* and various sabellid worms (Fig. 14.7). The hydroid attaches itself about the mouth of the worm's tube, pilfers some of the food gathered by the ciliary activity of its host and occasionally even seizes some of the latter's eggs (15, 24, 38, 68).

Scale worms (polynoids) frequent crevices and dark places, a behaviour that is governed by taxes of various kinds. Also, many species are commensals, and the same factors that determine choice of habitat in free-living polynoids may influence commensals to occupy inhabited burrows, etc. Indeed, some scale-worms are facultative commensals, either free-living or associating with other animals, e.g. *Harmothoë lunulata*; commensals of this species vary in appearance with different hosts. Degrees of facultative association terminate in obligate commensalism, when the commensal becomes closely associated with a particular host, e.g. *Acholoë* in the ambulacral grooves of the starfish *Astropecten* (16, 17)

Experimental analyses of host-commensal relationships in polynoid worms have shown that some species are attracted by specific substances given off by their co-partners. Thus *Arctonoë fragilis*, which is a commensal

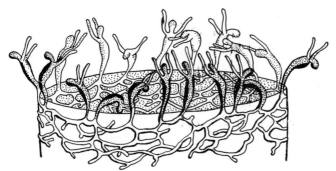

FIG. 14.7. *Proboscidactyla stellata* (= *Lar sabellarum*), A COMMENSAL HYDROID LIVING ON THE TUBE OF A SABELLID *Branchiomma vesiculosum*. (After Gosse, 1877.)

of various starfishes *Evasterias*, etc., is attracted by the scent of its host and can distinguish between water coming from its host and sea water alone. Moreover, the attraction is a specific one, and *Arctonoë* from one host species is not attracted to other species of starfish. Other commensal polynoids give positive responses to host and related species. *Polynoë scolopendrina*, for example, is attracted to its normal host, *Polymnia nebulosa*, and to other terebellids in lesser degree. The chemical attractants appear to be unstable or closely bound substances in the partnerships investigated (18, 41).

An often cited commensal is *Nereis fucata* which lives in whelk shells inhabited by hermit crabs (*Eupagurus bernhardus*). The worm usually lies withdrawn in the upper coils of the shell, where it maintains a current of water by steady or intermittent pulsations of its body. When the hermit crab is manipulating a piece of food, however, the worm extends its head outside the shell, and seizes some of the food from the crab's mandibles (7, 23). Gosse (33) has described the activities of the worm as follows.

> While I was feeding one of my Soldiers by giving him a fragment of cooked meat, which he having seized with one claw had transformed to the foot-jaws, and was munching, I saw protrude from between the body of the Crab and the Whelk-shell the head of a beautiful worm, *Nereis bilineata*, which rapidly glided out round the Crab's right cheek, and, passing between the upper and lower foot-jaws, seized the morsel of food, and, retreating, forcibly dragged it from the Crab's very mouth. I beheld this with amazement, admiring that, though the Crab sought to recover his hold, he manifested not the least sign of anger at the actions of the Worm. . . . I was surprised to observe what a cavern opened beneath the pointed head of the *Nereis* when it seized the morsel, and with what force comparatively large pieces were torn off and swallowed, and how firmly the throat-jaws held the piece when it would not yield. Occasionally it was dragged quite away from the Crab's jaws, and quickly carried into the recesses of the shell; sometimes in this case he put in one of his claws and recovered his morsel; at others he gave a sudden start at missing his grasp, which frightened the Worm and made it let go and retreat; but sometimes the latter made good his foray, and enjoyed his plunder in secret.

Among Crustacea many copepods are commensal in habit: *Hersiliodes*, for example, lives in the sand galleries of the burrowing shrimp *Callianassa*. Porcelain crabs of the genus *Polyonyx* are frequent associates of various tubicolous polychaetes, for example *Loimia* and *Chaetopterus*. Apart from protection certain of these commensal forms are undoubtedly dependent upon water currents created by their hosts.

Inquilinism

Inquilinism is one route to parasitism, and in some groups, such as copepods, species can be found that represent all steps from simple commensals sheltering within the host to specialized parasites. In the copepod sub-order Notodelphoida, living in ascidians, forms like *Notodelphys* and *Doropygus* have biting mouth parts resembling those of free-living copepods. They live in the branchial chamber of their hosts, and seize food particles brought in by water currents. Certain other forms such as *Enterocola* and *Enteropsis* have moved into the stomach or epicardial tubes of the ascidian and feed on the fluids of the host.

Pinnotherid (pea) crabs are usually regarded as inquiline commensals, but their behaviour is more suggestive of parasitism. They commonly live in the mantle cavity of lamellibranchs, but occasionally in other animals such as echinoids, holothurians and ascidians, or in the burrows of polychaetes and burrowing shrimps (*Callianassa*). The pea-crab obtains oxygen and food from the currents of water passing through the mantle cavity of the lamellibranch, and competes with the mollusc by removing some of the mucus-strings passing towards its mouth. As a result of its activities it often weakens or even injures the gills of its bivalve host. Usually there is only one pea-crab in a mollusc, and some forms are rather specific in their hosts (66, 85). Other inquiline crustacea are the shrimp *Pontonia* found in the mantle cavity of *Pinna*, and *Typton* living in the sponge *Desmacidon*. There are also certain inquiline polychaetes, for example the polynoid *Hipponoë* occurring in the mantle cavity of the goose barnacle *Lepas*, and inquiline nemertines among the Malacobdellidae, which are provided with suckers and live in the mantle cavity of lamellibranchs.

Certain teleosts have also adopted the habit of living inside other sedentary animals and display suitable modifications of structure. The genus *Carapus* contains slender eel-like fishes, some of which inhabit crevices, while others are inquiline in habit. The needle fish, *C. acus* for example, dwells in the intestine of a sea-cucumber, which it enters tail first. The fish appears to react first to a chemical stimulus (probably to a substance carried in the mucus of the holothurian), and then to the anal current (2). A small fish *Apogonichthys* utilizes the gastropod *Strombus*, and many gobies and blennies are inquilines in internal chambers of reef sponges. These fishes are generally small and slender in form and live in tubular sponges or those with large internal cavities (36, 37).

Most investigations of commensalism have been descriptive in nature, and it is only recently that these associations have been subjected to experimentation. On analysis it appears that three aspects need to be recognized in an appreciation of commensal associations. These are: the economics of the association, i.e. their effect on survival of both associates; their evolutionary origin; and the behaviour patterns concerned with initiating and maintaining the commensal condition. In many respects the same conditions of analysis are applicable to parasitic and symbiotic relationships, described in later sections.

Precise analyses of the economics of commensal associations have still to be sought, but it is obvious that there is often sharing of food, provision of sheltered environments, etc. It would be interesting to have information establishing ecological parameters, limits of tolerance and partition of foodstuffs in representative associations.

The behaviour of many commensals is obviously specialized and adapted towards cementing the association. Three problems in commensal behaviour can be distinguished. First, how do the commensals succeed in reaching their host? Second, once the host is reached, what factors bind the commensal to the host? Third, how does the reciprocal behaviour of the host affect the association?

It must be confessed that little is known about how commensals seek out and adopt their hosts. In species with planktonic stages it is suggested that the larva first chooses a suitable substrate, and then reacts to other, more precise, stimuli, in locating the host within that environment. Once the host is reached, other factors intervene to cement the association, among which thigmotaxis and chemotaxis are probably of great importance. The specific responses of pea-crabs and polynoids to certain host species show that the releasing stimuli are likewise highly specific in character. Where the host plays an active part, e.g. in associations between anemones and other animals, the behaviour patterns of both participants need precise analysis. Davenport in a disciplined review (18) has discussed these factors in terms of established associations and their evolutionary origin.

PARASITISM

Parasitism involves modes of life easily recognizable as such, but difficult to define because of their heterogeneity. Ectoparasites and endoparasites live on or within a host and derive their nutriment from the latter's tissues or fluids. As distinct from predators they do not immediately kill the animal upon which they subsist, although they may ultimately encompass its destruction by severely reducing its tissues or drastically curtailing its nourishment. There are, of course, many border-line cases which are referred by usage to commensalism, parasitism or symbiosis, and many which require further study for clarification.

In some groups—for example sporozoans and cestodes—all members are parasitic, whereas others contain only a few species which have assumed a parasitic existence. Among the latter are many excellent examples illustrating graduated modifications towards parasitic specialization. The numbers of parasites are incredibly vast: indeed it has been estimated that since every animal contains several species of parasites, the latter, in species and individuals, must far outnumber the free-living animals (42). Of that multitude several have been chosen from marine groups containing predominantly non-parasitic members.

Coelenterates and Ctenophores. Some interesting parasitic species occur among coelenterates. Ectoparasitic hydroids which live on the skin of fishes have already been mentioned (p. 579). A minute anthomedusan *Mnestra*, bearing abortive tentacles, is found attached to the nudibranch *Phyllirrhoe* (Fig. 13.5). This relationship, originally considered to be one of parasitization of the snail by the medusa, now receives a reverse explanation. *Mnestra* is regarded as the degenerate medusa of *Zanclea* and other coastal hydroids, which *Phyllirrhoe* utilizes as a pelagic vehicle in early stages of its life-history. As *Phyllirrhoe* matures it dispenses with its starved and degenerate host. Some of the Narcomedusae have a life-history complicated by parasitism in the actinula stage. The planulae, as in *Cunina*, attach themselves to other Trachymedusae or Hydromedusae where they live parasitically and bud off medusae. And larval actinians of the genus *Peachia* live for a time attached to the tissues of various Hydromedusae and Schyphomedusae (*Cyanea, Aequorea, Catostylus*) before taking up a benthic existence (1, 6, 55, 71).

Annelids. Only a few polychaetes have turned to parasitism, and these do not show any profound alteration in structure. A syllid *Ichthyotomus sanguinarius*, extensively investigated by Eisig (22), provides some interesting details. This animal attaches itself to the fins of eels (*Myrus, Conger*) by a pair of scissor-shaped stylets, which are opened out to hold the para-site in position. The worm feeds on the blood which escapes from the wound. *Ichthyotomus* still bears most of the characteristics of a free-living syllid, but the cephalic appendages have disappeared and the specialized stylets appear to be derived from the buccal teeth of carnivorous forms. In the head there are two pairs of large haemophilic glands, which secrete an anti-coagulant, and these have their homologues in the cutaneous glands of non-parasitic syllids (Fig. 14.8).

There are several species of eunicids which are parasitic during their young stages in various other polychaetes and echiuroids, for example, *Oligognathus bonelliae* in *Bonellia, Drilonereis* in *Protula* and *Labrorostra-tus parasiticus* in *Odontosyllis* (69). The parasites show no regression apart

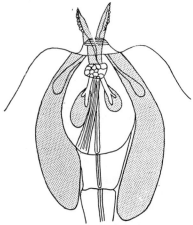

FIG. 14.8. PIERCING STYLETS AND HAEMOPHILIC GLANDS IN THE HEAD OF THE PARASITIC SYLLID *Ichthyotomus sanguinarius.* (From Eisig (22).)

from a slight simplification of jaws. They invade the host when the latter is still very small, increase in size with it and finally leave it to reproduce. Other polychaetes are also parasitic in their early stages. Thus the alciopid larva of *Corynocephalus albomaculatus* is found in the digestive cavity of the ctenophore *Cydippe*.

More highly specialized are the Histriobdellidae, of which *Histriobdella homari* is found in the gill chamber or among the eggs of the lobster. These animals are simple in structure and are sometimes included among the archiannelids. The myzostomarians are well-known associates of feather stars, crinoids and ophiuroids. Some species, e.g. *Myzostoma cirriferum* on *Antedon*, are commensals rather than parasites. Others, more sedentary, form lesions in the skin of the host, whereas true endoparasitic species like *M. pulvinar*, which is found in the crinoid *Septometra*, invade the digestive tract of their hosts (3).

The Hirudinea contain some marine species, for example *Pontobdella* and *Branchellion*, parasitic on rays, skates and sharks. These leeches are blood-suckers with biting mouth parts, and attach themselves by means of suckers to fish they encounter.

Molluscs. Molluscs, like annelids, constitute a group in which parasitism is the exception rather than the rule. One family of lamellibranchs, the Lucinidae, contains members more or less parasitic on echinoderms. Among gastropods there is a variety of ecto- and endoparasites showing different degrees of specialization and regression of organs as the result of parasitism. The forms associated with echinoderms, in particular, afford a remarkable series showing alterations of structure along the road of a parasitic existence (Fig. 14.9).

Certain species of *Eulima* (Eulimidae) are still free-living, or exist in commensalism with echinoderms. *Mucronalia variabilis* (Stiliferidae) is another gastropod living on the skin or in the digestive tube of holothurians (*Synapta*). *Mucronalia* pierces the wall of the sea cucumber with a long proboscis and sucks in the coelomic fluid of its host. It is little modified externally, but the digestive system shows profound changes: the proboscis is enlarged, the radula is absent and the oesophagus terminates as a short blind tube. *Stilifer linckiae*, an ectoparasite of the sea star *Linckia* is interesting in showing great development of a pseudopallium, which grows back to envelop the entire shell. This is a new structure, which takes the form of a collar surrounding the mouth region. There is some regression and modification in the gut: the proboscis is enlarged, the radula missing and the liver reduced. *Stilifer* pushes its proboscis into the coelom of its host and feeds on tissue fluids.

Thyca (Capulidae) is an ectoparasite of starfishes. It has a sucker by means of which it adheres to its host; opening into the centre of the latter is a muscular proboscis which is protruded and inserted into the skin of the starfish between the calcareous plates.

Two endoparasitic prosobranchs (Aglossa) will exemplify the final stages of regression achieved in this group. *Gasterosiphon deimatis* (Stiliferidae) lives inside a holothurian (*Deima*), but retains communication with the exterior by a long siphon which penetrates the skin of the sea-cucumber. This siphon swells into a bulb which encloses the visceral mass of the animal, and at the opposite pole of the latter a long thin proboscis extends to an intestinal blood vessel of the holothurian, from which the parasite obtains its nourishment. The structure within the central swelling is still recognizably a gastropod, although the foot is rudimentary and the shell has disappeared. The oesophagus leads into a stomach cavity from which ducts radiate out into a hepatopancreas. *Entoconcha* (Entoconchidae) is another endoparasite of holothurians. It is a mere vermiform tube, its siphon opens through the host's skin, and the proboscis ends in a blood vessel of the host.

Crustacea. Parasitism in crustaceans is very extensive and involves whole orders in some instances. The modifications are most diverse and range, as in gastropods, from incipient parasitism to marked degeneration.

The isopods embody three parasitic groups: the Gnathiidae, Cymo-

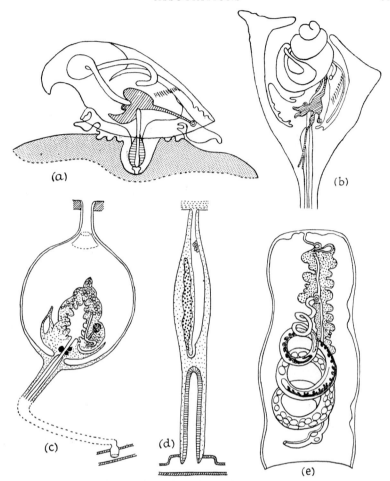

FIG. 14.9. PARASITISM IN GASTROPODS

(a) *Thyca ectoconcha*, an ectoparasite of starfish (*Linckia*); (b) *Stilifer linckiae*, parasitic in starfish; (c) *Gasterosiphon deimatus*, parasitic in holothurians; (d) *Entoconcha mirabilis*, parasitic in holothurians; (e) *E. mirabilis* in its host (*Synapta*). (Redrawn from Nancy, 1913; Ankel, 1936; Caullery (1952).)

thoidae and three families of the sub-order Epicaridea. The Gnathiidae are a rather homogeneous group of isopods in which the juveniles are blood-sucking ectoparasites of fish, and become free-living when mature. There is marked sexual dimorphism in these animals, and the two sexes were originally assigned to separate genera, *Ancaeus* for males, and *Praniza* for females and immature animals, and the term praniza is still used in refer-ring to the parasitic larvae. On hatching, a larva attaches itself to a fish by its mandibles, and perforates its skin: neither the species of host nor the position of attachment is fixed (p. 474). The blood of the host is ingested, fills the hepatic caeca of the parasite and is accommodated by a great dilation of the posterior thoracic segments. When development is complete the larvae fall off and metamorphose into adults, which no longer feed. After fertilization the embryos develop within the body of the female (62).

The cymothoids are mostly external parasites of fish. The Epicaridea are highly modified parasites found on other crustacea, and they recall the parasitic cirripedes in the extent of their transformations. The adults show considerable diversity in structure and habits but the larval forms are similar to one another and pass through three successive stages known as the epicaridium, microniscus and the cryptoniscus forms. The eggs are incubated in a special chamber situated either beneath the thorax or internally, and the eggs on hatching give rise to the epicaridium form, which has typical isopod features. This swims actively in the plankton until it encounters a copepod such as *Calanus* or *Acartia* to which it adheres by its thoracic appendages, and feeds by sucking in the haemolymph of its host. After a moult the parasite passes into the microniscus stage, and when about to quit its copepod host it undergoes a further transformation into a cryptoniscus larva which becomes free-swimming once more. The cryptoniscus larva is elongated, still with normal appendages, but possesses piercing mouth parts which it uses to attack its definitive host (Fig. 14.10).

Among the Epicaridea the bopyrid parasites are probably the best known. These animals are parasitic on prawns, anomurans and brachyurans. In *Bopyrus fougerouxi*, parasitic on the common prawn *Palaemon serratus*, the female is large, distinctly segmented and provided with appendages. A definite asymmetry is apparent and corresponds to the lateral position assumed by the parasite on the host. The prawn is attacked when still quite small, host and parasite grow in parallel and even moult together. Nourishment is obtained by sucking in the host's blood and storing it in the greatly enlarged hepatic diverticula. *Bopyrus* is dioecious and the female is accompanied by a dwarf male which adheres to its under-surface.

The cryptoniscid *Liriopsis pygmaea* is a highly modified epicaridian living as a hyperparasite on *Peltogaster*, itself a rhizocephalan parasite of the hermit crab *Eupagurus*. During its growing phase *Liriopsis* feeds on the body fluids of *Peltogaster*, and causes atrophy of the ovary in its host. Once mature, however, it ceases to feed, and the ovary of *Peltogaster* regenerates and becomes functional. This is an interesting instance of partial and temporary castration which may be compared with more profound changes induced by bopyrid and rhizocephalan parasites (3, 83).

The entoniscids inhabiting the visceral cavity of porcellanid and brachyuran crabs are the most specialized of epicaridian parasites. The cryptoniscus larva of *Portunion maenadis*, to mention one species, penetrates the hypodermis of the shore crab *Carcinus maenas*, where it moults and metamorphoses into a larval form devoid of appendages (Fig. 14.10). It gradually makes its way into the visceral cavity and, in the case of the female, becomes a saccular structure surrounded by a cellular sheath and devoid of all resemblance to an isopod. Segments and appendages are no

longer apparent, and the thorax becomes enveloped by enormous oosteg-
ites bounding an incubation chamber. The males are dwarf animals retaining the metameric appearance of isopods and are found in the incubation
chamber of the female. When the female parasite reaches maturity, an
opening is formed through the body wall of the host and larvae are discharged to the exterior through this opening (86).

Sex determination in these animals shows certain interesting features

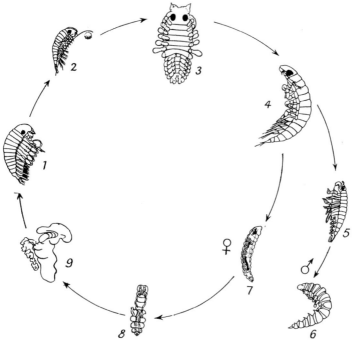

FIG. 14.10. DIAGRAM SUMMARIZING THE LIFE CYCLE OF THE
ENTONISCID PARASITE *Portunion maenadis*. (From Veillet (86).)

1: epicaridium larva, just before hatching; 2: epicaridium larva attached to a copepod
Acartia; 3: microniscus stage, fixed on a copepod; 4: free cryptoniscus stage; 5: immature male in a host *Carcinus*; 6: adult male; 7, 8, 9: stages in the development of a
female in a host crab.

which have been partially unravelled (Fig. 14.11). In the bopyrids a
cryptoniscus larva which reaches a host transforms into a new larval form
characterized by loss of pleopods. Further development of the male is
arrested at this stage, while the females continue to increase in size and
become equipped with plate-like respiratory pleopods. Experimentally it
has been shown, however, that when young male parasites are removed
from the female and placed in the branchial cavity of non-parasitized
hosts, the majority develop into normal females. Among cryptoniscids,
the cryptoniscus larva which fixes itself upon its definitive host becomes

firstly a male, then a female; there is, consequently, marked protandrous hermaphroditism since all larvae pass through a functional male stage. In explanation it appears that the first larva reaching the definitive host becomes a male and then a female, but later larvae attaching themselves to the same host become arrested in the male stage. Sex determination is regarded as epigamic in these animals and may be influenced by the supply of food available to the still neutral larvae, or to the direct action of the female on the other larval males (3, 43, 73, 78).

Epicaridian parasites produce considerable changes in their hosts, the magnitude and character of which vary with the species of parasite.

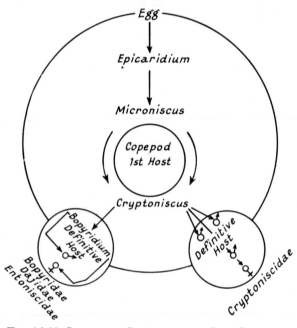

FIG. 14.11. SCHEMATIC OUTLINE OF THE LIFE CYCLE OF EPICARIDIAN PARASITES. (From Baer (3).)

Usually the gonads of the host are reduced or completely atrophied, a condition referred to as parasitic castration. Changes also occur in secondary sexual characters: males may be feminized to some extent (*Upogebia* parasitized by *Gyge*), and female breeding characters fail to develop (*Palaemon* parasitized by *Bopyrus*). An interesting instance of castration associated with hyperparasitism is recorded among the Epicaridea. A bopyrid *Bopyrina virbii*, which produces parasitic castration in its host *Hippolyte*, is parasitized and sterilized in turn by a cryptoniscid *Cabirops* (11, 44, 53, 76, 77).

Cirripedes. The sedentary habits of cirripedes and the utilization of living supports of attachment have permitted some species to form fairly intimate associations with other animals, and it is doubtless by this route that the parasitic cirripedes have evolved. *Tubicinella* found attached to whales and *Chelonobia* on marine turtles are provided with basal ramifications extending into the integument of their hosts; these animals, however, still feed normally. But *Anelasma*, which penetrates into the skin of sharks, feeds on the tissues of the latter by a system of ramifying roots. This is essentially the mode of feeding characteristic of all rhizocephalans.

Probably the best known of all marine parasites is the rhizocephalan *Sacculina*. This animal lives on crabs, and in the adult condition it presents the appearance of a fleshy bag lying on the lower surface of the abdomen

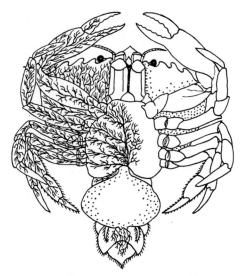

FIG. 14.12. DIAGRAMMATIC REPRESENTATION OF THE RHIZOCEPHALAN PARASITE *Sacculina carcini*, SHOWING THE EXTENSIVE SYSTEM OF ROOTS WHICH RAMIFY THROUGH THE TISSUES OF THE CRAB. (From various sources.)

and emerging from the cephalothorax of the crab. This sac shows a small orifice which leads into a flattened mantle cavity and consists largely of paired ovaries together with testes and a small ganglion (the animal is hermaphroditic). The sac is only the external manifestation of the parasite, which also bears a system of roots ramifying throughout the body of the crab (Fig. 14.12). It is by means of this root system that the parasite absorbs nourishment from its host, and supplies the reproductive tissues with food.

On hatching, the larva of *Sacculina* has typical cirripede features and resembles the nauplius of sedentary forms such as *Balanus* (Fig. 14.13). It differs, however, in the absence of a digestive system and the interior of the body is filled with lipoid food reserves. After four moults the nauplius transforms into a cypris larva, which settles on its proper host and attaches itself by its antennae. Fixation accomplished, the internal contents of the cypris contract into a cellular mass and the animal sheds its integument together with its appendages. A thin chitinous dart is then formed, which pierces the body wall of the crab, and through this opening the cellular mass of the cypris invades the visceral cavity of the host. Development is slow, occupying twelve months, and during that period the *Sacculina* migrates from the point of penetration along the intestine. It takes on the appearance of a mass of branching rootlets and, on arriving at the unpaired

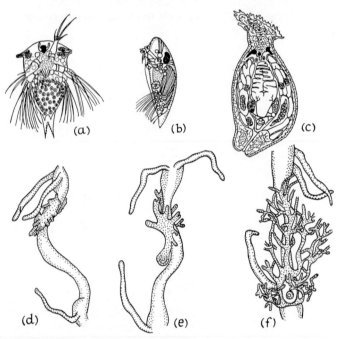

FIG. 14.13. *Sacculina*, A RHIZOCEPHALAN PARASITE OF CRABS

(*a*) Nauplius larva; (*b*) cypris larva; (*c*) section through external mass of *Sacculina*; (*d*), (*e*) and (*f*) growth of parasite internally along the intestine of the crab. ((*a*), (*b*), (*d*), (*e*) and (*f*), after Smith (83); (*c*) after Delage, 1884.)

intestinal caecum, it gives rise to a tumour-like nucleus, which develops into the saccular structure visible externally. On reaching the outer wall, the nucleus causes necrosis of the host's tissues and softening of the chitin, thus permitting access to the exterior (83).

Well-known rhizocephalan forms are *Sacculina* parasitic on *Carcinus*, *Portunus* and *Inachus*; *Peltogaster* on pagurids; *Parthenopea* on *Gebia* and *Callianassa*; and *Thompsonia* on *Melia*, *Thalamita* and *Alpheus*. In an infection with *Thompsonia* up to 200 reproductive sacs may appear on the outside of the prawn, and these arise from a common system of rootlets due to infection by a single cypris larva (72, 87).

Rhizocephalan parasites produce profound effects on the morphology and metabolism of their hosts. The *Sacculina* parasite of *Carcinus* accumulates large quantities of lipoid reserves which in the normal female crab would be deposited in the ovaries. In the non-parasitized crab the blood is not tinted, except when a moult is imminent or when the ovaries are nearing maturity, when it becomes coloured by carotenoids. The fat-content of the blood and ovaries also increases greatly in the female at sexual maturity. When infected with *Sacculina*, however, both sexes have coloured blood and a high fat-content. *Sacculina* thus alters the metabolism of the male crab to that characteristic of the female. In *Pagurus* infected by *Peltogaster* the fat-content of parasitized animals is reduced below that

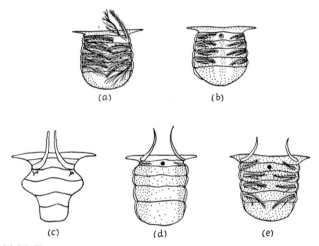

(a)   (b)

(c)   (d)   (e)

FIG. 14.14. EFFECTS OF THE RHIZOCEPHALAN PARASITE *Sacculina neglecta* ON ITS HOST, THE CRAB *Inachus mauritanicus*

(a) Abdomen of normal adult female (ventral view); (b) infected female; (c) abdomen of normal male (ventral view); (d) and (e) infected males. (Redrawn from Smith (83).)

of normal animals. Rhizocephalan parasites also affect the genital organs and secondary sexual characters, and so-called parasitic castration results. In infected males of brachyurans and pagurids the testes become more or less completely atrophied and the external sexual characters tend towards an intersexual or predominantly female type. The effects are seen in the shape of the abdomen, size of the chelae, reduction of copulatory stylets and the appearance of abdominal appendages of female appearance (Fig. 14.14). There is much variation in the extent of external modification which male crabs undergo as the result of parasitization. The degree of modification is correlated with size, smaller crabs being liable to greater alteration of secondary sexual characteristics (20, 27, 45, 74, 75).

The Ascothoracica are another group of parasitic cirripedes and are found in corals and echinoderms. They include the Lauridae and the

Synagogidae, which are external parasites of antipatharians and crinoids; the Petrarcidae, which live in the body cavities of abyssal madreporarian corals; and the Dendrogasteridae, which are endoparasites of madreporarian corals, echinoids and asteroids. Development in ascothoracids usually involves nauplius, metanauplius and cypris larvae. The nauplius, when present, lacks the anterolateral horns characteristic of cirripedes, and the cypris is provided with piercing and sucking mouth parts. The mantle sometimes becomes greatly enlarged in the adult female, and the eggs are retained for some time and commence their development in the mantle cavity.

Synagoga (Synagogidae) is a small ectoparasite found on the stems of the crinoid *Metacrinus*. It is provided with a bivalved carapace, buccal mouth parts organized for piercing the host's tissues, and possesses typical crustacean features recalling those of a cypris larva. In this form the sexes are separate and the males may be dwarf in size. *Myriocladus* (Dendrogasteridae), an endoparasite of *Asterias*, is much more specialized in organization. The bulk of the body in the female is made up of ramified digestive diverticula covered by a mantle layer, and it feeds by absorbing nourishment from the body fluids of its host. The dwarf males, on the other hand, retain the appendages and have a cypris-like organization (65).

Copepods. Parasitism is very extensive among copepods, which display all gradations from forms in which there is a slight reduction of appendages to highly modified species in which the body is reduced to a saccular mass. They infect a remarkably wide variety of marine animals, including alcyonarians, actinians, polychaetes, crustacea, molluscs, echinoderms, ascidians, fish and cetaceans (Fig. 14.15). Moreover, they have adapted themselves to most diverse modes of existence, and may be encountered outside the host, or internally in the alimentary canal, blood vessels and coelomic cavity. Sexual dimorphism is usually well marked, and the male is either free-living or minute in size and dependent upon the female. Nutrition is derived by sucking in fluids of the host.

Copepods of the family Caligidae are common parasites of fish and are known as fish-lice. Species of Monstrillidae resemble gnathiids in that the young stages are parasitic, while the adults lead an independent existence. These remarkable animals are internal parasites of polychaetes and are highly modified for their manner of life. In *Cymbasoma rigidum*, for example, the eggs hatch into free-swimming nauplii, which appear normal save for the absence of a gut. The nauplius finally invades a serpulid worm, *Salmacina*, in which it moults and becomes reduced to a cellular mass (Fig. 14.16). Then, by amoeboid movement, it migrates into a longitudinal blood vessel of its host and there assumes an elongate cylindrical form, with two long anterior appendages which are employed in absorbing nutriment from the host. The parasite is invested by a cuticle, in which a gradual transformation into the adult form takes place. This has a definite copepod appearance, although the gut has atrophied and buccal and thoracic appendages are wanting. After escaping from the host polychaete, the adults function solely as reproductive individuals, swim for a while actively in the plankton, produce their eggs and die (60).

Parasitism takes many bizarre forms but none is more unusual than that displayed by the copepod *Xenocoeloma brumpti* (Herpyllobiidae), occurring on the terebellid *Polycirrus arenivorus*. *Xenocoeloma* appears like a cylindrical sac attached to the side of the worm (Fig. 14.15). In reality, however, it is an internal parasite, for it is completely covered by the host, except for a terminal opening through which the ovaries discharge to the exterior. Fusion of host and parasite tissues is most subtle: the epidermis of *Xeno-*

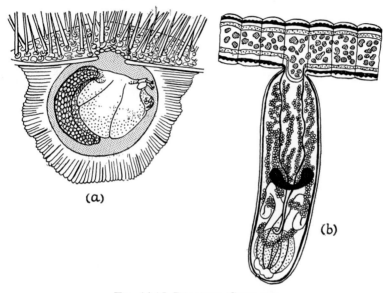

(a)

(b)

FIG. 14.15. PARASITIC COPEPODS

(a) *Pionodesmotes phormosomae* (♀) in an internal gall within the test of the urchin *Phormosoma uranus*; (b) *Xenocoeloma brumpti* attached to the body wall of *Polycirrus arenivorus*. ((a) after Koehler (1898); (b) after Caullery and Mesnil (12).)

coeloma has disappeared and it is covered, instead, by epidermis of its host, and the muscles of its body wall extend underneath the surface epithelium of the worm. The head region and the alimentary canal have disappeared, and the longitudinal axis of the parasite is occupied by a diverticulum of the coelomic cavity of the host. *Xenocoeloma* is hermaphroditic and the males have disappeared. The ovaries discharge into oviducts, which become filled with developing eggs and which occupy a large proportion of the mass of the animal. Terminally there are two large testes which open into a seminal vesicle, from which the spermatozoa pass into the oviducts and effect self-fertilization. The eggs mature on a pair of ovigerous cords and hatch into nauplius larvae, devoid of alimentary canal, and these infect new hosts (12).

Conclusions

Probably the most striking aspect of parasitism is the trend towards morphological degeneration. In incipient parasitism, such as seen in the copepod *Caligus*, the parasite differs only slightly from independent forms.

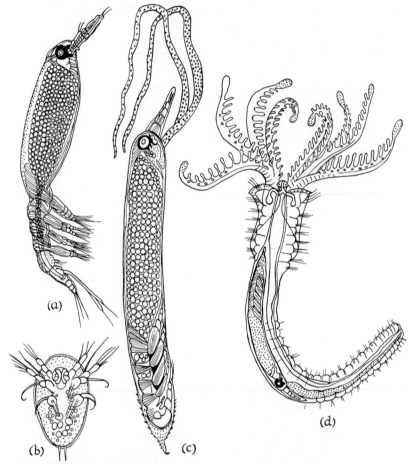

FIG. 14.16. DEVELOPMENTAL STAGES IN THE MONSTRILLID COPEPOD
Cymbasoma rigidum (= *Haemocera danae*)

(*a*) Pelagic adult; (*b*) nauplius larva; (*c*) female parasite removed from its host; (*d*) parasite in position in its host (*Salmacina dysteri*). (Redrawn from Malaquin (60).)

It is somewhat more clumsily built and possesses a suctorial proboscis, but still retains the ability to swim. Highly specialized species, such as *Xenocoeloma* and *Herpyllobius*, tend, however, to be little more than form-less sacs, absorbing fluids from their hosts and concentrating on egg production. As a general rule parasitism involves atrophy and finally loss of locomotory appendages and sense organs, which cease to have significance in fixed forms dependent on their hosts. The mouth parts frequently become converted into piercing and sucking organs, as in bopyrids; and in internal parasites, which derive their food by absorption of simple nutriments from the fluids of the host, there may be partial or complete atrophy of the gut—for example, in cestodes and entoconchid gastropods. The external surface of the animal may then assume the role of the gut in absorption, and it is frequently augmented by means of folds, ramifications and special appendages; for example, in rhizocephalans, dendrogasterids and monstrillids. Corresponding to the reduction in peripheral sensory and motor fields there is a diminution in the size and complexity of central nervous organs.

In those forms which are parasitic during only part of their life-history it is found that regression is slight in the free-living stages, and becomes most evident during the parasitic phase of the life-cycle, when a metamorphosis ensues. Nauplius larvae of peltogastrids and monstrillids, and adult stages of the latter, are significant examples. The actively-swimming stages, of course, are dependent upon an efficient sensori-neuromuscular organization for their continued existence. Feeding, however, may be suspended, the gut be atrophied and the animal be dependent on accumulated food reserves obtained from the host.

The female reproductive organs of parasites tend to become greatly hypertrophied. Often the females are much larger than the males—for example, in *Bopyrus*—in which a dwarf male is attached to the female. The ovaries become very large and, in extreme cases, occupy the major part of the body mass. A tendency towards hermaphroditism is also evident in many groups. In *Xenocoeloma* the males have disappeared, and in *Sacculina* the dwarf complementary males sometimes found on the body of the female are vestigial individuals which no longer appear to be functional. Self-fertilization is normal in many of these forms. Still other species show successive hermaphroditism in that each individual develops, first, the reproductive organs of one sex, and then gradually transforms into the opposite sex later in its life-history; for example, cryptoniscids and myzostomarians.

The hypertrophy of reproductive structures in the female and the various modes of hermaphroditism occurring among parasites are adaptations to ensure perpetuation of the species under conditions in which mortality of eggs and young stages is exceedingly high. Added to the normal hazards of predation are the difficulties of encountering a suitable host animal at the appropriate time and of securing access to the latter. The fecundity of parasitic species is very great. Meyerhof and Rothschild (61), for example, have recorded a case of a periwinkle *Littorina littorea* infected with *Cryptocotyle lingua*, which over the course of twelve months emitted about 1,300,000 cercariae. The complicated life-histories of heteroecious parasites, which have one or two provisional hosts, can likewise be regarded as adaptations for facilitating access to the final host (56).

The significance of the terms regression and degeneration is obviously one of definition. The atrophy of sensory, nervous, muscular and locomotory systems mentioned above is accompanied by equally great hypertrophy and specialization of vegetative systems—for example, in the appearance of piercing and sucking mouth parts, haemophilic glands and enlargement of the gut, of ovaries, uteri and brood chambers. Nevertheless, evolutionary advance has come to have certain definite connotations. It implies an increase in the animal's capacity to cope with its environment through an enlargement of its sensory field, an actual increase in the number of sensory modalities perceived and an augmentation of effector mechanisms. *Pari passu* there is an enlargement of central nervous organization permitting choice, diversity of control and utilization of past experience. It is evident that this whole field of evolutionary progression has been forsaken in the adoption of a parasitic life, and a narrow, fixed and inflexible life-history has resulted.

Different parasites display much variation in host specificity. In its extreme expression, as seen among gregarines and certain parasitic copepods, for example, a given species of parasite is confined to one particular species of host. Other parasites are slightly more adaptable in that they can live on related host species. On the other hand, there are certain external parasites such as gnathiids, which attack all kinds of fish indiscriminately and, experimentally, have even been reared on Amphibia. The behaviour of heteroecious parasites is somewhat peculiar in this regard, for strict host specificity may be characteristic of the stages infecting either the provisional or definitive host, and not necessarily of both. Thus in trematodes, the gastropod host of the sporocyst may be fixed whereas the sexual stage is found in many different host species (4).

The influence of the parasite on the host has been brought out in some of the life-histories summarized in previous pages. The parasite may affect the size, form and physiology of the host. In a study of the snail *Hydrobia ulvae* it has been found that individuals infected with trematode parasites are consistently larger than uninfected specimens, i.e. the parasites in some way favour an increase in size of the host (81).

The well-known condition of parasitic castration and the tendency towards intersexuality in parasitized crustaceans have received a number of explanations (8). Smith suggested that rhizocephalan parasites impose the same metabolic demands on the male crab as the ovary does in the female. Foodstuffs, especially lipoids, which normally nourish the gonads, were considered in some way to influence gonadal activity and, at the same time, the secondary sexual characteristics. Ovary and parasite each make similar and heavy inroads on trophic balances of the crab and produce similar effects in female and male animals. Other explanations involve hormone production by the parasite and alterations in the amount of hormone secreted in the host. Recent experiments suggest that the parasites exert their influence on secondary sexual characters through the eyestalks of the host. The latter structures, it will be recalled, are the site of important neurosecretory organs (p. 442) (54). It is not possible nor desirable to consider all the multifarious observations and interpretations recorded on this difficult subject, which awaits further experimental treatment for clarification.

An additional complication lies in the possibility of host resistance. Among trematodes it has been observed that heavy infections may set up immunity reactions in the final hosts, limiting the number of parasites (*Maritrema oöcysta* in the black-headed gull). The vertebrate host may show increased resistance to infection with age (herring gull infected with *Parorchis acanthus*) (10, 82). A racial difference exists in the resistance of populations of mussels *Mytilus edulis* to parasitic infection by the copepod *Mytilicola intestinalis* in that infected mussels in the Mediterranean show no adverse effects, whereas mussels in the North Sea are heavily infested and suffer from gross inanition. It is only recently that *Mytilicola* has appeared on the coasts of north Europe, but it has long been known in the Mediterranean, where the mussels have become more adjusted to the parasite (26). Dicyemid parasites, as we have observed, live in a balanced relationship with their cephalopod hosts, and a preliminary stage of parasitism of this kind may lead to a state of mutual adaptation, perhaps with benefit to both partners, that can be termed symbiosis.

SYMBIOSIS

Associations between marine animals and unicellular algae, termed symbiosis, are of great intrinsic interest and a considerable body of descriptive and experimental evidence is available about them (9, 90, 91). The algae involved are usually classified arbitrarily as green zoochlorellae and brown zooxanthellae, but these terms are without systematic significance. The associations, although usually labelled symbiotic, are seldom true balanced relationships, with equal benefits to both partners, and some symbiotic associations, indeed, are one-sided parasitism.

Green and brown unicellular organisms are found in the tissues of a host of marine invertebrates, namely in Protozoa, Porifera, Coelenterata, Turbellaria and Mollusca, and less frequently in compound ascidians, bryozoans, polychaetes and echinoderms. Some examples of animal species containing such symbionts are presented in Table 14.1.

Algal symbionts are small unicellular bodies ranging up to 10μ in diameter. The zooxanthellae from foraminifers are generally spherical in shape and possess a cellulose covering, chromatophore, pyrenoid body, oil bodies, starch grains and nucleus (21). In true symbiotic associations the algae are located within the tissue cells of the host, but there are some border-line cases in which the algal cells lie in body cavities, or between the cells of the host, as in the compound ascidian *Diplosoma virens*. Most of these algal symbionts carry on photosynthesis by means of chlorophyll; as an exception may be cited the flagellates occurring in *Beroë* which, although pigmented, lack chlorophyll and are incapable of photosynthetic

TABLE 14.1

EXAMPLES OF MARINE ANIMALS CONTAINING ALGAL SYMBIONTS
(ZOOCHLORELLAE AND ZOOXANTHELLAE)

Protozoa
    Rhizopoda: Foraminifera: *Trichosphaerium, Peneroplis, Orbitolites, Globigerina*
    Radiolaria: *Collozoum, Sphaerozoum, Thalassicolla, Lithocercus, Acanthometra,*
        Heliosphaera and many others
    Mastigophora: *Noctiluca miliaris, Leptodiscus medusoides*
    Ciliophora: *Spatostyla sertulariarum, Scyphidia scorpaenae, Trichodina patellae,*
        Mesodinium rubrum, Frontonia leucas, Vorticella, Cothurnia

Coelenterata
    Hydrozoa: Hydroida: *Halecium, Hydrichthella, Sertularella, Aglaophenia*
        Hydrocorallinae: *Millepora, Sporadopora*
        Siphonophora: *Velella, Porpita*
    Scyphozoa: *Cassiopeia, Catostylus, Cotylorhiza, Mastigias et al.*
    Anthozoa: Alcyonaria: *Lobophytum, Sclerophytum, Xenia, Heteroxenia, Sarco-*
        phyton, Gorgonia, Virgularia, Alcyonium (tropical species),
        Heliopora et al.
        Antipatharia: *Stichopathes, Hillopathes, Eucirripathes*
        Actiniaria: *Anemonia sulcata, Actinia bermudensis, Anthopleura balii,*
        Aiptasia diaphana, A. couchii, Cribrina xanthogrammica et al.
        Zoanthinaria: *Parazoanthus, Zoanthus, Zoanthella, Zoanthina, Isaurus*
        Madreporaria: Abundant in nearly all shallow water corals except
        Astrangia and *Phyllangia*

Platyhelminthes
    Turbellaria: *Convoluta, Amphiscolops, Monocelis, Enterostomum*

Annelida
    Polychaeta: *Eunice gigantea*

Mollusca
    Gastropoda: *Aeolidiella glauca, Tridachia crispata, Doridoedes gardineri, Melibe*
        rangii, Spurilla neopolitana, Phyllirrhoe bucephala, Placobranchus
        ocellatus
    Lamellibranchia: *Tridacna, Hippopus, Corculum*

Bryozoa
    Zoobothryon, Bicellaria

Tunicata
    Diplosoma virens, Didemnum viride, Trididemnum cyclops

(Based on Buchner (9), with additions)

activity (5, 84). The animals hosts will be reviewed in order before describing some general features of algal-animal symbiotic relationships.

Protozoa. Numerous Radiolaria contain symbiotic zooxanthellae. Generally, the algal cells are localized in the extracapsular protoplasm (sub-orders Spumellaria, Nassellaria) but in *Acanthometra* (sub-order Acantharia) they are intracapsular in position (Fig. 14.17). The Phaeodaria, which lack yellow cells, are deep-sea forms. The colonial forms, in particular, feed holozoically only when they are young and algal symbionts are few. Symbionts are absent from young individuals, which must be reinfected anew by free-living motile cells.

In a similar manner, many foraminifers have formed close associations with unicellular algae, e.g. *Orbitolites*. These may be extremely abundant, as many as 100,000 algal cells having been found in a large specimen of *Peneroplis*. Polythalamian foraminifers exist in two forms, microspheres and megalospheres, which reproduce asexually and sexually. The large asexual bodies or amoebulae which arise by multiple fission of the parent carry away some of the symbionts, but the gametes are free of algae and the microspheres must be reinfected from without.

A few marine ciliates and flagellates also contain symbiotic algae. The peritrich *Spatostyla sertulariarum* encloses a small number of zooxanthellae which are passed to the daughter cells during cell division. Of particular interest is the marine ciliate *Mesodinium rubrum* which contains small red algal symbionts. The young protozoans are colourless, but as they mature the cytosome becomes filled with algal cells and the animal ceases to take in preformed nourishment. Gohar (30) figures a ciliate that feeds upon xeniid alcyonarians and acquires zooxanthellae from the latter. *Noctiluca*

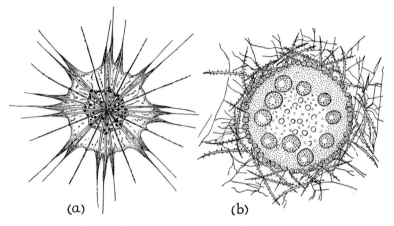

(a) (b)

FIG. 14.17. ZOOXANTHELLAE IN RADIOLARIANS

(a) *Acanthometra pellucida* in which the algae are intracapsular in position; (b) the colonial species *Sphaerozoum acuferum*, with extracapsular zooxanthellae. (Redrawn from Buchner (9).)

miliaris (Dinoflagellata) is sometimes infected with zoochlorellae, which may be very numerous and fill the cell.

Porifera. Many instances of algal symbiosis in sponges have been recorded (*see* Buchner (9)). The plant symbionts involve red algae (Rhodophyta) with *Reniera*, filamentous green algae (Chlorophyta) with *Halichondria*, Chrysophyta in *Grantia*, and blue-green algae (Cyanophyta) in *Hircinia*. Unicellular algae occur in the chambers of the sponge, or in the mesogloea; more striking is the case of certain red algae which have branches and thallus entirely enclosed in sponge tissue.

Coelenterates. Symbiosis with algae is of widespread occurrence in these animals and may be of considerable importance in their economy. Zooxanthellae are characteristic of numerous littoral coelenterates occurring in warm inter-tropical waters, namely Hydrozoa, Alcyonaria and

Zoantharia. They are almost invariably present in reef-building madreporarians, but in cold northern seas are confined to a few actiniarians such as *Anemonia sulcata*.

The zooxanthellae of coelenterates are highly specialized for life within the animal, are confined to the endoderm of corals and lie within carrier or wandering cells. They are the vegetative stage of dinoflagellates; these have motile free-living stages which, presumably, can invade suitable host coelenterates (59). Among those species of corals and anemones which normally harbour zooxanthellae, individuals which live in dark places can do without their algal symbionts and obtain all their nourishment holozoically. There are some coelenterates (Xeniidae) which have lost

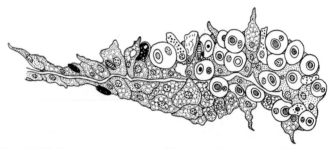

FIG. 14.18. SECTION THROUGH A VENTRAL MESENTERIAL FILAMENT
OF THE ALCYONARIAN *Sclerophytum capitale*
Zooxanthellae are numerous. (From Pratt, 1905.)

the capacity of capturing their own food, and are dependent upon their imprisoned algae for foodstuffs (30).

In hydrozoan corals (*Millepora*), alcyonarians and madreporarians, the zooxanthellae occur only in the endoderm (Fig. 14.18) and are most abundant in those regions, such as disc and tentacles, which are exposed more fully to the light. In the Scyphozoa, however, the zooxanthellae are situated in the mesogloea. In all cases the unicellular algae are intracellular, and are held in amoeboid wandering cells.

Turbellaria. The best-known example of symbiosis in marine turbellarians is afforded by *Convoluta* (Acoela) (Figs. 14.19 and 14.20). *C. convoluta* (= *paradoxa*) contains zooxanthellae which occur in large numbers just below the epidermis. This animal retains its alimentary canal and continues to feed normally, but it is also dependent upon lipoids manufactured by its algal symbionts and fails to develop in their absence. When starved it eventually digests the zooxanthellae, but can be infected again from the outside. The eggs are free of algae, and the larvae, colourless at first, are infected by free-living algal cells (49).

In *C. roscoffensis* the symbiotic association is still more intimate. At first the animal feeds holozoically, but when mature it depends on the excess of food manufactured by the algae. Finally, it consumes its algae, reproduces and perishes. Again, in this species the larvae when hatched are colourless. Free-living algae are attracted by chemotaxis to the egg case, and infect the young animals when they emerge. In this association we can regard the algae as really constituting an organ of the animal: the latter, in fact, is living parasitically on its contained algae (50).

Mollusca. Among marine forms, algal symbiosis has been described in several species of opisthobranch gastropods, and in a few lamellibranchs. In the nudibranch *Aeolidiella glauca*, zooxanthellae occur in cells of the

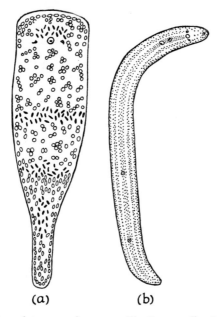

(a)   (b)

FIG. 14.19. (*a*) *Convoluta convoluta* AND (*b*) *C. roscoffensis*, TWO SPECIES OF ACOELOUS TURBELLARIANS HARBOURING SYMBIOTIC ALGAE ($\times$ 27). (From Keeble, 1912.)

liver tubules which extend into the cerata (finger-like processes arising from the dorsal surface of the body). These animals prey upon the anemone *Heliactis bellis*, from which they acquire their zooxanthellae (34). Other sea-slugs which feed upon anemones and contain zooxanthellae probably obtain them from the same source. In *Tridachia crispata*, which is a herbivore, the zooxanthellae lie in connective tissue and are localized in a band lying near the margin of the highly flattened body. The pelagic form *Phyllirrhoe* also harbours zooxanthellae in liver diverticula. Zoochlorellae in *Placobranchus* occur in folds of the branchial cavity, and in the liver where they may be undergoing digestion (9, 46).

Symbiosis with algae is highly developed among the Tridacnidae occurring on coral reefs of the Indo-Pacific region (Fig. 14.21). Two genera are involved, *Hippopus* and *Tridacna*, of which the giant clam

T. derasa sometimes attains a length of nearly one and a half metres. Immense numbers of zooxanthellae are present in these animals, and are housed chiefly in the inner lobes of the mantle-edges on the dorsal side of the body, but zooxanthellae also occur elsewhere in the connective tissue into which light can penetrate. The animals literally "farm" their algae, which synthesize starch and oil deposits. The zooxanthellae are contained in amoeboid cells within blood sinuses and are carried from the mantle to the digestive diverticula to be digested. *Corculum cardissa*, the

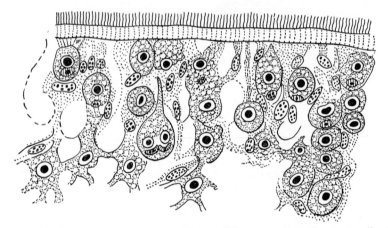

FIG. 14.20. SECTION THROUGH THE BODY WALL OF *Convoluta roscoffensis*, SHOWING GREEN ALGAL CELLS IN MESENCHYME BENEATH THE EPIDERMIS
The algal cells contain pyrenoid bodies and nuclei. (From Keeble and Gamble (50).)

Pacific heart shell, also contains abundant zooxanthellae in gills, mantle and liver tissue (48, 91).

Echinoderms. Several instances have been reported of green and blue-green algae occurring in the tissues of echinoderms (sea-urchins, brittle stars and starfish). These probably should be regarded as parasitic infections, rare in occurrence, which may culminate in the death of the infected animal (63, 64).

Bryozoa. Filamentous green, brown and red algae are found underneath the cuticle of certain marine bryozoans, e.g. *Flustra* and *Alcyonidium* (52).

General Consideration of Symbiosis between Algae and Animals

Symbiotic relationships between plants and animals are usually very intimate, a particular species of alga being confined to a single host species. The possession of algal symbionts is obligatory in most animal species in which this relationship exists, and it is more exceptional to find a facultative association. Populations of *Noctiluca miliaris* in the Indian Ocean contain zoochlorellae, but in the North Atlantic symbionts are absent. Specimens of the ciliate *Trichodina patellae* are infected with zooxanthellae on the coast of Normandy (Cap de la Havre), but not at Wimereux (Pas de Calais). Yonge (90) notes that reef-building corals are able to live with few or no zooxanthellae in dark places in nature, as well as under experimental conditions.

Structural Modifications of Animals in Conjunction with Algal Symbiosis

Various genotypic modifications are encountered among animals in which algal symbiosis is obligatory: examples are Turbellaria, Alcyonaria and Lamellibranchia. Tropical Alcyonacea show a reduction of the ventral mesenterial filaments in correlation with the number of zooxanthellae present. These are the regions which secrete protease for digestion of animal food. In *Lobophytum* there is little reduction of the filaments and few algae are present; in *Sclerophytum* the filaments are very small, gland cells are few and algae are abundant (Fig. 14.18). Xeniids show extreme adaptation to a symbiotic existence: the stomodaeum is very short, the tentacles do not react to animal food and the animal is entirely dependent upon the symbiotic activities of its algal associates (30).

In the reef clams (Tridacnidae) enormous numbers of zooxanthellae are found in those portions of the mantle edge concerned with the formation of the siphons (Fig. 14.21). Profound modifications in structure have occurred in that the mantle and shell have rotated about 180° in relation to the visceral mass and foot; consequently the siphonal tissues are transferred from the normal posterior to a dorsal position. This allows the mantle edges to be exposed fully to the light, which is focused deeply into the tissues by means of hyaline lens-like bodies, about which the zooxanthellae are congregated in enormous numbers. These are always contained in phagocytic cells and are carried to the digestive diverticula to be digested intracellularly. Heart shells *Corculum* are also modified in relation to algal symbiosis. The shell is very thin and transparent, allowing light to reach the algal symbionts which are concentrated in the gills, palps and lower mantle surface. Their occurrence in digestive diverticula indicates they are consumed by the animal (48, 91).

Special Habits in Connexion with Symbiosis

Owing to the photosynthetic activity of imprisoned algae, animals containing symbionts tend to seek out or settle in well-illuminated waters. Zooplanktonic species containing zooxanthellae tend to remain in surface waters during day-time, when other forms descend into deeper waters. Behaviour of this kind has been observed in Radiolaria, larvae of the zoantharians *Zoanthella* and *Zoanthina*, and the ephyrae of *Mastigias*.

The habits of littoral and sedentary forms are also strongly influenced by illumination. The scyphomedusan *Cassiopeia*, found in shallow tropical waters, is partially sedentary in habit and reposes on the bottom with the sub-umbrella surface uppermost. In this position the zooxanthellae, which are concentrated especially about the mouths, are exposed to the light. The planula larvae of different species of reef-building corals show positive phototaxis which appears to be associated with their algal content (47). In contrast, the planulae of *Dendrophyllia*, which is a deep-water coral lacking zooxanthellae, settle in darkness. Reef-building corals are typical inhabitants of shallow water, and display maximal development in depths of less than 30 m. This partiality for shallow waters is probably related to symbiosis with zooxanthellae. The effect of light on the growth of corals has been reviewed by Yonge, who concludes that reef-building corals are influenced in manner, speed and solidity of growth by light, whereas the growth of deep-water corals is not so affected. Phototropism is of great importance in the formation of reefs; in the absence of light zooxanthellae are sparse or absent, and growth and metabolism of the coral are probably depressed since the algae are not available to provide nourishment (92).

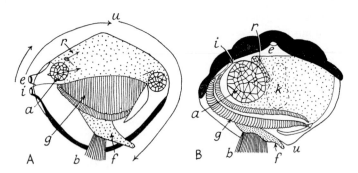

FIG. 14.21. STRUCTURAL SPECIALIZATION IN TRIDACNID BIVALVES

A. Diagram of an unspecialized lamellibranch for comparison with *Tridacna*. The arrows indicate the rotation of the umbo (*u*), exhalent and inhalent siphons (*e*, *i*), posterior adductor (*a*), and pedal retractor (*r*), involved in the morphological transformation of the Tridacnidae.

B. Lateral view of *Tridacna* showing the result of rotation. Byssus (*b*) and gills (*g*) remain in the same relative position. The extent of the large kidneys (*k*) is indicated by the broken lines. Enlarged mantle lobes above are shown in solid black. (From Yonge (90).)

The turbellarian *Convoluta roscoffensis*, intensively studied by Gamble and Keeble, lives on sandy shores at the level of high-water neaps within a drainage area where it obtains maximal light and safety from possible desiccation. Positive phototaxis and negative geotaxis cause the animals to migrate to the surface during the day. Mechanical stimulation, i.e. vibrations, will release positive geotaxis, and cause the animals to migrate downwards, and it is this factor which is operative in causing the animals to burrow into the sand when the tide reaches them. *C. convoluta*, which lives on weed at low-water mark, migrates up and down with spring and neap tides, and thus secures optimal illumination without danger of desiccation (28).

Functional Relations between the Associates

It is generally believed that in symbiotic relationships between plants and animals the alga benefits by deriving protection and securing carbon dioxide and nitrogenous waste products from the host, while the animal obtains oxygen and nourishment and secures the elimination of waste substances.

Life is probably more secure for an alga within an animal than in the surrounding medium, unless the animal eventually devours its symbionts as *Convoluta roscoffensis* does. It has been demonstrated experimentally that zooxanthellae utilize the CO_2 produced by various reef-building corals,

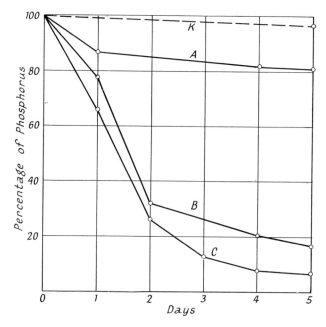

FIG. 14.22. A GRAPH SHOWING THE PERCENTAGE CHANGES IN PHOSPHORUS CONTENT OF SEA WATER CONTAINING DIFFERENT SPECIES OF CORALS

Animals in jars 2·5 l capacity; original level of P, 2·036 g/m³ of sea water. A. *Psammocora*; B. *Porites*; C. *Favia*; K. Control. (From Yonge (90).)

but this is probably important only when the algae are highly concentrated. Nutrient salts containing nitrogen and phosphorus, however, are limiting factors for plant growth, and algae living in animals are favourably situated to acquire these compounds at their source. Zooxanthellae utilize a wide range of phosphoric acids (Fig. 14.22), ammonia, and many nitrogen-containing organic compounds, including guanine, urea, uric acid and amino acids (90, 92).

When the reverse relationship is considered it is discovered that oxygen in abundance is produced by the algal symbionts when illuminated. The oxygen tension is normally adequate for aquatic animals under most conditions, but oxygen may become depleted in the heated shallow waters over reefs and in tidal pools during ebb. Under these conditions the oxygen produced by algae may have survival value.

There is evidence that many animals obtain nutriment from their imprisoned algae. A transference of foodstuffs has been demonstrated in *Convoluta convoluta* and in *C. roscoffensis*. *Orbitolites* utilizes the stored oil and starch grains which are released when its enclosed algal symbionts degenerate. In various other forms the algae are killed and digested by the host, namely, in later stages of the life-history of *C. roscoffensis*, in the Xeniidae and the Tridacnidae. The majority of coelenterates, however, do not digest their associated algae (21, 30, 90, 92).

It is possible to distinguish between associations in which the algal symbionts are not essential to the life of the animal, namely Madreporaria, Actiniaria, and those in which the animal is dependent upon the algae, from which it derives all its nourishment, namely *Convoluta roscoffensis* and tropical Alcyonaria such as the Xeniidae. Experimentally, in many animals the zooxanthellae can be removed only with difficulty. Under conditions of extreme starvation *Convoluta convoluta* eventually destroys and digests its algae, but can be reinfected. Madreporarians, actiniarians and Scyphomedusae (*Cassiopeia*) containing zooxanthellae gradually lose the latter when they are starved, kept in the dark or otherwise subjected to adverse conditions, but the algae are extruded or excreted through the gastric filaments or mesenteries, and are not digested. Madreporarian corals possessing zooxanthellae show the effects of starvation as quickly as those lacking zooxanthellae, thus demonstrating that the latter are not consumed.

Another functional role ascribed to algal symbionts is the automatic removal of waste products, namely carbon dioxide, and nitrogen and phosphorus end-products. The algae would thus be acting as adventitious excretory organs. In this connexion Yonge notes that the kidneys of *Tridacna* are enlarged, in conjunction with the necessity for disposing of the remnants of the zooxanthellae digested by the blood phagocytes (90).

The presence of algal symbionts in corals increases metabolic efficiency and produces a higher rate of growth. A direct effect on formation of skeleton and metabolism of calcium is involved. The zooxanthellae favour the deposition of aragonite (for the reactions involved see Yonge (92)); they also utilize nitrogen and phosphorus wastes in synthesis of protein. It is not clear, however, what kind and quantity of food materials, produced by the algae, become available to the host.

Symbiosis with Heterotrophic Algae

A few instances are known of animals containing algal associates which, although pigmented, lack chlorophyll, and no doubt many more such cases remain to be discovered. In the two associations now to be described the plant cells are sufficiently abundant and coloured to tint the soft parts of the animals in which they occur.

The first concerns a deep-water ctenophore *Beroë abyssicola*, occurring below 180 metres. In this animal the stomodaeum is coloured red due to the presence of numerous red flagellates in the vacuolated cellular tissue lying underneath the epithelial lining. Other species of ctenophores are suspected of harbouring similar organisms (5).

The green colour of Marenne oysters is due to infection by a green diatom, *Navicula ostrearia*, located in gills and palps. Again, the pigment, in this case known as "marénnine," is produced by the algal symbiont; chemically it appears to be a carotiprotein (70).

There is little information about the interrelations between these algal associates and their animal hosts, and it is premature to characterize them as symbionts or parasites.

Fungal Symbionts in Excretory Organs

A single instance of this kind of association is known in the Molgulidae (colonial ascidians). These animals possess a small closed excretory vesicle or storage kidney containing renal concretions (urates), and in this vesicle flourish peculiar fungal bodies. These are said to propagate by sexual and asexual means, and infection of new hosts takes place by means of zoospores. The significance of the association remains obscure, but it is assumed that the fungal hyphae make use of the excretory material of *Molgula* (9).

Symbiotic Bacteria and Luminescence

Certain luminescent organisms owe their light to symbiotic bacteria, and the physiological and morphological implications of this relationship have been outlined in Chapter 13. Following the discovery of symbiotic bacteria and mycetozoa in various higher plants and animals, frequent claims have been made that the luminescence of many groups of animals is due to symbiotic bacteria, but few of these conjectures have been substantiated. Luminescent animals which owe their light to bacteria are various myopsid squid and teleosts, and bacteria have also been implicated in the luminescence of tunicates.

The luminescent bacteria of myopsid squid have been studied in some detail, especially by Pierantoni, Kishitani and Herfurth. The subject is reviewed by Harvey (39), who also gives a detailed account of factors affecting the luminescence of free-living bacteria. In myopsid squid the luminous glands or accessory glands lie close to the anus and ink sac, and are intimately associated with the accessory nidamental glands (Figs. 13.19 and 14.23). The simplest condition is seen in *Loligo*, where the accessory glands are open to the exterior and consist of a mass of epithelial tubes which enclose luminous bacteria. In many cuttlefish the accessory glands are distinct and more complex, and contain several kinds of epithelial tubes and bacteria, only one variety of which is luminescent.

The luminescence of the accessory glands has been observed in *Sepiola rondeletii, S. birostrata, Loligo edulis* and others. The accessory organs open into the mantle cavity, and in *S. birostrata* a luminous secretion is actually discharged, but not in *S. rondeletii*. It has already been pointed out that some individuals of a species only are luminous, and sexual differences also occur: in *Rossia* and *Sepietta*, for example, accessory glands are confined to the female, whereas in *Sepiola* they are present in both sexes.

Luminous bacteria have been isolated from various myopsid squid and

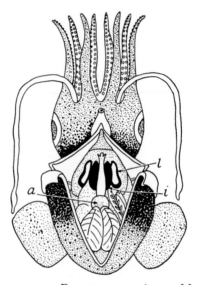

FIG. 14.23. SPECIMEN OF *Euprymna morsei* WITH MANTLE CAVITY
OPENED TO EXPOSE INK SAC AND LIGHT-ORGANS
a, Accessory nidamental gland; *i*, ink sac; *l*, light-organ (× 1). (After Kishitani, 1928.)

have been cultured. Special growth characteristics and luminous reactions have been ascertained, which indicate close adjustments to particular hosts, but Kishitani also discovered so-called symbiotic species living as saprophytes on the inner mantle surface. According to Herfurth (40), the bacteria are not transmitted from one generation to another through the egg, and each generation must be reinfected anew. Consequently it is by no means certain that a true symbiotic relationship is involved, and the biological significance of luminescence in these animals is most obscure (9, 39).

The luminous test cells which lie at the entrance of the branchial chamber of *Pyrosoma* contain convoluted tubular bodies with an internal granular reticulum (Fig. 13.13). These have been regarded as bacterial bodies which reproduce by spore formation and infect the next generation through those test cells which invade the developing embryo (9). There are, however, certain cogent reasons for taking exception to this interpretation. It has been observed that luminescence in *Pyrosoma* is discontinuous and appears only after stimulation of the animal. The luminescent material can be dried, and caused to lighten by the addition of fresh water. Finally, potassium cyanide, which depresses luminescence in bacteria, is without effect on the luminescence of *Pyrosoma*. It would appear, then, that the production of light may be an intrinsic characteristic of this animal (39).

Symbiotic relationships with luminescent bacteria are frequent among marine teleosts, and the light-organs concerned are diverse and frequently very complex (p. 553). The bacteria lie in epithelial tubes or folds, and in the anomalopids, for example, the light-organ is made up of rows of epithelial tubules containing rod-like bacteria, and possesses a well-developed vascular supply. The bacteria have been cultured in some instances, but little is known of the development of the relationship. In all these forms light is emitted continuously by the symbiotic bacteria. In some species, e.g. the macrourid *Malacocephalus*, a luminous material can be extruded from the gland (Fig. 13.20). Frequently, the fish is able to control the actual emission by means of screening devices, e.g. *Photoblepharon*.

Some instances of luminescence have been described in which the light is due not to symbiosis but to an attack by pathogenic luminescent bacteria. In the amphipod *Talitrus* a small proportion of individuals are luminescent and so infected, and the disease eventually leads to the death of the animal. The bacterium has been successfully inoculated into other species of amphipods and isopods, which subsequently become luminous. Luminescent bacteria have also been recovered from the gut of non-luminous amphipods, and Harvey suggests that infection of the body tissues occurs by this route under suitable conditions. Other marine invertebrates can be readily infected with luminescent bacteria and become luminous; for example, *Palaemon*, *Sepia*, *Ciona* and many teleosts. If the infection is not fatal the animal recovers in the course of a few weeks and the light gradually disappears (9, 39).

REFERENCES

1. ANKEL, W. E., "*Phyllirrhoe bucephala* Per. & Les. und die Meduse *Mnestra parasites* Krohn," *Pubbl. Staz. Zool. Napoli*, **23**, 91 (1952).
2. ARNOLD, D. C., "Further studies on the behaviour of the fish *Carapus acus*," ibid., **30**, 263 (1957).
3. BAER, J. G., *Le Parasitisme* (Lausanne, F. Rouge et Cie., 1946).
4. BAER, J. G., *Ecology of Animal Parasites* (Urbana, Univ. Illinois Press, 1952).
5. BERKELEY, C., "Symbiosis of *Beroe* and a flagellate," *Contr. Canad. Biol. Fish.*, **6**, 13 (1930).

6. BLACKBURN, M., "Notes on some parasitic actinian larvae," *J. Coun. Sci. Industr. Res. Aust.*, **21**, 183 (1948).
7. BRIGHTWELL, L. R., "Some experiments with the common hermit crab (*Eupagurus bernhardus*) Linn.," *Proc. Zool. Soc.*, **121**, 279 (1951).
8. BROWN, F. A. JR., "Hormones in Crustacea," in Vol. I, *The Hormones*, Ed. Pincus, G. and Thimann, K. V. (New York, Academic Press, 1948).
9. BUCHNER, P., *Endosymbiose der Tiere mit pflanzlichen Mikroorganismen* (Basel/Stuttgart, Verlag Birkhäuser, 1953).
10. CABLE, R. M., "The resistance of the herring gull, *Larus argentatus*, to experimental infections of the trematode, *Parorchis acanthus*," *J. Parasit.*, **23**, 559 (Abstr.) (1937).
11. CALLAN, H. G., "The effects of castration by parasites on the secondary sex characters of prawns (*Leander*)," *J. Exp. Biol.*, **17**, 168 (1940).
12. CAULLERY, M. and MESNIL, F., "*Xenocoeloma brumpti* C. & M. Copépode parasite de *Polycirrus arenivorus* C.," *Bull. Biol.*, **53**, 161 (1919).
13. COLES, J. W., "Nematodes parasitic on sea weeds of the genera *Ascophyllum* and *Fucus*," *J. Mar. Biol. Ass. U.K.*, **37**, 145 (1958).
14. COTT, H. B., *Adaptive Coloration in Animals* (London, Methuen, 1940).
15. DALES, R. P., "Feeding and digestion in terebellid polychaetes," *J. Mar. Biol. Ass. U.K.*, **34**, 55 (1955).
16. DALES, R. P., "Commensalism," in *Treatise on Marine Ecology and Palaeoecology*," Ed. Hedgpeth, J. W. (*Geol. Soc. Amer. Mem.*, **67**, Pt. 1, 391, 1957).
17. DALES, R. P., *Annelids* (London, Hutchinson University Library, 1963).
18. DAVENPORT, D., "Specificity and behavior in symbioses," *Quart. Rev. Biol.*, **30**, 29 (1955).
19. DAVENPORT, D., ROSS, D. M. and SUTTON, L., "The remote control of nematocyst-discharge in the attachment of *Calliactis* to shells of hermit crabs," *Vie et Milieu*, **12**, 197 (1961).
20. DAY, J. H., "The life-history of *Sacculina*," *Quart. J. Micr. Sci.*, **77**, 549 (1935).
21. DOYLE, W. L. and DOYLE, M. M., "The structure of Zooxanthellae," *Pap. Tortugas Lab.*, **32** (8), 127 (1940).
22. EISIG, H., "*Ichthyotomus sanguinarius*, eine auf Aalen schmarotzende Annelide," *Fauna u. Flora Neapel*, **28** (1906).
23. ELMHIRST, R., "Ecology of *Eupagurus bernhardus*, the hermit crab," *Annu. Rep. Scot. Mar. Biol. Ass.*, 1946–7, p. 18 (1947).
24. FISHER, W. K. and MACGINITIE, G. E., "The natural history of an echiuroid worm," *Ann. Mag. Nat. Hist.*, Ser. 10, **1**, 204 (1928).
26. FLEURY, G., LUBET, P. and DANTEC, J. LE, "Note sur le *Mytilicola intestinalis* Steuer," *Ann. Pharm. Franc.*, **9**, 569 (1951).
27. FOXON, G. E. H., "Notes on the life history of *Sacculina*," *J. Mar. Biol. Ass. U.K.*, **24**, 253 (1940).
28. FRAENKEL, G. S. and GUNN, D. L., *The Orientation of Animals* (Oxford, Clarendon Press, 1940).
29. FRITSCH, F. E., "Algae in association with heterotrophic or holozoic organisms," *Proc. Roy. Soc. B.*, **139**, 185 (1952).
30. GOHAR, H. A. F., "Studies on the Xeniidae of the Red Sea," *Publ. Mar. Biol. Sta. Ghardaqa*, No. 2, p. 25 (1940).
31. GOHAR, H. A. F., "Commensalism between fish and anemone," ibid., No. 6, p. 35 (1948).

32. GOODEY, T., *Plant Parasitic Nematodes and the Diseases They Cause* (London, Methuen, 1933).
33. GOSSE, P. H., *The Aquarium* (London, van Voorst, 1854).
34. GRAHAM, A., "The structure and function of the alimentary canal of aeolid molluscs," *Trans. Roy. Soc. Edinb.*, **59**, 267 (1938).
35. GUDGER, E. W., "Association between sessile colonial hydroids and fishes," *Ann. Mag. Nat. Hist.*, Ser. 10, **1**, 17 (1928).
36. GUDGER, E. W., "Inquilinism between the cheilodipterid fish, *Apogonichthys puncticulatus*, and the univalve mollusk, *Strombus bituberculatus*," *Zoologica, N.Y.*, **9**, 193 (1934).
37. GUDGER, E. W., "Fishes that live as inquilines (lodgers) in sponges," ibid., **35**, 121 (1950).
38. HAND, C. and HENDRICKSON, J. R., "A two-tentacled, commensal hydroid from California," *Biol. Bull.*, **99**, 74 (1950).
39. HARVEY, E. N., *Bioluminescence* (New York, Academic Press, 1952).
40. HERFURTH, A. H., "Beiträge zur Kenntnis der Bakteriensymbiose der Cephalopoden," *Z. Morph. Ökol. Tiere*, **31**, 561 (1936).
41. HICKOCK, J. F. and DAVENPORT, D., "Further studies in the behavior of commensal polychaetes," *Biol. Bull.*, **113**, 397 (1957).
42. HINDLE, E., "Heteroecism in animals," *Proc. Linn. Soc.*, **162**, 5 (1950).
43. HIRAIWA, Y. K., "Studies on a bopyrid, *Epipenaeon japonica*. 3. Development and life cycle," *J. Sci. Hiroshima Univ.*, Ser. B, **4**, 101 (1936).
44. HIRAIWA, Y. K. and SATO, M., "On the effect of parasitic Isopoda on a prawn, *Penaeopsis*," ibid., Ser. B, **7**, 105 (1939).
45. HUGHES, T. E., "The effects on the fat and starch metabolism of *Gebia* by the parasite *Gyge branchialis*," *J. Exp. Biol.*, **17**, 331 (1940).
46. KAWAGUTI, S., "Study on the invertebrates associating unicellular algae. 1. *Placobranchus ocellatus*, a nudibranch," *Palao Trop. Biol. Stud.*, **2**, 307 (1941).
47. KAWAGUTI, S., "Zooxanthellae as a factor of positive phototropism in those animals containing them," ibid., **2**, 681 (1944).
48. KAWAGUTI, S., "Observations on the heart shell, *Corculum cardissa*, and its associated zooxanthellae," *Pacif. Sci.*, **4**, 43 (1950).
49. KEEBLE, F., "The yellow-brown cells of *Convoluta paradoxa*," *Quart. J. Micr. Sci.*, **52**, 431 (1908).
50. KEEBLE, F. and GAMBLE, F. W., "The origin and nature of the green cells of *Convoluta roscoffensis*," *Quart. J. Micr. Sci.*, **51**, 167 (1907).
51. KESSEL, E., "Beobachtungen an *Eupaguras*-Wohngehäusen mit *Hydractinia*-Bewuchs," *Verh. dtsch. Zool. Ges.*, **40**, 154 (1938).
52. KNIGHT, M. and PARKE, M. W., *Manx Algae*, L.M.B.C. Mem. 30, 155 pp. (1931).
53. KNOWLES, F. G. W. and CALLAN, H. G., "A change in the chromatophore pattern of Crustacea at sexual maturity," *J. Exp. Biol.*, **17**, 262 (1940).
54. KNOWLES, F. G. W. and CARLISLE, D. B., "Endocrine control in the Crustacea," *Biol. Rev.*, **31**, 396 (1956).
55. KRAMP, P. L., "Medusae. Part 3. Trachylina and Scyphozoa," *Dan. Ingolf-Exped.*, **5** (14), 66 pp. (1947).
56. LAPAGE, G., *Parasitic Animals* (Cambridge Univ. Press, 1951).
57. LIMBAUGH, C., "Cleaning symbiosis," *Sci. Amer.*, **205**, 42 (Aug., 1961).

58. LIMBAUGH, C., PEDERSON, H. and CHACE, F. A., JR., "Shrimps that clean fishes," *Bull. Mar. Sci. Gulf Caribbean*, **11**, 237 (1961).
59. MCLAUGHLIN, J. J. A. and ZAHL, P. A., "Studies in marine biology. 2. *In vitro* culture of zooxanthellae," *Proc. Soc. Exp. Biol.*, *N.Y.*, **95**, 115 (1957).
60. MALAQUIN, A., "Le parasitisme évolutif des Monstrillides," *Arch. Zool. Exp. Gén.*, **9**, 81 (1901).
61. MEYERHOF, E. and ROTHSCHILD, M., "A prolific trematode," *Nature*, **146**, 367 (1940).
62. MONOD, T., "Les Gnathiidae: essai monographique," *Mém. Soc. Sci. Nat. Maroc*, No. 13, 668 pp. (1926).
63. MORTENSEN, T. and ROSENVINGE, L. K., "Sur une nouvelle Algae, *Coccomyxa astericola*, parasite dans une Astérie," *Biol. Medd. Copenhagen*, **10** (9), 8 pp. (1933).
64. MORTENSEN, T. and ROSENVINGE, L. K., "Sur une Algae cyanophycée, *Dactylococcopsis echini*, n. sp., parasite dans un Oursin," ibid., **11** (7), 10 pp. (1934).
65. OKADA, Y. K., "Les Cirripèdes ascothoraciques," *Trav. Sta. Zool. Wimereux*, **13**, 489 (1938).
66. ORTON, J. H., "Mode of feeding and sex-phenomena in the pea-crab (*Pinnotheres pisum*)," *Nature*, **106**, 533 (1920).
67. ORTON, J. H., "On the mode of feeding of the hermit-crab *Eupagurus Bernhardus*," *J. Mar. Biol. Ass. U.K.*, **14**, 909 (1927).
68. ORTON, J. H. and SMITH, C. L., "Experiments with *Amphitrite* and its commensals," *Ann. Mag. Nat. Hist.*, Ser. 10, **16**, 644 (1935).
69. PÉRÈS, J.-M., "Sur un cas nouveau de parasitisme chez les Polychètes," *Bull. Inst. Océanogr. Monaco*, No. 945, 4 pp. (1949).
70. RANSON, G., *Les Huîtres* (Paris, Paul Lechevalier, 1951).
71. REES, W. J., "Note on *Phyllirrhoe bucephala* and *Mnestra parasites*," *Proc. Malac. Soc. Lond.*, **29**, 219 (1953).
72. REINHARD, E. G., "The endoparasitic development of *Peltogaster paguri*," *J. Morph.*, **70**, 69 (1942).
73. REINHARD, E. G., "Experiments on the determination and differentiation of sex in the bopyrid *Stegophyrxus hyptius* Thompson," *Biol. Bull.*, **96**, 17 (1949).
74. REINHARD, E. G., "An analysis of the effects of a sacculinid parasite on the external morphology of *Callinectes sapidus* Rathbun," ibid., **98**, 277 (1950).
75. REINHARD, E. G. and BRAND, T. VON, "The fat content of *Pagurus* parasitized by *Peltogaster*," *Physiol. Zool.*, **17**, 31 (1944).
76. REINHARD, E. G. and BUCKERIDGE, F. W., "The effect of parasitism by an entoniscid on the secondary sex characters of *Pagurus longicarpus*," *J. Parasitol.*, **36**, 131 (1950).
77. REVERBERI, G., "Parassitismo, iperparassitismo e sesso nei Crostacei," *Pubbl. Staz. Zool. Napoli*, **23**, 284 (1952).
78. REVERBERI, G. and PITOTTI, M., "Il ciclo biologico e la determinazione fenotipica del sesso di *Ione thoracica*," ibid., **19**, 111 (1943).
79. ROSS, D. M. and SUTTON, L., "The response of the sea anemone *Calliactis* to shells of the hermit crab *Pagurus*," *Proc. Roy. Soc.*, B, **115**, 266 (1961).
80. ROSS, D. M. and SUTTON, L., "The association between the hermit crab *Dardanus* and the sea anemone *Calliactis*," *Proc. Roy. Soc.*, B, **115**, 282.

81. ROTHSCHILD, A. and ROTHSCHILD, M., "Some observations on the growth of *Peringia ulvae* (Pennant) 1777 in the laboratory," *Nov. Zool. Tring*, **41**, 240 (1939).

82. ROTHSCHILD, M., "A note on immunity reaction in the black-headed gull (*Larus ridibundus* L.) infected with *Maritrema oöcysta* Lebour, 1907," *J. Parasitol.*, **28**, 423 (1942).

83. SMITH, G., "Rhizocephala," *Fauna u. Flora Neapel*, Monogr., 29 (1906).

84. SMITH, H. G., "On the presence of Algae in certain Ascidiacea," *Ann. Mag. Nat. Hist.*, Ser. 10, **15**, 615 (1935).

85. STAUBER, L. A., "*Pinnotheres ostreum*, parasitic on the American oyster, *Ostrea (Gyphaea) virginica*," *Biol. Bull.*, **88**, 269 (1945).

86. VEILLET, A., "Recherches sur le parasitisme des Crabes et des Galathées par les Rhizocéphales et les Epicarides," *Ann. Inst. Océanogr. Monaco*, **22**, 193 (1945).

87. VEILLET, A., "Métamorphose de la larve cypris du *Rhizocéphale Septosaccus*," *C. R. Acad. Sci.*, **224**, 957 (1947).

88. VERWEY, J., "Coral reef studies. 1. The symbiosis between damsel fishes and sea anemones in Batavia Bay," *Treubia*, **12**, 305 (1930).

89. WAHLERT, G. et H., "Le comportement de nettoyage de *Crenilabrus melanocercus* en Méditerranée," *Vie et Milieu*, **12**, 1 (1961).

90. YONGE, C. M., "Experimental analysis of the association between invertebrates and unicellular algae," *Biol. Rev.*, **19**, 68 (1944).

91. YONGE, C. M., "Symbiosis," in *Treatise on Marine Ecology and Paleoecology*, Vol. I, *Ecology*, Ed. Hedgpeth, J. W. (*Geol. Soc. Amer. Mem.*, 67, 1957).

92. YONGE, C. M., "The biology of coral reefs," *Adv. Mar. Biol.*, **1**, 209 (1963).

CHAPTER 15

SKELETONS, SHELTERS AND SPECIAL DEFENCES

> For they had heard that in certain parts of the ocean a kind of worm is
> bred, which many times pierceth and eateth through the strongest oak
> that is: and therefore that the mariners and the rest to be employed in
> this voyage might be free and safe from this danger, they cover a
> piece of keel of the ship with thin sheets of lead . . .
>
> HAKLUYT: *Chancellor's North-Easterly Voyage,* 1553

PREVIOUSLY we have noted how certain inorganic substances are concentrated in skeletal structures (Chapter 2). In the following pages the skeletons of marine animals are considered in more detail. Skeletons are
internal in some animals, but more often appear as external coverings,
shells, etc. Instead of forming hard exoskeletons, many animals secrete
hard tubes of calcareous or organic matter, and others utilize external
secretions for binding together foreign materials or for lining burrows.
Empty, or even inhabited, shells and burrows are invaded by soft-bodied
species seeking protection. This leads us to a consideration of burrowing
and boring species, and the mechanisms which they employ. Finally, we
shall examine special protective devices, such as poison glands, which are
frequently associated with piercing spines and lancets, and this will afford
an opportunity for dealing with poisons and poisonous secretions among
marine animals. This assemblage of topics may appear somewhat hetero-
geneous, but the structures under discussion are linked by a common protective and defensive role in the economy of the organism.

SKELETONS

Animals are provided with hard skeletons for support, protection and
defence. Endoskeletons protect soft and delicate tissues, e.g. the brain of
cephalopods, cyclostomes and fishes. They give internal support to the
body wall and appendages, e.g. in cephalopods, fish; and form rigid supports and lever systems for the operation of muscles in certain molluscs, in
crustaceans and in chordates. The exoskeletons of different animals have
similar protective and functional roles and also provide barriers to the
diffusion of water and solutes.

Endoskeletons

Endoskeletal structures lie either just beneath the surface or at deeper
levels in the body. Although particularly characteristic of vertebrates, we
find endoskeletons present in several invertebrate phyla, especially sponges

and echinoderms, and to a limited extent in certain molluscs, decapod crustaceans, brachiopods, etc. The classification is arbitrary, and some groups of invertebrates show much lability in skeletal organization. The following sections are organized on a phyletic basis.

Protozoa. Radiolarians possess a central capsule of organic material together with an internal spicular skeleton (Fig. 14.17). The latter frequently takes the form of a lattice-work bearing projecting spines, e.g. *Heliosphaera*, *Actinomma*. Spicules are absent in *Thalassicolla* and *Collozoum*.

Organic material in the skeleton of Protozoa is usually classified as tectin, a variety of glycoprotein. The membrane of the central capsule of *Thalassicolla* contains quinone-tanned protein (*see* p. 632). In most radiolarians the internal lattice-work and spicular skeleton consist of silica. In *Acanthometra* and other members of the Acantharia, however, the skeleton is composed mainly of celestite (strontium sulphate). Values for $SrSO_4$ lie around 65%; SiO_2 forms about 9% of shell, and calcium occurs in traces (96).

Porifera. All sponges, with the exception of the Myxospongiae, are provided with an internal structural framework of mineral or organic composition. It is usual to define the skeletons of the three classes of Porifera as follows: Calcarea, skeletons consisting solely of calcareous spicules; Hexactinellida, sponges with a purely siliceous skeleton composed of six-rayed (triaxonid) spicules; Demospongiae, skeleton composed of siliceous spicules which are not triaxonid, or of spongin, or of an admixture of both.

The skeleton of sponges has supporting and defensive functions. In *Euplectella* (Hexactinellida) the skeleton is a delicate cylindrical framework of siliceous spicules consisting of longitudinal, circular and oblique components. The arrangement is such as to offer maximal resistance to torsion and compression, and combines lightness with high rigidity. Myxospongiae, lacking a skeleton, are encrusting in habit. The mineral matter of sponge skeleton is made up of spicules of definite and characteristic shapes, amply described in taxonomic text-books. Analyses of the skeletons of calcareous sponges give values for $CaCO_3$ of 71–85%; these may be lower than true values because of impurities (*Hircinia*, *Grantia*, *Leucilla*). There is some evidence that the calcareous sponges may contain significant amounts of $MgCO_3$, up to 7% in *Leuconia* (Table 15.1). $CaCO_3$ exists as calcite in the spicules. In siliceous sponges, such as Venus' flower-basket *Euplectella*, the skeleton is composed of nearly pure opaline silica. Boron is a constant minor constituent of siliceous spicules (*Suberites*, *Tethya*).

Organic skeletons consist of fibres of a proteid substance, spongin, arranged in a network, or in branching formation. In many Demospongiae the siliceous spicules are bound together by spongin material, or incorporated in spongin. In the sub-class Keratosa the skeleton is composed entirely of spongin fibres. This group includes the bath sponges of commerce (*Spongia*, *Hippospongia*). On the basis of X-ray analysis, spongin

TABLE 15.1

INORGANIC CONSTITUENTS IN THE SKELETON OF SOME MARINE ANIMALS

Animal group and species	Organic matter % dry weight	Percentage of mineral matter						
		SiO_2	$(Al,F)_2O_3$	$MgCO_3$	$CaCO_3$	$Ca_3(PO_4)_2$	$CaSO_4$	Other
Protozoa—Foraminifera								
Sphaeroidinella dehiscens	2·38	8·89[a]	4·94	1·79	84·38	?	—	Fe_2O_3–0·27
Orbitolites marginatis	1·30	0·31	0·13	10·55	89·01	trace	—	$SiO_2+(Al,F)_2O_3$ —10·47
Porifera								
Calcarea								
Leuconia aspera	0·43	—	—	7·17	90·20	—	1·63	—
Grantia ciliata	—	—	—	4·61	84·92	?	—	—
Hircinia campana	—	1·36	5·45	8·00	81·64	3·55	?	—
Hexactinellida								
Euplectella speciosa	—	99	—	—	—	—	—	—
Demospongiae								
Halichondria panicea	—	82	—	—	—	—	—	—
Spongia officinalis	>96	—	—	—	—	—	—	—
Coelenterata								
Hydrocorallinae								
Millepora alcicornis	3·31	0·02	0·07	0·22	99·63	0·06	trace	—
Alcyonaria								
Heliopora cerulea	1·55	0·15	0·07	0·35	98·93	trace	0·50	—
Corallium rubrum	0·06	—	—	9·18	88·84	0·72	1·26	—
Tubipora purpurea	2·27	1·40	0·57	12·23	84·61	trace	1·19	—
Alcyonium carneum	40·90	1·50	trace	6·60	84·50	5·19	2·15	—
Madreporaria								
Porites clavaria	3·70	0·04	0·10	0·37	99·49	trace	?	—
Polychaeta								
Hyalinoecia tubicola	50·68[b]	—	—	—	—	trace	trace	—
Hydroides dianthus	4·36	—	—	9·72	89·66	0·62	—	—
Echinodermata								
Crinoidea								
Parametra granulata	13·67	0·42	0·33	10·09	87·16	trace	—	—
Echinoidea								
Strongylocentrotus drobachiensis	8·61	0·13	0·37	5·99	93·13	trace	0·38	—
Asteroidea								
Asterias vulgaris	29·34	0·64	0·30	7·79	91·06	0·21	?	—

Ophiuroidea								
Ophiothrix angulata	13·93	0·31	0·77	11·68	87·24	?	?	—
Holothuria								
Holothuria floridana	46·72[c]	0·15	0·34	13·84	83·29	trace	2·38	—
Polyzoa								
Microporella grisea	6·86[a]	0·18	0·12	1·11	96·90	0·24	1·45	$SiO_2 + (Al,F)_2O_3$ −4.82
Membranipora membranacea	35·06[a]	—	—	6·94	87·92	0·32	?	
Brachiopoda								
Gryphus cubensis	0·93	0·06	0·04	0·93	98·61	trace	0·36	—
Crania anomala	3·52	0·22	0·27	8·63	88·59	0·57	1·72	—
Lingula unguis	40	0·91	0·54	2·70	1·18	91·74	2·93	—
Mollusca								
Laevicardium substriatum	2·44	0·11	0·09	trace	99·80	trace	?	—
Dentalium solidum	2·04	0·40	0·27	0·20	99·13	trace	0·35	—
Mopalia muscosa	2·61	0·61	0·22	0·45	98·37	trace	?	—
Nucella lapillus	3·21	0·15	0·16	0·41	99·28	trace	—	—
Nautilus pompilius	5·37	0·19	0·15	0·16	99·50	trace	—	—
Spirula spirula	2·37	—	—	0·48	95·75	3·39	0·38	—
Sepia sp.	2·98	0	0·06	1·62	98·32	trace	—	—
Argonauta argo	6·86	0·09	0·13	6·02	93·76	trace	—	—
Crustacea								
Cirripedia								
Lepas anatifera	2·13	0·04	0·20	2·49	97·27	trace	—	—
Balanus hameri	1·92	0·03	0·15	0·75	99·07	0	—	—
Amphipoda								
Tryphosa pinguis	45·20	1·12	0·67	4·84	74·64	18·02	0·71	—
Decapoda								
Homarus americanus	37·74	0	0·34	8·02	79·50	10·91	1·23	—
Grapsus grapsus	47·79	trace	8·86	6·18	72·77	12·19	trace	—
Crangon dalii	77·50	2·94	0·95	10·05	54·83	27·44	3·79	—
Vertebrata (skeleton)								
Squalus acanthias	—	—	—	—	7·34	80·0	—	$Mg_3(PO_4)_2$ −2.09 Excess Ca −3.06
Lophius piscatorius	—	—	—	—	7·27	82·5	—	$Mg_3(PO_4)_2$ −1.99 Excess Ca −2.08
Scomber scombrus	—	—	—	—	6·35	83·85	—	$Mg_3(PO_4)_2$ −2.74 Excess Ca −1.90

a, impurities; *b*, onuphin; *c*, soft parts of body; *d*, body and skeleton.
Data from Clarke and Wheeler (23) and Morgulis and Janecek (85)

fibres are classed with collagen. Amino-acid composition is markedly different from both keratin and gelatin (81).

Mineral spicules and organic fibres are secreted by cells termed scleroblasts. Both siliceous and calcareous spicules are laid down around an axial thread of organic matter. More is known about spicule formation in calcareous sponges. At first intracellular, the spicules frequently become larger than the scleroblasts secreting them. In this event the scleroblasts become apposed to the sides of the spicule, on which they continue to deposit $CaCO_3$ extracellularly. Carbonate ions are necessary for formation of spicules. Larvae reared in carbonate-free sea water fail to produce spicules, and spicules of young sponges regress in such media, probably due to increased acidity occasioned by action of respiratory CO_2. Spongin fibres are also secreted by mesenchyme cells. These arrange themselves in rows and each gives rise to part of an elongated fibre (23, 111, 132).

Echinoderms. The majority of echinoderms are protected by an endoskeleton of calcareous plates termed ossicles. These are embedded in the skin and frequently bear spines which are movably articulated with the plates. When the ossicles are scattered the integument has a leathery texture; when closely apposed they encase the animal in armour.

In echinoids the skeleton usually forms a compact cuirass except for a space about mouth and anus. The ossicles bear large movable spines. A peculiarity of these animals is the presence about the oesophagus of a calcareous framework known as Aristotle's lantern, which supports a set of teeth. In asteroids there is a well-developed system of ossicles, which are not united, however, into a continuous shell. Ophiuroids have the body covered with closely-set plates, those of the arms articulating so as to afford free movability. Large ossicles occur on the aboral surface, in the arms and in the stalk of crinoids. In holothurians the ossicles are greatly reduced and scattered through the integument. They have varied shapes, such as wheels, anchors and crosses. The planktonic *Pelagothuria* lacks ossicles. *Psolus* has the dorsal ossicles enlarged to form a complete mail of plates.

The skeleton forms a high proportion of total body material in starfish and brittle stars. Starfish contain about 30% dry matter and brittle stars over 50%, of which some 34% is protein and 42% $CaCO_3$.

Echinoderm skeletons contain a small proportion of organic matter (10–20%), which presumably forms a substrate on which mineral matter is deposited. Amino-acid residues have been determined for skeletal protein of *Arbacia*, and X-ray diffraction studies have revealed the presence of collagen-type fibrils (105). Although preponderantly calcareous the skeletons also contain much magnesia. $CaCO_3$, as calcite, occurs in amounts ranging from 78–95% (mineral matter); average calcareous content lies around 88% (starfish, sea-urchins, holothurians, crinoids). $MgCO_3$ is present in all groups (5–16% of skeletal material, Table 15.1). As in certain other marine organisms, the proportion of $MgCO_3$ in the skeleton appears to be a function of temperature, animals from warmer waters being richer

in magnesia than those from cold water. This is revealed in the accompanying table (15.2) showing selected data for crinoids from Clarke and
Wheeler (23). Since the magnesium and calcium content of sea water is
universally constant, we must look to some effect of temperature on
physiological mechanisms to account for this phenomenon (21, 22).

TABLE 15.2

PERCENTAGE OF MAGNESIUM CARBONATE IN ASH FROM CRINOIDS

Genus	Locality	Latitude	Depth (m)	Tempera- ture (°C)	MgCO$_3$
Heliometra	N. Japan	43° N	315	1·5	7·28
Promachocrinus	Antarctic	67° S	375	− 1·8	7·86
Ptilocrinus	Br. Columbia	52° N	2,858	1·8	7·91
Anthometra	Antarctic	67° S	375	− 1·8	8·23
Hathrometra	Mass.	40° N	329	7·8	9·36
Florometra	Wash.	47° N	1,145	3·3	9·44
Pentametrocrinus	S. Japan	34° N	1,123	3·4	10·15
Hypalocrinus	Philippines	9° N	612	10·2	10·16
Metacrinus	S. Japan	31° N	278	13·3	10·34
Parametra	Philippines	9° N	502	12	11·08
Crinometra	Cuba	23° N	59	26·2	11·69
Tropiometra	Tobago	11° N	Shoal	28	13·74

The physiology of skeleton-formation in adult echinoderms has not been
investigated. In the larvae, spicules are formed by mesenchyme cells after
gastrulation (sea-urchin, starfish). Salts for spicule formation are derived
from sea water. Mineral matter is absorbed from sea water throughout
development: ash increases from 1·5% (dry weight) at fertilization to
16·8% at 40 hours (pluteus). Sea-urchin and starfish eggs fail to develop in
sea water lacking Ca^{++} and $CO_3^=$ ions and spicule-formation is delayed
in Ca^{++}-poor media; Mg^{++} and $SO_4^=$ ions are also necessary for spicule-
formation. However, Ca^{++} and certain other ions are required for tissue
differentiation and growth apart from skeletal formation, as evidenced by
requirements of *Beroë* and *Ciona* larvae. At the time of spicule formation
the pH of sea-urchin larvae rises owing to incorporation of $CO_3^=$ ions
in the skeleton. At the same time HCO_3^- ions are absorbed from the
environment to supplement those derived from respiratory CO_2 (60, 76,
82, 87, 98, 111, 132).

Endoskeleton of Fishes. The internal skeleton of cyclostomes and fishes
consists of cartilage or bone. Cartilage contains chondromucoid (gluco-
protein), elastin and collagen. In elasmobranchs the cartilage is to some
extent calcified. This takes the form of a deposition of crystalline plates of
calcium phosphate over the surfaces of the cartilage.

Bone consists of an organic base impregnated with mineral matter. The
water content is about 50%. Dry matter consists of 60% organic and 40%
mineral material. The organic substratum contains collagen, glycoprotein
and protein. Most of the mineral matter is calcium phosphate, which forms
about 83% of total mineral matter in teleost bone; $CaCO_3$ forms some

6–7% (Table 15.1). The bones of marine fishes contain only about 60% as much $CaCO_3$ as found in higher vertebrates, apparently owing to lower carbonate reserves in the body fluids of fishes. Much of the calcium phosphate is probably arranged in the form of the mineral apatite ($10Ca:6PO_4$) (6, 59, 85).

Phosphatases are involved in ossification and deposition of calcareous matter. Alkaline phosphatase appears at the time of ossification, and probably catalyses the local deposition of PO_4 ions in insoluble form. At the same time Ca^{++} is liberated from the blood and calcium phosphate is laid down in crystalline form in the organic matrix. Calcifying cartilage of the selachian *Scyliorhinus* contains phosphatase, as does developing bone of teleosts and higher vertebrates. Differences in the properties of true bone (teleost) and calcified cartilage (elasmobranch) arise from different methods of ossification (deposition of calcium phosphate) (74).

Scales (Fig. 12.9) are somewhat similar to bone in structure. The teleost scale consists of an organic base of collagen and an albuminoid ichthylepidin. About 25% of the scale is dry matter. Menhaden scales (*Brevoortia*) contain 59% organic matter and 41% ash. Collagen forms 76% of organic matter, ichthylepidin 24%. Selachian denticles and scales of certain teleosts (*Mola, Spheroides*) have an organic framework of collagen alone. The mineral matter is largely calcium phosphate ($Ca(H_2PO_4)_2$) (44, 110).

In temperate and arctic waters seasonal changes in growth and metabolism of teleost fishes are also attended by variations in deposition of skeletal material. The annual growth rings on scales and otoliths, consisting of alternating bands of rapid summer and slow winter growth, are well known. Similar growth rings also occur in the bones of many species. They are, for example, well marked in the dragonet *Callionymus* (20, 35, 83).

Variations in scale pattern can be noted only briefly. In some species, e.g. conger eel, scales are greatly reduced or absent. In others, the scales are enlarged or strengthened to form an external armour. Armoured teleosts include needle-fishes (Centriscidae), in which the body is enclosed in a bony cuirass; knight-fish (Monocentridae) and trunk-fish (Ostracionti-dae), which bear thick scales so as to enclose the body in a kind of box. Spicules and spines are a common form of external armament. In puffers or globe-fishes (Tetraodontidae) the body is naked except for numerous small movable spines set in the skin. By means of a large sac connected with the gullet, the puffer-fish can inflate itself with air or water until the body is blown out like a balloon and spines stand erect. Porcupine-fishes (Diodontidae) are covered with fixed or movable spines. In trigger-fishes (*Balistes*) the first spine in the dorsal fin is strong and hollowed out posteriorly to receive a bony knob at the base of the second spine. By this mechanism the first spine remains firmly erect until the second spine, which acts after the manner of a trigger, is lowered. An account of venomous mechanisms associated with spines is given in a later section.

Exoskeletons. Many protozoa are protected externally by plates, tests or other coverings. The plant-like flagellates are provided with a polysac-charide membrane, which in dinoflagellates takes the form of stout plates of cellulose. Other species are enclosed in shells bearing pores or apertures through which the animal emerges or sends forth strands of cytoplasm. Secreted tests of organic matter are found in foraminifers (*Gromia, Allogromia*), folliculinid and tintinnid ciliates. Some of these tests are said to have a nitrogenous basis and may be proteinaceous. Those of fora-minifers are covered externally by a layer of cytoplasm. Foreign bodies are frequently incorporated in the shell, e.g. tests of foraminifers, loricae of tintinnids. The tests of the majority of foraminifers are calcareous, and take the form of loose-fitting shells with wide mouths, or chambered shells perforated by numerous pores. In some groups the skeleton is arranged in the form of an external lattice, siliceous in Silicoflagellata and calcareous in Coccolithophoridae.

Siliceous foraminiferan tests are constructed largely of sand grains on an organic base and contain 76–95 % silica. Calcareous foraminifers, such as *Orbitolites* and *Polytrema*, have tests composed largely of $CaCO_3$ (86–89 %). Variable amounts of $MgCO_3$ are also present (2–16 %). The con-tent of the latter is appreciably greater in warm-water species. Spectro-scopic analysis also demonstrates the accumulation of surprisingly large amounts of strontium and silica in calcareous tests. In the Xenophyophora, deep-sea forms sometimes grouped with Foraminifera, the skeleton con-sists of grains of barium sulphate (21, 23, 28, 114, 132).

Coelenterates. An external secreted skeleton is a characteristic feature of many sedentary coelenterates, notably the corals.

The soft parts of hydroids are covered by a chitinous perisarc which is secreted by the epidermis, probably by specialized glandular cells. This is occasionally strengthened by deposition of calcareous matter, e.g. *Hydrac-tinia*. The pneumatophore or air sac of siphonophores has a chitinous lining. Chitin is said to be absent from the Anthozoa (65).

Corals. Millepore corals (Hydrozoa) possess a calcareous exoskeleton which takes the form of leaf-like or branching growths. Tubes from the polyps ramify through the skeleton, which corresponds to the perisarc of hydroid colonies. Analyses of *Millepora* and of *Distichopora*, another coralline hydroid, show that the skeleton consists largely of aragonite. Organic matter forms about 3 % of the skeleton (dry weight); mineral matter is predominantly $CaCO_3$ (Table 15.1).

Alcyonaria are colonial in habit and are supported by a skeleton secreted by mesogloeal cells. The skeleton is calcareous or horny in composition and differs greatly in construction in different groups. Organic skeletons consist of strands and lamellae of horny material. Calcareous skeletons may consist of spicules embedded in a horny network, e.g. gorgonians; of separate calcareous spicules, e.g. soft corals (Alcyonacea); or of spicules fused by calcareous cement, e.g. organ-pipe coral *Tubipora*.

The skeleton of *Alcyonium*, a typical genus, consists of mesogloeal spicules. These contain an organic axis, secreted by scleroblasts, on which crystals of calcite are deposited. In the blue coral *Heliopora* the skeleton consists of crystalline fibres of aragonite fused into lamellae. In the horny corals or gorgonians the axial skeleton consists of a horn-like material, gorgonin, arranged in branched and lamellated fashion. Calcareous matter sometimes occurs in the axis. Overlying the axial skeleton is a system of calcareous spicules and plates of various shapes. In the red coral *Corallium* gorgonin is absent and the skeleton consists of a solid axis of calcareous spicules cemented together by calcium carbonate (125).

Gorgonin is a protein which, from X-ray diffraction evidence, shows affinities with collagen (*Balticina*). The sulphur content is lower than in keratin; high tyrosine content is characteristic; cystine residue is higher than in gelatin. In addition, monoiodotyrosine, diiodotyrosine and bromine analogues appear to be constituent amino-acids of the skeletal protein (p. 73) (81).

A few analyses of alcyonarian corals are listed in Table 15.1. The contribution of organic matter to the skeleton shows much variation. It is very low in *Corallium* (0·06%), about 1·6% in blue coral *Heliopora*, 2·3% in the organ-pipe coral *Tubipora*, 29% in the sea-pen *Pennatula* and 52% in the sea-fan *Gorgonia*. The axis of the latter is almost entirely organic matter (about 95%). The chief mineral constituent of *Heliopora* is $CaCO_3$ (99%). In skeletons of other alcyonarians, $CaCO_3$ accounts for 80–92% of mineral matter. Content of $MgCO_3$ is high, from 6–17%. Species from warm waters contain proportionately much more magnesia than those from cold northern or cold deep waters (21, 23).

Madreporaria (true or stony corals) are mostly colonial in habit. They are provided with a hard calcareous exoskeleton, which is secreted by the epidermis and lies wholly outside the polyp body. The skeleton of each polyp is a cup-shaped structure containing vertical ridges radiating from the centre to the periphery. The skeleton of a whole colony is made up of the conjoined skeletons secreted by each polyp. In the solitary corals, *Fungia, Caryophyllia, Balanophyllia*, the skeletal cup of each polyp is large, 0·5–25 cm in diameter. Most corals are colonial, with small or minute polyps, 1–30 mm in diameter. The colonies vary from flat to spherical in shape, and consist predominantly of $CaCO_3$, of which only the surface is occupied by living substance.

Madreporarian corals have been repeatedly analysed. Organic material forms up to 7% of dry matter; most of this probably resides in encrusting material or polyps. The skeleton is almost entirely $CaCO_3$ in the form of aragonite (21, 23, 58).

Skeletal material is continually being secreted by the bases of the polyps and the colony increases in length and diameter. By the formation of horizontal plates in the cups the polyps are pushed upward and so retain their position on the surface of the mass.

Annelids. Annelids are essentially soft-bodied animals. Some, like the Aphroditidae, are covered with scales or dense felt-works of chaetae. The chaetae of *Aphrodite* consist of chitin and aromatically tanned protein (in the ratio 35:65) (103). The tubes and burrows of polychaetes are described in later sections.

Crustacea. Arthropods, as a group, are characterized by a chitinous cuticle. This is usually stout, but at intervals on the trunk and limbs it becomes flexible so as to form joints. The cuticle is an external armour protecting soft parts and moulding body form. It provides attachment for muscles and a skeleton for development of limbs, jaws and other mouth parts.

The organic constituents of the cuticle are chitin and proteins, and often it is further hardened by the deposition of lime salts. These give the cuticle a stony hardness in certain ostracods, barnacles and crabs. Periodically, during the growth of the animal, the hard outer layers of the cuticle are separated from the inner layers, ruptured and shed in a moult or ecdysis. The soft inner layers then expand to accommodate the body. Expansion is effected by osmotic changes in the blood and by absorption of sea water (*see* Chapter 2). In *Uca*, for example, the water content of the body increases by about 16% immediately after ecdysis. Moulting processes are regulated by temperature; in temperate and cold regions the frequency of ecdysis is highest in summer, and declines or ceases in winter months (49, 127).

Many groups of crustaceans are provided with a shell or carapace. This is a dorsal fold of skin and cuticle which arises from the hind border of the head and extends for a greater or lesser distance over the trunk. Ostracods possess a bivalved carapace covering the whole body; in Malacostraca it covers the thorax. The carapace has disappeared in isopods and amphipods. An internal skeleton is sometimes present as ingrowths of the cuticle. These structures, known as apodemes, serve for insertions of muscles; in decapods they unite to form a framework, the endophragmal skeleton.

On the basis of skeletal composition, crustaceans fall into two main categories—namely barnacles with predominantly calcareous shells, and softer-bodied forms, shrimps, lobsters, etc., the skeletons of which contain much organic matter. The shells of barnacles (*Lepas, Balanus*) contain a minor fraction of organic matter (2–5% dry weight). $CaCO_3$ is the major inorganic constituent, forming 96–99% of mineral matter; $MgCO_3$ is present in amounts up to 2·5% (Table 15.1).

The proportion of organic matter is high in the shrimp skeleton, 77% (dry weight) in *Crangon*; in *Homarus* it forms 38%; and is low in crab, 29% in *Eriphia*. Absolute values of organic and inorganic constituents show much variation with age and species. $CaCO_3$ predominates among mineral constituents. It is low in shrimps, 60% ash or less; lobsters and crayfish show values around 74–78%. Calcium phosphate ($Ca_3(PO_4)_2$) is present in notable quantities (11% mineral matter in *Homarus*, and 27–49% in shrimps *Crangon* and *Pandalus*). Magnesium is also a conspicuous constituent, $MgCO_3$ forming 8–15% of skeletal ash in various decapods. Inorganic material in the skeletons of minute crustaceans (copepod *Temora*, euphausiid *Thysanoessa*) consists almost entirely of calcium phosphate.

The relative proportions of mineral constituents in the skeleton vary in different regions of the animal, and with age. The latter factor is brought out in the analyses from Clarke and Wheeler (23) for *Homarus* shown in Table 15.3. As the animal ages, $CaCO_3$ decreases relative to other con-

TABLE 15.3

MEAN ANALYSES OF LOBSTER SHELLS
(percentage ash)

	Length of animal		
	21·6 cm	29·3 cm	42 cm
$MgCO_3$	9·27	9·70	9·88
$CaCO_3$	75·69	68·02	61·01
$Ca_3(PO_4)_2$	13·45	24·92	26·35
$CaSO_4$	1·24	1·85	2·32

stituents and there is a marked relative increase of $Ca_3(PO_4)_2$. Slight relative increases of $CaSO_4$ and $MgCO_3$ are also evident.

ORGANIC COMPOSITION OF CRUSTACEAN EXOSKELETON. The cuticle is formed by the underlying epidermis (hypodermis) and comprises two

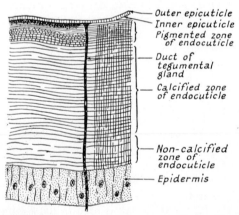

FIG. 15.1. DIAGRAMMATIC REPRESENTATION OF THE FULLY FORMED CUTICLE OF A DECAPOD CRUSTACEAN, AS SEEN IN CROSS-SECTION. (From Dennell (27).)

regions—a relatively thick inner layer containing chitin, the endocuticle; and a thin outer layer, the epicuticle, containing protein but lacking chitin (Fig. 15.1). An extensive treatment of the arthropod cuticle is given by Richards (109).

Chitin present in the endocuticle is bound with protein in a protein-chitin complex. Chitin occurs not only in the body wall, but also in the

TABLE 15.4

OCCURRENCE OF CHITIN IN MARINE ANIMALS

Group and Animal	Structure	Occurrence
Protozoa		—
Porifera		—
Coelenterata		
Hydrozoa-Hydroida	Perisarc	+
Scyphomedusae		—
Anthozoa		—
Ctenophora		—
Nematoda	{ Body wall	—
	Egg shell	+
Chaetognatha		
Sagitta	Hooks	+
Annelida		
Polychaeta	Body wall	—
Eunice, Aphrodite, Glycera,	} Jaws, bristles, gut lining	+
Lepidonotus, Arenicola, Pectinaria		
Mollusca		
Cephalopoda		
Sepia, Loligo, Nauplius	Shell or dorsal shield	+
Amphineura	?	+
Gastropoda		
Aplysia, Patella, Haliotis, Buccinum,	} Radula, jaws	+
Littorina, et al.		
Lamellibranchia	Shell	—
Sipunculoidea		
Sipunculus	Body wall	—
Polyzoa		
Ectoprocta		
Bugula, Flustra, Cristatella, et al.	Exoskeleton, operculum	+
Brachiopoda		
Terebratalia	Pedicle	+
Lingula, Discinisca	Shell, pedicle	+
Crania		—
Phoronidea		
Phoronis, Phoronopsis	Tubes	+
Pognophora	Tubes	+
Arthropoda		
Xiphosura		
Limulus	Body wall	+
Crustacea		
Copepoda		
Lernaeopoda	Body wall	+
Cirripedia		
Balanus, Lepas	Body wall	+
Mysidacea		
Mysis	Body wall	+
Isopoda		
Ligia	Body wall	+
Amphipoda		
Gammarus, Caprella	Body wall	+
Decapoda	{ Body wall, gills, gut,	+
Cancer, Crangon, Homarus, et al.	setae, egg shell	
Insecta	Body wall, tracheae	+

(Various sources.)

cuticle lining the fore- and hindgut, in apodemes and in the eggshell. It appears to be universally present in arthropods and has also been identified in members of certain other phyla, a survey of which is presented in Table 15.4. Chitin forms a substantial proportion of the crustacean cuticle, from 60–80% of total organic matter. Protein, representing the remainder of organic matter, is present in two forms, a water-soluble arthropodin, and a water-insoluble sclerotin. The rigidity of the organic skeleton is due largely to the presence of tanned scleroproteins. Some analyses of crustacean integuments (organic constituents) are presented in Table 15·5. Arthropodin has been analysed into its amino-acid constituents (30).

Structurally, chitin is a long-chain polymer. It is similar to cellulose, but with N-acetylglucosamine, linked $1:4(\beta)$, forming the repeating unit.

Chitin

Active systems obviously exist for the synthesis and destruction of chitin, the relative and absolute amounts of which change during the life of the animal. At each moult the cuticle is largely digested, resorbed and formed anew, and chitin in the new cuticle is synthesized from sugars derived ultimately from glycogen reserves of the animal. During the moulting period reserves of protein, lipoid and glycogen in the hepatopancreas are mobilized, both for nutrition of the animal during its fast and for fabrication of new cuticle. Part is transferred to the epidermis, where glucose molecules are aminated and acetylated, leading to the formation of chitin (Fig. 15.2). At the end of the moult, levels of glycogen and glucosamine in the epidermis are greatly reduced (107, 109).

MOULTING. In crustaceans moulting begins with a loosening of the old cuticle from the underlying epidermal cells. At the same time a fluid is secreted which dissolves part of the old cuticle, and this cuticular material is resorbed. New cuticle—endocuticle and epicuticle—is laid down underneath the old endocuticle which is to be discarded. The old cuticle splits at certain predetermined lines, which are weakened by the action of moulting fluid, and the animal emerges. The exuvium which is cast off consists of the epicuticle and that portion of the old endocuticle which was not dissolved.

The cuticle, when first produced, is soft, but in most crustaceans it gradually becomes hardened or sclerotized (decapods, isopods, amphipods). This hardening or tanning process produces rigid lateral binding of the protein chains by powerful cross-linkages. The agents responsible for tanning are orthoquinones, which form the lateral linkages between the protein chains. Quinones are produced by oxidation of polyphenols through activity of an enzyme, polyphenol oxidase. Polyphenols themselves are derived from blood tyrosine through the action of tyrosinase, also circulating in the blood. A suggested scheme of events is the following. Some

TABLE 15.5

Composition of Integument of Crustaceans

	Nephrops norvegicus Cephalothorax	*Cancer paguras* Cephalothorax	*Palaemon serratus* Cephalothorax	*Ligia oceanica* Tergites	*Lepas anatifera* Integument of peduncle
Water (percentage fresh carapace)	25·4	17·7	24·2	—	—
Organic matter (percentage dry carapace)	26·9	11·4	37·5	41·6	>99
Chitin (percentage organic matter)	77·5	71·4	64·5	78·5	58·3
Calculated protein (amino-N × 6·25) (percentage organic matter)	13·7	11·2	14	9·5	19

(From Lafon (70).)

hormonal stimulus releases the activity of tyrosinase, and blood tyrosine is converted into hydroxyphenol. The polyphenols diffuse outwards to the epicuticle, where they are oxidized to orthoquinones; the latter harden the epicuticle and outer layers of the endocuticle. The tegumental glands appear to be the source of polyphenol oxidase (10, 11, 27, 68, 69).

Another important, and sometimes dominant, factor in hardening is the deposition of lime salts. After moult, calcification of the cuticle takes place rapidly. In *Cancer* and *Carcinus* the outer layer of the cuticle becomes calcified in 1–2 days, followed by deeper lamellae. The degree of calcification stands in inverse relationship to the amount of protein present in the cuticle. In newly formed cuticle prior to calcification, and in species with

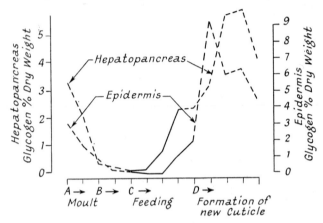

FIG. 15.2. VARIATIONS IN AMOUNT OF GLYCOGEN CONTAINED IN THE HYPODERMIS AND HEPATOPANCREAS OF *Cancer pagurus* DURING COURSE OF AN INTERMOULT

– – – non-feeding period; —— feeding period. Moult at *A*. *A–B*, period of absorption of water immediately after moult and of calcification. *B–C*, water absorption and calcification complete; period of hardening of integument. *C–D*, completion of integument, feeding and tissue growth. *D–A*, premoult, new integument forming. (From Renaud (107).)

non-calcified cuticle, there are roughly equivalent quantities of chitin and protein. With the progress of calcification the quantity of protein added to the cuticle decreases. Calcification thus replaces a large proportion of protein that would otherwise be needed for hardening the cuticle, and is an economical process in an environment rich in calcium.

Prior to the moult, calcium is resorbed from the cuticle. The fate of this calcium varies in different species. Calcium is stored in the hepatopancreas (crabs, spiny lobsters), in gastroliths (lobsters), sternal plates and pleopods (isopods), and held in the haemolymph (Fig. 15.3). A certain proportion is also excreted by marine decapods. As the new cuticle hardens, calcium is reabsorbed from the environment and mobilized from stores in gastroliths, hepatopancreas and elsewhere. Blood-calcium concentrations vary in correlation with these changes in the cuticle and may rise to five times normal values. Changes also occur during the moulting cycle in blood-phosphate levels, which are highest immediately preceding a moult and lowest following it (*Homarus*). Phosphates are removed from the skeleton prior to moulting, and stored as spherules of calcium phosphate in cells of the hepatopancreas. Following the moult these phosphate reserves are mobilized for hardening the new skeleton (spiny lobster, *Panulirus*) (53, 57, 72, 111, 116, 127 128).

HORMONAL CONTROL OF MOULTING. Moulting in crustaceans is under hormonal control, and both moult-accelerating and moult-inhibiting hormones are involved. A moult-inhibiting hormone is produced by special neurosecretory organs, notably the x-organ in the eye-stalk of decapods. From the x-organ the hormone is transferred to the sinus gland for storage

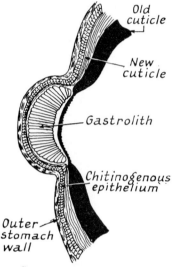

Old cuticle

New cuticle

Gastrolith

Chitinogenous epithelium

Outer stomach wall

FIG. 15.3. DIAGRAMMATIC SECTION THROUGH THE STOMACH WALL OF A MOULTING LOBSTER *Homarus*, CUTTING THE GASTROLITH. (From Herrick, 1896.)

and release (Fig. 12.7). Eye-stalk removal accelerates ecdysis and shortens subsequent intermoult periods (*Uca*, *Eriocheir*, etc.). The changes induced by eye-stalk ablation resemble closely those observed in the normal premoult period, viz. removal of calcium from the cuticle, formation of gastroliths, increase in oxygen consumption and in water-content of the body (*Cambarus*, *Uca*, etc.). Moulting and associated changes are inhibited in eye-stalkless animals by implanting whole eye-stalk or the x-organs of normal donors into their bodies. In some species, removal of the eye-stalks during the moulting season does not initiate proecdysis. Production of a moult-inhibiting hormone by the eye-stalk neurosecretory organs may thus be limited to the non-moulting season. A moult-inhibiting factor may also be produced in sites additional to the eye-stalks (*Palaemon*, *Carcinus*) (8, 13, 17, 29, 32, 100).

Growth is normally associated with moult in crustaceans. Several investigators have found that eye-stalkless specimens become larger than normal. This is ascribed to the induction of extra moults and to an excessive increase in volume at the time of moulting. The latter results from derangement of water metabolism (117). It has long been known that female crustaceans, carrying eggs, do not moult in spring as the males do, but postpone their moult until after the young are liberated (*Crangon* and other species). Egg-bearing female *Cambarus* can be induced to moult by removal of the eye-stalks. The normal postponement of moult in the breeding female, so essential to the survival of the species, is thus a function of the eye-stalk neurosecretory organs.

Moulting is attended by a series of complex metabolic changes, the interrelations of which still await clear definition. Similarly, eye-stalk ablation produces diverse alterations in physiological state which vary with species, sex and stage of the moulting cycle.

In the premoult period (stage *D*, Fig. 15.2) glycogen stores in the epidermis and hepatopancreas reach a maximum; they fall to a minimum after ecdysis during completion of the new cuticle (stage *C*). Calcium is mobilized from stores in the digestive gland and elsewhere during the period when the exoskeleton is being mineralized. Removal of the eye-stalks produces no change in total glycogen, but does raise the glycogen content of the epidermis. Other changes following loss of the eye-stalks are hypoglycaemia, increase in calcium content of the digestive gland (*Hemigrapsus*, *Panulirus*) and loss of ability to regulate respiration (*Gecarcinus*). It has been suggested that the eye-stalk principle or principles restrain intermediary metabolism, especially those processes connected with preparation for moulting (deposition of glycogen in the epidermis, deposition of calcium in the hepatopancreas) (7, 32, 49, 88, 115, 116).

Evidence has also been adduced for a moult-accelerating principle in decapods (prawns *Lysmata*, *Palaemon*). Extracts of the eye-stalks of fast-moulting (summer) female prawns accelerate the rate of moulting, while comparable extracts from eye-stalks of males or slow-moulting (winter) females are less effective. It is suggested that the moulting cycle is initiated by a fall in level of the moult-inhibiting hormone, but the moult, once begun, is controlled by a moult-accelerating principle. This principle is produced by neurosecretory cells in brain, thoracic ganglia, Y-organs and eye-stalks (16, 19, 66).

Xiphosurans. The cuticle of *Limulus* is structurally similar to that of decapod crustaceans. It contains very little inorganic matter (1% dry weight). Organic matter consists of 25% chitin, 75% scleroprotein. The latter is hardened by quinone tanning (10, 71).

Mollusca. Several kinds of hard skeletons are found in the different classes of molluscs. These are transverse articulating shell plates (Amphineura); a single shell, often coiled (Gastropoda); a pair of hinged shell valves (Lamellibranchia); tubular shell open at both ends (Scaphopoda); and chambered external or reduced internal shells in cephalopods. The shell of the argonaut is a peculiar and specialized structure. In the following account we shall be concerned chiefly with the shells of gastropods and lamellibranchs, which have been most investigated.

SHELL COMPOSITION. The shells of gastropods and lamellibranchs consist of an outer organic membrane of conchiolin, the periostracum, and a series of crystalline layers containing $CaCO_3$ as aragonite or calcite in a conchiolin matrix. Tables and lists showing the mineralogical form in which $CaCO_3$ is present in molluscan shells are available (75, 80, 120). Conchiolin is predominantly protein, with traces of polysaccharide. In gastropods and lamellibranchs the amount of organic matter is small, ranging from 1–10% (dry weight). $CaCO_3$ constitutes 98–99% of inorganic matter. Small amounts of $MgCO_3$ occur in many species, and reach levels of 1–2% in shells of *Nassarius*, *Pinna* and *Pecten* (Table 15.1). Analyses of scaphopod (*Dentalium*) and amphineuran (*Mopalia*) shells reveal similar values (5, 12, 21, 42, 108, 124, 129).

The lamellibranch shell typically consists of two valves closely apposed along the dorsal side where they articulate through interlocking teeth. A ligament, which may be internal or external, occurs along the mid-dorsal line. This ligament is mechanically opposed to the adductor muscles of the shell, and by its elasticity it holds the valves open when the muscles are relaxed. Typically the shell consists of three layers, an external periostracum and two calcareous layers. The ligament is largely organic and consists of inner and outer regions. The outer is prismatic, consisting of crystals arranged in a columnar pattern; the inner is laminate, consisting of parallel crystalline sheets. This layer is called nacreous when the crystals are aragonite and calcitostracum when calcite. The outer layer is subject to tensile strain transverse to the longitudinal plane of the shell, and this strain is increased when the valves are closed. The inner layer is elastic and is compressed when the valves close (130).

In marine prosobranchs the shell has essentially the same layered structure, but shows much variation in finer composition.

ORIGIN OF SHELL MATERIAL. Most of the calcareous material of the shells of marine molluscs is absorbed directly from sea water as calcium ions, which are secreted as $CaCO_3$ at the edge of the mantle. Metabolic CO_2 is the primary source of the carbonate radicle.

Shell growth in oysters can occur in sterile sea water in the virtual absence of food. From analysis of oyster shell it has been calculated that some 75 g of shell are laid down in 12 months; this corresponds to about 25 g of Ca^{++}, and a deposition-rate of 70 mg Ca^{++}/day. Direct measurements of calcium deposition, using ^{45}Ca, give a rate of 30 mg/day for *Crassostrea virginica* (25–26°C). Shell is formed throughout the year, even during the colder winter months when the oyster is not feeding and deposition of soft tissues is at a standstill (42, 124, 135).

FORMATION OF SHELL. The innermost layer of the shell (nacreous layer) is formed by the epithelium of the entire mantle; the outer layers and periostracum are usually formed by the mantle edge alone. Under certain circumstances, e.g. during shell regeneration, the periostracum may be formed by the epithelium of the general mantle.

The $CaCO_3$ used in shell formation is liberated by cells of the mantle edge into extrapallial fluid between the epithelium and periostracum. Subsequent crystallization of $CaCO_3$ from this fluid takes place outside the epithelial cells. Calcium ions enter through the general external surface, mantle, gills and especially the gut. Experiments with mussels show that ^{90}Sr and [45]Ca are absorbed on mucous feeding sheets from whence

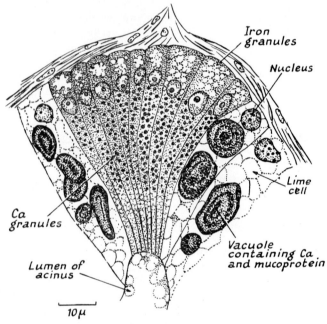

FIG. 15.4. SECTION THROUGH ACINUS OF DIGESTIVE GLAND OF *Haliotis tuberculata*, SHOWING GLANDULAR CELLS CONTAINING CALCAREOUS GRANULES.
(After Manigault (80).)

they enter the body through gills, mantle and gut. In *Aplysia* [90]Sr passes through the general body surface, especially the gill. Phosphate ions (measured by uptake of ^{32}P) are absorbed principally by the gills (oyster) (40, 62, 75, 104, 106, 111).

It is well known that terrestrial gastropods (pulmonates) accumulate calcium reserves in special lime cells of the digestive gland, and are able to draw upon this supply for shell growth and regeneration. Lime cells are found in the digestive gland of chitons, and calcium stores in the connective tissue and digestive gland of *Littorina*, *Haliotis* and *Nucella* (Fig. 15.4). The significance of these tissue deposits in an environment rich in calcium is not clear (39, 80).

Shell formation involves two phases—elaboration of the fibrous organic framework, followed by concentration and deposition of mineral salts.

Shell which is regenerated in calcium-free sea water has a normal organic matrix but lacks calcium. The mantle can shift calcium at a high rate in either direction; the amount deposited and the rate of deposition are affected by the concentration of calcium in the medium. Carbonic anhydrase is found in mantle as well as other tissues of many molluscs, and is probably involved in shell formation (conversion of CO_2 to carbonate). During calcification of the nacre minute crystalline nuclei are deposited on the organic matrix or on previously formed crystals. The nuclei are the sites of crystal formation as calcium carbonate is laid down. The character of the organic matrix influences the type of crystals formed on its surface; as the crystals increase a pattern develops. In the oyster, for example, the crystal develops a main stem, side branches and dendritic growths, the result being the formation of overlapping rows of crystals. These are either calcite or aragonite in marine gastropods and lamellibranchs. In the prismatic layer the growing crystals unite with one another to form polygons, which become invested by a hardened matrix (4, 5, 80, 120, 131, 134).

In typical lamellibranchs two kinds of shell can be distinguished on the basis of surface markings. In the first type there are a number of well-marked rings on the shell, which are laid down in winter when growth is retarded; the wider areas between the rings are formed when growth is rapid. Each ring, therefore, represents a winter period. In the second type of shell, growth rings are poorly marked. Bivalves which show pronounced growth rings are oyster *Ostrea*, cockle *Cardium*, etc. *Tellina tenuis* is an example of a species without well-marked winter rings. In some gastropods, e.g. the periwinkle *Littorina littorea*, shell formation takes place throughout the year, but is slowed down in winter and accelerated during spring and summer. In the limpet *Patella vulgata*, shell growth may be arrested in winter and resumed in spring (42, 67, 84).

STRUCTURAL PROTEINS IN MOLLUSCS. In lamellibranchs, such as *Mytilus*, structural proteins are present in the periostracum, hinge, byssus and in the supporting material of the gills. With the exception of the latter, these structures contain quinone-tanned protein (conchiolin). Analyses of amino-acid residues point to the existence of distinct species of conchiolins in prismatic and nacreous layers, and X-ray diffraction pictures reveal collagen-type fibrils. Under electron microscopy, thin layers from decalcified shells appear to be continuous or riddled with fine pores, the patterning of which varies with the species (45, 46).

The byssus threads of lamellibranchs are formed in the posterior groove of the foot from the secretions of two glands, a "white" gland which supplies most of the protein of the thread and a "purple" gland which supplies the aromatic material responsible for the tanning (*Mytilus*). A polyphenol oxidase is present which converts polyphenol to the quinone tanning agent. Similar reactions take place in the hardening of the periostracum, hinge and conchiolin ground substance of the shell. The periostracum is secreted by the mantle edge; it originates as a single homogeneous sheet, which soon becomes differentiated into three layers (Fig. 15.5). The hinge is divided into two main layers, inner and outer, both of which consist of tanned protein. The inner layer also contains $CaCO_3$ and the outer layer deposits of lipoid. The internal cavities of the gills are lined by a supporting substance which is a fibrillar protein resembling the untanned protein of the byssus (9, 12, 105).

INTERNAL SPICULES. Apart from exoskeletons, the tissues of certain molluscs are strengthened by spicules of various kinds. These are characteristic especially of gastropods which have lost the external shell. In nudibranchs the tissues of the body wall contain numerous calcareous

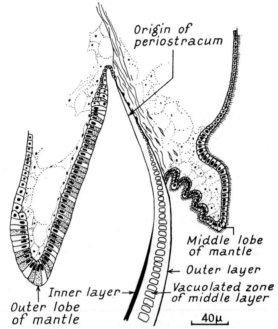

FIG. 15.5. SECTION ACROSS THE MANTLE EDGE OF *Mytilus*, SHOWING THE PERIOSTRACUM. (After Brown (12).)

spicules. According to Odum (97) these consist of amorphous $CaCO_3$ and form 50 % of dry weight (*Archidoris*). The spicules are responsible for the high levels of calcium reported for tissues of nudibranchs. Remarkably large quantities of magnesium and fluorine also occur in the body wall of *Archidoris* (7 and 3 % of dry matter). Strontium content is almost 0·5 %. These last three elements may be associated with the skeletal spicules. When *Acanthodoris* is placed in sea water activated with ⁹⁰Sr, the strontium becomes concentrated about calcium concretions in the mantle. Strontium and calcium are probably taken in through the body wall as well as the gut (37, 40, 77, 78, 132).

Integumentary spicules are not always calcareous. Marine pulmonates

Onchidella contain siliceous spicules, and pholads possess siliceous granules. The former animals lack a test.

Cephalopod Skeleton. Primitive cephalopods were provided with a chambered shell, in the last compartment of which the animal lived. *Nautilus* (Tetrabranchiata) still retains this external shell, but in dibranchiate cephalopods the shell is internal or wanting. In *Nautilus* the shell is spirally coiled and consists of a series of chambers, separated from one another by curved septa (Fig. 15.6). The terminal living chamber is the largest of these, and is occupied by the body of the animal; the other chambers are filled with gas. All the septa are perforated in the middle, and are traversed by a siphuncle, a tubular prolongation of the visceral

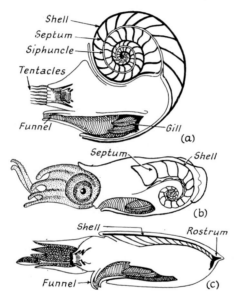

FIG. 15.6. SHELLS OF CEPHALOPODS, PRESENTED AS SCHEMATIC HALF-SECTIONS
(a) *Nautilus*; (b) *Spirula*; (c) *Sepia*. (Redrawn from Naef and Chun.)

hump. As the *Nautilus* grows it adds to the shell, and on occasion the animal moves forward and shuts off a chamber behind it by the secretion of a new septum. The *Nautilus* shell consists of two calcareous layers, the outer porcellanous (dull in texture), the inner nacreous; septa are also nacreous.

The shell in decapods is wholly internal (Fig. 15.6). In *Spirula* it takes the form of a loose spiral, which is divided by septa into a series of chambers. In *Sepia* the shell or cuttle-bone is entirely internal and functions as an endoskeleton. The primitive chambered condition is still recognizable in the presence of oblique calcareous partitions. Cuttle-bone is composed of horny matter on which calcareous material is deposited. Additional internal skeletons are present in the form of cephalic and other cartilages. In *Loligo* the endoskeleton is reduced to a horny pen (126).

Chemical analyses are available for the shells of *Nautilus, Spirula* and *Sepia*. Organic matter is small in amount, around 2–5%, somewhat higher values occurring in cuttle-bone than in the hard shell of *Nautilus*. Chitin occurs in the shell or endoskeleton of all groups (Table 15.4). The mineral matter is predominantly aragonite (94–99·7%) (23).

Brachiopods. The shells of brachiopods, which superficially are so similar to those of lamellibranchs, are likewise bivalved. The two valves are dorsal and ventral; the posterior end of the ventral valve projects beyond the dorsal, and bears a notch or aperture through which a stalk protrudes, attaching the animal to the substratum. Brachiopods are divided into two groups with the following skeletal characteristics—

1. Ecardines. Shells usually soft (chitinous), only lightly strengthened

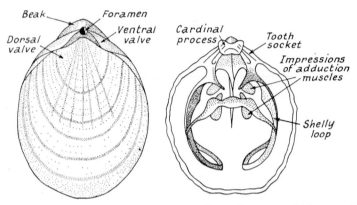

Fig. 15.7. Valves of a Brachiopod *Magellania flavescens*. (After Davidson)
(*Left*) Entire shell, viewed dorsally; (*right*) interior of dorsal valve showing shelly loops (skeletal supports).

with lime salts (except *Crania*). A hinge and internal supports for the arms are lacking.

2. Testicardines. Shells heavily charged with calcareous spicules. The valves are hinged and there is usually an internal skeleton supporting the arms (Fig. 15.7).

Most brachiopods are attached by a stalk or pedicle to some rock or other support. In some species, e.g. *Crania*, the ventral valve is firmly attached to its support. *Lingula* possesses a long free stalk and lives in a burrow in sandy bottom. In testicardinate brachiopods there are two lateral teeth at the posterior margin of the ventral valve, and these fit into corresponding sockets in the dorsal valve so as to form a hinge. An endo-skeleton is present in the form of plate-like processes or spiral lamellae, which project into the shell cavity and support various parts of the soft structures.

The valves of ecardines, with the exception of *Crania*, contain a high proportion of organic matter, from 25–40% dry weight (*Lingula, Discinisca,*

Glottidia). In contrast are testicardinate and craniid brachiopods, the valves of which contain less than 4 % organic matter. Analyses of inorganic constituents show that brachiopod shells fall into two groups; calcareous shells, and shells with high phosphate content (Table 15.1). In ecardinate brachiopods, whose shells contain much organic matter, the predominant mineral constituent is calcium phosphate; in craniids and testicardines, calcium phosphate is replaced by calcium carbonate. The nature of the organic matter in the shell is imperfectly known. Chitin has been identified in the shell and pedicle of *Lingula* (ecardine) and the pedicle of *Terebratalia* (testicardine).

The brachiopod shell is secreted by the outer epithelium. It consists of an external cuticle secreted by a chitinogenous band in the posterior region

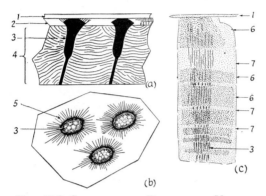

FIG. 15.8. STRUCTURE OF BRACHIOPOD VALVES

(*a*), (*c*) Vertical section, (*b*) surface view; (*a*), (*b*) *Magellania* (testicardine); (*c*) *Lingula* (ecardine). 1: periostracum; 2: outer calcareous layer; 3: canal; 4: inner calcareous layer; 5: radiating canaliculi; 6: chitinous layers; 7: calcareous layers ((*a*), (*b*) from King, 1870; (*c*) from Helmcke after Blochmann.)

of the body, and underlying layers of mineral and organic matter. The shells of different families differ somewhat in structure (Fig. 15.8). In lingulids the shell consists of alternating layers of chitinous material and $Ca_3(PO_4)_2$. In discinids the shell is composed of parallel chitinous lamellae impregnated with $Ca_3(PO_4)_2$. Shells of Craniidae are composed of fine organic lamellae interspersed with thick layers of $CaCO_3$. Outside is a thick cuticle. In the testicardinate families Terebratulidae and Rhynchonellidae the shell has three layers: outer cuticle, thin mineral layer and thick prismatic layer. The cuticle consists of organic ground substance impregnated with $CaCO_3$.

Polyzoa. Polyzoans are usually colonial in habit, and the individuals are enclosed in small cells which are aggregated to form colonies. In encrusting forms like *Membranipora* and *Flustra* the cells are closely packed together in a single layer. Others form slender branching growths, e.g. *Bugula*, or coral-like colonies, e.g. *Heteropora*. Externally the body wall is bounded by a skeletal layer known as the ectocyst. This is flexible and horny in some species, sometimes strengthened with sand grains, etc., and rigid and hard when heavily impregnated with calcareous matter. The organic substratum of the exoskeleton, opercula, etc., contains chitin (61).

Encrusting or fern-like forms contain much organic matter (35–85%), and have predominantly organic skeletons, e.g. *Flustra*. Others, largely calcareous, such as *Cellepora*, contain about 5% organic matter (Table 15.1). Skeletal mineral matter is predominantly $CaCO_3$.

Tunicates. All tunicates are covered by a test of some sort, which is usually composed in large part of tunicin (cellulose). In simple ascidians the tunic has a leathery or cartilaginous consistency, whereas in compound forms the test exists as a gelatinous or viscous matrix. Its main constituent is cellulose. The cartilaginous test of *Ascidia* is about 90% water, compared with 65% in the leathery test of *Pyura*. Analysis of *Ciona* test reveals cellulose 60·3%, nitrogenous material 27% and inorganic matter 12·7% (119).

Test material is constantly sloughed off and lost at the surface, and new test is secreted next to the epidermis. Secretion of tunicin is an epidermal function, but mesenchyme cells are involved in growth and maintenance of the tissue. Denuded areas of tunic are quickly replaced and regenerated through the activity of epidermal cells (3).

Of the pelagic tunicates (Thaliacea), Pyrosomas are colonies existing in gelatinous tubes, doliolids and salps bear delicate barrel-shaped or cylindrical tests. Older analyses for the tests of Pyrosoma show: water content, 94·8%; cellulose, 1·2%; nitrogenous material, 3·2%; and ash, 0·7%.

The tubes of the Pogonophora contain chitin.

TUBES AND EXTERNAL CASES

Tubes and cases are secreted and constructed by many kinds of animals. They are usually characteristic of sedentary species, but we find some active species that drag their cases along with them, and pelagic species that inhabit special shelters. These structures are built of most diverse materials, of organic and inorganic origin. In some species they are entirely secreted; in others, built of environmental materials which are cemented together. Tubes and cases afford shelter and protection; they also form an integral part of respiratory and food-collecting mechanisms in various species.

Calcareous Cases and Tubes

Calcareous tubes are characteristic of serpulid polychaetes. Other instances of animals fabricating calcareous cases are the paper nautilus, which makes a limy shell, and the shipworm, which deposits a calcareous lining in its burrow. Calcareous shells and cases of foraminifers, molluscs, etc., are described under exoskeletons in another section (p. 626).

Serpulids are housed in tubes composed of a groundwork of so-called mucoid material in which calcium carbonate is deposited (Fig. 15.9). This is largely in the form of aragonite (*Pomatoceros*). There is no organic union between the tube and the animal. The tubes of serpulids have characteristic shapes and arrangements, varying from species to species. They are solitary (*Spirorbis*), aggregated (*Serpula*), semicolonial (*Filograna*) or cemented together to form crusts or masses (*Pomatoleios*). The anterior

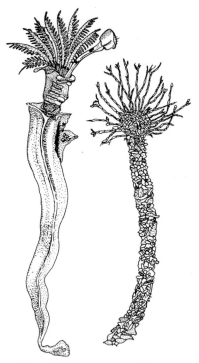

Fig. 15.9. Polychaete Tubes

(*Left*) Calcareous tube of a serpulid *Pomatoceros triqueter*. Branchial crown, operculum and anterior region of animal are shown protruding from the tube; (*right*) sand- and gravel-encrusted tube of *Lanice conchilega* (Terebellidae). (After McIntosh, 1922–23.)

opening of the tube can be closed by a specially developed operculum formed by modified gill filaments.

CaCO$_3$ predominates in serpulid tubes, forming 90–99 % mineral matter; organic matter is small, 3–6 % dry weight. MgCO$_3$ is sometimes present (*Serpula*) (Table 15.1) (21, 23).

The tube is secreted by tubiparous (major subcollar glands) lying in the first setigerous segment. Alkaline phosphatase occurs in this region and is possibly concerned with liberation of phosphate radicles as part of the process of calcium secretion. The calcareous material secreted by these glands is moulded by the collar at the anterior end of the worm. Normally the tube is added to at the anterior end as the animal grows. In *Pomato-*

ceros, tube production continues from March to September, i.e. during the feeding season. Calcium for tube building is obtained from sea water, and there is some evidence that calcium and radioactive strontium, which is handled in the same way as calcium, are absorbed in the anterior region of the alimentary canal; some part of the calcium secreted by the tubiparous glands is derived from this source (*Serpula, Mercierella, Pomatoceros*) (52, 121).

Serpulids are capable of dissolving the calcareous matter of their tubes, as well as secreting fresh material. Species of *Salmacina* and *Filograna* practise asexual reproduction and new individuals are formed at the posterior end of the parent. The new individual crawls down the parent's tube and makes a fresh opening to the exterior through which it protrudes

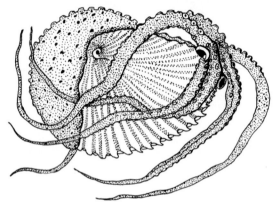

FIG. 15.10. FEMALE ARGONAUT IN SHELL

its crown; furthermore, it may destroy the posterior part of the parent's tube, thus separating it from the rest of the colony. These serpulids may be compared with the sabellid *Potamilla*, which is able to bore into calcareous shells. The mechanism by which these animals dissolve $CaCO_3$ is unknown (52).

Argonaut. The female paper nautilus *Argonauta argo* dwells in a symmetrical spiral shell which is secreted by thin terminal expansions of the two dorsal arms (Fig. 15.10). This shell is unique among molluscs in its mode of formation. The shell is also repaired by these same dorsal arms when portions are broken off. The argonaut shell is composed of outer prismatic layers and a middle fibrous layer. Its composition resembles that of other molluscan shells: it consists largely of $CaCO_3$ (93% mineral matter), but also contains significant amounts of $MgCO_3$ (7%) (21, 23).

Organic Tubes

Tubes and cases of organic material are formed by many different marine animals, including coelenterates, polychaetes, phoronids, small crustaceans and lamellibranchs. These shelters vary greatly in shape and composition. A burrowing sea-anemone (*Cerianthus*) lines its burrow in the mud with mucoid material strengthened by nematocysts. Some amphipods, such as *Amphithoë rubricata*, live in tubular nests formed of weed fragments held together with threads secreted from pedal glands. A few lamellibranchs, e.g. *Lima*, build nests of byssus threads. Tubes of phoronids have an organic base containing chitin, and are leathery, impregnated with calcareous material or strengthened with sand grains (61, 79, 136).

Tubicolous animals, *par excellence*, are polychaetes, many of which secrete tubes of so-called mucoid material. Mucoid tubes vary in consistency from soft jelly (*Myxicola, Flabelligera*) to leather- or horn-like consistency (*Chaetopterus, Hyalinoecia*) (Figs. 4.2, 5.3 and 15.11). Frequently, foreign materials are deposited on a mucoid base, e.g. sand grains, mud and fine gravel in tubes of *Lanice, Branchiomma*, etc. (Fig. 15.9).

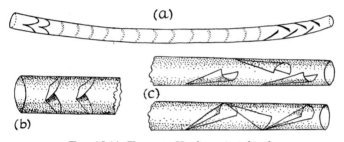

FIG. 15.11. TUBE OF *Hyalinoecia tubicola*

(*a*) Entire tube; (*b*) two pairs of valves at anterior end of tube in closed positions; (*c*) posterior end of tube, valves open (above), closed (below) (after Watson, 1903).

Arenaceous tubes of some sabellariids may be aggregated together in such dense masses as to constitute sandstone reefs (*Sabellaria, Gunnarea*).

It is generally agreed that mucoid tubes are secreted by epidermal glandular cells, widespread (*Myxicola*), or concentrated in certain regions which mould the form of the tube, e.g. epidermis of peristomial collar and thoracic membrane of *Sabella*. The process of tube formation has been described in several species. In *Sabella pavonina* a sorting mechanism exists on the gill filaments whereby medium-sized particles are carried by ciliary activity to ventral sacs lying below the mouth. Additions are made to the anterior end of the tube with material stored in the ventral sacs (Fig. 15.12). The particles are mixed with mucoid material into a string; by rotation of the anterior end of the animal and moulding action of the collar-folds the string is laid along the edge of the tube and cemented into place with mucoid secretion (89).

The mucoid constituents of polychaete tubes are variants of glycoproteins (polysaccharide-protein complexes). Mucoproteins have been identified in tubes of *Myxicola, Sabella, Spirographis, Lanice, Pectinaria, Hyalinoecia et al.* Acid hydrolysis yields the common protein amino-acids;

carbohydrate constituents are sugars (glucose, galactose, arabinose, fructose, etc.), acetylglucosamine, glucosamine and glucuronic acid. The presence of hyaluronic acid has been established in integumentary glands of certain species. Older analyses of the horny tubes of certain eunicids (*Onuphis, Hyalinoecia*) reveal a high content of phosphorus which may be incorporated in the organic matter (23, 25, 26).

Polychaetes possess the faculty of dissolving the organic material of tubes when occasion demands. When the tube of *Sabella* is artificially closed, the animal can make a hole in the side of the tube, from which it protrudes its branchial crown. Sabellids are among the few animals which show true phototropism, and are able to bend their tubes so that the

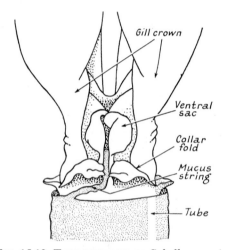

FIG. 15.12. TUBE-BUILDING IN *Sabella pavonina*

Ventral view of the base of the crown and the anterior end of the tube, showing the method by which the string of mucus and sand is applied to the edge of the tube. (From E. A. T. Nicol (89).)

animal continues to direct its branchial crown towards the light when the direction of the latter is altered. *Chaetopterus* normally enlarges its U-shaped tube by establishing a new opening at the base of the U, building a new and larger extension and closing off the old arm. It is suggested that in all these instances the animals, by release of suitable enzymes, are able to dissolve the mucoid walls of the tube (36, 90).

Tubicolous worms frequently possess some mechanism for closing the mouth of the tube when they withdraw. The tube of *Hyalinoecia* is provided with neat protective valves at either end (Fig. 15.11). The mouth of the tube of *Branchiomma* and other sabellids usually collapses when the animal withdraws. We have already noted the opercula of serpulids (p. 645). Somewhat similar are the opercula of sabellariids, formed by enlarged anterior chaetae, which effectively block the opening of the tube.

Boring Animals

The reefs, rock, coral and wooden materials found in the inter-tidal zone and shallow inshore waters provide niches and crevices in which many animals lodge themselves. Beginning with efforts to enlarge and shape such ready-made cavities, or to burrow into soft shale, animals from several phyla have acquired the capacity to excavate hard materials—stone, wood or shell—and fashion their own burrows or galleries. The specialization of structure and function entailed by the adoption of this mode of life is amply compensated by the protection conferred, and in at least two groups of wood-borers, the gribble and shipworm, a new source

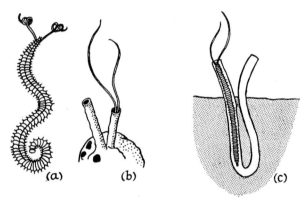

FIG. 15.13. A ROCK-BORING POLYCHAETE, *Polydora ciliata*

(*a*) Worm extracted from its burrow; (*b*) mud tubes erected at the two openings of the burrow, from one of which the tentacles of the worm are extended; (*c*) diagrammatic section of the burrow with worm in position. Enlarged. (After Calman (14).)

of food is also exploited. The following account deals first with animals that excavate stone, shell or coral, followed by wood-borers.

EXCAVATION OF STONE AND SHELL. Animals that bore into stone include sponges, polychaetes, sipunculoids, crustaceans, sea-urchins and molluscs.

The monaxonellid sponge *Cliona* excavates limestone rock and molluscan shells. The borings are rather shallow, seldom exceeding 5 cm in depth, and consist of a series of branching passages which open at frequent intervals to the surface and which accommodate the sponge. *Cliona* sometimes riddles shells, including those of the oyster, and causes much damage. Actual penetration is ascribed to chemical action by the sponge.

Several species of polychaetes bore into limestone rock and shell, including *Polydora* (Spionidae) and *Potamilla* (Sabellidae). *Polydora* is a common form which makes U-shaped cavities in shell or rock (Fig. 15.13). The excavations are often prolonged by a tubular extension of mud over each of the openings. Since the body of the worm, apart from parapodial chaetae, is soft, it is believed that burrowing is probably accomplished or aided by chemical means (14, 123).

It is among lamellibranchs that the largest and most efficient rock-borers are encountered. The family Pholadidae includes a series of forms that live in various kinds of soft rocks, shell and wood. The piddock *Pholas dactylus* is a rather large species which sometimes reaches a length of 15 cm and makes burrows up to 30 cm long (Fig. 15.14). It bores indifferently into a

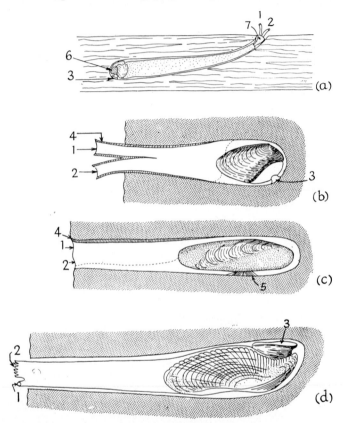

FIG. 15.14. BORING LAMELLIBRANCHS

(a) *Teredo navalis* in wood (× ½), remainder in stone; (b) *Gastrochaena cuneiformis* (× ¾); (c) *Lithophaga cumingiana* (× ½); (d) *Pholas dactylus* (× ¾). 1: exhalant siphon; 2: inhalant siphon; 3: foot; 4: calcareous lining; 5: byssus; 6: shell; 7: pallet. (Partly after Otter (99).)

wide variety of rocks—limestone, shale, sandstone, mica-schist—and occasionally peat and wood. The piddock attaches itself at the head of its burrow by means of a sucker-like foot. The valves are stout and bear spines on the external surface. There is no hinge ligament, the hinge takes the form of a ball joint and the two valves rock on this joint as a fulcrum through alternate contractions of two adductor muscles. The piddock bores by rasping action of its shell, the spines gradually cutting away the rock. During this process the animal fastens itself by its foot, and the valves rock to and fro, scraping away the walls.

Other common forms of bivalves with similar habits are *Barnea*, *Pholadidea* and *Gastrochaena*. *Hiatella* (*Saxicava*) is a related genus boring into limestone and sandstone. Boring is accomplished mainly, if not exclusively, by mechanical means. During this process the siphons are closed and partly withdrawn, the contained water is pressed into the mantle cavity and the shell valves are forced apart and scraped against the walls of the burrow. Repetition of this process slowly wears away the stone.

Besides the piddocks, rock-boring habits are found in two other bi-valves, namely *Petricola* (Petricolidae) and the date mussel *Lithophaga* (Mytilidae). The shell of *Petricola* superficially resembles that of pholads and it burrows into the same kind of rocks. *Lithophaga*, on the other hand, has a thin and fragile shell, devoid of teeth and spines and covered ex-ternally with a thick periostracum (Fig. 15.14). The date mussel restricts its attacks to limestone and other calcareous rocks, which it excavates by chemical means. Special glands in the mantle produce an acid secretion which attacks the stone, while the calcareous shell of the mollusc is pro-tected by the thick periostracum (137).

Sea-urchins which bore into rock occur commonly in the littoral region in many parts of the world. The excavations vary from shallow depressions in the rock surface to deep cells. Boring is accomplished by mechanical action of the teeth and peripheral spines, and is a means of protection against strong wave action. *Paracentrotus lividus*, found in the Mediter-ranean and on west European coasts, excavates deep cells on surf-swept shores, but does not display this habit in quiet Mediterranean waters. *Paracentrotus* is reported to bore into wood as well as stone.

Wood-borers

Wooden structures are attacked by two groups of marine animals, namely lamellibranchs and crustaceans. Of these the shipworm *Teredo* and its allies are the most important. Furthering the destructive activity of the shipworm are various isopods, especially the gribble *Limnoria*.

The shipworms (Teredinidae) are highly modified for excavating and living in wood, which provides shelter, protection and food. The body is elongated and almost naked except for a pair of small valves at the anterior end by which boring is accomplished (Fig. 15.14). The valves are globular in shape and are composed of three lobes; the outer surfaces of the two anterior lobes are provided with fine ridges bearing sharp teeth (Fig. 15.15). In shipworms, as in pholads, a hinge ligament is absent, and the inner surfaces of the valves possess articulating knobs on which they rock to and fro. The valves are moved by contractions of the adductor muscles. When the strong posterior adductor muscle contracts, the anterior lobes of the shell are drawn apart and rasp the sides of the burrow. During this activity the shipworm is held in position by the sucker-like foot, and a constant hydrostatic pressure is maintained in the mantle fluid, which keeps the boring end of the animal pressed against the head of the burrow. *Teredo* lines the burrow with a calcareous secretion, and can close the external

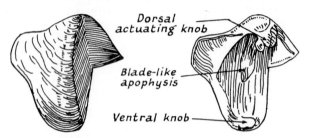

FIG. 15.15. VALVES OF *Teredo norvegica*
External view of right valve; internal view of left valve. (After Calman (14).)

opening with a pair of shelly pallets borne on the posterior end of the body (73).

A tropical genus of shipworms *Bankia* attains large dimensions, exceeding one metre. Two genera of pholads also bore in wood. *Xylophaga* excavates shallow burrows in floating timber and bores in the same manner as *Teredo*. *Martesia*, found in the tropics, has similar habits.

Species of gribble *Limnoria* (Fig. 15.16) are found throughout the world and are very destructive to marine timbers. This animal is about 4 mm

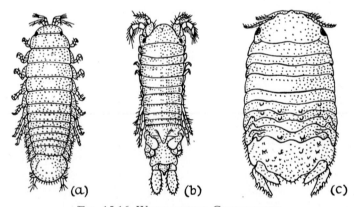

FIG. 15.16. WOOD-BORING CRUSTACEANS
(a) *Limnoria lignorum*; (b) *Chelura terebrans*; (c) *Sphaeroma terebrans*. Enlarged. (Redrawn from Calman (14).)

long and excavates galleries some 25 mm in length immediately under the surface of the wood. The galleries open to the surface at regular intervals by small apertures, forming respiratory pits through which the animals draw in water. A male and female are usually found together, but the gallery is excavated solely by the female. Boring is accomplished by the mandibles: these are dissimilar in shape, the right one having a sharp point and roughened edge, which fits into a groove with a rasp-like surface on the left mandible. The density of infection sometimes reaches 45–60 animals per square centimetre.

Other crustacean wood-borers are *Sphaeroma*, a large isopod which burrows into timber and soft rocks, and the amphipod *Chelura* (Fig. 15.16). The latter usually occurs in association with the gribble. It works closer to the surface than the gribble, and appears to require the pioneer assistance of the latter before it can effectively attack the wood (14, 137).

Coral-reef Dwellers

Coral reefs are inhabited by a great variety of boring animals. Many species bore into dead coral or coral limestone, including sponges (*Spirastrella*), polychaetes (*Eunice*), molluscs (Lamellibranchia, Amphineura), sipunculoids, cirripedes (*Lithotrya*) and sea-urchins (*Cidaris, et al.*). Reference has already been made to the rock-boring habits of bivalves such as *Lithophaga*, *Gastrochaena* and *Petricola*, which also attack reef coral. The most remarkable of reef-boring bivalves is *Tridacna*. Small species bore downwards into calcareous rock by grinding action of their valves, until they are flush with the surface. Since the shell has rotated with reference to the body in these animals so that the hinge now lies on the under-side, the free edges of the valves face upwards at the surface.

A reef chiton *Acanthopleura* rasps out shallow burrows with the radula, and various polychaetes excavate burrows in calcareous rock by means of hard jaws, aided perhaps by stiff bristles. Reef-burrowing sipunculoids are provided with bands of hard skeletal material about the anterior and posterior ends. A rock-boring barnacle *Lithotrya* excavates burrows in coral rock, into which it withdraws when the tide is out. Boring is accomplished by means of studs on the peduncle: the studs consist of a chitinous core overlain by a calcareous covering, and they are shed and renewed at intervals. These various animals assist in eroding and destroying coral reefs.

Living coral colonies are not attacked to the same extent as dead coral masses by boring animals. Borers found in living coral include sponges (*Cliona*), polychaetes, sipunculoids, cirripedes and various bivalves (especially *Lithophaga*).

There is a great variety of animals which settle on coral when young, and grow with the colony. Some of these coral dwellers are highly specialized. Various species of terebellids and sabellids settle on growing coral colonies and increase in size with the latter. Crabs of the family Hapalocarcinidae live commensally with reef corals. These curious creatures settle on the coral which grows up around them. The mechanical activity of the crab and the respiratory currents which it creates in some way influence the growth of the coral, resulting in the formation of pits or galls. Other decapods with similar commensal habits are *Paratypton*, a prawn living in coral, and *Caphyra*, a crab inhabiting depressions in *Alcyonium*.

Certain operculate cirripedes (*Creusia*, *Pyrgoma*) are confined to living corals. Different species of *Pyrgoma* display host specificity and are found on particular reef or deep-water corals. The growth of these cirripedes is correlated with that of the host. Another commensal of madreporarian coral is the gastropod *Magilus antiquus*, which lengthens the last convolution of its shell in a linear fashion, and thus keeps pace with outward growth of the coral (55, 56, 99).

ADVENTITIOUS SHELTERS

Commensal relationships are very common among marine animals, and there are many instances of animals seeking shelter in the burrow and tubes of their rightful owners (endoecism), or even in body cavities of other species (inquilinism). Intimate associations of this nature between different species are described in Chapter 14.

Empty tubes, shells and other skeletal structures are frequently utilized for shelter by marine animals, especially crustaceans. Some sea-urchins, e.g. *Psammechinus*, have the habit of covering themselves with shells, pebbles, etc. There are holothurians, e.g. *Pseudostichopus*, which cover themselves with siliceous sponge spicules. Some brachyurans employ shields for protection and defence. *Dorippe* has the last two pairs of legs modified for holding objects over the back, and tropical species carry around molluscan shells, mangrove leaves, etc.

The habit of dwelling in empty gastropod shells is widespread among hermit crabs. When young the crabs select small shells and discard these for larger shells as they grow in size. In conformity with this habit we find that hermit crabs usually have twisted abdomens which can fit into coiled gastropod shells, e.g. *Eupagurus*. Terrestrial hermit crabs *Coenobita* procure shells from the shore, but on occasion make use of other structures, e.g. coco-nut shells. These pagurids have soft unarmoured abdomens. The terrestrial robber-crab *Birgus* has abandoned the habit of carrying a shell about, and the abdomen has secondarily acquired hard terga.

Pomatochelids are a family of primitive hermit crabs possessing symmetrical abdomens. Shelters utilized include Dentalium shells (*Pomatocheles*) or water-logged tubes of bamboo and mangrove (*Pylocheles*).

A curious example of the utilization of another animal's covering is afforded by the pelagic amphipod *Phronima*. This animal inhabits the hyaline barrel-like cases of *Pyrosoma* and *Doliolum*. The female *Phronima* attacks the Pyrosoma or salp and, after eating the ascidiozooids, continues to dwell in the test. *Phronima* is able to navigate its house: holding on to the case by the thoracic legs, it protrudes the rear portion of the body and propels the case forwards by alternate flexion and extension of the abdomen. Water drawn in at the front end of the case provides a feeding and respiratory current for female and young.

POISONS AND VENOMOUS DEVICES

The use of toxic and noxious substances for offence and defence is widespread among marine animals. The substances involved act as repellents, deterrents or are definitely poisonous. We find them incorporated in the tissues, or associated with stings, darts, etc. An account of venomous marine animals has been prepared by Russell (112).

Some species of dinoflagellates are toxic, and have been regarded as being responsible for the death of marine fish, mass mortalities associated with "red-tides," and paralytic shell-fish poisoning. Toxin extracted from *Gymnodinium veneficum* affects the nervous system of animals, especially ganglionic synapses. Its mode of action appears to involve membrane depolarization (1).

Sponges are said to be repellent to most other animals, but this has not prevented lodgers from making use of sponge cavities (see Chapter 14), or certain animals from feeding upon sponges. Sponge-eaters are generally specialized in feeding habits and restricted to this particular food, e.g. various snails and nudibranchs (38).

Coelenterates, as a group, are characterized by stinging nematocysts, which are poisonous to other animals (102). These independent effectors have already been described (p. 370).

Various worms and molluscs possess noxious properties, frequently in conjunction with bright warning coloration. Brightly coloured dorids and a terebellid *Polycirrus caliendrum* are distasteful to predatory fish. A tectibranch *Pleurobranchus membranaceus* secretes acid (H_2SO_4) from the body-surface and is repellent to fish. The cerata of nudibranchs (*Aeolidiella, Facelina*, etc.) enclose cnidophorous sacs. These contain nematocysts derived from the coelenterates on which these nudibranchs feed, and have a protective function. Cone-shells (Conidae) of tropical Indo-Pacific shores are venomous: the radula is used for wounding and as a penetrant for introducing a poison with curare-like properties. Other gastropods regarded as venomous are dog-whelks and allies (*Nucella, Murex*). *Murex* is the source of Tyrian purple, which is produced by a hypobranchial gland in the mantle cavity. Extracts of this gland are highly toxic when injected into test animals (crabs, fish, frogs). Apart from the colouring material, the hypobranchial gland contains serotonin, choline esters and substances with curare-like activity (15, 33, 63, 64, 122).

Poisonous and Repellent Devices in Echinoderms. Poisonous echinoderms include certain sea-urchins and sea-cucumbers. Urchins of the family Toxopneustidae bear poisonous pedicellariae; other echinoids have poisonous spines, e.g. the tropical urchin *Asthenosoma* (31, 86, 101).

Defensive structures, known as organs of Cuvier, are peculiar organs occurring in certain holothurians (*Holothuria, Actinopyga*). They consist of short tubes opening into the cloaca, and represent modified basal branches of the respiratory tree. The walls of the tubes contain muscles, spirally wound connective-tissue fibres and glandular cells capable of discharging a sticky slime which swells to enormous extent on contact with sea water. When irritated *Holothuria* contracts strongly, rupturing the cloaca, and ejects its viscera, including the Cuvierian organs. These elongate greatly when autotomized, seemingly as the consequence of raised hydrostatic pressure, and unfolding of spirally wound fibrils. When an enemy comes into contact with these sticky tubes, they become pulled out into a snarl of glutinous white threads, in which the predator may be completely entangled and immobilized. Cuvierian organs sometimes contain a highly toxic material termed holothurin. Extracts from *Actinopyga* are lethal to fish and mice, and poison protozoan cultures (24, 34, 41, 91, 92).

Fishes with Poisonous Flesh. Certain fishes are known to have poisonous flesh and to cause food-poisoning when eaten by man. Poisons are localized in particular organs, e.g. gonads, or are widespread throughout the body of the fish. There are instances of fishes, such as square-tails, wrasses and parrot-fishes (Tetragonuridae, Labridae and Scaridae), which occasionally become toxic through having eaten poisonous food. In the file-fishes (Monacanthidae) and trigger-fishes (Balistidae) the flesh is reported to be poisonous, at least at certain seasons. Still other fish are more or less permeated with poison at all times. Puffers and globe-fishes (Tetraodontidae) are always more or less poisonous to man.

The poisonous principles are classified as endotoxins or ichthyosarcotoxins, but their chemical nature is unknown. The relative toxicities of various tissues from puffer-fish have been determined by tests on laboratory animals. Liver shows high incidence of toxicity; frequently gonads, intestine and muscles are poisonous as well. The principal symptoms are neurological disturbances and gastric derangements. Information is not available to answer the natural query whether the poisonous character of the flesh of these fishes has survival value against predators other than man (43, 50, 54, 93, 122, 133).

Venomous Stings and Spines among Fishes. Some fishes with spines for stinging or lacerating have special glands for producing poisonous secretions in conjunction with these devices. Like the poisonous fangs of snakes these devices in fishes probably have offensive as well as protective functions. An interesting account of poisonous fishes is available in Evans' *Sting-fish and Seafarer*.

Poisonous spines occur in several elasmobranchs, the most formidable of which are sting- and eagle-rays (Dasyatidae and Myliobatidae). In these animals there is a large serrated spine on the tail which is capable of inflicting severe wounds when the tail is lashed from side to side (Fig. 15.17). Along either side of the spine there is a narrow groove containing specialized glandular tissue which produces a powerful venom. Some of this material becomes injected into any wounds inflicted by the spine. The poison of the sting-ray causes great pain, paralysis and swelling of the affected part in man. The poisonous spine of *Trygon* (*Dasyatis*) is not an effective protection against the natural foes of this fish, namely hammer-headed and tiger sharks. A specimen of the former is reported to have had fifty sting-ray spines embedded in various parts of its body, especially in the mouth and gullet. It is suggested that the sting-ray uses its spine mainly as an offensive weapon (47, 94, 95).

Other elasmobranchs bearing poisonous spines are the Port Jackson shark *Heterodontus*, the spiny dogfish *Squalus acanthias* and the chimaeroids *Chimaera monstrosa* and *Hydrolagus colliei*. These animals have a grooved spine in front of the dorsal fin. The arrangement is much the same as in the sting-ray, for the groove contains glandular tissue which secretes a venomous substance.

Among teleosts in British waters the weever-fishes (Trachinidae) are well-known venomous species. In these fishes spines on the gill-covers and

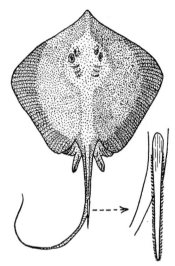

Fig. 15.17. Sting Ray (*Dasyatis pastinaca*) ($\times \frac{1}{9}$), and Enlarged View of the Poisonous Spine. (After Norman (93).)

first dorsal fin are equipped with poison-glands. Each opercular spine is grooved and bears a small mass of glandular tissue. Wounds are inflicted when the fish is stepped on or handled. Under these conditions venom is released by rupture of the glandular cells and flows along the groove into the wound. The spines of the weever-fish are reported to cause severe and painful wounds.

Poisonous spines resembling those of the weever-fish are found on the operculum and in the dorsal fin of other teleosts. Poison glands are located in grooves or occur at the base of the spine. Notable poisonous fishes are scorpion-fishes (*Scorpaenidae*) and poison-fishes (Synanceiidae). The poison glands discharge their secretions into ducts leading into a deep groove on either side of the spine. The stonefish *Synanceia* has bag-like glands lying on either side of the dorsal spines (Fig. 15.18). These fishes lie on the bottom and, if trodden upon, the erect spines penetrate the skin, and pressure on the glands causes venom to be forced into the wound. The poison of the stonefish is excruciatingly painful and sometimes fatal. More complex is the poison apparatus of the toadfish *Thalassophryne*. In this animal the two spines of the first dorsal fin are hollow, and the base of each spine bears a special poison gland leading into the duct. In other toad-fishes poison spines and glands also occur on the operculum (2, 118, 133).

The poisonous spines just described in teleosts are employed in defence. The actual release of poison does not appear to be under control of the animal. Experiments have shown that extracts of the poison glands cause sickness and death of test animals. The toxin of the sting-ray causes vaso-

FIG. 15.18. STONEFISH *Synanceichthys verrucosus* DISSECTED TO SHOW THE POISON GLANDS ON THE DORSAL SPINES. (From Whitley (133).)

constriction and cardiac arrest, acting on the cardiac pacemaker. The poison of the weever-fish contains a histamine-releaser, 5-hydroxytrypt-amine, and some principle having a deleterious effect on the heart. The poison of the stonefish increases capillary permeability and directly para-lyses muscle, apparently by blocking the conductile process. Although toxins may differ in various fishes, common effects are neurotoxic and myotoxic, causing pain and muscular malfunctioning and disturbances of the circulatory system of the victim (18, 48, 51, 112, 113).

REFERENCES

1. ABBOTT, B. C. and BALLANTINE, D., "The toxin from *Gymnodinium veneficum* Ballantine," *J. Mar. Biol. Ass. U.K.*, **36**, 169 (1957).
2. AUSTIN, L., GILLIS, R. G. and YOUATT, G., "Stonefish venom," *Austr. J. Exp. Biol. Med. Sci.*, **43**, 79 (1965).
3. BERRILL, N. J., *The Tunicata: with an account of the British species* (London, Ray Soc., 1950).
4. BEVELANDER, G., "Calcification in molluscs. 3. Intake and deposition of Ca^{45} and P^{32} in relation to shell formation," *Biol. Bull.*, **102**, 9 (1952).
5. BEVELANDER, G. and BENZER, P., "Calcification in marine molluscs," *Biol. Bull.*, **94**, 176 (1948).

6. BIEDERMANN, W., "Physiologie der Stütz- und Skelettssubstanzen," *Handbuch vergl. Physiol.* 3, 1 (I Teil), p. 319 (1914).
7. BLISS, D. E., "Endocrine control of metabolism in the land crab, *Gecarcinus lateralis,*" *Biol. Bull.*, 104, 275 (1953).
8. BLISS, D. E. and WELSH, J. H., "The neurosecretory system of brachyuran crustacea," *Biol. Bull.*, 103, 157 (1952).
9. BROWN, C. H., "Protein skeletal materials in the invertebrates," *Proc. Sixth Inter. Conger. Exp. Cytol.*, p. 351 (*Exp. Cell Res.*, *Supp.* 1) (1949).
10. BROWN, C. H., "A review of the methods available for the determination of the types of forces stabilizing structural proteins in animals," *Quart. J. Micr. Sci.*, 91, 331 (1950).
11. BROWN, C. H., "Quinone tanning in the animal kingdom," *Nature*, 165, 275 (1950).
12. BROWN, C. H., "Some structural proteins of *Mytilus edulis,*" *Quart. J. Micr. Sci.*, 93, 487 (1952).
13. BROWN, F. A., "Hormones in crustaceans," in *The Hormones*, Ed. Pincus, G. and Thimann, K. V., Vol. I (New York, Academic Press, 1948).
14. CALMAN, W. T., *Marine Boring Animals* (London, Brit. Mus. (Nat. Hist.), Econ. Ser., No. 10, 1936).
15. CARDOT, H. and JULLIEN, A., "Action de la pourpre sur l'excitabilité du nerf et du muscle," *C.R. Soc. Biol., Paris*, 133, 521 (1940).
16. CARLISLE, D. B., "Studies on *Lysmata seticaudata*, 4," *Pubbl. Staz. Zool. Napoli*, 24, 279 (1953).
17. CARLISLE, D. B., "Studies on *Lysmata seticaudata*. 6," ibid., 24, 435 (1953).
18. CARLISLE, D. B., "On the venom of the lesser weeverfish, *Trachinus vipera,*" *J. Mar. Biol. Ass. U.K.*, 42, 155 (1962).
19. CARLISLE, D. B. and DOHRN, P. F. R., "Studies on *Lysmata seticaudata*. 2. Experimental evidence for a growth- and moult-accelerating factor," *Pubbl. Staz. Zool. Napoli*, 24, 69 (1953).
20. CHANG, H.-W., "Age and growth of *Callionymus lyra,*" *J. Mar. Biol. Ass. U.K.*, 30, 281 (1951).
21. CHAVE, K. E., "Calcareous marine organisms," *J. Geol.*, 62, 266 (1954).
22. CLARKE, F. W. and WHEELER, W. C., "The composition of crinoid skeletons," *Prof. Pap. U.S. Geol. Surv.*, No. 90-D, p. 33 (1914).
23. CLARKE, F. W. and WHEELER, W. C., "The inorganic constituents of marine invertebrates," ibid., No. 124, 62 pp. (1922).
24. CUÉNOT, L., "Echinoderms," in *Traité de Zoologie*, Ed. Grassé, P.-P., T. XI (Paris, Masson, 1948).
25. DEFRETIN, R., "Sur les acides aminés entrant dans la constitution des mucoprotéides des tubes de quelques Polychètes sédentaires," *C.R. Soc. Biol., Paris*, 145, 115 (1951).
26. DEFRETIN, R., "Le système glandulaire de *Lanice conchilega,*" ibid., 146, 91 (1952).
27. DENNELL, R., "The occurrence and significance of phenolic hardening in the newly formed cuticle of Crustacea Decapoda," *Proc. Roy. Soc. B.*, 134, 485 (1947).
28. DOFLEIN, F. and REICHENOW, E., *Lehrbuch der Protozoenkunde*. Teil I (Jena, Fischer, 1949).
29. DRACH, P., "Gland du sinus, mue et métabolisme chez les Crustacés," *Bull. Biol. Fr. Belg.*, Suppl. 33, p. 164 (1948).

30. DUCHÂTEAU, G. and FLORKIN, M., "Sur la composition de l'arthropodine et de la scléroprotéine cuticulaires de deux Crustacés décapodes (*Homarus vulgaris* Edwards, *Callinectes sapidus* Rathbun)," *Physiol. Comp. Oecol.*, **3**, 365 (1954).

31. EARLE, K. V., "Pathological effects of two West Indian echinoderms," *Trans. R. Soc. Trop. Med. Hyg.*, **33**, 447 (1940).

32. EDWARDS, G. A., "The influence of eyestalk removal on the metabolism of the fiddler crab," *Physiol. Comp. Oecol.*, **2**, 34 (1950).

33. EMERSON, G. A. and TAFT, C. H., "Pharmacologically active agents from the sea," *Tex. Rep. Biol. Med.*, **3**, 302 (1945).

34. ENDEAN, R., "The Cuvierian tubules of *Holothuria leucospilota*," *Quart. J. Micr. Sci.*, **98**, 455 (1957).

35. FORD, E., "Vertebral variation in teleostean fishes," *J. Mar. Biol. Ass. U.K.*, **22**, 1 (1937).

36. FOX, H. M., "On the blood circulation and metabolism of sabellids," *Proc. Roy. Soc. B.*, **125**, 554 (1938).

37. FOX, H. M. and RAMAGE, H., "A spectrographic analysis of animal tissues," ibid., **108**, 157 (1931).

38. FRETTER, V., "Observations on the life history and functional morphology of *Cerithiopsis*," *J. Mar. Biol. Ass. U.K.*, **29**, 567 (1951).

39. FRETTER, V., "Experiments with P³² and I¹³¹ on species of *Helix*, *Arion*, and *Agriolimax*," *Quart. J. Micr. Sci.*, **93**, 133 (1952).

40. FRETTER, V., "Experiments with radioactive strontium (⁹⁰Sr) on certain molluscs and polychaetes," *J. Mar. Biol. Ass. U.K.*, **32**, 367 (1953).

41. FREY, D. G., "The use of sea cucumbers in poisoning fishes," *Copeia*, **1951**, 175 (1951).

42. GALTSOFF, P. S., "The biochemistry of the invertebrates of the sea," *Ecol. Monogr.*, **4**, 481 (1934).

43. GOE, D. R. and HALSTEAD, B. W., "A preliminary report of the toxicity of the Gulf puffer, *Sphoeroides annulatus*," *Calif. Fish Game*, **39**, 229 (1953).

44. GREEN, E. H. and TOWER, R. W., "The organic constituents of the scales of fish," *Bull. U.S. Bur. Fish.*, **21**, 97 (1902).

45. GRÉGOIRE, C., DUCHÂTEAU, G. and FLORKIN, M., "Trames organiques de nacres de Gastéropodes étudiées au microscope électronique," *Arch. Int. Physiol.*, **58**, 483 (1951).

46. GRÉGOIRE, C., DUCHÂTEAU, G. and FLORKIN, M., "La trame protidique des nacres et des perles," *Ann. Inst. Océanogr. Monaco*, **31**, 1 (1955).

47. GUDGER, E. W., "Does the sting ray strike and poison fishes?" *Sci. Mon.*, **63**, 110 (1946).

48. GUDGER, E. W., "Is the sting ray's sting poisonous to vertebrates other than men and fishes?" *Amer. Nat.*, **81**, 297 (1947).

49. GUYSELMAN, J. B., "An analysis of the molting process in the fiddler crab, *Uca pugilator*," *Biol. Bull.*, **104**, 115 (1953).

50. HALSTEAD, B. W., "Some general considerations of the problem of poisonous fishes," *Copeia*, **1953**, 31 (1953).

51. HALSTEAD, B. W. and BUNKER, N. C., "The venom apparatus of the ratfish, *Hydrolagus colliei*," ibid., **1952**, 128 (1952).

52. HANSON, J., "Formation and breakdown of serpulid tubes," *Nature*, **161**, 610 (1948).

53. HARRISON, F. M. and MARTIN, A. W., "Calcium distribution and con-

servation during the molting period in *Limnoria lignorum*," *J. Cell. Comp. Physiol.*, **43**, 247 (1954).

54. HASHIMOTO, Y. and MIGITA, M., "On the assay method of puffer poison," *Bull. Tokai Fish. Res. Lab.*, No. 3 (B), Contrb. 30 (1952).

55. HIRO, F., "Studies on the animals inhabiting reef corals. 1. *Hapalocarcinus* and *Cryptochirus*," *Palao Trop. Biol. Stud.*, **1**, 137 (1937).

56. HIRO, F., "Studies on the animals inhabiting reef corals. 2. Cirripeds of the genera *Creusia* and *Pyrgoma*," ibid., **1**, 391 (1938).

57. HOLLETT, A., "Relation between moult cycle and phosphorus content of blood and muscle in lobster," *J. Fish. Res. Bd Can.*, **6**, 152 (1943).

58. HOSOI, K., "Contribution to the biochemistry of the coral. 6. Calcium and carbonate in the skeleton of *Fungia*," *Palao Trop. Biol. Stud.*, **2**, 57 (1940).

59. HUGGINS, C., "The composition of bone and the function of the bone cell," *Physiol. Rev.*, **17**, 119 (1937).

60. HUTCHINSON, G. E., SETLOW, J. K. and BROOKS, J. L., "Biochemical observations on *Asterias forbesi*," *Bull. Bingham Oceanogr. Coll.*, **9**, Art. 3, 3 (1946).

61. HYMAN, L. H., "The occurrence of chitin in the lophophorate phyla," *Biol. Bull.*, **114**, 106 (1958).

62. JODREY, L. H., "Studies on shell formation. 3. Measurement of calcium deposition in shell and calcium turnover in mantle tissue," ibid., **104**, 398 (1953).

63. JULLIEN, A. and BONNET, A., "Action de la cholinestérase sur l'extrait de glande à pourpre de *Murex*," *C.R. Acad. Sci.*, Paris, **212**, 813 (1941).

64. JULLIEN, A. and BONNET, A., "Toxicité de la pourpre en rapport avec la présence des substances à action stimulante sur le muscle de Sangsue," ibid., **212**, 932 (1941).

65. KESSEL, E., "Beobachtungen an *Eupagurus*-Wohngehäusen mit *Hydractinia*-Bewuchs," *Verh. dtsch Zool. Ges.*, **40**, 154 (1938).

66. KNOWLES, F. G. W. and CARLISLE, D. B., "Endocrine control in the Crustacea," *Biol. Rev.*, **31**, 396 (1956).

67. KORRINGA, P., "Recent advances in oyster biology," *Quart. Rev. Biol.*, **27**, 266 (1952).

68. KRISHNAN, G., "Sinus gland and tyrosinase activity in *Carcinus maenas*," *Nature*, **165**, 364 (1950).

69. KRISHNAN, G., "Phenolic tanning and pigmentation of the cuticle in *Carcinus maenas*," *Quart. J. Micr. Sci.*, **92**, 333 (1951).

70. LAFON, M., "Sur la composition du tégument des Crustacés," *C. R. Soc. Biol.*, Paris, **135**, 1003 (1941).

71. LAFON, M., "Sur la structure et la composition chimique du tégument de la Limule (*Xiphosura polyphemus*)," *Bull. Inst. Océanogr. Monaco*, No. 850 (1943).

72. LAFON, M., "Nouvelles recherches biochimiques et physiologiques sur le squelette tégumentaire des Crustacés," ibid., No. 939 (1948).

73. LANE, C. E. and TIERNEY, J. Q., "Hydrodynamics and respiration in *Teredo*," *Bull. Mar. Sci. Gulf Caribbean*, **1**, 104 (1951).

74. LORCH, I. J., "The distribution of alkaline phosphatase in relation to calcification in *Scyliorhinus canicula*," *Quart. J. Micr. Sci.*, **90**, 381 (1949).

75. LOWENSTAM, H. A., "Factors affecting the aragonite-calcite ratios in carbonate-secreting marine organisms," *J. Geol.*, **62**, 284 (1954).

76. LOWNDES, A. G., "Densities of the embryonic stages of sea-urchins," *Nature*, **154**, 55 (1944).
77. MCCANCE, R. A. and MASTERS, M., "The chemical composition and the acid base balance of *Archidoris britannica*," *J. Mar. Biol. Ass. U.K.*, **22**, 273 (1937).
78. MCCANCE, R. A. and SHACKLETON, L. R. B., "The metallic constituents of marine gastropods," ibid., **22**, 269 (1937).
79. MACGINITIE, G. E. and MACGINITIE, N., *Natural History of Marine Animals* (London, McGraw-Hill, 1949).
80. MANIGAULT, P., "Recherches sur le calcaire chez les Mollusques," *Ann. Inst. Océanogr. Monaco*, **18**, 331 (1939).
81. MARKS, M. H., BEAR, R. S. and BLAKE, C. H., "X-ray diffraction evidence of collagen-type protein fibres in the Echinodermata, Coelenterata and Porifera," *J. Exp. Zool.*, **111**, 55 (1949).
82. MAXWELL, B. E., "The distribution of vitamin B_{12}-active substances in some marine invertebrates of British Columbia," *J. Fish. Res. Bd Can.*, **9**, 164 (1952).
83. MENON, M. D., "The use of bones, other than otoliths, in determining the age and growth-rate of fishes," *J. Cons. Int. Explor. Mer*, **16**, 311 (1950).
84. MOORE, H. B., "The biology of *Littorina littorea*. 1. Growth of the shell and tissues," *J. Mar. Biol. Ass. U.K.*, **21**, 721 (1937).
85. MORGULIS, S. and JANECEK, E., "Studies on the chemical composition of bone ash," *J. Biol. Chem.*, **93**, 455 (1931).
86. MORTENSEN, T., *A Monograph of the Echinoidea*. **2** (1) and **3** (2) (Copenhagen, C. A. Reitzel, 1935, 1943).
87. NEEDHAM, J., *Chemical Embryology*, Vol. 3 (Cambridge Univ. Press, 1931).
88. NEILAND, K. A. and SCHEER, B. T., "The influence of fasting and of sinus gland removal on body composition of *Hemigrapsus nudus*," *Physiol. Comp. Oecol.*, **3**, 321 (1953).
89. NICOL, E. A. T., "The feeding mechanism, formation of tube, and physiology of digestion in *Sabella pavonina*," *Trans. Roy. Soc. Edinb.*, **56**, 537 (1930).
90. NICOL, J. A. C., "Responses of *Branchiomma vesiculosum* to photic stimulation," *J. Mar. Biol. Ass. U.K.*, **29**, 303 (1950).
91. NIGRELLI, R. F., "The effects of holothurin on fish, etc.," *Zoologica, N.Y.*, **37**, 89 (1952).
92. NIGRELLI, R. and ZAHL, P. A., "Some biological characteristics of holothurin," *Proc. Soc. Exp. Biol. Med.*, **81**, 379 (1952).
93. NORMAN, J. R., *Illustrated Guide to the Fish Gallery* (London, Brit. Mus. (Nat. Hist.), 1937).
94. NORMAN, J. R. and FRASER, F. C., *Giant Fishes, Whales and Dolphins* (London, Putnam, 1948).
95. OCAMPO, R. R., HALSTEAD, B. W. and MODGLIN, F. R., "The microscopic anatomy of the caudal appendage of the spotted eagleray, *Aëtobatus narinari*," *Anat. Rec.*, **115**, 87 (1953).
96. ODUM, H. T., "Notes on the strontium content of sea water, celestite Radiolaria, and strontianite snail shells," *Science*, **114**, 211 (1951).
97. ODUM, H. T., "Nudibranch spicules made of amorphous calcium carbonate," ibid., **114**, 395 (1951).
98. OKAZAKI, K., "Skeleton formation of sea urchin larvae," *Biol. Bull.*, **110**, 320 (1956).

99. OTTER, G. W., "Rock-destroying organisms in relation to coral reefs," *Sci. Rep. Gt. Barrier Reef Exp.*, **1**, 323 (1937).

100. PASSANO, L. M., "Neurosecretory control of molting in crabs by the x-organ sinus gland complex," *Physiol. Comp. Oecol.*, **3**, 155 (1953).

101. PÉRÈS, J. M., "Recherches sur les pédicellaires glandulaires de *Sphaerechinus granularis*," *Arch. Zool. Exp. Gén.* (Notes et Rev.), **86**, 118 (1950).

102. PHILLIPS, J. H. Jr. and ABBOTT, D. P., "Isolation and assay of the nematocyst toxin of Metridium senile," *Biol. Bull.*, **113**, 296 (1957).

103. PICKEN, L. E. R. and LOTMAR, W., "Oriented protein in chitinous structures," *Nature*, **165**, 599 (1950).

104. POMEROY, L. R. and HASKIN, H. H., "The uptake and utilization of phosphate ions from sea water by the American oyster, *Crassostrea virginica*," *Biol. Bull.*, **107**, 123 (1954).

105. RANDALL, J. T., FRASER, R. D. B., JACKSON, S., MARTIN, A. V. W. and NORTH, A. C. T., "Aspects of collagen structure," *Nature*, 169, 1029 (1952).

106. RAO, K. P. and GOLDBERG, E. D., "Utilization of dissolved calcium by a pelecypod," *J. Cell. Comp. Physiol.*, **43**, 283 (1954).

107. RENAUD, L., "Le cycle des reserves organiques chez les Crustacés décapodes," *Ann. Inst. Océanogr.*, **24**, 259 (1949).

108. REYNE, A., "On the structure of the shells and pearls of Tridacna squamosa Lam. and Hippopus hippopus (Linn.)," *Arch. Néerl. Zool.*, **8**, 206 (1951).

109. RICHARDS, A. G., *The Integument of Arthropods* (Oxford Univ. Press, 1951).

110. RIDDELL, W. A., "The nutritive value of marine products. 13. Mineral constituents of coho salmon," *J. Biol. Bd Can.*, **2**, 473 (1936).

111. ROBERTSON, J. D., "The function and metabolism of calcium in the Invertebrata," *Biol. Rev.*, **16**, 106 (1941).

112. RUSSELL, F. E., "Marine toxins and venomous and poisonous marine animals," *Adv. Mar. Biol.*, **3** (1965).

113. RUSSELL, F. E. and EMERY, J. A., "Venom of weevers Trachinus," *Ann. N.Y. Acad. Sci.*, **90**, 805 (1960).

114. SAID, R., "Preliminary note on the spectroscopic distribution of elements in the shells of some recent calcareous Foraminifera," *Contr. Cushman Fdn.*, **2**, 11 (1951).

115. SCHEER, B. T. and SCHEER, M. A. R., "Blood sugar in spiny lobsters," *Physiol. Comp. Oecol.*, **2**, 198 (1951).

116. SCHWABE, C. W., SCHEER, B. T. and SCHEER, M. A. R., "The molt cycle in *Panulirus japonicus*," ibid., **2**, 310 (1952).

117. SCUDAMORE, H. H., "The influence of the sinus glands upon molting and associated changes in the crayfish," *Physiol. Zool.*, **20**, 187 (1947).

118. SMITH, J. L. B., "A case of poisoning by the stonefish, *Synanceja*," *Copeia*, **1951**, 207 (1951).

119. SPENCE, J. and RICHARDS, O. W., "Native cellulose in the ascidian *Phallusia nigra*," *Publ. Carneg. Instn.* No. 517, p. 163 (1940).

120. STOLKOWSKI, J., "Essai sur le déterminisme des formes minéralogiques du calcaire chez les êtres vivants (calcaires coquilliers)," *Ann. Inst. Océanogr. Monaco*, **26**, 1 (1950).

121. SWAN, E. F., "The calcareous tube secreting glands of the serpulid polychaetes," *J. Morph.*, **86**, 285 (1950).

122. TAFT, C. H., "Poisonous marine animals," *Tex. Rep. Biol. Med.*, **3**, 339 (1945).

123. TAKAHASHI, K., "Notes on the polychaetous annelid, *Polydora pacifica*, which bores holes in *Pinctada*," *Palao Trop. Biol. Stud.*, **1**, 155 (1937).
124. TANAKA, S. and HATANO, H., "Studies on the seasonal changes in the chemical constituents of the pearl oyster," *Publ. Seto Mar. Biol. Lab.*, **2** (2), 341 (1952).
125. TIXIER-DURIVAULT, A., "Contribution à l'étude du métabolisme du calcium et du fer chez l'*Alcyonium palmatum*," *Ann. Inst. Océanogr. Monaco*, **20**, 311 (1940).
126. TOMPSETT, D. H., *Sepia*, L.M.B.C. Mem. No. 32 (Liverpool Univ. Press, 1939).
127. TRAVIS, D. F., "The molting cycle of the spiny lobster, *Panulirus argus*. 1," *Biol. Bull.*, **107**, 433 (1954).
128. TRAVIS, D. F., "The molting cycle of the spiny lobster, *Panulirus argus*. 4," ibid., **113**, 451 (1957).
129. TRUEMAN, E. R., "Occurrence of strontium in molluscan shells," *Nature*, **153**, 142 (1944).
130. TRUEMAN, E. R., "The structure, development, and operation of the hinge ligament of *Ostrea edulis*," *Quart. J. Micr. Sci.*, **92**, 129 (1951).
131. WATABE, N., "Decalcification of thin sections for electron microscope studies of crystal-matrix relationships in mollusc shells," *J. Cell. Biol.*, **18**, 701 (1963).
132. WEBB, D. A., "Studies on the ultimate composition of biological material. 2. Spectrographic analyses of marine invertebrates," *Sci. Proc. R. Dublin Soc.*, **21**, 505 (1937).
133. WHITLEY, G. P., *Poisonous and Harmful Fishes*, Bull. 159 (C.S.I.R., Melbourne, Australia, 1943).
134. WILBUR, K. M., "Shell formation and regeneration," in *Physiology of Mollusca*, Ed. Wilbur, K. M. and Yonge, C. M., Vol. 1, p. 243 (New York and London, Academic Press, 1964).
135. WILBUR, K. M. and JODREY, L. H., "Studies on shell formation 1. Measurement of the rate of shell formation using Ca⁴⁵," *Biol. Bull.*, **103**, 269 (1952).
136. YONGE, C. M., *The Sea Shore* (London, Collins, 1949).
137. YONGE, C. M., "Marine boring organisms," *Research*, **4**, 162 (1951).

APPENDIX

SALINE MEDIA

Sea Water

The composition of sea water in terms of hypothetical combinations of ions appears in the following table. Concentration: chlorinity, 19‰; salinity 34·325‰. Depression of freezing point, $-1·872°C$. Density, 1·026 at 17·5°C.

Salt	g/kg	g/l
NaCl	23·477	24·087
KCl	0·664	0·681
$CaCl_2$	1·102	1·131
$MgCl_2$	4·981	5·111
Na_2SO_4	3·917	4·019
$NaHCO_3$	0·192	0·197
KBr	0·096	0·098
H_3BO_3	0·026	0·027
$SrCl_2$	0·024	0·025
NaF	0·003	0·003
H_2O to	1,000g	1,000 c.c.

(From Lyman and Fleming (10).)

Osmotic pressures of sea-water solutions at different salinities and temperatures are given by Wilson and Arons (23).

Isosmotic Solutions

The table on page 667 shows concentrations of salt solutions approximately isosmotic with sea water (salinity, 34·325‰).

Actual concentrations of hygroscopic salts, $CaCl_2$, $MgCl_2$, choline Cl, should be determined by argentometric titration.

The pHs of these isosmotic solutions differ greatly from sea water, and for particular experiments may need adjustment by addition of appropriate acid or base.

Over the range 9–21‰ Cl, the ratio of NaCl molality to sea water chlorinity can be expressed as

$$R = 0·02782 + 0·000079 \, (‰ \, Cl)$$

Solutions of salts isosmotic with sea water in this range are described in the following table—

Molality of solution of equal vapour pressure at 25° C

Cl °/oo	Salinity °/oo	R	NaCl	KCl	CaCl₂	MgCl₂	MgSO₄	Na₂SO₄	Sucrose	Urea
10	18·08	0·02861	0·2861	0·2908	0·2039	0·2005	0·5056	0·2374	0·5065	0·5400
11	19·89	0·02869	0·3156	0·3211	0·2240	0·2199	0·5597	0·2643	0·5560	0·5965
12	21·69	0·02877	0·3452	0·3516	0·2441	0·2393	0·6138	0·2918	0·6053	0·6534
13	23·50	0·02885	0·3751	0·3825	0·2642	0·2588	0·6675	0·3196	0·6546	0·7112
14	25·30	0·02893	0·4050	0·4134	0·2841	0·2780	0·7206	0·3477	0·7040	0·7695
15	27·11	0·02901	0·4352	0·4447	0·3043	0·2975	0·7738	0·3762	0·7534	0·8285
16	28·91	0·02908	0·4653	0·4760	0·3243	0·3165	0·8264	0·4051	0·8025	0·8880
17	30·72	0·02916	0·4957	0·5077	0·3445	0·3356	0·8786	0·4347	0·8516	0·9482
18	32·52	0·02924	0·5263	0·5397	0·3645	0·3546	0·9300	0·4648	0·9008	1·010
19	34·33	0·02932	0·5571	0·5719	0·3845	0·3738	0·9803	0·4954	0·9497	1·071
20	36·13	0·02940	0·5880	0·6043	0·4044	0·3929	1·028	0·5264	0·9982	1·133
21	37·94	0·02948	0·6191	0·6370	0·4243	0·4122	1·076	0·5578	1·047	1·197
22	39·74	0·02956	0·6503	0·6698	0·4440	0·4313	1·123	0·5896	1·095	1·260

(From measurements made by Robinson (18), with the isopiestic method (see also Barnes (2).)

Salt	Molality	g/kg water	Molarity	g/l solution (20°C)
NaCl	0·557	32·55	0·552	32·27
KCl	0·572	42·64	0·562	41·90
CaCl$_2$	0·384	42·62	0·380	42·14
CaCl$_2$.6H$_2$O	—	84·13	—	83·18
MgCl$_2$	0·374	35·62	0·370	35·30
MgCl$_2$.6H$_2$O	—	76·05	—	75·37
Na$_2$SO$_4$	0·495	70·31	0·489	69·55
Na$_2$SO$_4$.10H$_2$O	—	159·50	—	157·76
MgSO$_4$.7H$_2$O	0·980	241·57	0·867	213·73
NaHCO$_3$	0·590	49·57	—	—
KBr	0·563	67·0	0·552	65·74
Chloride Cl	0·60 (?)	83·8	—	—
Non-electrolytes	1·006	—	—	—
Sucrose	0·950	325·18	0·783	267·95
Urea	1·071	64·32	—	—

(Based on cryoscopic data and isopiestic measurements)

Artificial Sea Water

This may be made up by weighing out the amounts of salts shown in the preceding table (p. 665), or by using isosmotic solutions in the following proportions, if these are at hand.

Isosmotic solution	c.c.
0·55 M NaCl	747·8
0·56 M KCl	16·3
0·38 M CaCl$_2$	26·8
0·37 M MgCl$_2$	145·03
0·49 M Na$_2$SO$_4$	58·21 (4·019 g)
NaHCO$_3$	0·197 g
0·55 M KBr[1]	1·5 (0·098 g)
Water to	1,000 c.c.

(1) For most purposes KBr may be omitted.

Balanced Salt Solutions Suitable for Marine Animals

The tissues of many lower invertebrates will continue to function normally in sea water, which can be used as a physiological medium. Even in more complex forms, crustaceans and cephalopods, isolated tissues can survive and function in sea water, although the blood differs considerably in composition from the latter. Thus the heart beat of *Maia* persists in sea water, and giant-axons of squid and cuttlefish transmit normally. A variety of physiological media have been advocated and employed by different investigators. Some of these recipes are entirely empirical; others are based on analyses of the chief constituents of body fluids. Some suitable tissue media appear in the following table. See also McClendon (11), Young (24), Pantin (14), Prosser (16).

ARTIFICIAL

Quantities in grammes/litre.

Animal	NaCl	KCl	CaCl$_2$	MgCl$_2$	NaHCO$_3$
Sipunculoidea					
Golfingia gouldii[1]	26·29	0·75	1·17	5·01	0·22
Mollusca					
Crassostrea virginica	26·54	0·75	1·11	3·33	to pH 7·3
Loligo forbesi[1]	26·29	0·75	1·17	5·01	0·22
Crustacea					
Homarus americanus	26·42	1·12	2·78	0·38	—
Maia squinado	30·36	0·97	1·54	2·37	to pH 7
Carcinus maenas, and other decapods	} 31·31	0·99	1·38	2·37	to pH 7
Cancer irroratus	26·89	0·88	1·33	0·38	—
Callinectes danae[2]	24·43	0·86	1·42	1·66	to pH 7·5
Echinoderms					
Lytechinus variegatus	23·52	1·09	1·48	1·98	—
Cyclostomes					
Myxine glutinosa	22·0	0·4	0·5	0·4	0·3
Petromyzon (freshwater)	5·5	0·14	0·12	—	—
	6·5	0·12	0·15	—	—
Selachians					
Scyliorhinus, Raja	22·0	0·52	0·44	0·47	—
	18·0	0·5	0·4	0·5	0·5
	16·38	0·894	1·11	—	0·378
Torpedo torpedo[1]	15·99	0·57	0·47	0·15	0·10
Teleosts					
Lophius piscatorius	13·5	0·6	0·25	0·35	—
	12·0	0·60	0·25	0·21	0·19
Fundulus, Syngnathus	11·0	0·55	0·4	0·24	0·5
Pseudopleuronectes americanus and other marine teleosts	} 7·8	0·19	0·17	0·10	1·26
Anguilla anquilla (freshwater)	6·5	0·14	0·12	—	—

[1] g/1000 g H$_2$O.   [2] g/1000 g solution.

Sources: 1, Otis (12); 2, Cole (3); 3, Welsh (22); 4, Pantin (13); 5, Smith (20); 6, Fänge (5); 7, Young (24); Valente and Bruno (21); 15, Forster and Taggart (7); 16, Hodgkin and Katz (9); 17, Prosser and Melton (17);

PHYSIOLOGICAL MEDIA

Add water to make 1000 c.c.

Other substances	Source
	17
MgSO$_4$, 2·05 g	1
	16
MgSO$_4$, 0·48 g; 18 c.c. 0·5 M boric acid; 1 c.c. 0·5 M NaOH; pH 7·4	2
Urea, 1·04 g	3
	4
MgSO$_4$, 2·17 g; 17·6 c.c. 0·5 M boric acid; 0·96 c.c. 0·5 M NaOH	5
Glucose, 1 g	12, 13
MgSO$_4$, 2·13 g	14
pH 7·8	6
	7
"phosphates," 0·2 g; pH 7·5	8
Urea, 29 g	7
Urea, 10 g	9
Urea, 21·6 g; NaH$_2$PO$_4$, 0·06 g; glucose, 1 g; pH 7·8	10
Urea, 24·92 g	18
	7
KH$_2$PO$_4$, 0·07 g	11
	9
NaH$_2$PO$_4$ 0·06 g	15
	7

8, Galloway (8); 9, Dreyer (4); 10, Babkin, *et al.* (1); 11, Young (25); 12, Pereira (15); 13, Sawaya (19); 14, 18, Fatt and Woodin (6).

REFERENCES

1. BABKIN, B. P., BOWIE, D. J. and NICHOLLS, J. V. V., "Structure and reactions to stimuli of arteries in *Raja*," *Contr. Canad. Biol. Fish.*, **8**, 207 (1933).
2. BARNES, H., "Some tables for the ionic composition of sea water," *J. Exp. Biol.*, **31**, 582 (1954).
3. COLE, W. H., "A perfusing solution for the lobster (*Homarus*) heart," *J. Gen. Physiol.*, **25**, 1 (1941).
4. DREYER, N. B., "Intestinal reaction to drugs in different fishes," *Proc. N.S. Inst. Sci.*, **17**, 199 (1930).
5. FÄNGE, R., "Effect of drugs on the intestine of a vertebrate without sympathetic nervous system," *Ark. Zool.*, **40A**, No. 11 (1948).
6. FATT, P. and WOODIN, A. M., "The release of phosphate from the electric organ of *Torpedo*," *J. Exp. Biol.*, **30**, 68 (1953).
7. FORSTER, R. P. and TAGGART, J. V., "Use of isolated renal tubules for the examination of metabolic processes associated with active cellular transport," *J. Cell. Comp. Physiol.*, **36**, 251 (1950).
8. GALLOWAY, T. M., "The osmotic pressure and saline content of the blood of *Petromyzon fluviatilis*," *J. Exp. Biol.*, **10**, 313 (1933).
9. HODGKIN, A. L. and KATZ, B., "The effect of sodium ions on the electrical activity of the giant axon of the squid," *J. Physiol.*, **108**, 37 (1949).
10. LYMAN, J. and FLEMING, R. H., "Composition of sea water," *J. Mar. Res.*, **3**, 134 (1940).
11. McCLENDON, J. F., "The composition, especially the hydrogen ion concentration of sea water in relation to marine organisms," *J. Biol. Chem.*, **28**, 135 (1916).
12. OTIS, A. B., "Effects of certain drugs and ions on the oyster heart," *Physiol. Zool.*, **15**, 418 (1942).
13. PANTIN, C. F. A., "On the excitation of crustacean muscle. 1," *J. Exp. Biol.*, **11**, 11 (1934).
14. PANTIN, C. F. A., *Notes on Microscopical Technique for Zoologists* (Cambridge Univ. Press, 1946).
15. PEREIRA, R. S., "Sôbre a composição mineral do sangue do *Callinectes danae*," *Zoologia, S. Paulo*, No. 8, p. 147 (1944).
16. PROSSER, C. L. (Ed.), *Comparative Animal Physiology* (London, Saunders, 1950).
17. PROSSER, C. L. and MELTON, C. E. JR., "Nervous conduction in smooth muscle of Phascolosoma proboscis retractors," *J. Cell. Comp. Physiol.*, **44**, 255 (1954).
18. ROBINSON, R. A., "The vapour pressure and osmotic equivalence of sea water," *J. Mar. Biol. Ass. U.K.*, **33**, 449 (1954).
19. SAWAYA, P., "Solução perfusora para *Callinectes danae*," *Zoologia, S. Paulo*, No. 9, p. 5 (1945).
20. SMITH, R. I., "The action of electrical stimulation and of certain drugs on cardiac nerves of the crab, *Cancer irroratus*," *Biol. Bull.*, **93**, 72 (1947).
21. VALENTE, D. and BRUNO, A., "Contéudo mineral do sangue de invertebrados marinhos," *Zoologia, S. Paulo*, No. 16, p. 303 (1951).
22. WELSH, J. H., "Chemical mediation in crustaceans," *J. Exp. Biol.*, **16**, 198 (1939).
23. WILSON, K. G. and ARONS, A. B., "Osmotic pressures of sea water solutions

computed from experimental vapor pressure lowering," *J. Mar. Res.*, **14**, 195 (1955).

24. YOUNG, J. Z., "The preparation of isotonic solutions for use in experiments with fish," *Pubbl. Staz. Zool. Napoli*, **12**, 425 (1933).

25. YOUNG, J. Z., "The innervation and reactions to drugs of the viscera of teleostean fish," *Proc. Roy. Soc. B.*, **120**, 303 (1936).

INDEX

abalone. *See Haliotis*
Abraliopsis, 545, 570
A. morisii, 546, 548
absorption, 271
Abudefduf saxatilus, 160
abyssal plain, 7
abyssal region, 2
Acantharia, skeleton, 621
Acanthephyra, 555
Acanthodoris, 230, 270, 640
Acanthometra, 604, 621
A. pellucida, 605
Acartia, 592, 593
accommodation, eye, 308, 309
Acerina, 342
acetylcholine, 109, 110, 112, 378, 390,
    438, 522
acetylcholinesterase, 438
Acholoë, 543, 544
A. astericola, 544, 564, 565, 568, 585
Acipenser. See sturgeon
Acmaea, 38, 147
A. limatula, 101, 107
acorn barnacles. *See* cirripedes
Acropoma japonicum, 554
Actinia, 482, 583
A. equina, 160, 468, 481, 483
actinians—
    excretion, 284
    feeding, 233
    See also sea anemones
Actinoloba reticulata, 581
Actinomma, 621
Actinophrys sol, 41
Actinopyga, 655
action potential—
    electric organs, 396
    muscle, 378
    nerve, 415
    Noctiluca, 558
action spectra, 323, 325
actomyosin, 391
Adamsia palliata, 582, 583
adaptive coloration, 490
adductor muscle, 388
Adélie penguin, 169
adenase, 290
adenine, 278, 290
adenosine triphosphate, ATP, 392
adrenaline, 92, 109, 378, 438, 522
adrenergic systems, 438
adventitious shelters, 654
Aeolidiella, 655
A. glauca, 373
Aeolis, 373
Aequorea, 445, 555, 558

A. aequorea, 30
A. forskalea, 418, 532, 564
aerial gills, 146
aerial respiration, 146
Agalma, 398
agar, 264
air-bladder. *See* swim-bladder
Akera, 472, 474
albatrosses, feeding, 241, 242
albedo, 484, 510
Alca torda, 169, 245
Alcyonidium, 608
Alcyonium, 627
A. carneum, 622
Alexandrowicz, J. S., 114
algae, 579, 608
algal symbionts, 603
alkali reserve—
    blood, 190
    sea water, 13
allantoic acid, 278, 291
allantoicase, 291
allantoin, 278, 291
allantoinase, 291
Alle alle, 169, 241
Allogromia, 627
allophores, 501
Alloteuthis, 260
Alopias, 238
Alpheus, 596
Ameiurus, 333, 342
A. nebulosus, 341
amine oxidase, 113
amino acids, 60, 74, 278, 284
ammonia, 278
ammonotelism, 278, 284
Amoeba—
    effect of pressure, 24
    feeding, 200, 232
A. lacerta, 41
A. mira, 41
amoebocytes, 122, 257
Ampelisca, 222
ampharetids, feeding, 203
Amphibia, 55
Amphioxus, 100, 101, 106, 219, 220, 261,
    303
A. lanceolatus, 151
Amphipnous, 149
amphipods—
    colour responses, 509
    excretion, 288
    feeding, 222, 228
    osmoregulation, 50
Amphiporus, 234
Amphiprion, 587

673